College Chemistry

HARPERCOLLINS COLLEGE OUTLINE

College Chemistry

Drew Wolfe
Hillsborough Community College
Tampa, Florida

HarperPerennial
A Division of HarperCollinsPublishers

Developed by American BookWorks Corporation

Library of Congress Cataloging-in-Publication Data

Wolfe, Drew H.
    College chemistry/Drew H. Wolfe
        p.   cm.
    ISBN 0-06-467120-8
    1. Chemistry.   I. Title.
    QD31.2.W637   1993
    540—dc20   93-5137

94 95 96 97 TB/RRD 10 9 8 7 6 5 4 3 2 1

Contents

Preface

College Chemistry has been written for beginning college chemistry students. It covers the core topics found in the General Chemistry curriculum. It can be used as a supplementary text for any comprehensive General Chemistry textbook. The order of chapters in *College Chemistry* follows many of the popular chemistry textbooks.

Chapters 1 and 2 introduce chemistry and chemical measurements. Chapter 3 covers the nature of atoms, elements, ions, and compounds. Chapter 4 considers the mole concept and quantitative chemical relationships. Chapter 5 is an introduction to the principal types of inorganic reactions: precipitation, acid-base, and redox reactions. Chapter 6 covers the gases so that properties of gases can be used in future chapters. The remaining physical states, liquids and solids, are discussed in Chapter 12.

Chapter 7 is the first of two chapters that cover chemical thermodynamics. The first law of thermodynamics is discussed in Chapter 7, and the second and third laws of thermodynamics are considered in Chapter 18. Chapter 8 discusses the quantum theory and the electron configuration of atoms. The material in this chapter is completed in Chapter 9, which is a discussion of the periodic properties of atoms and elements. Chapters 10 and 11 are devoted to chemical bonding. In Chapter 10, the fundamental concepts are considered, and in Chapter 11, molecular geometry, hybrid orbitals, and the basic concepts of the molecular orbital theory are reviewed.

Chapter 13 considers the nature and properties of solutions and colloids. Chapter 14 surveys the topic of chemical kinetics. Chapter 15 is the first chapter devoted to the topic of chemical equilibrium systems, and it principally considers gas-phase equilibria. Chapters 16 and 17 discuss the topic of aqueous equilibria. Chapter 16 covers acids, bases, and salts, and acid-base equilibria. Chapter 17 completes the topic of aqueous equilibria by considering buffer solutions, titrations, solubility equilibria, and complex ion equilibria. The final two topics are electrochemistry found in Chapter 19 and nuclear chemistry in Chapter 20.

Each chapter in *College Chemistry* has many problems with complete solutions that make use of the factor-label (unit conversion) method when appropriate. At the end of each chapter is a Review Exercise with answers to all problems. An effective way to use this book is to study a solved problem and then find a similar one to work in the Review Exercise. Also, each chapter contains succinct discussions of the principal aspects of the topics considered.

In conclusion, I would like to express my appreciation and thanks for the assistance I received from Bill Hamill and Fred Grayson. I would also like to thank my wife, Cyndy, and daughter, Natasha, who always provide me with love and support.

1

Introduction to Chemistry

Chemistry is one of the three major areas of science, along with biology and physics. In this chapter we will first propose a definition for chemistry and discuss its scope. Then we will turn our attention to the principal concern of chemistry—matter.

1.1   WHAT IS CHEMISTRY?

*Chemistry—
Definition,
Practitioners,
and History*

Chemistry is the science of matter and the changes it undergoes. This main focus of chemistry is matter. All objects in the world are types of matter.

A chemist is a person who studies the composition, structure, and properties of matter and seeks to explain the changes that matter undergoes.

Modern chemistry grew out of the pseudoscience called alchemy. Alchemists searched for methods to convert base metals to gold. Robert Boyle was one of the first scientists to suggest that ideas and thoughts about matter must be supported by reproducible experiments. Antoine Lavoisier is credited with being the father of modern chemistry as a result of his pioneering experiments on the properties of matter.

MATTER, MASS, AND ENERGY

Matter is anything that has mass and occupies space. The mass of an object is a measure of the amount of matter it has. Closely related to matter is energy. Thus, chemistry also considers the relationship of matter and energy.

Energy is the capacity to do work, or more simply, the capacity to change something.

1.2   MATTER AND ITS PROPERTIES

*Composition
and Structure*

Composition refers to the identity and amount of the components of matter. Structure describes the physical arrangement of its particles (atoms, ions, or molecules). Some types of matter have a highly organized structure while others are random.

Physical Properties and Changes

Chemists distinguish one type of matter from another by identifying their properties, just as people are differentiated by observing their physical appearance and personality traits. Properties are classified as being either physical or chemical. Physical properties are characteristics of a particular type of matter that can be measured without changing its composition. Density, color, melting point, boiling point, physical state, heat conductivity, and electrical conductivity are examples of physical properties of matter.

If a change occurs in the physical properties of a sample of matter without a change in composition, then a physical change occurs. After such a change, the same type of matter is present but has a different set of physical properties. Changes in shape, size, and physical state are other examples of physical changes.

Chemical Properties and Changes

A chemical property describes what happens to one type of matter when it changes composition. When matter changes its composition, a chemical reaction or chemical change occurs. Therefore, chemical properties describe the chemical reactions that matter undergoes. For example, a chemical property of gasoline is that it burns (undergoes oxidation) when ignited. Gasoline is a liquid mixture of carbon-hydrogen compounds.

Problem 1.1 Classify each of the following as a physical property, physical change, chemical property or chemical change. (a) A blue solid, (b) an explosive liquid, and (c) a solid changes directly to a vapor without becoming a liquid.

Solution 1.1
   (a) A physical property, because it is a characteristic of a solid without reference to any other substance.
   (b) A chemical property, because explosive describes a chemical change that the liquid undergoes.
   (c) A physical change, because the solid does not change composition.

1.3   CLASSIFICATION OF MATTER

Samples of matter can be classified as being either pure substances or mixtures.

Pure Substances

Pure substances (or, simply, substances) have a constant composition, cannot be separated into simpler components by physical methods, and undergo state changes at a constant temperature. Examples of pure substances include gold, copper, water, and carbon dioxide. Pure substances can be further subdivided into elements or compounds.

Mixtures

A mixture results when pure substances that do not react are combined. Mixtures have a variable composition, can usually be separated by physical methods, and undergo state changes over a range of temperatures. Mixtures can either be homogeneous (those with one phase) or heterogeneous (those with two or more phases). Ocean water, concrete, air, and asphalt are four examples of mixtures.

Elements

Elements are the basic units of matter. All of the other types of matter contain elements. About 110 different elements have been identified. Of these elements, 92 occur in nature and the remaining are synthetic. At 25°C, 97 elements are solids, 2 are liquids, and 11 are gases.

PERIODIC TABLE OF THE ELEMENTS

The symbols of the elements are found in the periodic table. This table is one of the most important tables in chemistry (Fig. 1). Each element is located in a horizontal row called a period and in a vertical column called a group (sometimes called a family). Each period is numbered consecutively from 1 to 7. Each group of elements is assigned a Roman numeral and a letter. It has been recommended that the groups be numbered consecutively from 1 to 18. Thus, two numbering systems are now used.

SYMBOLS OF THE ELEMENTS

Chemists often use symbols to represent elements. The use of symbols for elements dates back to the ancient Greeks, who originally suggested that matter was composed of elements. Symbols can be one, two, or three letters. Usually they are the first letters of the English or Latin names. It is important to learn the symbols of the elements in the beginning of your study of chemistry.

Problem 1.2   Name the following elements: (a) B, (b) Cu, (c) Mn, (d) Ag, (e) Au, (f) Pb

Solution 1.2   (a) boron, (b) copper, (c) manganese, (d) silver, (e) gold, (f) lead

Problem 1.3   What are the symbols for the following elements? (a) cobalt, (b) manganese, (c) fluorine (d) tin, (e) mercury, (f) potassium

Solution 1.3   (a) Co, (b) Mn, (c) F, (d) Sn, (e) Hg, (f) K

Compounds

Compounds are substances that may be broken down chemically to two or more elements. Many compounds are composed of small particles called molecules; others are composed of formula units of positive and negative ions. Molecules and formula units result when atoms combine chemically. Water is a familiar compound that results when the element hydrogen combines chemically with the element oxygen. During this reaction, two H atoms bond with one O atom.

A chemical formula is used to show the number of atoms of each element in a molecule. To the right of each symbol that has more than one atom in the formula, a subscript is written that shows the number of atoms in the molecule. Thus, the formula for water is H_2O. Other examples of compounds are carbon dioxide, CO_2, table salt, $NaCl$, table sugar, $C_{12}H_{22}O_{11}$, calcium nitrate, $Ca(NO_3)_2$, and aluminum sulfate, $Al_2(SO_4)_3$.

Problem 1.4   How many atoms of each type are found in a formula unit of calcium acetate, $Ca(C_2H_3O_2)_2$?

Solution 1.4   One formula unit of calcium acetate contains: one Ca atom, four C atoms, six H atoms, and four O atoms.

Types of Mixtures— Homogeneous and Heterogeneous

Mixtures are divided into two classes: homogeneous and heterogeneous. "Homogeneous" is a word derived from *homo* which means the "same" or "equal," and *genus* which means "kind" or "structure." "Hetero" is a prefix that means "different."

Homogeneous mixtures are also called solutions. Only one phase is found in homogeneous mixtures. For example, consider a sugar-water solution. It is prepared by mixing solid sugar and liquid water. After the sugar dissolves, a homogeneous mixture results. When looking at sugar water you cannot tell if it is pure water or a solution. Other examples of solutions are alcohol and water, air, and most alloys.

A heterogeneous mixture is one that exhibits more than one phase. A phase is an observable region of matter with a composition different from the surrounding regions. Each phase can be distinguished from bordering regions by its properties. For example, when sand is added to water, the sand does not dissolve. It falls to the bottom of the water. When observing sand and water, you

Periodic Table of the Elements

1(IA)	2(IIA)	3(IIIB)	4(IVB)	5(VB)	6(VIB)	7(VIIB)	8	9 — VIIIB	10	11(IB)	12(IIB)	13(IIIA)	14(IVA)	15(VA)	16(VIA)	17(VIIA)	18(VIII)
1 H 1.0079																	2 He 4.003
3 Li 6.939	4 Be 9.012											5 B 10.81	6 C 12.01	7 N 14.01	8 O 16.00	9 F 19.00	10 Ne 20.18
11 Na 22.990	12 Mg 24.312											13 Al 26.98	14 Si 28.08	15 P 30.97	16 S 32.06	17 Cl 35.45	18 Ar 39.95
19 K 39.102	20 Ca 40.08	21 Sc 44.96	22 Ti 47.90	23 V 50.94	24 Cr 52.00	25 Mn 54.94	26 Fe 55.85	27 Co 58.93	28 Ni 58.69	29 Cu 63.55	30 Zn 65.39	31 Ga 69.72	32 Ge 72.61	33 As 74.92	34 Se 78.96	35 Br 79.90	36 Kr 83.80
37 Rb 85.47	38 Sr 87.62	39 Y 88.90	40 Zr 91.22	41 Nb 92.21	42 Mo 95.94	43 Tc (98)	44 Ru 101.1	45 Rh 102.9	46 Pd 106.4	47 Ag 107.9	48 Cd 112.4	49 In 114.8	50 Sn 118.7	51 Sb 121.8	52 Te 127.6	53 I 126.9	54 Xe 131.3
55 Cs 132.9	56 Ba 137.3	57 La** 138.9	72 Hf 178.5	73 Ta 180.9	74 W 183.8	75 Re 186.2	76 Os 190.2	77 Ir 192.2	78 Pt 195.1	79 Au 197.0	80 Hg 200.6	81 Tl 204.4	82 Pb 207.2	83 Bi 209.0	84 Po (209)	85 At (210)	86 Rn (222)
87 Fr 223	88 Ra 226	89 Ac** 227	104 Unq (261)	105 Unp (262)	106 Unh (263)	107 Uns (262)	108 Uno (265)	109 Uno (266)									

Lanthanides (*)

58 Ce 140.1	59 Pr 140.9	60 Nd 144.2	61 Pm (145)	62 Sm 150.4	63 Eu 152.0	64 Gd 157.2	65 Tb 158.9	66 Dy 162.5	67 Ho 164.9	68 Er 167.3	69 Tm 168.9	70 Yb 173.0	71 Lu 175.0

Actinides (**)

90 Th 232.0	91 Pa 231.0	92 U 238.0	93 Np (237)	94 Pu (244)	95 Am (243)	96 Cm (247)	97 Bk (247)	98 Cf (251)	99 Es (252)	100 Fm (257)	101 Md (258)	102 No (259)	103 Lr (260)

Fig. 1. *Periodic Table of the Elements*

see the solid sand phase and the liquid water phase. Oil and water, salt and sand, and granite are all examples of heterogeneous mixtures.

Problem 1.5 Classify each of the following as an element, compound, homogeneous mixture or heterogeneous mixture. (a) 18 karat gold, (b) nitrogen dioxide, NO_2, (c) pure uranium.

Solution 1.5
    (a) Gold that is 18 karat is a solution of gold and other metals such as silver, copper, and platinum. Thus, 18 karat gold is a homogeneous mixture.
    (b) Nitrogen dioxide is a compound because it is a chemical combination of nitrogen and oxygen.
    (c) Pure uranium is one of the elements.

Separation of Mixtures

Mixtures, whether homogeneous or heterogeneous, may be separated into their components by physical methods. For example, a solution of salt and water can be separated by heating. During heating, water changes to a vapor which is condensed, leaving the salt behind. This is the basis of the process called distillation.

Filtration is a method used to separate some heterogeneous mixtures. Such mixtures are poured into a funnel that contains a filter paper, which is paper containing small, uniform openings or pores. Sand and water are separated by pouring the mixture into a filter.

Problem 1.6 How can a mixture of sand and salt be separated?

Solution 1.6 A combination of sand and salt is a heterogeneous mixture. A convenient separation takes into account the difference in the solubility of sand and salt in water. Salt is soluble in water, but sand is not. If water is added to the mixture, the salt dissolves, leaving the sand undissolved. The salt-water solution that results is then filtered. Sand is trapped by the filter paper while the salt water passes through. To recover the salt, the water is evaporated.

1.4 PHYSICAL STATES OF MATTER

On earth, matter exists in three physical states: solids, liquids, and gases. Each physical state has its own general set of properties.

Solids

Solids are usually the most compact state of matter. They have a fixed shape, constant volume, and do not flow to any appreciable extent. The particles that compose solids are closely packed and bonded by fairly strong forces of attraction. The structure of most solids is an organized pattern of atoms, molecules, or ions. Solids have the most organized structure of the three physical states.

Liquids

The structure of liquids is more disorganized than that of solids because the forces among the liquid particles are generally weaker than those in solids. Thus, liquids are usually less compact (less dense) and more fluid than solids. Like solids, liquids have a constant volume. In other words, liquids are nearly incompressible. A substance is incompressible if its volume remains constant with increasing applied pressure (a force exerted on an area). Liquids take the shapes of their containers to the level they fill.

Gases

Gases are the least compact (most diffuse) state of matter. The randomly distributed particles in gases are widely separated with only weak attractive forces. Gases have a variable shape, variable volume, totally fill their containers, and may be compressed. Of the three physical states, gases have the greatest ability to flow. Stated differently, gases are the most fluid of the three physical states of matter.

Changes of State

The addition or removal of heat from a substance can cause its physical state to change.

MELTING AND FREEZING

When a solid is heated, its temperature increases until it reaches its melting point. The melting point of a solid is the temperature at which it changes to a liquid and both the solid and liquid phases coexist. Each substance has its own characteristic melting point. For example, ice, $H_2O(s)$, melts at $0°C$ and sodium chloride, $NaCl(s)$, melts at $801°C$. If heat is removed from a liquid, it cools and changes to a solid at the freezing point. The freezing and melting temperatures of a substance are the same.

$$\text{Solid} \underset{\text{freezing}}{\overset{\text{melting}}{\rightleftharpoons}} \text{Liquid}$$

BOILING AND CONDENSING

When a liquid is heated, its temperature increases until the boiling point is reached. At the boiling point, bubbles of vapor form throughout the liquid and the liquid changes to a vapor. A vapor is the gaseous form of a substance. Removing heat from the vapor ultimately causes it to cool and condense back to a liquid.

$$\text{Liquid} \underset{\text{condensing}}{\overset{\text{boiling}}{\rightleftharpoons}} \text{Vapor}$$

SUMMARY

Chemistry is the study of matter and its interactions. Our universe is composed entirely of matter and energy. Matter is anything that has mass and occupies space. Energy is the capacity to do work.

Physical properties are characteristics of individual substances that can be measured without changing the composition of a substance. Chemical properties describe how the composition of a substance changes when it interacts with other substances or energy forms.

Matter is subdivided into two general classes, pure substances and mixtures. Pure substances are subdivided into elements and compounds. Mixtures are subdivided into homogeneous and heterogeneous mixtures.

Solids, liquids, and gases are the three physical states. Solids are the most dense and most viscous of the physical states. Gases are the least dense and least viscous. The structures of liquids more closely resemble those of solids than gases. Liquids have a relatively high average density and are incompressible.

CHAPTER 1 REVIEW EXERCISES

1. Classify each of the following as either a physical or chemical property: (a) existence in the solid state, (b) magnetic properties, (c) explosiveness, (d) combustibility, (e) flammability, (f) boiling point.

2. Classify each as a physical or chemical change: (a) formation of an ice cube from liquid water, (b) frying an egg, (c) fizzing of an Alka-Seltzer tablet, (d) gasoline evaporating, (e) distillation of alcohol, (f) digesting food.

3. Sulfur is a yellow solid that burns in air to yield poisonous sulfur oxides. On heating, sulfur discolors and turns dark brown at 180°C. Sulfur melts at 115°C and boils at 445°C. Identify all stated chemical and physical properties of sulfur.

4. Classify each of the following as pure substances or mixtures: (a) wine, (b) beef, (c) gold jewelry, (d) tap water, (e) carbon dioxide, (f) baking soda.

5. Write the name for each of the following elements: (a) He, (b) Fe, (c) Li, (d) Se, (e) Ne, (f) Zr.

6. Write the name for each of the following elements: (a) Hg, (b) Zn, (c) W, (d) Xe, (e) Sr, (f) Al.

7. Write the symbols for each of the following elements: (a) nickel, (b) nitrogen, (c) neodymium, (d) neon, (e) niobium, (f) nobelium.

8. Write the symbols for each of the following elements: (a) indium, (b) silicon, (c) chlorine, (d) potassium, (e) manganese, (f) beryllium.

9. Write the names and symbols for all eight elements in the second period of the periodic table.

10. State the name and number of each atom in the following formulas. (a) RbH_2PO_4, (b) $Al(OH)_3$, (c) $(NH_4)_2C_2O_4$, (d) $XePtCl_6$, (e) CCl_2Br_2.

11. Classify the following as being homogeneous or heterogeneous mixtures: (a) brass, (b) coffee, (c) cement, (d) motor oil, (e) carbonated beverage, (f) oil and water.

12. What physical state of matter is most commonly found under each of the following conditions: (a) very high temperatures and low pressures, (b) very low temperatures and high pressures?

13. What type(s) of matter possesses the following properties: (a) has a variable composition with one phase, (b) is inseparable by chemical means, (c) exhibits two or more phases, (d) changes state at constant temperature and has components that can be separated by chemical means?

14. (a) How can a mixture of sugar and water be separated? (b) How can a mixture of iron filings and salt be separated?

15. Some of the names of elements are derived from the names of geographical locations. Write the names and symbols for the elements that describe the following locations: (a) two continents, (b) a state in the U.S., (c) three countries in Europe, (d) a city in California.

ANSWERS TO REVIEW EXERCISES

1. (a) physical, (b) physical, (c) chemical, (d) chemical, (e) chemical, (f) physical

2. (a) physical, (b) chemical, (c) chemical, (d) physical, (e) physical, (f) chemical

3. Chemical: burns in air, discolors and turns dark brown, Physical: yellow solid, melts at 115°C, boils at 445°C

4. (a) mixture, (b) mixture, (c) mixture, (d) mixture, (e) pure substance, (f) pure substance

5. (a) helium, (b) iron, (c) lithium, (d) selenium, (e) neon, (f) zirconium

6. (a) mercury, (b) zinc, (c) tungsten, (d) xenon, (e) strontium, (f) aluminum

7. (a) Ni, (b) N, (c) Nd, (d) Ne, (e) Nb, (f) No

8. (a) In, (b) Si, (c) Cl, (d) K, (e) Mn, (f) Be

9. Lithium, Li; Beryllium, Be; Boron, B; Carbon, C; Nitrogen, N; Oxygen, O; Fluorine, F; and Neon, Ne

10. (a) rubidium, 1; hydrogen, 2; phosphorus, 1; oxygen, 4. (b) aluminum, 1, oxygen, 3, hydrogen, 3; (c) nitrogen, 2, hydrogen, 8, carbon, 2, oxygen, 4; (d) xenon, 1, platinum, 1, chlorine, 6;

11. (a) homogeneous, (b) homogeneous, (c) heterogeneous, (d) homogeneous, (e) heterogeneous, (f) heterogeneous

12. (a) gas phase, (b) solid phase

13. (a) homogeneous mixtures, (b) elements, (c) heterogeneous mixture, (d) compound

14. (a) evaporate the water, (b) use a magnet to remove the iron filings

15. (a) Europium, Eu; Americium, Am; (b) Californium, Cf; (c) Francium, Fr; Germanium, Ge; Polonium, Po; (d) Berkelium, Bk

2

Chemical Measurements

In this chapter we will first discuss the International System of Units, the measurement system used by scientists throughout the world. Then we will consider uncertainty in measurements and significant figures.

2.1   INTERNATIONAL SYSTEM OF UNITS

Measurements

Chemists make both qualitative and quantitative laboratory measurements. Each quantitative measurement expresses the magnitude, the units or label, and the degree of uncertainty.

The SI System –A Metric System

The Systéme International d'Unités, or the International System of Units (SI), is the measurement system used in chemistry. The International System is a metric system. In the metric system, the conversion of a measurement from one unit to another only requires the shifting of the decimal point.

SI PREFIXES

To scale an SI unit to the proper size for a measurement, the SI system has a series of prefixes that are added to units. Problems 2.1 and 2.2 review some of the more important prefixes.

Problem 2.1   What is the meaning of each of the following SI prefixes? (a) micro (μ), (b) mega (M), (c) milli (m), (d) deci (d)

Solution 2.1   (a) $1 \times 10^{-6}\times$, (b) $1 \times 10^{6}\times$, (c) $0.001\times$, (d) $0.1\times$

Problem 2.2   What prefix is used for each of the following? (a) $0.01\times$, (b) $1 \times 10^{-9}\times$, (c) $1000\times$, (d) $1 \times 10^{-12}\times$

Solution 2.2   (a) centi (c), (b) nano (n), (c) kilo (k), (d) pico (p)

Base and Derived SI Units

All SI units can be derived from seven base units. They include the following: meter (m)—unit of length; kilogram (kg)—unit of mass; second (s)—unit of time; Kelvin (K)—unit of temperature; mole (mol)—unit of amount of substance; ampere (A)—unit of electric current; and candela (cd)—unit of luminous intensity.

All other units in the SI system are derived from combinations of the seven base units. These are called derived units. Examples of derived SI units include m^2 (area), m^3 (volume), kg/m^3 (density), and $kg\ m^2/s^2$ (energy).

2.2 IMPORTANT CHEMICAL MEASUREMENTS

Length Measurements

The SI unit of length is the meter. Other commonly used units of length that are encountered in chemistry are the centimeter, cm, and the millimeter, mm. Centi, c, is the prefix that means one-hundredth. Thus, one centimeter is 1×10^{-2} m. The unit that most closely resembles 1 cm in the U. S. Customary System is the inch. One inch is equivalent to 2.54 cm.

Problem 2.3 Convert 475 mm to nm. One nanometer, nm, is 10^{-9} m.

Solution 2.3 First convert the millimeters to meters using the conversion factor, 1 m/1000 mm, and then convert from meters to nanometers using, 1×10^9 nm/1 m.

$$475 \text{ mm} \times 1\text{m}/1000 \text{ mm} \times 1 \times 10^9 \text{ nm}/1 \text{ m} = 4.75 \times 10^8 \text{ nm}$$

Problem 2.4 If one meter is 39.37 *in*, calculate the number of inches in 1.000 nm.

Solution 2.4 Using the conversion factor, 1 m/39.37 in, and knowing that 1 nm is 1×10^{-9} m, the number of inches per nanometer is calculated.

$$1.000 \text{ nm} \times 1 \times 10^{-9}\text{m/nm} \times 39.37 \text{ in/m} = 3.937 \times 10^{-8}\,in$$

Volume Measurements

Volume is the amount of space occupied by matter. A unit of volume in the SI system can be derived from the base units for length, the meter and its submultiples. To measure the volume of a rectangular box, multiply its length times width times height. If the centimeter is used for the unit of length, then the unit of cubic centimeters, cm^3 or cc, is obtained. Cubic centimeters are one of the most commonly used SI units of volume. In addition, the cubic decimeter, dm^3, is also used. One decimeter is 10 cm. Hence, $1\ dm^3$ has the same volume as $1000\ cm^3$.

In addition to the SI units of volume, two non-SI units of volume are often encountered. One liter, 1 L, is equivalent to one decimeter cubed, $1\ dm^3$, and one milliliter, 1 mL, is the same volume as one cubic centimeter, $1\ cm^3$. Hence 1 L is 1000 mL, just as $1\ dm^3$ is $1000\ cm^3$. One liter is equivalent to 1.057 quarts in the U.S. system.

Problem 2.5 How many cm^3 are contained in $1\ m^3$?

Solution 2.5 One hundred centimeters equals one meter, 100 cm/1 m. Hence to find the number of cm^3 per $1\ m^3$ this relationship should be cubed as follows.

$$\left(\frac{10^2 \text{ cm}}{1 \text{ m}}\right)^3 = \frac{10^6 \text{ cm}^3}{1 \text{ m}^3}$$

Problem 2.6   Convert 502 cm^3 to mm^3.

Solution 2.6   The simplest way to solve this problem is to realize that 1 cm is 10 mm; thus, 1 cm^3 equals 10^3 mm^3.

$$502 \text{ cm}^3 \times 1 \times 10^3 \text{ mm}^3/1 \text{ cm}^3 = 5.02 \times 10^5 \text{ mm}^3$$

Problem 2.7   How many microliters, μL, are contained in 1.00 m^3?

Solution 2.7   First, convert m^3 to dm^3. One dm^3 is exactly equivalent to 1 L. To complete the problem, use the conversion factor, 1 μL/1 $\times$ 10^{-6} L.

$$1.00 \text{ m}^3 \times 1 \text{ dm}^3/0.001 \text{ m}^3 \times 1 \text{ L}/1 \text{ dm}^3 \times 1 \mu\text{L}/1 \times 10^{-6} \text{ L} = 1 \times 10^9 \mu\text{L}$$

Problem 2.8   What is the volume in cm^3 of a solid with the following dimensions: 6.55 cm $\times$ 81.2 mm $\times$ 0.102 m?

Solution 2.8   First, convert the lengths in mm and m to cm.

$$81.2 \text{ mm} \times 1 \text{ cm}/10 \text{ mm} = 8.12 \text{ cm}$$
$$0.102 \text{ m} \times 10^2 \text{ m}/1 \text{ m} = 10.2 \text{ cm}$$

Then, multiply the three length measures to obtain the volume in cm^3.

$$V = 6.55 \text{ cm} \times 8.12 \text{ cm} \times 10.2 \text{ cm} = 542 \text{ cm}^3$$

Problem 2.9   An automobile engine has a displacement of 3.80 L. What is its displacement in cubic inches? \

Solution 2.9   To find the relationships between dm^3 and m^3, and in^3 and m^3, cube the conversion factors 10 dm/m and 39.37 in/m as follows.

$$(10 \text{ dm})^3/(1 \text{ m})^3 = 10^3 \text{ dm}^3/1 \text{ m}^3$$
$$(39.37 \, in)^3/(1 \text{ m})^3 = 6.102 \times 10^4 \, in^3/1 \text{ m}^3$$

Then, use these conversion factors to convert L to in^3.

$$3.80 \text{ L} \times 1 \text{ dm}^3/1 \text{ L} \times 1 \text{ m}^3/10^3 \text{ dm}^3 \times 6.102 \times 10^4 \, in^3/1 \text{ m}^3 = 232 \, in^3$$

Mass Measurements

Mass is a measure of the amount of matter in an object. The most commonly used SI units for mass are the kilogram, kg, and gram, g. One kilogram, 1 kg, is equivalent to 1000 g. For most routine chemistry laboratory measurements, the kilogram is too large. Hence, the gram and its submultiples are the most common units of mass in the lab.

MASS VERSUS WEIGHT

What is the difference between mass and weight? If equal forces are applied to large and small masses, the small mass accelerates more than the larger mass. The mass of a body is fixed and does not change when moved to another part of the universe. In contrast, the weight of an object depends on both its mass and the gravitational force of attraction. Because the gravitational field of the earth is not uniform, the weight of a body varies, depending on its location. However, it is common practice to use the terms mass and weight interchangeably.

Problem 2.10 A small object is found to have a mass of 327 mg. What is the mass of the object in pounds?

Solution 2.10 Use the conversion factor 1 g/1000 mg to convert to g and then 1 lb/454 g to convert grams to pounds.

$$327 \text{ mg} \times 1 \text{ g}/1000 \text{ mg} \times 1 \text{ lb}/454 \text{ g} = 0.000720 \text{ lb}$$

Problem 2.11 A chemistry student performs an experiment in which the mass of a sample must be determined in mg. The student first measures the mass of an empty beaker and finds that it is 74.111 g. Then the student measures the combined mass of the sample and beaker and finds that it is 76.984 g. What is the mass of the sample in mg?

Solution 2.11 Subtract the mass of the empty beaker from the mass of the beaker plus the sample to obtain the mass of the sample in grams.

$$\text{Mass of sample} = 76.984 \text{ g} - 74.111 \text{ g} = 2.873 \text{ g}$$

Then convert the grams to milligrams using the conversion factor 1000 mg/1 g.

$$2.873 \text{ g} \times 1000 \text{ mg}/1 \text{ g} = 2873 \text{ mg}$$

Density Measurements

Density is the ratio of mass to volume of a sample of matter.

$$\text{Density} = \frac{\text{mass}}{\text{volume}}$$

Most often the density of an object has the SI units of either g/cm^3 or g/dm^3, or the non-SI units g/mL and g/L. Knowing the density of an object tells you how compact it is. More dense objects have more matter in a given volume than less dense objects.

INTENSIVE AND EXTENSIVE PROPERTIES

Density is classified as an intensive property of matter. An intensive property is independent of the quantity of matter present. For instance, the density of an object does not depend on the sample size. Fifty cm^3 of water has a mass of 50 g, and 100 cm^3 of water has a mass of 100 g. In both cases, the density of water is 1.0 g/cm^3. Another intensive property of matter is temperature. The opposite of an intensive property is an extensive property, which depends on the amount or extent of matter present. Two examples of extensive properties are mass and volume.

Problem 2.12 An empty 25-mL graduated cylinder has a mass of 77.31 g. After it is filled with 25.0 mL of an unknown liquid, the combined mass is 107.81 g. Calculate the density of the unknown liquid.

Solution 2.12 To calculate the density, d, of the unknown liquid, divide the mass of the liquid by its volume.

$$\text{Density} = \frac{\text{mass}}{\text{volume}}$$

First, calculate the mass of the unknown liquid.

$$\text{mass of unknown liquid} = (\text{mass of unknown liquid} + \text{graduated cylinder})$$
$$- \text{mass of graduated cylinder}$$
$$= 107.81 \text{ g} - 77.31 \text{ g} = 30.50 \text{ g}$$

Then, calculate the density of the unknown liquid.

$$d = \text{mass/volume}$$
$$= 30.50 \text{ g}/25.0 \text{ mL} = 1.22 \text{ g/mL}$$

Problem 2.13 What volume in L does 3.5 kg mercury, Hg, occupy? The density of mercury is 13.6 g/cm^3.

Solution 2.13 First convert the mass of Hg to grams and then use the density, 13.6 g/cm^3, to calculate the volume in cm^3. Complete the problem by converting cm^3 to L.

$$3.5 \text{ kg} \times 1000 \text{ g/kg} \times 1 \text{ cm}^3/13.6 \text{ g} \times 1 \text{ L}/1000 \text{ cm}^3 = 0.26 \text{ L Hg}$$

Problem 2.14 Calculate the mass in kg of air in a room that has the dimensions of 8.50 m by 9.11 m by 2.52 m. The density of air is 1.29 g/dm^3.

Solution 2.14 First, calculate the volume of air in the room.

$$V = 8.50 \text{ m} \times 9.11 \text{ m} \times 2.52 \text{ m} = 195 \text{ m}^3$$

Then, convert the volume in m^3 to dm^3.

$$195 \text{ m}^3 \times 1 \times 10^3 \text{ dm}^3/\text{m}^3 = 1.95 \times 10^5 \text{ dm}^3$$

Finally, use the density, 1.29 g/dm^3, to calculate the mass in grams and then convert to kilograms.

$$1.95 \times 10^5 \text{ dm}^3 \times 1.29 \text{ g/dm}^3 \times 1 \text{ kg}/1000 \text{ g} = 252 \text{ kg}$$

Problem 2.15 An empty density bottle (pycnometer) has a mass of 37.234 g. It is filled with distilled water and has a combined mass of 57.177 g. The water is removed and is replaced with ethanol (grain alcohol). The mass of the bottle and ethanol is 53.021 g. If the density of water at room temperature, 298 K, is 0.99707 g/cm^3, what is the density of ethanol?

Solution 2.15 To calculate the density, d, of ethanol divide the mass by the volume.

$$d = \frac{\text{mass}}{\text{volume}}$$

First, calculate the mass of ethanol.

$$\text{Mass of ethanol} = (\text{mass of bottle} + \text{ethanol}) - \text{mass of bottle}$$
$$= 53.021 \text{ g} - 37.234 \text{ g} = 15.787 \text{ g ethanol}$$

Next, calculate the volume of the bottle. To accomplish this, calculate the mass of the water that fills the bottle. Then use the density of water to obtain its volume.

$$\text{Mass of water} = (\text{mass of bottle} + \text{water}) - \text{mass of bottle}$$
$$= 57.177 \text{ g} - 37.234 \text{ g} = 19.943 \text{ g water}$$
$$\text{Volume of water} = 19.943 \text{ g } H_2O \times 1.0000 \text{ cm}^3 \text{ } H_2O/0.99707 \text{ g } H_2O$$
$$= 20.002 \text{ cm}^3$$

Then, calculate the density of ethanol.

$$d = \text{mass/volume}$$
$$= 15.787 \text{ g}/20.002 \text{ cm}^3 = 0.78929 \text{ g/cm}^3$$

Problem 2.16 What volume of gold, Au, has the same mass as 15.0 cm^3 of lead, Pb? The densities of Au and Pb are 19.3 and 11.4 g/cm^3, respectively.

Solution 2.16 First, calculate the mass of lead, Pb, using its density, 11.4 g/cm^3. This mass of Pb equals that of Au

$$15.0 \text{ cm}^3 \times 11.4 \text{ g Pb/cm}^3 = 171 \text{ g Pb} = 171 \text{ g Au}$$

Then, calculate the volume of gold, Au, using its density 19.3 g/cm^3.

$$171 \text{ g Au} \times 1 \text{ cm}^3/19.3 \text{ g Au} = 8.86 \text{ cm}^3$$

Temperature and Heat

Temperature is a measure of the hotness or coldness of an object. If a warmer object contacts a colder one, the temperature of the warmer object decreases and the temperature of the colder one increases spontaneously until the temperatures equalize. Heat flows or transfers from the hotter object to the colder one. Heat is a form of kinetic energy detected when objects of different temperatures contact each other. Thus, a better way to define temperature is the property of a body that determines the direction that heat flows. Temperature is an intensive property of matter, while heat is an extensive property.

CELSIUS AND KELVIN TEMPERATURE SCALES

Most laboratory thermometers have calibration marks in degrees Celsius, °C, a non-SI temperature unit. The SI unit of temperature is the Kelvin, K. The magnitude of one Celsius degree is equivalent to that of one Kelvin. However, the zero points of these scales differ. The zero point of the Kelvin scale is absolute zero, the lowest possible temperature. On the Celsius scale, absolute zero is −273.15°C.

$$K = °C + 273.15$$

CELSIUS AND FAHRENHEIT TEMPERATURE SCALES

The relationship of the Fahrenheit temperature scale and the Celsius scale is as follows:

$$°C = 5/9(°F - 32)$$

Rearranging and solving the equation for $°F$ gives the following:

$$°F = 9/5°C + 32 = 1.8°C + 32$$

Problem 2.17   Convert $-56.9°F$ to $°C$ and K.

Solution 2.17   First, convert $°F$ to $°C$.

$$°C = 5/9(-56.9°F - 32) = -49.4°C$$

Then, convert $°C$ to K.

$$K = °C + 273.15$$
$$= -49.4°C + 273.15 = 223.8 \text{ K}$$

Problem 2.18   Standard temperature for chemical reactions is 298 K. What temperature is this in $°C$ and $°F$?

Solution 2.18   First, convert K to $°C$.

$$K = °C + 273$$
$$°C = K - 273$$
$$= 298 \text{ K} - 273 = 25°C$$

Then, convert $°C$ to $°F$.

$$°C = 5/9(°F - 32)$$
$$°F = 9/5 \, °C + 32$$
$$= 9/525°C + 32 = 77°F$$

Problem 2.19   One temperature is the same on both the Celsius and Fahrenheit scales. Calculate this temperature.

Solution 2.19   For $°F$, substitute $°C$ in the following temperature conversion equation because they are equal. Then solve for $°C$.

$$°C = 5/9(°F - 32)$$
$$= 5/9(°C - 32) = -40°C = -40°F$$

Energy Measurements

POTENTIAL AND KINETIC ENERGY

Energy is the capacity to do work. All different types of energy can be divided into two broad categories: potential and kinetic energy. Potential energy is stored energy. Kinetic energy is energy of motion. Energy may be stored as a result of its position or condition, but most important to chemists is the energy stored in matter—chemical potential energy.

CALCULATING KINETIC ENERGY

The kinetic energy possessed by a body depends on both its mass and velocity. Bodies that have equal masses possess the same kinetic energy, if they travel at the same velocity, but have different kinetic energies if they travel at different velocities. The kinetic energy of a body can be calculated from Equation 2.1.

$$E_k = 1/2mv^2 \tag{2.1}$$

in which E_k is kinetic energy in J, m is the mass of the body in kg, and v is its velocity in m/s.

THE JOULE

The SI unit for energy is the joule, J. One joule is 1 kg m^2/s^2. A 1 kg mass that travels at 1 m/s has a kinetic energy of 1 kg(m/s)^2 or 1 J. A joule is a rather small unit of energy for chemical reactions. Therefore, the kilojoule, kJ, is most often encountered.

Problem 2.20 What is the kinetic energy in joules of a 5.0-kg body that has a velocity of 25 m/s?

Solution 2.20 Use Equation 2.1 to solve this problem.

$$E_k = 1/2mv^2$$
$$= 1/2 \times 5.0 \text{ kg} \times (25 \text{ m/s})^2 = 1.6 \times 10^3 \text{ J}$$

THE CALORIE

The non-SI unit for energy is the calorie, cal. One calorie is exactly equivalent to 4.184 J. Historically, one calorie was defined as the amount of heat needed to raise one gram of water by one degree Celsius.

Problem 2.21 Calculate the energy in J and cal of a 2.00-kg body that moves with a constant velocity of 15.0 m/s.

Solution 2.21 Use Equation 2.1 to calculate the energy in joules.

$$E_k = 1/2mv^2$$
$$= 1/2 \times 2.00 \text{ kg} \times (15.0 \text{ m/s})^2 = 225 \text{ J}$$

Then, convert from joules to calories.

$$225 \text{ J} \times 1 \text{ cal}/4.184 \text{ J} = 53.8 \text{ cal}$$

2.3 UNCERTAINTY IN MEASUREMENTS

Accuracy

Whenever chemical measurements are made, both precision and accuracy are considered. The accuracy of a measurement is how close the measured value is to a standard or "true" value. A more accurate measurement is one closer to the standard value than a less accurate measurement. Accuracy is measured in terms of the deviation of the measurement(s) (called the error) from the "true" value.

Problem 2.22   A student performs an experiment to find the density of a pure sample of chromium, Cr. The results of the experiment indicated that the density of the Cr was 7.00 g/cm^3. If the actual value of the density of Cr is 7.19 g/cm^3, calculate the percent deviation of this measurement.

Solution 2.22   To calculate the percent deviation, divide the deviation by the true value and multiply by 100 to get a percent.

$$\% \; deviation = \frac{measured \; value - true \; value}{true \; value} \times 100$$
$$\% \; deviation = (7.00 \; g/cm^3 - 7.19 \; g/cm^3)/7.19 \; g/cm^3 \times 100$$
$$= -2.6\%$$

The percent deviation is a negative number because the measured value is below the true value. Sometimes percent deviations are expressed as the absolute value, and the minus sign is dropped.

Precision

Precision is how closely repeated measures are grouped, that is, how reproducible the measurements are. The smaller the range of values obtained when measuring the same quantity, the greater the precision. Most often, but not always, good precision is an indication of high accuracy.

ERRORS IN MEASUREMENT

Measurement errors account for the range of different values that are obtained when making the same measurement repeatedly. Two types of errors are generally found in chemical measurements: systematic and random errors.

Systematic errors result from: poor procedures and methods; malfunctioning and uncalibrated instruments; human error; impure samples; and some unrecognized factors that influence the results. Systematic errors are reduced by finding their causes and eliminating them.

Random errors occur in all chemical measurements. Even if every precaution is taken to avoid systematic errors, small deviations or random errors arise that are unavoidable and not identifiable. Random errors, by definition, are impossible to illustrate. If random errors could be identified, they would be corrected, and thus would not be random errors.

ERRORS AND MEASUREMENT UNCERTAINTY

Collectively, systematic and random errors introduce uncertainty—or lack of confidence—in all measured values. Thus, all reported measurements should indicate the degree of uncertainty of the measurement. In chemistry, this is most frequently accomplished through the use of significant figures, which is described in the following section.

Range of Uncertainty of Measurements

Measurement uncertainty can be expressed by showing the range of uncertainty. More precise measuring devices give a smaller range of uncertainty than less precise ones.

Problem 2.23   The mass of an unknown metal was found to be $68.33 \pm 0.05 \; g$. The volume of this metal was $8.3 \pm 0.2 \; cm^3$. (a) Calculate the maximum limit of density by dividing the maximum mass by the minimum volume. (b) Calculate the minimum limit of density by dividing the minimum mass by the maximum volume. (c) Calculate the average of these two densities. (d) Subtract the average from the maximum density and determine the range of uncertainty in the calculated density.

Solution 2.23
(a) To obtain the maximum limit of density, divide the maximum mass, m, by the minimum volume, V.

$$d_{max} = m_{max}/V_{min}$$
$$= 68.38 \; g/8.1 \; cm^3 = 8.4 \; g/cm^3$$

(b) To obtain the minimum limit of density, divide the minimum mass by the maximum volume.

$$d_{min} = m_{min}/V_{max}$$
$$= 68.28 \ g/8.5 \ cm^3 = 8.0 \ g/cm^3$$

(c) Next, calculate the average of these two densities.

$$d_{av} = (8.0 \ g/cm^3 + 8.4 \ g/cm^3)/2 = 8.2 \ g/cm^3$$

(d) Finally, subtract the average from the maximum density and determine the range of uncertainty in the calculated density ($d = 8.0 \pm 0.2 \ g/cm^3$).

2.4   SIGNIFICANT FIGURES

What Are Significant Figures?

Significant figures, also called significant digits, are measured digits in a number that are known with certainty plus one uncertain digit. Stated differently, significant figures are all known digits plus the first doubtful or estimated digit.

It is important to note that significant figures only apply to measured values, and do not apply to exact numbers. Significant figures only apply to measurements that are to some degree uncertain.

Significant Figures and Uncertainty

Usually, the last significant figure is thought to be uncertain by ± 1. For example, stating that the volume of a liquid is 35.5 mL indicates that the measured volume is at most 35.6 mL (+0.1) and at least 35.4 mL (−0.1). If the same liquid is totally transferred to a more precise volumetric instrument—let's say one that has a scale with 0.1-mL marks etched accurately on the side—it is possible to obtain an additional significant figure.

The Number of Significant Figures

Whenever a measurement is encountered, always remember that besides the numerical value and units, the number also indicates the precision with which the measurement was made, by the number of significant figures in the measurement. Consider the following three measurements and the indicated number of significant figures.

1.25 m indicates three significant figures (1, 2, 5) (range 1.26 m–1.24 m)

434.56 K indicates five significant figures (4, 3, 4, 5, 6) (range 434.57 K–434.55 K)

ZEROS AND SIGNIFICANT FIGURES

All nonzero numbers in measurements are always significant, but zeros pose a special problem because a zero in a number that acts as a placeholder is not significant. Placeholders are not measured quantities; therefore, they are not significant figures.

The following rules summarize all possible cases in which zeros are found in measurements:

Rule 1. Zeros located in the middle of a number.
In all cases, zeros in the middle of a number are significant. In each of the following, the zero is a significant figure. Zeros in the middle of measured quantities are measured digits and are not placeholders; accordingly, they are significant in all cases.

Rule 2. Zeros located in front of a number.
Zeros in front of numbers are usually to the right of the decimal point. These zeros act as placeholders (they are not measured), so they are not significant figures.

Sometimes a zero is placed in front of the decimal point to show that no other digit is present. Similarly this zero is not significant.

Rule 3. Zeros located after a number to the right of the decimal point.

For this specific case, the zero is either a measured quantity (certain) or a good estimate (the first uncertain digit); consequently, zeros after a number and to the right of the decimal point are all significant.

For each of the above measurements, the zeros were measured by some instrument. All of the zeros are certain except the last zero, which is uncertain but still significant.

Rule 4. Zeros located after a number to the left of the decimal point.

Zeros found after a number and to the left of the decimal point are significant if they are measured, and are not significant if they are placeholders.

An object with a measured mass of 500 g has a questionable number of significant figures because more information is required to determine the correct number. The measurement, 500 g, contains three significant figures only if the second zero (units place) is the first uncertain figure. It contains two significant figures if the first zero (tens place) is the first uncertain figure. Lastly, the 5 could be the uncertain digit; if this is the case, the measurement only has one significant figure.

To avoid the confusion generated by the ambiguous nature of zeros to the left of decimal points, such measurements are often expressed in scientific notation in which the decimal factor represents the correct number of significant figures. Thus, 500 grams is expressed as 5×10^2 g (one significant figure) or 5.0×10^2 g (two significant figures) or 5.00×10^2 g (three significant figures), depending on the proper number of significant figures.

Problem 2.24   Write the number of significant figures indicated by each of the following measurements: (a) 55,9977 g, (b) 0.2937 cm, (c) 1000.0200 L, (d) 0.0000500 kg, (e) 2.001010×10^{12} mg

Solution 2.24   (a) Six significant figures, (b) Four significant figures, (c) Eight significant figures, (d) Three significant figures, (e) Seven significant figures

Problem 2.25   A college chemistry professor counts the number of students in his laboratory class. The count indicates the presence of 21 students. How many significant figures does this represent?

Solution 2.25   Significant figures do not apply in this case because there is no uncertainty in counting students.

Addition and Subtraction of Significant Figures

When measured quantities are added and subtracted, the answer can have no more digits to the right of the decimal point than does the measured quantity with the least number of decimal places.

Problem 2.26   Add the masses 2.0965 g and 1.41 g and express the answer to the correct number of significant figures.

Solution 2.26   The answer can only have two decimal places. First calculate the sum of the two numbers:

$$
\begin{array}{r}
2.0965 \text{ g} \\
+ \quad 1.41 \text{ g} \\
\hline
3.5065 \text{ g} \quad = 3.51 \text{ g}
\end{array}
$$

Then round off the answer to the correct number of decimal places. Because the second mass was only measured to two decimal places, the answer can only have two decimal places. The answer to this problem is 3.51 g.

Rules for Rounding Off Measurements

When rounding off, look at the first nonsignificant figure—one place to the right of the least significant figure. The least significant figure is the last figure in the number retained after rounding off. Then apply the following three rounding rules.

RULE 1

If the value of the first nonsignificant figure is greater than 5, add 1 to the least significant figure and drop all nonsignificant digits.

RULE 2

If the value of the first nonsignificant figure is less than 5, retain the least significant figure and drop all nonsignificant digits.

RULE 3

(a) If the first nonsignificant figure is 5 and is followed by nonzero digits, increase the value of the least significant figure by one and drop all nonsignificant digits.
(b) If the 5 is followed by zeros or nothing, add 1 to the least significant figure and drop all nonsignificant digits; however, if the least significant figure is an even number, retain the least significant figure and drop all nonsignificant figures.

Problem 2.27   What is the sum of 10.0043 mL + 5.5 mL + 9.250 mL?

Solution 2.27

$$
\begin{array}{ll}
10.0043 \text{ mL} & \text{(four decimal places)} \\
5.5 \text{ mL} & \text{(one decimal places)} \\
+\quad 9.250 \text{ mL} & \text{(three decimal places)} \\
\hline
24.7543 \text{ mL} & \text{(round to one decimal place)}
\end{array}
$$

The answer, 24.7543 mL, must be rounded to one decimal place because the second measured quantity, 5.5 mL, only contains one decimal place. Because the first nonsignificant figure is 5 followed by nonzero digits and the least significant figure is 7 add one to the least significant figure and drop all nonsignificant digits. This gives a final answer of 24.8 mL.

Multiplication and Division of Significant Figures

When measurements are multiplied and divided, the answer can have no more significant figures than the measurement with the least number of significant figures. If two numbers are multiplied, one with six and the other with three significant figures, the answer can only have three significant figures. Problem 2.28 illustrates such a problem.

Problem 2.28   Find the area of a surface that is 5.82131 cm by 4.11 cm.

Solution 2.28   To find the area multiply the length times the width.

$$
\begin{array}{ll}
57.82131 \text{ cm} & \text{(six significant figures)} \\
\times\quad 4.11 \text{ cm} & \text{(three significant figures)} \\
\hline
23.92558410 \text{ cm}^2 &
\end{array}
$$

The first nonsignificant digit in the answer is 2, which is less than 5; thus, Rule 2 is applied and the answer is rounded off to 23.9 cm^2 (three significant figures).

Problem 2.29   Perform the indicated arithmetic operations and express the answer to the correct number of significant figures.

$$\frac{7.290 \text{ m} \times 2.0400 \text{ m}}{0.95 \text{ m}} =$$

Solution 2.29 The denominator contains a measurement with only two significant figures; hence, this limits the answer to two significant figures. Perform the indicated math operations and round off the resulting answer to two significant figures.

$$\frac{7.290 \text{ m} \times 2.0400 \text{ m}}{0.95 \text{ m}} = 15.65431579 \text{ m} = 16 \text{ m}$$

The first nonsignificant figure is 6; hence, the answer is rounded off by adding 1 to 5 and dropping the nonsignificant figures, which leaves 16 m as the answer.

Multiplication and Addition of Significant Figures

It is not uncommon to perform calculations in which both addition and multiplication are required. Problem 2.30 shows how to solve such problems.

Problem 2.30 Perform the indicated arithmetic operations and express the answer to the correct number of significant figures.

$$(11.2050 \text{ mm} - 10.322 \text{ mm}) \times 6.030000 \text{ mm} = ?$$

Solution 2.30 After subtracting, the answer can have only three decimal places because 10.322 mm only contains three decimal places.

$$11.2050 \text{ mm} - 10.322 \text{ mm} = 0.8830 \text{ mm} = 0.883 \text{ mm}$$

After multiplying 0.883 mm (three significant figures) by 6.030000 mm (seven significant figures), the answer can only have three significant figures.

$$0.883 \text{ mm} \times 6.030000 \text{ mm} = 5.32449 \text{ mm}^2 = 5.32 \text{ mm}^2$$

SUMMARY

*T*he International System of Units, SI, has seven base units from which all of the others are derived. Prefixes are added to units to scale the unit to the proper size.

Mass is a measure of the quantity of matter contained in an object. Volume is the amount of space occupied by a mass. The density of matter is the ratio of mass to volume. Temperature is a measure of the degree of hotness of a body, and determines the direction of heat flow. Energy is the capacity to do work. Stored energy is called potential energy. Energy that involves motion is kinetic energy.

All measurements are uncertain to some degree because of experimental errors. Systematic errors can be identified and in many cases corrected. Random errors are errors that cannot be identified. The combination of systematic and random errors produces measurement uncertainty. To indicate the degree of uncertainty of a measurement, scientists use significant figures, which are the measured digits that are certain plus one digit that is uncertain.

CHAPTER 2 REVIEW EXERCISE

1. Perform each of the following length conversions: (a) 616 m = ? mm, (b) 2059 cm = ? nm, (c) 0.71 km = ? μm

2. If exactly 16 oz are contained in a pound and 2000 lb are contained in a ton, change each to the designated SI unit. (a) 12 lbs = ? g, (b) 446 oz = ? mg, (c) 2.128 tons = ? Mg

3. Convert 98.6°F to °C and K.

4. Change each to the indicated unit: (a) 721.1 mL = ? qt, (b) 2.010 m^3 = ? mm^3, (c) 9.502 cm^3 = ? dm^3

5. (a) What Fahrenheit temperature is numerically equal to twice the Celsius temperature?, (b) What Celsius temperature is numerically equal to twice the Fahrenheit temperature?

6. Vanadium, an element, has a density of 6.11 g/mL. Calculate the mass in grams of vanadium contained in the following volumes: (a) 55.0 mL, (b) 707 cm^3, (c) 904.5 μL

7. A sample of cadmium, Cd, has a mass of 1.94 kg. What volume does the Cd occupy? The density of Cd is 8.65 g/cm^3.

8. Air has a density of 1.29 g/L. Express the density of air in each of the following units: (a) g/cm^3, (b) kg/m^3, (c) mg/mm^3, (d) kg/km^3.

9. An empty 10-mL graduated cylinder has a mass of 49.01 g. After it is filled with 10.00 mL of an unknown liquid, the combined mass is 58.71 g. Calculate the density of the unknown liquid.

10. An empty density bottle (pycnometer) has a mass of 57.004 g. When filled with distilled water, it has a mass of 82.901 g. An unknown liquid is then added to the density bottle and the combined mass of the bottle and liquid is 84.040 g. The density of water at room temperature is 0.99707 g/cm^3. What is the density of the unknown liquid?

11. The mass of the water in the oceans is 4.0 × 10^{20} kg. The concentration of bromine in the oceans is about 60 kg per million kg of water (60 parts per million by mass). (a) What mass of bromine in metric tons is in the oceans? (b) Calculate the mass of ocean water that contains 175 metric tons of Br. One metric ton is equivalent to 1000 kg.

12. A bar of pure Zn ($d = 7.14$ g/cm^3) has the following dimensions: 0.560 m × 11.3 cm × 853.1 mm. What is the mass of the Zn bar in kilograms?

13. A cylinder is measured and is found to have a mass of 124.54 g. Its height is 3.22 cm with a circular diameter of 1.88 cm. The formula for the volume of a cylinder is $V = \pi r^2 h$. Calculate the density of the cylinder.

14. (a) What mass of iron ($d = 7.86$ g/cm^3) has the same volume as 1.00 kg U? The density of U is 18.9 g/cm^3. (b) What volume of iron has the same mass as 100 mL U?

15. (a) What is the kinetic energy in J and cal of a 4.5 kg body that has a velocity of 3.9 m/s? (b) What is the kinetic energy in J when the velocity of this body doubles?

16. How many kcal are equivalent to 1.070 kJ?

17. How many significant figures do each of the following express? (a) 2.914 g, (b) 0.00001 m, (c) 0.0010100 mL?

18. Perform the indicated additions and subtractions and express the answer to the correct number of significant figures.

    (a) 32.55 g − 1.9889 g = ?
    (b) 0.02 mL + 0.183 mL = ?
    (c) 34.0000 s − 11.0 s + 55.3458702 s = ?

19. Perform the indicated multiplications and divisions and express the answer to the correct number of significant figures.

   (a) 183.22 g/5.4 mL = ?
   (b) 0.210 cm × 6.388 cm × 16.5495 cm =?
   (c) 206.00 L/0.000276131 L = ?

20. Perform the indicated arithmetic operations and express the answer to the correct number of significant figures.

   (a) (13.983 m − 12.98551 m) × 8.319 m =?
   (b) (28.070 g − 28.069 g)/(5.623 s + 25.134 s) =?

21. The density of germanium, Ge, is 5.23 g/cm^3. (a) What is the mass of a cube of Ge, in kg, that has an edge length, l, of 884 mm? ($V_{cube} = l^3$) (b) What is the mass of a cylinder of Ge, in kg, that has a radius of 4.50 cm and a height of 12.1 cm? ($V_{cylinder} = \pi r^2 h$) (c) What is the mass of a sphere of germanium, in kg, that has a radius of 118 mm? ($V_{sphere} = 4/3\pi r^3$) (d) What is the radius of a sphere of Ge that has a mass of 1.000 kg?

ANSWERS TO REVIEW EXERCISE

1. (a) 6.16×10^5 mm, (b) 2.059×10^{10} nm, (c) 7.1×10^8 μm

2. (a) 5.4×10^3 g, (b) 1.27×10^7 mg, (c) 1.932 Mg

3. $37.0°C$, 310.2 K

4. (a) 0.7622 qt, (b) $2.010 \times 10^9 mm^3$, (c) 9.502×10^{-3} dm^3

5. (a) $320°F$, (b) $-24.62°C$

6. (a) 336 g, (b) 4.32×10^3 g, (c) 5.53 g

7. $224 cm^3$

8. (a) $0.00129 g/cm^3$, (b) $1.29 kg/m^3$, (c) $0.00129 mg/mm^3$, (d) $1.29 \times 10^9 kg/km^3$

9. $0.970 g/mL$

10. $1.0409 g/cm^3$

11. (a) 2.4×10^{16} kg Br, (b) 2.9×10^9 kg ocean water

12. 385 kg

13. $13.9 g/cm^3$

14. (a) 416 g, (b) 240 mL

15. (a) 34 J, 8.1 cal, (b) 1.4×10^2 J

16. 0.2557 kcal

17. (a) 4, (b) 1, (c) 5

18. (a) 30.56 g, (b) 0.20 mL, (c) 78.3 s

19. (a) 34 g/mL, (b) $22.2 cm^3$, (c) 7.4602×10^5

20. (a) $8.30 m^2$, (b) 3×10^{-5} g/s

21. (a) 3.61×10^3 kg, (b) 4.03 kg, (c) 36.0 kg, (d) 3.574 cm

3

Atoms and Elements, Molecules and Compounds

In this chapter we will consider the fundamental particles that compose matter: atoms, ions, and molecules. The properties of these small particles (their microscopic properties) determine the overall properties (their macroscopic properties) of the substances and mixtures they compose. The chapter concludes with a discussion of the rules for naming and writing formulas of inorganic compounds.

3.1 BASIC STRUCTURE OF THE ATOM

Early History of Atoms

Democritus (460–370 B.C.) and Leucippus, ancient Greek philosophers, were the first people to propose the idea that matter is made up of atoms. They stated that matter was composed of very small, indivisible, indestructible particles.

Dalton Model of the Atom

Almost 2300 years elapsed before the proposal of a scientific atomic theory. In 1803, John Dalton (1766–1844) proposed the first generally accepted theory of atoms. Dalton's hypotheses are as follows: All matter is composed of small indivisible and indestructible particles called atoms; The atoms of a given element have the same properties, e.g., weight and size; Atoms of different elements have different properties; In chemical reactions, atoms (in elements) combine with other atoms in fixed ratios to form molecules (in compounds), but cannot be created or destroyed.

LAW OF CONSERVATION OF MASS

The longevity of Dalton's theory may be attributed to its incorporation and explanation of two fundamental laws of chemistry: the law of conservation of mass and the law of constant composition. The law of conservation of mass states that matter cannot be created or destroyed under normal conditions.

LAW OF CONSTANT COMPOSITION (LAW OF DEFINITE PROPORTIONS)

The law of constant composition, also known as the law of definite proportions, states that the composition of a pure substance is fixed. Recall that the composition of a substance is the amount and identity of its components. Therefore, the law of constant composition tells us that a compound always has the same elements in the same mass ratio.

LAW OF MULTIPLE PROPORTIONS

John Dalton used his atomic model to explain compounds that result when one atom combines with a second atom in different ratios. Dalton stated that if two elements can combine to form more than one compound, the masses of one element that combine with a fixed mass of the second element are in a ratio of small whole numbers. Today, this statement is called the law of multiple proportions.

Problem 3.1 Use carbon dioxide and carbon monoxide to illustrate the law of multiple proportions. The ratio of the mass of O to the mass of C in 100 g CO_2 is 72.7 g O to 27.3 g C. The ratio of the mass of oxygen to the mass of carbon in 100 g CO is 57.1 g O to 42.9 g C.

Solution 3.1 The ratio of the mass of O to the mass of C in 100 g CO_2 is 72.7 g O to 27.3 g C or 2.66 to 1.00. The ratio of the mass of oxygen to the mass of carbon in 100 g CO is 57.1 g O to 42.9 g C or 1.33 to 1.00.

According to the law of multiple proportions, the ratio of the mass of O in CO_2 per gram of C in CO_2 to the mass of O in CO per gram of C in CO is a whole number. This mass ratio is two to one–a simple ratio of whole numbers.

$$\frac{\frac{2.66\ g\ O}{g\ C\ in\ CO_2}}{\frac{1.33\ g\ C}{g\ C\ in\ CO}} = \frac{2.00}{1.00}$$

Problem 3.2 The percent of S in one iron-sulfur compound is 36.4% and the percent of S in another iron-sulfur compound is 53.3%. Use these data to illustrate the law of multiple proportions.

Solution 3.2 The ratio of the mass of S to the mass of Fe in 100 g is 36.4 g S to 63.6 g Fe, or 0.572 to 1.00 in the first compound. The ratio of the mass of S to the mass of Fe is 53.3 g S to 46.7 g Fe, or 1.14 to 1.00, in the second compound. The ratio of S to Fe in the second compound compared to that of the first is 1.14 to 0.572, or 2.00 to 1.00—a ratio of whole numbers.

Electricity and the Atom

Michael Faraday (1791–1867) performed some of the pioneering experiments on the nature of electricity. Faraday passed electric currents through salt solutions and found that dissolved salts undergo chemical reactions. Later he discovered that the masses of the new substances produced were related to the duration and magnitude of the electric current that flowed through the solutions.

DISCHARGE TUBES EXPERIMENTS

Faraday, with Geissler, Crooks, and Hittorf, investigated the flow of electricity through gases by constructing glass discharge tubes with embedded electrodes. They discovered that if they added gases to these tubes and applied a high voltage to the electrodes, the gas glowed with a characteristic color.

Additional investigations revealed that an electric current flowed from the negative electrode, the cathode, to the positive electrode, the anode. This glow was the result of the electric discharge hitting the anode. Because these rays were emitted from the cathode, they became known as cathode rays.

Charged Bodies

Experimental evidence suggested that cathode rays were negatively charged because like electric charges repel and unlike electric charges attract. Scientists attempted many other discharge tube experiments and the majority of the results suggested that cathode rays were small particles.

Protons (Goldstein Experiment)

The discovery of protons, the positively charged particles in atoms, also was the result of a discharge tube experiment. In 1886, E. Goldstein discovered that positively charged particles were accelerated from the anode to the cathode at the same time that cathode rays accelerated from the cathode to the anode.

The Charge-to-Mass Ratio of an Electron (Thomson Experiment)

In 1897, the British scientist Joseph John (J. J.) Thomson (1856–1940) performed a classic discharge tube experiment that established the particle nature of electricity. From this experiment, he suggested that cathode rays were composed of small negatively charged particles called electrons. Thomson measured the charge, e, to mass, m, ratio of the electron. It has the value -1.76×10^8 coulombs/g. A coulomb, C, is a unit of electric charge. Because of the large magnitude of the charge-to-mass ratio, Thomson showed that an electron has a relatively large negative charge compared to its small mass.

Problem 3.3 The charge-to-mass ratio for a proton, p^+, is 1/1837 times that of the charge-to-mass ratio for an e^-, -1.76×10^8 C/g. What does this indicate about the charge and mass of protons compared with those of electrons?

Solution 3.3 Because the charge-to-mass ratio of the proton, p^+, is 1/1837 that of the e^- and the charge of the electron is equal but opposite to that of the proton, the mass of the proton is 1837 times that of the electron.

The Charge on an Electron (Millikan Experiment)

In 1911, the American scientist Robert A. Millikan (1868–1953) measured the charge on an electron by performing what is now known as the oil-drop experiment. He calculated that one electron has a charge of -1.602×10^{-19} C. Millikan also showed that the charge on an electron was the most fundamental unit of electric charge.

Problem 3.4 Combine the results of Thomson's and Millikan's experiments, and calculate the mass of the electron.

Solution 3.4

$$-1.602 \times 10^{-19} \text{ C/e}^- \times 1 \text{ g}/-1.76 \times 10^8 \text{ C} = 9.10 \times 10^{-28} \text{ g/e}^-$$

X-Rays

In 1895, using a discharge tube, the German scientist Wilhelm Roentgen (1845–1923) discovered a new type of radiation. He noticed that when a discharge tube covered with black cardboard was switched on, it emitted radiation that caused barium platinocyanide coated paper to glow. Roentgen called this unknown radiation x-rays. Unlike cathode rays, x-rays were not affected by electrical and magnetic fields. They could also pass easily through many different types of matter.

Nuclear Radiation

Shortly after the discovery of x-rays, the French scientist Henri Becquerel (1852–1908) discovered accidentally that some substances spontaneously emit radiations. Becquerel found that his photographic plates were exposed when he placed them near rocks that contained a uranium compound. During the next two years, Marie Curie (1867–1934) and Pierre Curie (1859–1906) showed that many substances could emit radiation. In their extensive investigation of radiation, they discovered the elements polonium, Po, and radium, Ra.

ALPHA, BETA, AND GAMMA RADIATION

Ernest Rutherford (1871–1937) studied the properties of radiation and found that matter releases three principal types of radiation which he termed alpha (α), beta (β), and gamma (γ) rays. Rutherford showed that alpha rays are positively charged, beta rays are negatively charged, and gamma rays have no charge. The particles in α rays are the most massive of the three with a mass equivalent to that of a He nucleus, He^{2+}. Beta rays have the same mass as electrons. Gamma rays are massless because they are a form of electromagnetic radiation that closely resemble x-rays.

The Gold Leaf Experiment

In 1909, Rutherford and his students Hans Geiger (1882–1945) and Ernest Marsden probed the atom with α rays. They bombarded gold leaf, a thin target of gold foil, with a narrow beam of α particles. Surrounding the gold leaf target was a screen that detected the α radiation. Much to their surprise they discovered that a small percent of the α particles were deflected through large angles.

The Nuclear Model of the Atom

From the results of the gold-leaf experiment, Rutherford proposed a new model of the atom. The Rutherford atom was composed mainly of empty space where the electrons resided; at the center of the atom was a very small positively charged nucleus with most of the atom's mass.

Atomic Number (Moseley Experiment)

In 1914, H. G. J. Moseley (1887–1915), a student of Rutherford, devised a method for measuring the magnitude of the positive charge on the nucleus of an atom. In other words, he devised a means for counting the number of protons in the nuclei of atoms.

The Neutron (Chadwick Experiment)

The neutron, $n°$, is elusive because of its neutral charge, which means that it does not readily interact with matter. In 1932, James Chadwick (1891–1974), one of Rutherford's colleagues, produced neutrons when he bombarded Be atoms with α rays. What he found was a neutral particle that had approximately the same mass as a proton.

3.2 COMPOSITION OF ATOMS

Atomic Number, Z

Each atom has its own complement of protons, neutrons, and electrons. Because atoms are electrically neutral, the number of positive charges equals the number of negative charges. Stated differently, the atomic number of an atom also equals the number of electrons—the negatively-charged particles in an atom.

Atomic number = number of protons = number of electrons

Mass Number, A

Mass number, A, is the sum of the protons, p^+, and neutrons, $n°$, in the nucleus of an atom. Because mass numbers are *not* listed on standard periodic tables, they are given when needed. To display the mass numbers and atomic numbers for an atom, write the mass number as a superscript and the atomic number as a subscript on the left side of the symbol. For example, the mass number of an atom of scandium is 45 and its atomic number is 21. The symbol for this atom is written as $^{45}_{21}Sc$

The Number of Neutrons in an Atom

To calculate the number of neutrons in an atom, subtract the atomic number from the mass number.

$$\text{Number of neutrons} = \text{mass number} - \text{atomic number}$$
$$= (\text{number of p}^+ + \text{n}^\circ) - \text{number of p}^+$$
$$= A - Z$$

For example, to calculate the number of neutrons in the nuclei of $^{45}_{21}\text{Sc}$ atoms subtract 21 from 45 to obtain 24 neutrons.

$$\text{Number of neutrons} = 45 - 21 = 24 \text{ n}^\circ$$

Therefore, $^{45}_{21}\text{Sc}$ atoms have 21 p$^+$, 21 e$^-$, and 24 n$^\circ$.

Problem 3.5　How many neutrons are in the nuclei of $^{235}_{92}\text{U}$?

Solution 3.5　To calculate the number of neutrons, subtract the atomic number, 92, from the mass number, 235, of this U atom.

$$\text{Number of neutrons} = \text{mass number} - \text{atomic number}$$
$$= 235 - 92 = 143 \text{ n}^\circ$$

Problem 3.6　What is the atomic number, mass number, and symbol for the element that has 46 protons and 60 neutrons?

Solution 3.6　The atomic number, Z, is the number of protons. Thus, this atom has an atomic number of 46. The periodic table shows that the atom with an atomic number of 46 is palladium, Pd. Mass number, A, is the number of protons and neutrons.

$$\text{Mass number} = \text{number of p}^+ + \text{number of n}^\circ$$
$$= 46 \text{ p}^+ + 60 \text{ n}^\circ = 106$$

The symbol for this atom of palladium has the mass number, 106, as a superscript to the left and the atomic number as a subscript to the left—$^{106}_{46}\text{Pd}$.

Problem 3.7　What is the atomic number, mass number, and symbol for the element that has 56 protons and 82 neutrons?

Solution 3.7　The atomic number, Z, is 56. The mass number, A, is 138 (56 p$^+$ + 82 n$^\circ$), and the symbol is $^{138}_{56}\text{Ba}$.

Problem 3.8　What is the composition of $^{226}_{88}\text{Ra}$ atoms?

Solution 3.8　^{226}Ra contains 88 protons and 138 (226 − 88) neutrons in its nucleus.

Isotopes

Atoms with the same atomic number but different mass numbers are called isotopes. $^{1}_{1}\text{H}$ and $^{2}_{1}\text{H}$ are the two naturally occurring isotopes of hydrogen. $^{1}_{1}\text{H}$ atoms have one proton, one electron, and no neutrons, and $^{2}_{1}\text{H}$ atoms have one proton, one neutron, and one electron.

ISOTOPES OF CARBON

Carbon is also composed of an isotopic mixture. Analysis of the identities of atoms in a sample of carbon reveals 98.89% $^{12}_{6}C$ atoms and 1.11% $^{13}_{6}C$ atoms. Additionally, natural samples of C have a trace amount of the radioactive isotope $^{14}_{6}C$ (a β emitter). $^{14}_{6}C$ is used to date old objects in a procedure called radiocarbon dating.

Problem 3.9 Consider the following atoms: $^{31}_{15}P$, $^{30}_{16}S$, $^{34}_{15}P$, $^{35}_{16}S$, $^{33}_{17}Cl$. (a) Which have the same number of electrons? (b) Which have the same number of neutrons? (c) Which are isotopes?

Solution 3.9

(a) $^{31}_{15}P$ and $^{34}_{15}P$ each have the 15 electrons, $^{30}_{16}S$ and $^{35}_{16}S$ each have 16 electrons.
(b) $^{31}_{15}P$ and $^{33}_{17}Cl$ each have 16 neutrons, and $^{34}_{15}P$ and $^{35}_{16}S$ each have 19 neutrons.
(c) $^{31}_{15}P$ and $^{34}_{15}P$ are isotopes, $^{30}_{16}S$ and $^{35}_{16}S$ are isotopes.

Atomic Mass (Atomic Weight)

Atomic mass (often called atomic weight) is the weighted average of the masses of the naturally occurring isotopes of an element relative to ^{12}C. Instead of using a tiny number of grams as a measure of the atomic mass of atoms, a relative scale is used based on the mass of ^{12}C. The relative atomic mass scale compares the masses of atoms to the mass of the standard, ^{12}C. Chemists from around the world decided to assign exactly 12 atomic mass units, u, to the mass of one ^{12}C atom. Therefore, a value of 24 u is assigned to an atom that has twice the mass of ^{12}C and 4 u to an atom that has one-third the mass of ^{12}C. Looking at this from the other direction, if an atom has a mass of 52 u, then its mass is 52 u/12 u or 4.3 times as great as a ^{12}C atom. One atomic mass unit, 1 u, equals one-twelfth the mass of a ^{12}C atom.

Calculating Atomic Masses

To obtain the atomic mass of an element, calculate the weighted average of the masses of the isotopes. A weighted average takes into account the percent abundances of the naturally occurring isotopes.

Problem 3.10 Gallium is composed of two isotopes, ^{69}Ga and ^{71}Ga. ^{69}Ga has a mass of 68.926 and comprises 60.4% of the Ga atoms. ^{71}Ga has a mass of 70.925 and comprises 39.6% of the Ga atoms. Calculate the atomic mass of gallium.

Solution 3.10 Calculate the weighted average of the two Ga isotopes from the percent abundances and the masses of its isotopes. Thus, multiply the mass of each isotope times its percent abundance. After the sum of these products is obtained, divide by 100.

$$\text{Atomic mass (Ga)} = \frac{(68.926 \times 60.4) + (70.925 \times 39.6)}{100} = 69.7$$

Problem 3.11 Calculate the atomic mass of rubidium, Rb, using the following data:

Isotope	Relative Mass, u	Percent Abundance,%
^{85}Rb	84.912	72.15
^{87}Rb	86.909	27.85

Solution 3.11 The atomic mass of Rb is obtained by calculating the average mass of its naturally occurring isotopes:

$$\text{Atomic mass of Rb} = [(84.912 \text{ u} \times 72.15) + (86.909 \text{ u} \times 27.85)]/100$$
$$= 85.49 \text{ u}$$

Problem 3.12   Lithium is composed of two isotopes, ^{6}Li and ^{7}Li. The mass of ^{6}Li is 6.015 and the mass of ^{7}Li is 7.016. If the atomic mass of lithium is 6.941, calculate the percent abundances of ^{6}Li and ^{7}Li.

Solution 3.12   The sum of the percents of the isotopes must equal 100%. If x is allowed to equal the percent of ^{6}Li and y equals the percent of ^{7}Li, then, $x + y = 100\%$. In addition, the atomic mass equals the weighted average of the masses of the isotopes.

$$\text{Atomic mass}_{Li} = \frac{6.015x + 7.016y}{100} = 6.941$$

Solve this equation by substituting $100 - x$ for y.

$$x + y = 100$$
$$y = 100 - x$$
$$\textit{Atomic mass}_{Li} = \frac{6.015x + 7.016(100 - x)}{100} = 6.941$$
$$x = 7.5\%$$
$$y = 100.0 - x = 100.0 - 7.5 = 92.5\%$$

Problem 3.13   Silver, Ag, has an atomic mass of 107.9. It is composed of ^{107}Ag with a mass of 106.9 and ^{109}Ag with a mass of 108.9. Calculate the percent abundances of ^{107}Ag and ^{109}Ag.

Solution 3.13   Solve this equation in a manner similar to Problem 3.12. The percent abundance for ^{107}Ag is 51.8%, and the percent abundance for ^{109}Ag is 48.2%.

3.3   ELEMENTS AND THE PERIODIC TABLE

Periodic Table   The periodic table of the elements is the most widely used table in chemistry because of the important information it contains regarding elements and atoms.

A periodic table lists each element with its chemical symbol, atomic number, and atomic mass. Some periodic tables give additional information regarding the element. The most commonly used form of the periodic table (the long form) is found in Fig. 1.1. The periodic table lists the elements in order of their atomic numbers, Z.

Problem 3.14   Use the periodic table to find the symbols and atomic numbers for each of the following elements: (a) antimony, (b) molybdenum, (c) cerium, (d) selenium, (e) zirconium.

Solution 3.14   (a) Sb, 51; (b) Mo, 42; (c) Ce, 58; (d) Se, 32; (e) Zr, 40

GROUPS AND PERIODS

Each element is in a vertical column and a horizontal row. A vertical column is a chemical group or family. A horizontal row is a chemical period. Each chemical group is assigned a number from 1 to 18. However, in the past chemical groups were given a Roman numeral and either the letter A or B. Because some chemists use the newer system for designating groups and others use the older one, both systems are used in this book. Each period is assigned a number from 1 to 7.

Problem 3.15   In what period and group are each of the following elements located? (a) Al, (b) Br, (c) Be, (d) Co, (e) Xe

Solution 3.15   The periods/groups are: (a) 3/13 (IIIA); (b) 4/17 (VIIA); (c) 2/2 (IIA); (d) 4/9 (VIIIB); (e) 5/18 (VIIIA).

METALS, NONMETALS, AND METALLOIDS (SEMIMETALS)

The elements on the left side of the periodic table are metals. Those on the right side are non-metals. In general, metals are usually silver-gray solids that conduct heat and electricity. They have a wide range of melting and boiling points, and are among the most dense substances known. Metals share the common properties of being malleable (the ability to be hammered into different shapes) and ductile (the ability to be drawn into wires).

Nonmetals may be solids, liquids, or gases, and are poor conductors (insulators) of heat and electricity. On an average, nonmetals have lower boiling points, melting points, and densities than metals.

Elements with intermediate properties are called metalloids or semimetals. The metalloids are along a bold zigzag line that separates the metals from the nonmetals.

Problem 3.16   Classify each of the following elements as metal, nonmetal, or metalloid: (a) Ga, (b) I, (c) As, (d) H, (e) Sc.

Solution 3.16   (a) metal, (b) nonmetal, (c) metalloid, (d) nonmetal, (e) metal

Chemical Groups

Elements within a chemical group have similar properties and are given a group name.

ALKALI METALS

Elements in group 1 (IA) are called the alkali metals. They are reactive metals with low melting points and densities.

ALKALINE EARTH METALS

Group 2 (IIA) elements are the alkaline earth metals. Their properties are somewhat similar to the alkali metals, but are less reactive and have higher melting points.

TRANSITION METALS

The next ten groups of elements are known as the transition metals or transition elements. These elements are assigned the numbers 3 to 12 in the newer numbering system and a Roman numeral and the letter B in the older system. Sometimes the transition metals are called the B group elements. All of the metals in groups 3 (IIIB) to 12 (IIB) and the two series of elements written below the main body of the table are transition metals.

GROUPS 13 TO 15

Group 13 (IIIA) is often called the boron-aluminum group. Boron is a metalloid, and the remaining members (Al, Ga, In, and Tl) have metallic properties. Group 14 (IVA) is the carbon-silicon group. Carbon is a nonmetal, silicon and germanium are metalloids, and tin and lead are metals. Group 14 (IVA) is a diverse chemical group. Group 15 (VA) is the nitrogen-phosphorus group. Nitrogen and phosphorus are nonmetals, arsenic and antimony are metalloids, and bismuth is a metal.

CHALCOGENS

Group 16 (VIA) is the chalcogens or oxygen group. Oxygen, sulfur, and selenium are nonmetals, tellurium is a metalloid, and polonium is a radioactive metal.

HALOGENS

Group 17 (VIIA) contains the halogens. The members of the halogens include fluorine, chlorine, bromine, iodine, and astatine. They are reactive nonmetals.

NOBLE GASES

Group 18 (VIIIA) consists of the noble gases. Helium, neon, argon, krypton, xenon, and radon are unreactive gaseous nonmetallic elements.

Problem 3.17   To which chemical group does each of the following belong? (a) Te, (b) Ba, (c) Kr, (d) Ti, (e) Ge

Solution 3.17   (a) chalcogens, (b) alkaline earth metals, (c) noble gases, (d) transition metals, (e) C-Si group

3.4   IONS AND ION FORMATION

Ions

Ions are charged atoms or charged groups of atoms. A cation (*cat'i on*) is a positively charged atom. An anion (*an' i on*) is a negatively charged atom.

Formation of Monopositive Cations

Under the proper conditions, atoms can either lose or gain electrons. Adding the proper amount of energy to an atom removes one or more electrons. For example, when sufficient energy is added to a gaseous sodium atom, Na, one electron is removed, and a positively charged sodium ion, Na^+, results.

$$Na(g) \longrightarrow Na^+(g) + e^-(g)$$

Whenever one or more electrons, negatively charged bodies, is removed from an atom, a positive ion results that has more protons than electrons. A sodium atom has 11 p^+ and 11 e^-. After an electron is removed, the resulting sodium ion has 11 p^+ and 10 e^-. An ion is the charged particle that results when atoms or groups of atoms lose or gain electrons.

Formation of Dipositive Cations

If two electrons are removed from an atom, then a cation with a 2+ charge results. For example, Ca forms cations with a 2^+ charge.

$$Ca(g) \longrightarrow Ca^{2+}(g) + 2e^-(g)$$

In general, metals tend to lose electrons and form cations. Group 1 (IA) atoms tend to lose one electron and form ions with a 1+ charge and group 2 (IIA) atoms tend to lose two electrons and form ions with a 2+ charge.

Stability of Noble Gas Configuration

When group 1 (IA) atoms lose one electron or group 2 (IIA) atoms lose two electrons, they have the same number of electrons as the preceding noble gases, group 18 (VIIIA) elements. Noble gases are the most stable of all elements. Ions with the same number of electrons as noble gases are usually more stable than those with more or less electrons. In other words, ions with 2, 10, 36, 54, or 86 electrons are most stable.

Problem 3.18 (a) How many electrons does an Al atom lose to form a stable noble gas configuration? (b) What is the charge on Al ions? (c) How many protons and electrons are in Al ions?

Solution 3.18

(a) Aluminum has an atomic number of 13, which means that it has 13 electrons. Thus, it loses three electrons to have the same number of electrons as the noble gas Ne.

(b) The charge on an Al ion is 3+, Al^{3+}.

(c) An Al ion has 13 protons and 10 electrons.

Formation of Anions

Nonmetals tend to gain electrons and form negative ions, anions, with the same number of electrons as the noble gases that follow them. For example, chlorine, a halogen atom [group 17 (VIIA)], gains one electron, giving it the same number of electrons as the noble gas Ar. A negative chloride ion, Cl^-, results. To write the name of an anion, drop the ending of its name and add *ide*. For chlorine, drop the *ine* ending and add *ide*. This yields the name chloride. Oxygen, a chalcogen atom [group 16 (VIA)], gains two electrons and reaches the Ne electron configuration. The resulting anion has a 2-charge and is called the oxide ion (oxygen−*ygen* + *ide*). Anions are negatively charged because they have more electrons than protons.

Problem 3.19 (a) How many electrons does an N atom gain to form a stable noble gas configuration? (b) What is the charge on N ions? (c) How many protons and electrons are in N ions?

Solution 3.19

(a) Nitrogen has an atomic number of 7, which means that it has 7 electrons. It must gain three electrons to have the same number of electrons as the noble gas Ne.

(b) The charge on an N ion is 3−, N^{3-}.

(c) An N ion has 7 protons and 10 electrons.

Formation of Transition Metal Cations

Many transition metals and metals in groups 13 to 15 can form two or more cations with different positive charges. For example, copper produces both Cu^+ and Cu^{2+} cations. To distinguish these ions, Cu^+ is called the copper(I) cation and Cu^{2+} is the copper(II) cation. To write the name of metal cations that can have more than one charge, write the name of the metal followed by the Roman numeral, enclosed in parentheses, that corresponds to the charge.

Polyatomic Ions

A monatomic ion results when one atom loses or gains electrons. However, a polyatomic ion results when a group of bonded atoms either loses or gains electrons. For example, the nitrate polyatomic ion has the formula NO_3^-. A nitrate ion consists of one N atom and three O atoms, and carries a 1− charge. The nitrate ion is a polyatomic anion.

OXYANIONS

An oxyanion is a polyatomic ion that has one or more O atoms. If an element forms two different oxyanions, the ending *ate* is given to the oxyanion with the larger number of O atoms and *ite* is given to the one with one less O atom. Let's consider the two oxyanions with one S atom: sulfate, SO_4^{2-}, and sulfite, SO_3^{2-}.

Sulfate has one S atom and four O atoms, and sulfite has one S atom and three O atoms. Both sulfate and sulfite carry a 2− charge.

Some elements form four different oxyanions. In addition to the *ate* and *ite* endings, two prefixes are added to their names. The prefix *per* is added to the ion that has one more O than the *ate* ion. The prefix *hypo* is affixed to the name of the ion that has one less O than the *ite* ion. For example, the four oxyanions of chlorine are as follows: perchlorate, ClO_4^-; chlorate, ClO_3^-; chlorite, ClO_2^-; and hypochlorite, ClO^-.

Problem 3.20   Write the names of the following ions: (a) $C_2H_3O_2^-$, (b) NH_4^+, (c) HSO_4^-, (d) BrO^-, (e) PO_3^{3-}.

Solution 3.20   (a) acetate, (b) ammonium, (c) hydrogensulfate or bisulfate, (d) hypobromite, (e) phosphite

3.5   MOLECULES AND FORMULA UNITS

Molecules and Covalent Compounds

Nonmetal atoms react with each other and form molecules. Usually molecules result because they are more stable (more resistant to change) than the atoms from which they form. The atoms in molecules are bound by chemical bonds. A chemical bond in a molecule results from the attraction of the positively charge nuclei of two atoms for overlapping regions in which the negatively charged electrons are located. Compounds composed of molecules are termed covalent compounds.

Formula Units and Ionic Compounds

When a metal reacts with a nonmetal, an ionic compound results. In this reaction, a metal atom releases one or more electrons that is taken in by one or more nonmetal atoms. The resulting cations and anions attract and produce a formula unit, which is the simplest repeating unit that makes up ionic compounds.

Diatomic Molecules

The simplest covalent molecules result when two nonmetal atoms bond to form a diatomic molecule. Hydrogen, H_2, is the simplest diatomic molecule because it consists of two bonded H atoms, the atom with the smallest atomic mass. At room temperature, $25°C$, the element hydrogen is composed of diatomic molecules of hydrogen, H_2. Individual H atoms do not exist at $25°C$. Other nonmetals composed of diatomic molecules include the following: N_2, O_2, F_2, Cl_2, Br_2, and I_2.

Binary Compounds– Ionic and Covalent

A binary compound results when two different elements undergo a chemical reaction. For example, sulfur combines with oxygen to form sulfur dioxide, SO_2. Other examples of binary compounds are water, H_2O; sodium chloride, NaCl; and carbon dioxide.

Binary compounds may be subdivided into two groups. Some consist of a metal and a nonmetal and others two nonmetals. If a compound has a metal bonded to a nonmetal, it is a binary ionic compound. If it has two bonded nonmetals, it is a binary covalent compound.

PROPERTIES OF IONIC COMPOUNDS

In general, most ionic compounds resemble NaCl–they are solids with relatively high melting and boiling points, are nonconductors of heat and electricity except in the liquid (molten) state, and dissociate to form hydrated ions in aqueous solutions.

PROPERTIES OF COVALENT COMPOUNDS

In general, binary covalent compounds are either gases, liquids, or soft solids. Their average boiling and melting points are lower than those of binary ionic compounds.

Ternary Ionic Compounds

Three different elements make up ternary compounds. Ternary ionic compounds consist of a metal cation and a polyatomic anion or a polyatomic cation and a nonmetal anion. Examples of ternary ionic compounds are potassium sulfate, K_2SO_4; lead(II) nitrate, $Pb(NO_3)_2$; and gold(I) phosphate, Au_3PO_4. The properties of ternary ionic compounds resemble those of binary ionic compounds.

Ternary Covalent Compounds

Ternary covalent substances have three bonded nonmetals. Examples include dichlorodifluoromethane, $C_2Cl_2F_2$ and phosphorus monofluorodichloride, $PFCl_2$.

TERNARY ACIDS

Acids are one of the most important groups of ternary covalent compound. Acids, HA, are compounds that increase the hydrogen ion [$H^+(aq)$] concentration in water.

$$HA \xrightarrow{H_2O} H^+(aq) + A^-(aq)$$

Acids ionize and produce hydrated ions when they dissolve. Thus, they increase the concentration of H^+ ions in water. Examples of ternary acids are nitric acid, $HNO_3(aq)$; sulfuric acid, $H_2SO_4(aq)$; perchloric acid, $HClO_4(aq)$; and phosphoric acid, $H_3PO_4(aq)$. These ternary acids are all corrosive liquids at room temperature.

Problem 3.21   Classify each of the following as binary or ternary and ionic or covalent: (a) BrF, (b) NaOCl, (c) K_3PO_4, (d) H_2SO_4, (e) $CuCl_2$

Solution 3.21   (a) binary, covalent; (b) ternary, ionic; (c) ternary, ionic; (d) ternary covalent; (e) binary, ionic

3.6   NAMES AND FORMULAS OF INORGANIC COMPOUNDS

Chemical Nomenclature

Chemical nomenclature is the system used to assign unique names to individual elements, ions, and compounds. The rules for chemical nomenclature are established by the International Union of Pure and Applied Chemists, IUPAC.

Stock System of Nomenclature

The system principally used for inorganic compounds is the Stock System of Nomenclature (adopted by the IUPAC). This system is used almost exclusively throughout this book although many scientists still use an old system derived from the Latin and Greek names of elements.

The Names of Binary Ionic Compounds

Use the following rules to write the names of binary ionic compounds.
1. Write the name of the metal. If the metal can have more than one charge, as is the case with many transition metals and metals in Groups 13 to 15, write a Roman numeral in parentheses that shows the charge directly after the name of the metal.
2. Modify the name of the nonmetal by dropping its ending and adding *ide*. For example, drop *ygen* from oxygen, *ogen* from nitrogen, *ur* from sulfur, *orus* from phosphorus, and *ine* from the halogens.

Problem 3.22   Write the names of: (a) RbF, (b) K_2S, and (c) $CaBr_2$.

Solution 3.22

(a) The name of the metal is rubidium. A Roman numeral representing the charge is not required because the group 1 metals always carry a 1+ charge. Then, modify the name of fluorine by dropping the ine and adding *ide* in its place–fluoride. Thus, RbF is rubidium fluoride.

(b) K_2S is potassium sulfide

(c) $CaBr_2$ is calcium bromide

NAMES OF BINARY IONIC COMPOUNDS WITH TRANSITION METALS

Binary ionic compounds that contain either transition metals or metals in groups 13 to 15 have names that include the charge on the metal cation. For example, what is the name of $FeBr_3$? Because the Fe atom can form more than cation, add the charge of the cation in parentheses to the name of the metal. The Fe ion in $FeBr_3$ has a charge of 3+ to balance the 3− from three Br^- ions. Hence, the name of $FeBr_3$ is iron(III) bromide.

The charge, written as a Roman numeral in parentheses, is added to the name of the metal. The ending *ine* is replaced with the ending *ide*. The charge must be included in the name to distinguish $FeBr_3$ from $FeBr_2$, another bromide of iron. The name of $FeBr_2$ is iron(II) bromide.

Determining the Charge on a Transition Metal. Since all compounds are neutral chemical species, the sum of the charges of the ions in ionic compounds equals zero. To calculate the charge on the metal ion, first determine the total charge on the nonmetal ions.

Problem 3.23   (a) Write the name of SnS_2. (b) Write the name of BiN.

Solution 3.23

(a) Sulfur is directly below O on the periodic table. Like O, sulfur takes in two electrons to obtain the same number of electrons as a noble gas. Therefore, its charge is 2−. Because the formula has two S ions, the total negative charge is 4−. The sum of the charges in a compound equals zero; hence, the charge on the Sn ion is 4+.

   The name of the metal ion is tin(IV). Modifying the name of the nonmetals requires removing the "ur" and adding "ide." The name of this compound is tin(IV) sulfide.

(b) BiN is the formula for bismuth(III) nitride.

Problem 3.24   Write the names for each of the following: (a) HgS, (b) PbO_2.

Solution 3.24

(a) HgS is mercury(II) sulfide. Sulfide has a charge of 2−, thus the Hg ion must be mercury(II), Hg^{2+}.

(b) PbO_2 is lead(IV) oxide. Oxide has a charge of 2−. Two oxides have a total charge of 4−. Hence, the lead ion is lead(IV), Pb^{4+}.

Formulas of Binary Ionic Compounds

To write the formula of a binary ionic compound given its name, write the two ions with their charges and then determine the quantity of each ion that produces a total charge of zero. For example, what is the formula of strontium chloride? Strontium is in group 2 (IIA) and Sr ions always carry a 2+ charge. Chlorine belongs to group 17 (VIIA) and Cl ions always have a 1− charge. A convenient means for identifying the subscripts in the formula is to calculate the lowest common multiple of the charges and then divide each charge into this multiple. The lowest common multiple for Sr^{2+} and Cl^- is 2. Dividing 2 into 2 give one Sr^{2+} ion and dividing 1 into 2 gives two Cl^- ions. The formula of strontium chloride is $SrCl_2$.

Problem 3.25   Write the formula of titanium(III) oxide.

Solution 3.25   The titanium(III) ion is Ti^{3+} and the oxide ion is O^{2-}. The lowest common multiple between the charges is 6. Dividing the charges into the lowest common multiple gives three Ti ions and two O ions. Thus, the formula of titanium(III) oxide is Ti_2O_3.

Problem 3.26 (a) What is the formula of vanadium(V) oxide? (b) What is the formula of gold(III) selenide?

Solution 3.26
- (a) The formula of vanadium(V) oxide is V_2O_5. The charge on the oxide ions is 2− and the charge on the vanadium ions is 5+. The lowest common multiple is 10; hence, there are two V^{5+} ions and five O^{2-} ions in the formula.
- (b) The formula of gold(III) selenide is Au_2Se_3. Selenide ions have a charge of 2− because they are members of group 16. The lowest common multiple is 6; hence, the formula contains two Au^{3+} ions and three Se^{2-} ions.

Names of Ternary Ionic Compounds

A different set of rules is used to write the names of ternary ionic compounds. If the compound has a metal and a polyatomic ion, use the following rules.
1. Write the name of the metal. If it can have more than one charge, add a Roman numeral with the charge inside of parentheses.
2. Write the name of the polyatomic ion with no change in spelling. If the compound has a polyatomic cation such as the ammonium ion, write the name of the polyatomic cation and then write the modified name of the monatomic anion, replacing its ending with ide.

Problem 3.27 Write the name of $Fe_2(SO_4)_3$.

Solution 3.27 Iron is a transition metal and can have ions with more than one charge. Thus, the charge is included in the name. Sulfate ions, SO_4^{2-}, have a charge of 2− and three sulfate ions carry a total charge of 6−. Therefore, the two Fe ions have a charge of 6+, and each iron ion has a charge of 3+.

To assign a name to $Fe_2(SO_4)_3$, write the name of the metal ion, iron(III) followed by the name of the polyatomic anion, sulfate. The name of $Fe_2(SO_4)_3$ is iron(III) sulfate

Problem 3.28 Write the Stock names for each of the following compounds: (a) K_2CrO_4, (b) $(NH_4)_2S$, (c) $FeCO_3$

Solution 3.28
- (a) K_2CrO_4 is potassium chromate. The metal is potassium, an alkali metal with a fixed oxidation state, and the polyatomic ion is chromate.
- (b) $(NH_4)_2S$ is ammonium sulfide. In this compound an ammonium ion is found in place of a metal, and the nonmetal, sulfur. Remove the ending from sulfur and add *ide*.
- (c) $FeCO_3$ is iron(II) carbonate. Iron is a metal with a variable oxidation state. Consequently, the name must indicate the charge on the iron ion. Carbonate, CO_3^{2-}, has a 2− charge; thus the charge on Fe is 2+ to add to zero.

Formulas of Ternary Ionic Compounds

To write the formula of a ternary ionic compound given its name, follow the same procedure used to write the formula of a binary ionic compound.

Problem 3.29 Write the formula for cobalt(III) hydroxide.

Solution 3.29 Begin by writing the ions with their charges (Co^{3+} OH^-). The lowest common multiple of 3+ and 1− is 3. Divide the charge of each ion into the lowest common multiple. Therefore, the formula of cobalt(III) hydroxide is $Co(OH)_3$.

Problem 3.30 Write the formulas of each of the following: (a) zinc(II) cyanide, (b) gold(III) sulfate

Solution 3.30

(a) Zinc(II) cyanide is $Zn(CN)_2$. Zinc(II) is Zn^{2+} and cyanide is CN^-. To produce a neutral compound, two cyanide ions are required per zinc ion.

(b) Gold(III) sulfate is $Au_2(SO_4)_3$. Gold(III) is Au^{3+} and sulfate is SO_4^{2-}. To produce a neutral compound two Au^{3+} ions are needed to balance three SO_4^{2-} ions.

Problem 3.31 (a) Write the name of $MgCrO_4$. (b) Write the formula of platinum(IV) sulfate.

Solution 3.31

(a) Mg is a metal that can have only one charge, 2+, because it is a member of group 2. Its symbol is Mg^{2+}. The name of the CrO_4^{2-} is the chromate ion. Thus, the name of this compound is magnesium chromate.

(b) The platinum(IV) ion is Pt^{4+} and the sulfate ion is SO_4^{2-}. The lowest common multiple between the charges is 4. Dividing the charges into the lowest common multiple gives one Pt ion and two SO_4^{2-} ions. Thus, the formula of platinum(IV) sulfate is $Pt(SO_4)_2$.

Names and Formulas of Binary Covalent Compounds

Because nonmetals combine with each other in many different ways, the names of binary covalent compounds include prefixes that show the number of a particular nonmetal in the formula. Use the following rules to write the names of binary covalent compounds.

1. Write the name of the first nonmetal in the formula. If the formula has two or more atoms, add the appropriate prefix to its name. If only one is listed, the prefix *mono* is usually not added. Note that the first nonmetal listed is generally to the left and/or below the second listed nonmetal on the periodic table.

2. Write the modified name of the second nonmetal–remove the ending and add *ide*. Add a prefix to this name to show the number of atoms in the formula.

Let's begin by writing the names of the two oxides of carbon, CO and CO_2. The first is carbon monoxide and the second is carbon dioxide. To avoid the double vowel "oo" in the name of carbon monoxide, add *mon* instead of *mono*. Two oxides of N are dinitrogen trioxide, N_2O_3, and dinitrogen pentoxide, N_2O_5.

Names and Formulas of Binary Acids

An acid is a compound that increases the H^+ ion concentration in water. Different rules are used to write the names of acids. For example, the name of a binary acid is derived from the name of the nonmetal atom in the molecule. First add the prefix *hydro* to the name of the nonmetal and then replace the ending with *ic acid*. For example, the name of $HCl(aq)$ is hydrochloric acid. Another example of binary acids is hydrofluoric acid, $HF(aq)$. If these compounds are not dissolved in water, and thus not behaving as acids, use the normal rules for naming binary covalent compounds. Pure gaseous HCl is hydrogen chloride.

Names and Formulas of Ternary Acids

The names of ternary acids are derived from the names of the oxyanions in the compound. If the name of the oxyanion ends in *ate*, replace it with *ic acid*. If it ends in *ite*, replace it with *ous acid*. Let's write the names of HNO_3 and HNO_2. The oxyanion in HNO_3 is nitrate and the one in HNO_2 is nitrite. Therefore, remove *ate* from nitrate and add *ic acid*, and likewise remove *ite* from nitrite and add *ous acid*. This yields the names nitric acid and nitrous acid.

Problem 3.32 Write the names for the following series of oxyacids, and the polyatomic ions contained within the molecules: (a) $HBrO_4$, (b) $HBrO_3$, (c) $HBrO_2$, (d) HBrO

Solution 3.32

(a) $HBrO_4$ is perbromic acid, and it contains the perbromate ion, BrO_4^-.

(b) $HBrO_3$ is bromic acid, and it contains the bromate ion, BrO_3^-.

(c) $HBrO_2$ is bromous acid, and it contains the bromite ion, BrO_2^-.

(d) HBrO is hypobromous acid, and it contains the hypobromite ion, BrO^- or OBr^-.

SUMMARY

The first scientific model of the atom was proposed by John Dalton in 1803. The Dalton model could explain the law of conservation of mass which states that matter cannot be created or destroyed, and the law of constant composition which states that the composition of a pure substance is constant. Dalton also proposed the law of multiple proportions which states that if two elements can combine to form more than one compound, the masses of one element that combine with a fixed mass of the second element are in a ratio of small whole numbers.

After the discovery of electricity and with experimentation with discharge tubes, scientists found that the atom had a substructure. J. J. Thomson measured the charge-to-mass ratio for the electron and found that the electron had a small mass and high negative charge. R. A. Millikan measured the charge on the electron in the oil-drop experiment. From the results of Thomson's and Millikan's experiments, the mass of the electron was calculated. Research into the nature of radioactivity lead E. Rutherford to the discovery of the nucleus. He showed the existence of the nucleus when he bombarded gold leaf with α particles. H. G. J. Moseley used x-rays to measure the charge on the nucleus—the atomic number.

The atomic number, Z, is the number of protons in the nucleus, and the mass number, A, is the total number of protons and neutrons in the nucleus. Isotopes are atoms with the same atomic numbers but have different mass numbers. The atomic mass of an element is the average mass of the naturally occurring isotopes of an element relative to ^{12}C.

The periodic table lists all of the elements. Each element is a member of a chemical group or family (a vertical column) and a chemical period (a horizontal row). The members of a chemical group share many common properties. Metals are on the left side and nonmetals are on the right side of the periodic table. Metals are usually solids that are good conductors, have high melting and boiling points, and are malleable and ductile. Nonmetals are gases, liquids, or low-melting solids that are usually insulators of heat and electricity.

If an atom loses an electron, it becomes a positive ion, a cation. If it gains an electron, it becomes a negative ion, an anion. Ions are most stable when they obtain the same number of electrons as noble gases, group 18. Ions that result when one atom loses or gains electrons are monatomic ions. A charged group of bonded atoms is a polyatomic ion.

Molecules result when two or more nonmetal atoms bond in chemical reactions. The atoms in a molecule are held by chemical bonds. Compounds composed of molecules are known as covalent compounds, and those composed of ionic formula units are ionic compounds. Binary compounds have two different atoms, and ternary compounds have three different atoms. Chemists use the Stock System of Nomenclature to assign names to inorganic compounds.

CHAPTER 3 REVIEW EXERCISE

1. What contribution did each of the following make to the structure of the atom? (a) Rutherford, (b) the Curies, (c) Thomson, (d) Goldstein, (e) Millikan, (f) Chadwick

2. The mass ratio of O to N is 53.3 g O/46.7 g N in 100.0 g of NO and the mass ratio of O to N is 69.6 g O/30.4 g N in 100.0 g NO_2. Use these data to illustrate the law of multiple proportions.

3. What were the outcomes and how did the following experiments change our ideas about atoms? (a) discharge tube experiments, (b) the oil-drop experiment, (c) the gold leaf experiment

4. How many protons, neutrons, and electrons are in each of the following atoms? (a) $^{59}_{27}Co$, (b) $^{70}_{32}Ge$, (c) $^{93}_{41}Nb$

5. Write the symbols for atoms with the following properties: (a) $Z = 53$, number of neutrons = 74, (b) $Z = 35$, $A = 81$, (c) number of protons = 22, number of neutrons = 26, (d) number of electrons = 46, $A = 105$

6. (a) What is the magnitude of the charge-to-mass ratio for an electron? (b) What does the charge-to-mass ratio of an electron indicate about the properties of an electron? (c) How can the charge-to-mass ratio of the electron be used to calculate the mass of an electron?

7. Natural samples of copper contain ^{63}Cu and ^{65}Cu. ^{63}Cu has a mass of 62.930 and ^{65}Cu has a mass of 64.928. If the percent abundance of ^{63}Cu is 69.09% and the percent abundance of ^{65}Cu is 30.91%, calculate the atomic mass of copper.

8. Bromine is composed of two isotopes, ^{79}Br and ^{81}Br. The mass of ^{79}Br is 78.9183 and the mass of ^{81}Br is 80.9163. If the atomic mass of bromine is 79.90, calculate the percent abundance of each Br isotope.

9. Consider the following data for the three naturally occurring isotopes of the element silicon.

Isotope	Mass	Percent abundance, %
^{28}Si	27.9769	92.21
^{29}Si	28.9765	4.70
^{30}Si	29.9738	3.09

Calculate the atomic mass of Si.

10. Element 18, Ar, has an atomic mass of 39.95 and element 19, K, has an atomic mass of 39.10. What is a possible explanation for the fact that Ar has a larger atomic mass than K?

11. What are the two numerical designations associated with each of the following chemical groups? (a) chalcogens, (b) halogens, (c) noble gases, (d) transition metals, (e) alkali metals, (f) alkaline earth metals

12. In what chemical groups on the periodic table do each of the following elements belong? (a) He, (b) Sn, (c) Si, (d) Rn, (e) Ba (f) Cs, (g) Zn

13. An element has the following properties: (1) white solid at 25°C, (2) melting point is 44°C, (3) density is 1.83 g/cm^3. From the properties, would you expect the element to be a metal or a nonmetal?

14. Classify the following elements as metals, nonmetals, or metalloids: (a) S, (b) Ni, (c) Cs, (d) Ge, (e) Ce, (f) Xe, (g) Si

15. From their placement on the periodic table, write the expected charge on each of the following ions: (a) lithium ions, (b) sulfide ions, (c) bromide ions, (d) barium ions, (e) nitride ions

16. How many protons and electrons are in each of the following ions? (a) Hg^{2+}, (b) Rb^+, (c) Cd^{2+}, (d) Se^{2-}, (e) P^{3-}

17. Which of the following atoms forms ions with more than one possible charge? (a) Na, (b) Cl, (c) V, (d) Mn, (e) Al, (f) Pb

18. Calculate the charge on the cation in each of the following ionic compounds: (a) NiO, (b) Ni_2O_3, (c) CrO_3, (d) $PbCl_4$, (e) $TaCl_5$

19. Write the formula of the compound that results when the ammonium ion is combined with each of the following ions. (a) sulfate, (b) sulfite, (c) nitrite, (d) periodate, (e) chlorate, (f) hydrogencarbonate, (g) phosphate

20. Write the formulas of the compounds that result when acetate ions are combined with each of the following ions: (a) lithium, (b) zinc(II), (c) ferrous, (d) gallium(III), (e) lead(IV)

21. Write the formulas for each of the following: (a) xenon tetrafluoride, (b) cesium oxide, (c) chromium(III) iodide, (d) cobalt(II) phosphide, (e) germanium(IV) selenide, (f) diiodine pentoxide

22. Write the formulas for each of the following: (a) tin(IV) nitrate, (b) aluminum hypochlorite, (c) cobalt(III) chromate, (d) magnesium borate, (e) mercury(II) cyanide, (f) molybdenum(III) hydroxide

23. Write the name for each of the following oxyacids: (a) H_3BO_3, (b) $HClO$, (c) HIO_3, (d) H_2CO_3, (e) $HBrO_4$

24. Write the name and formula of an example for each of the following classes of compounds: (a) ternary ionic compound, (b) binary covalent compound, (c) oxyacid, (d) hydrate, (e) binary ionic compound, (f) ternary covalent compound

25. An element has the following properties: (1) melting point is 1495°C, (2) boiling point is 2870°C, (3) density is 8.9 g/cm^3, (4) forms 2+ ions. From these properties, determine which of the following elements is described: Ni, Ne, N, or Na.

ANSWERS TO REVIEW EXERCISE

1. (a) the nucleus, (b) radioactivity, (c) e/m for e$^-$, (d) protons, (e) charge of the electron, (f) neutron

2. 1.14 g N/g O, 2.29 g N/g O, 2.00/1.00

3. (a) nature of electrons, (b) charge on the electron, (c) discovery of the nucleus

4. (a) 27 p$^+$, 27 e$^-$, 32 n°; (b) 32 p$^+$, 32 e$^-$, 38 n°; (c) 41 p$^+$, 41 e$^-$, 52 n°

5. (a) $^{127}_{53}I$, (b) $^{81}_{35}Br$, (c) $^{48}_{22}Ti$

6. (a) e/m(e$^-$) = -1.76×10^8 C/g, (b) the electron has a high charge and a small mass, (c) knowing the charge on the electron, -1.602×10^{-19} C, the mass is calculated: -1.602×10^{-19} C $\times$ 1g/ $- 1.76 \times 10^8$ C $= 9.10 \times 10^{-28}$ g

7. 63.55

8. 50.666% ^{79}Br, 49.334% ^{81}Br

9. 28.09

10. Ar has some higher mass isotopes, which raises the average above that of K

11. (a) 16 (VIA), (b) 17 (VIIA), (c) 18 (VIIIA), (d) 3-12, B group elements, (e) 1 (IA), (f) 2 (IIA)

12. (a) noble gas, (b) C group, (c) C group, (d) noble gas, (e) alkaline earth metal, (f) alkali metal, (g) transition metal

13. nonmetal

14. (a) nonmetal, (b) metal, (c) metal, (d) metalloid, (e) metal, (f) nonmetal, g. metalloid

15. (a) 1+, (b) 2−, (c) 1−, (d) 2+, (e) 3−

16. (a) p$^+$ = 80, e$^-$ = 78, (b) p$^+$ = 37, e$^-$ = 36, (c) p$^+$ = 48, e$^-$ = 46, (d) p$^+$ = 34, e$^-$ = 36, (e) p$^+$ = 15, e$^-$ = 18

17. V, Mn, Pb

18. (a) 2+, (b) 3+, (c) 6+, (d) 4+, (e) 5+

19. (a) $(NH_4)_2SO_4$, (b) $(NH_4)_2SO_3$, (c) NH_4NO_2, (d) NH_4IO_4, (e) NH_4ClO_3, (f) NH_4HCO_3, (g) $(NH_4)_3PO_4$

20. (a) $LiC_2H_3O_2$, (b) $Zn(C_2H_3O_2)_2$, (c) $Fe(C_2H_3O_2)_2$, (d) $Ga(C_2H_3O_2)_2$, (e) $Pb(C_2H_3O_2)_4$

21. (a) XeF_4, (b) Cs_2O, (c) CrI_3, (d) Co_3P_2, (e) $GeSe_2$, (f) I_2O_5

22. (a) $Sn(NO_3)_4$, (b) $Al(OCl)_3$, (c) $Co_2(CrO_4)_3$, (d) $Mg_3(BO_3)_2$, (e) $Hg(CN)_2$, (f) $Mo(OH)_3$

23. (a) boric acid, (b) hypochlorous acid, (c) iodic acid, (d) carbonic acid, (e) perbromic acid

24. (a) NaOH, sodium hydroxide; (b) HCl, hydrogen chloride; (c) HNO_3, nitric acid; (d) $CuSO_4 \cdot 5H_2O$, copper(II) sulfate pentahydrate; (e) NaF, sodium fluoride; (f) $HClO_3$, chloric acid

25. Ni—metals have high melting and boiling points and only Ni can form 2+ ions

4

Stoichiometry

4.1 THE MOLE CONCEPT

The Mole a Counting Unit

The mole is a base SI unit for the amount of substance. What is a mole, and how is it applied in chemistry? A mole, abbreviated mol, is a counting unit, a unit that allows us to keep track of the number and mass of atoms, molecules, and ions.

Moles

The number of objects in one mole is 6.022×10^{23}. This number is called Avogadro's number, N_A.

$$N_A = 6.022 \times 10^{23} \text{ particles/mole}$$

What is the importance of Avogadro's number, 6.022×10^{23}? If a sample of an element contains 6.02×10^{23} atoms, its mass equals the atomic mass in grams.

In all cases one mole of atoms contains Avogadro's number of atoms, which has a mass equal to the atomic mass in grams.

The SI definition for a mole is: One mole is the amount of pure substance that contains the same number of particles as there are atoms in exactly 12 g of ^{12}C.

Molar Mass of Atoms

The molar mass of an element is obtained by writing the value for the atomic mass (from the periodic table), and placing the unit grams after the number.

Problem 4.1

(a) What are the molar masses expressed to four significant figures of each of the following elements: As, Kr, Na, Al?

(b) How many atoms are in the molar masses of each of the elements listed in part (a)?

Solution 4.1   (a) 74.92 g/mol As, 83.80 g/mol Kr, 22.99 g/mol Na, and 26.98 g/mol Al, (b) These samples contain Avogadro's number of atoms–6.022×10^{23} atoms.

Mole Calculations Involving Elements

The advantage of using moles is that after making a simple mass measurement in a laboratory the investigator can readily calculate the number of moles of atoms or individual atoms in the sample. Mole calculations are easily done using the factor-label method (unit-conversion method).

Two conversion factors are used in mole calculations that involve elements: g/mol or mol/g and 6.022×10^{23} atoms/1 mol atoms or 1 mol atoms/6.022×10^{23} atoms.

Problem 4.2   (a) How many moles of Cr atoms are in a 0.500-g sample of Cr? (b) How many atoms of Cr are in a 0.500-g sample?

Solution 4.2

(a) 0.500 g Cr × 1 mol Cr/52.0 g Cr = 0.00962 mol Cr The mass of Cr is converted to moles using the molar mass of Cr, 52.0 g/mol.

(b) 0.00962 mol Cr × 6.02 × 10^{23} atoms Cr/mol Cr = 5.79 × 10^{21} atoms Cr To convert mole of Cr to atoms use the relationship between one mole and Avogadro's number, 6.02 × 10^{23} atoms Cr/mol.

Problem 4.3   Aluminum, Al, is the most abundant metal in the earth's crust. What is the mass of a 0.10-mol sample of Al?

Solution 4.3

$$0.10 \text{ mol Al} \times 27.0 \text{ g Al/1 mol Al} = 2.7 \text{ g Al}$$

Problem 4.4   Calcium is a silvery white metal. How many Ca atoms are in a 0.6000-mol sample of Ca?

Solution 4.4

$$0.6000 \text{ mol Ca} \times 6.022 \times 10^{23} \text{ atoms Ca/1 mol Ca} = 3.613 \times 10^{23} \text{ atoms Ca}$$

Problem 4.5   Gold along with silver and copper are called the coinage metals. A sample of Au contains 9.70 × 10^{23} atoms Au. What is the mass of this sample of gold?

Solution 4.5

$$9.70 \times 10^{23} \text{ atoms Au} \times 1 \text{ mol Au/6.02} \times 10^{23} \text{ atoms Au} \times 197 \text{ g Au/mol} = 317 \text{ g Au}$$

Problem 4.6   Because lead, Pb, is easily extracted from its ore, it was known and used by the ancient Egyptians. How many Pb atoms are found in a 100.0-gram sample of pure Pb?

Solution 4.6

$$100.0 \text{ g Pb} \times 1 \text{ mol Pb/207.2 g Pb} \times 6.022 \times 10^{23} \text{ atoms Pb/1 mol Pb} = 2.906 \times 10^{23} \text{ atoms Pb}$$

Problem 4.7   Uranium is a dense radioactive metal that can burst into flames if finely divided. What is the mass in kg of 5.64 × 10^{23} atoms of uranium?

Solution 4.7

$$5.64 \times 10^{23} \text{ atoms U} \times 1 \text{ mol U/6.022} \times 10^{23} \text{ atoms U} \times 238 \text{ g U/1 mol U} \times 1 \text{ kg/1000 g} = 0.223 \text{kg U}$$

Problem 4.8   How many Ag atoms are in a 90.1-mg sample of pure Ag?

Solution 4.8

90.1 mg Ag × 1 g Ag/1000 mg Ag × 1 mol Ag/108 g Ag ×

$$6.022 \times 10^{23} \text{ atoms Ag/1 mol Ag} = 5.0 \times 10^{20} \text{ atoms Ag}$$

Molecular Mass

Molecular mass (traditionally, molecular weight) is the sum of the atomic masses of atoms within a molecule. What is the molecular mass of water, H_2O? Each water molecule has two H atoms and one O atom. The atomic masses of H and O are 1.0 and 16.0, respectively. To find the molecular mass of water, multiply 2 times 1.0 to obtain the total mass of H, and add that to 16.0, resulting in 18 as the molecular mass.

If the molecular mass of water is 18, then its molar mass is 18.0 grams. This means that an 18.0-g sample of H_2O contains Avogadro's number of molecules, 6.02×10^{23} molecules of H_2O.

Problem 4.9 Calculate the molar masses of each of the following to at least three significant figures. (a) CH_4, (b) HNO_3, (c) $B_{10}H_{16}$.

Solution 4.9

(a) 1 mol C×12.0 g C/mol = 12.0g
     4 mol H×1.0 g H/mol = +4.0g
     Molar mass of CH_4 = 16.0g/mol

(b) 1 mol H×1.0 g H/mol =   1.0g
     1 mol N×14.0 g N/mol = 14.0g
     3 mol O×16.0 g O/mol = +48.0g
     Molar mass of HNO_3 = 63.0g/mol

(c) 10 mol B×10.81 g B/mol = 108.1g
     16 mol×1.01 g H/mol   = +16.1g
     Molar mass of $B_{10}H_{16}$ = 124.2g/mol

Mole Calculations Involving Compounds

Mole calculations with molecules are the same as those with atoms, except that the fundamental particle is a molecule. Therefore, the molar mass of a compound is the molecular mass in grams, and Avogadro's number of molecules are contained within the molar mass of a compound.

Problem 4.9 shows that the molar masses of CH_4, HNO_3, and $B_{10}H_{16}$ are 16.0 g, 63.0 g, and 124.2 g, respectively. Each of these samples contains Avogadro's number of molecules–6.022×10^{23} molecules.

Problem 4.10 Nitrous oxide, N_2O, often called laughing gas, is a colorless gas with a pleasant odor. Nitrous oxide has been used as a general anesthetic for medical and dental operations for over 50 years. What is the mass of a 4.05-mol sample of N_2O?

Solution 4.10 First, calculate the molar mass of N_2O.

   2 mol N×14.0 g N/mol N = 28.0g N
   1 mol O×16.0 g O/mol O = +16.0g O
                          = 44.0g/mol N_2O

Then, calculate the mass of N_2O of a 4.05 mole sample as follows.

$$4.05 \text{ mol } N_2O \times 44.0 \text{ g } N_2O/1 \text{ mol } N_2O = 178 \text{ g } N_2O$$

Problem 4.11 Sulfuric acid, H_2SO_4, is the industrial chemical produced in greatest amount in the United States. How many sulfuric acid molecules are contained in a 0.100-g sample of H_2SO_4?

Solution 4.11   First, calculate the molar mass of H_2SO_4.

$$2 \text{ mol H} \times 1.0 \text{ g H/mol H} = \quad 2.0 \text{ g H}$$
$$1 \text{ mol S} \times 32.1 \text{ g S/mol S} = \quad 32.1 \text{ g S}$$
$$4 \text{ mol O} \times 16.0 \text{ g O/1 mol O} = +64.0 \text{ g O}$$
$$= \overline{\quad 98.1 \text{ g/mol } H_2SO_4}$$

Using the molar mass and Avogadro's number, calculate the number of molecules.

$$0.100 \text{ g } H_2SO_4 \times 1 \text{ mol } H_2SO_4/98.1 \text{ g } H_2SO_4 \times$$
$$6.022 \times 10^{23} \text{ } H_2SO_4 \text{ molecules/1 mol } H_2SO_4 = 6.14 \times 10^{20} \text{ molecules } H_2SO_4$$

Problem 4.12   Glucose, $C_6H_{12}O_6$, is also known as blood sugar because it circulates in the blood. What is the mass of 3.39×10^{23} molecules of glucose?

Solution 4.12   First, calculate the molar mass of glucose.

$$6 \text{ mol C} \times 12.0 \text{ g C/mol C} = \quad 72.0 \text{ g C}$$
$$12 \text{ mol H} \times 1.0 \text{ g H/mol H} = \quad 12.0 \text{ g H}$$
$$6 \text{ mol O} \times 16.0 \text{ g O/mol O} = +96.0 \text{ g O}$$
$$= \overline{\quad 180.0 \text{ g } C_6H_{12}O_6}$$

Use the molar mass and Avogadro's number to calculate the mass of glucose.

$$3.39 \times 10^{23} \text{ molecules } C_6H_{12}O_6 \times 1 \text{ mol } C_6H_{12}O_6/6.02 \times 10^{23} \text{ molecules } C_6H_{12}O_6$$
$$\times 180.0 \text{ g } C_6H_{12}O_6/1 \text{ mol } C_6H_{12}O_6 = 101 \text{ g } C_6H_{12}O_6$$

Problem 4.13   How many moles of C and H atoms are in a 125-g sample of C_5H_{10} (cyclopentane)?

Solution 4.13   First, calculate the molar mass of C_5H_{10}.

$$5 \text{ mol C} \times 12.0 \text{ g C/mol C} = \quad 60.0 \text{ g C}$$
$$10 \text{ mol H} \times 1.0 \text{ g H/mol H} = +10.0 \text{ g H}$$
$$= \overline{\quad 70.0 \text{ g } C_5H_{10}}$$

One mole of C_5H_{10} contains 5 mol C and 10 mol H.

$$125 \text{ g } C_5H_{10} \times 1 \text{ mol } C_5H_{10}/70.0 \text{ g } C_5H_{10} \times 5 \text{ mol C/1 mol } C_5H_{10} = 8.93 \text{ mol C}$$

It is not necessary to write the full set-up to calculate the number of moles of H. The ratio of H to C in C_5H_{10} is 10 to 5 or 2 to 1 : 2 mol H/1 mol C. After calculating the number of moles of C, use this conversion factor to find the moles of H.

$$8.93 \text{ mol C} \times 2 \text{ mol H/1 mol C} = 17.9 \text{ mole H}$$

Problem 4.14   What mass of carbon tetrachloride, CCl_4, contains the same number of molecules as a 5.000-g sample of CO_2?

Solution 4.14   First, calculate the molar masses of CCl_4 and CO_2. The molar masses of CCl_4 and CO_2 are 153.80 g/mol and 44.01 g/mol, respectively. If the two samples contain the same number of molecules, then they also contain the same number of moles of molecules, 1 mol CO_2/1 mol CCl_4.

Hence, calculate the number of moles of CO_2, which equals the moles of CCl_4. Then, convert the moles of CCl_4 to grams.

5.000 g CO_2 × 1 mol CO_2/44.01 g CO_2 × 1 mol CCl_4/1 mol CO_2

× 153.8 g CCl_4/1 mol CCl_4 = 17.47 g CCl_4

Formula Mass

Covalent compounds, such as CO, NO, CH_4, and H_2O, are composed of discrete molecules. However, ionic compounds, such as NaCl, K_2O, $CuCl_2$, and $MgSO_4$, are not comprised of discrete molecules. Instead, their structure is a network of ions chemically bonded together. For these compounds, the term molecular mass has no real meaning because no molecules are present. A more accurate term is applied to these compounds: formula mass. Formula mass is used for those substances not composed of discrete molecules in the same way that molecular mass is used for compounds composed of molecules.

To calculate the formula mass of an ionic compound, follow the same procedure that is used to find the molecular mass of a substance composed of molecules. Usually, the formula mass is treated the same as molecular mass.

4.2   CHEMICAL FORMULA CALCULATIONS

Mole and mass data can be used to calculate formulas of compounds, mass relationships in chemical reactions, and concentrations of solutions and mixtures. In this section, formula calculations and determinations are considered.

Percent Composition

A direct result of the law of constant composition (Sec. 3.1) is that each element within a compound can be expressed as a mass percent. Collectively, all mass percents of elements in a compound are called the percent composition of the substance.

Problem 4.15   Nitrogen(V) oxide, N_2O_5, is a gas that combines with water to produce nitric acid, HNO_3–one of the most important industrial acids. What is the percent composition of N_2O_5?

Solution 4.15   First, determine the molar mass of N_2O_5. Its molar mass is 108.0 g/mol. To calculate the mass percent of N and O, divide the mass of N by molar mass of N_2O_5 and multiply by 100. The mass percent of O is found similarly.

% N = (g N/g N_2O_5) × 100 = (28.0 g N/108.0 g N_2O_5) × 100 = 25.9% N

% O = (g O/g N_2O_5) × 100 = (80.0 g O/108.0 g N_2O_5) × 100 = 74.1% O

Problem 4.16   Ethanol, C_2H_6O, is produced when grains or fruits are fermented by yeast. Calculate the percent composition of ethanol.

Solution 4.16   First, calculate the molar mass of ethanol. The molar mass of ethanol is 46.10 g/mol. Then, calculate the mass percent of C, H, and O in 1.00 mol C_2H_6O.

% C = (g C/g C_2H_6O) × 100 = (24.0 g C/46.1 g) × 100 = 52.1%

% H = (g H/g C_2H_6O) × 100 = (6.06 g H/46.1 g) × 100 = 13.1%

% O = (g O/g C_2H_6O) × 100 = (16.0 g O/46.1 g) × 100 = 34.7%

Empirical Formula Calculations

Empirical formulas express the smallest whole-number ratio of atoms within a molecule. To calculate the empirical formula of a compound, either the percent composition or the mass ratio of the elements must be known. The masses of each element in the compound are converted to moles to yield the mole ratio. The empirical formula is obtained when the simplest mole ratio is calculated. In most cases, the empirical formula is a ratio of whole numbers, such as 3 to 1 or 5 to 2.

MOLECULAR AND EMPIRICAL FORMULAS

Let us consider hydrogen peroxide, a commonly used antiseptic and bleaching agent. Its molecular formula is H_2O_2. A molecular formula expresses the actual number of atoms in the molecule. One hydrogen peroxide molecule contains two H atoms and two O atoms. Its empirical formula, HO (H_1O_1), is obtained by dividing the subscripts of the molecular formula by 2.

Many compounds have the same molecular and empirical formulas, e.g., propane, C_3H_8. Whenever the subscripts of the molecular formula of a compound are not divisible by a common number, the empirical formula is the same as the molecular formula. Other examples of such compounds are potassium nitrate, KNO_3, and sulfur trioxide, SO_3.

Problem 4.17 A nitrogen-fluorine compound contains 26.9% N and 73.1% F. What is the empirical formula of the compound?

Solution 4.17 First, calculate the number of moles of each element. The percents given are mass ratios of each element per 100 g of compound; specifically, 26.9% N is 26.9 g N/100 g compound and 73.1% F is 73.1 g F/100 g compound.
Thus, convert these masses to moles.

26.9 g N × 1 mol N/14.0 g N = 1.92 mol N
73.1 g F × 1 mol F/19.0 g F = 3.85 mol F

Then, calculate the simplest whole-number mole ratio. Find the element with the smallest number of moles, and then divide this value into the number of moles of each element. In our problem, 1.92 mol N is the smallest quantity of moles. Therefore, it is divided into itself, giving exactly 1, and then divided into 3.85 moles F, which gives 2.01.

1.92 mol N/1.92 mol N = 1.00
3.85 mol F/1.92 mol N = 2.01 mol F/1 mol N

The simplest ratio is 2 mol F to 1 mol N or, translated into an empirical formula, NF_2. If the simplest mole ratio is 1 to 2, this indicates that the ratio of atoms in the molecule is also 1 to 2.

Problem 4.18 Calculate the empirical formula of a compound whose percent composition by mass is 7.195% P and 92.805% Br.

Solution 4.18 Calculate the mole ratio of elements in the compound.

$$7.195 \text{ g P} \times 1 \text{ mol P}/30.97 \text{ g P} = 0.2323 \text{ mol P}$$

$$92.805 \text{ g Br} \times 1 \text{ mol Br}/79.904 \text{ g Br} = 1.1615 \text{ mol Br}$$

Note, pay careful attention to significant figures when doing empirical formula calculations or the wrong mole ratio is obtained.
Then, calculate the simplest ratio of whole numbers.

$$0.2323 \text{ mol P}/0.2323 \text{ mol P} = 1.000$$

$$1.1615 \text{ mol Br}/0.02323 \text{ mol P} = 4.999 \text{ mol Br/mol P}$$

Our results show a ratio of 4.999 mol Br per 1.000 mol P. Within the limits of significant figures, round this to 5 because this is a ratio of whole numbers. The empirical formula of the compound is PBr_5.

Problem 4.19   Ascorbic acid is the chemical name for vitamin C. Vitamins are essential substances required in the human diet almost every day. A 2.642-g sample of ascorbic acid is found to contain 1.081 g C, 0.121 g H, and the remainder is oxygen. What is the empirical formula of ascorbic acid?

Solution 4.19   First, determine the masses of all substances. The total mass of ascorbic acid is given and the masses of C and H. The mass of O can be obtained by subtracting the sum of the masses of C and H from the total mass.

$$\text{Mass of O = total mass} - (\text{mass C + mass H})$$
$$= 2.642 \text{ g total} - (1.081 \text{ g C} + 0.121 \text{ g H}) = 1.440 \text{ g O}$$

Next, calculate the number of moles of each element.

$$1.081 \text{ g C} \times 1 \text{ mol C}/12.01 \text{ g C} = 0.09001 \text{ mol C}$$
$$0.121 \text{ g H} \times 1 \text{ mol H}/1.01 \text{ g H} = 0.120 \text{ mol H}$$
$$1.440 \text{ g O} \times 1 \text{ mol O}/16.00 \text{ g O} = 0.09000 \text{ mol O}$$

Then calculate the simplest mole ratio.

Because 0.09000 mol O is the smallest number of moles, divide 0.09000 mol O into each quantity to find the ratio of whole numbers.

$$0.09001 \text{ mol C}/0.09000 \text{ mol O} = 1.000 \text{ mol C/mol O}$$
$$0.120 \text{ mol H}/0.09000 \text{ mol O} = 1.33 \text{ mol H/mol O}$$
$$0.09000 \text{ mol O}/0.09000 \text{ mol O} = 1.000$$

To eliminate the fraction obtained in the mole ratio of H to O, multiply the numbers by small integers starting with 2 to find the ratio of whole numbers. Multiplying by 2 does not give a ratio of whole numbers, but multiplying by 3 gives 3.000 mol C, 3.99 mol H, and 3.000 mol O. Thus, the empirical formula for ascorbic acid is $C_3H_4O_3$.

Problem 4.20   An 8.456-g sample of a silicon–chlorine compound contains 6.519 g Cl. Calculate the empirical formula of the compound.

Solution 4.20   First, calculate the mass of Si. To obtain the mass of Si in the compound, subtract the mass of Cl from the total mass of the compound.

$$\text{Mass of Si = total mass} - \text{mass of Cl}$$
$$= 8.456 \text{ g total} - 6.519 \text{ g Cl} = 1.937 \text{ g Si}$$

Then, calculate the moles of Si and Cl.

$$1.937 \text{ g Si} \times 1 \text{ mol Si}/28.09 \text{ g Si} = 0.06896 \text{ mol Si}$$
$$6.519 \text{ g Cl} \times 1 \text{ mol Cl}/35.45 \text{ g Cl} = 0.1839 \text{ mol Cl}$$

Divide each by the smallest number of moles.

$$0.06896 \text{ mol Si}/0.06896 \text{ mol Si} = 1.000$$
$$0.1839 \text{ mol Cl}/0.06896 \text{ mol Si} = 2.667 \text{ mol Cl/mol Si}$$

To convert to a ratio of whole numbers, multiply each by small integers. Multiplying each by 2, does not give a ratio of whole numbers. However, multiplying the initial ratio by 3 gives a 3–to–8 ratio. The empirical formula of this silicon–chlorine compound is Si_3Cl_8.

Molecular Formula Calculations

While knowledge of the empirical formula gives the simplest ratio of atoms within a molecule, the molecular formula expresses the actual ratio of each atom in a molecule.

Once the empirical formula is known, only the molecular mass of a compound is needed to calculate its molecular formula. Because the molecular formula is a higher multiple of the empirical formula (or the same), if the mass of the empirical formula unit (empirical formula mass) is divided into the molecular mass, a whole number is obtained. This value gives the number of empirical formula units per molecular formula.

Problem 4.21   The molecular mass of a phosphorus–oxygen compound is 280.4. A 10.000-g sample of this compounds contains 4.364 g P. What is the molecular formula of the compound?

Solution 4.21   First, calculate the mass of O in the sample.

$$\text{Mass of O} = \text{total mass} - \text{mass of P}$$
$$= 10.000 \text{ g} - 4.364 \text{ g P} = 5.636 \text{ g O}$$

Then determine the mole ratio of P and O.

$$4.364 \text{ g P} \times 1 \text{ mol P}/30.97 \text{ g P} = 0.1409 \text{ mol P}$$
$$5.636 \text{ g O} \times 1 \text{ mol O}/16.00 \text{ g O} = 0.3523 \text{ mol O}$$

Calculate the simplest mole ratio.

$$0.1409 \text{ mol P}/0.1409 \text{ mol P} = 1.000$$
$$0.3523 \text{ mol O}/0.1409 \text{ mol P} = 2.500 \text{ mol O/mol P}$$

After multiplying 2 times $PO_{2.5}$, the correct empirical formula, P_2O_5, is obtained.
The molecular formula is found by dividing the empirical formula mass into the molecular mass. The empirical formula mass is 142 ($(2 \times 31) + (5 \times 16)$).

$$\text{Molecular mass/Empirical formula mass} = 284/142 = 2$$

Two formula units compose the total molecular mass; accordingly, the molecular formula is $2 \times P_2O_5$, or P_4O_{10}.

Problem 4.22   An analytical chemist analyzes a sample of a boron–hydrogen compound and finds 6.876 g B and 1.069 g H. If the molecular mass of the compound is 74.94, calculate the molecular formula of the compound.

Solution 4.22   First, calculate the number of moles of each element by dividing each by its molar mass.

$$6.876 \text{ g B} \times 1 \text{ mol B}/10.81 \text{ g B} = 0.6361 \text{ mol B}$$
$$1.069 \text{ g H} \times 1 \text{ mol H}/1.008 \text{ g H} = 1.061 \text{ mol H}$$

Calculate the simplest ratio of whole numbers by dividing by the smallest number of moles.

$$0.6361 \text{ mol B}/0.6361 \text{ mol B} = 1.000$$
$$1.061 \text{ mol H}/0.6361 \text{ mol B} = 1.668 \text{ mol H/mol B}$$

Next, calculate the simplest ratio of whole numbers by multiplying the mole ratio by 3 to obtain a whole-number ratio.

$$1.000 \text{ mol B} \times 3 = 3.000 \text{ mol B}$$
$$1.668 \text{ mol H} \times 3 = 5.004 \text{ mol H}$$

Thus, the empirical formula of the compound is B_3H_5.

To calculate the molecular formula, add the atomic masses of each element in the empirical formula. This yields the empirical formula mass.

$$10.81 \times 3 = 32.43$$
$$1.008 \times 5 = +5.040$$
$$\text{Empirical formula mass} = \overline{37.47}$$

Divide the empirical formula mass into the molecular mass.

$$\frac{\text{Molecular mass}}{\text{Empirical formula mass}} = \frac{74.94}{37.47} = 2$$

Finally, calculate the molecular formula, by multiplying the subscripts in the empirical formula by 2.

$$B_3H_5 \times 2 = B_6H_{10}$$

The molecular formula of the compound is B_6H_{10}.

4.3   CHEMICAL EQUATIONS

Components of Chemical Equations

Chemical changes occur when substances undergo changes in their composition. When a substance undergoes a chemical change, we say "a chemical reaction has taken place." It is inconvenient and time-consuming to express what happens during chemical reactions by writing the complete names of all substances involved (a word equation). Instead, a concise statement, called a chemical equation, is written using the symbols of the elements and the formulas of compounds. Other special symbols are added to the equation to express exactly what changes occur during chemical changes.

REACTANTS AND PRODUCTS

A chemical equation has two parts: reactants and products. Reactants, sometimes called starting materials, are all substances present before the chemical change. Each reactant is listed by writing its symbol or formula separated by a plus (+) sign. All reactants are written to the left of an arrow (→) that separates the reactants from the products.

All products (that is, substances) produced after the chemical change occurs, are written to the right of the arrow, and are separated by plus signs. Hence, chemical equations have the following format:

$$A + B \rightarrow C + D$$

In our example, hypothetical substances A and B are the reactants, and C and D are the products of the reaction.

PHYSICAL STATES OF REACTANTS AND PRODUCTS

Often additional information is added to the equation. For example, it is important to know what physical state the reactants and products exist in. Four symbols are employed to indicate physical states: solid, (s); liquid, (l); gas, (g); and water or aqueous solution, (aq). Enclosed in parentheses, these symbols are written next to the formula within the equation.

Problem 4.23   Translate the following to a word equation.

$$SO_3(g) + H_2O(l) \rightarrow H_2SO_4(aq)$$

Solution 4.23   This equation states that gaseous SO_3, sulfur trioxide, combines with liquid H_2O, water, and produces an aqueous solution of H_2SO_4, sulfuric acid.

Balancing Chemical Equations

When an equation is written, it must obey the law of conservation of mass, i.e., matter cannot be created or destroyed. Specifically, the number of atoms of each different element in an equation must be the same on the left and right side of the arrow. After a chemical change, the same type and number of atoms are present; they are merely rearranged.

To obey the law of conservation of mass, an equation is balanced. Balancing an equation involves placing coefficients in front of all reactants and products so that the same number of atoms of each element appears on either side of the equation.

THE INSPECTION METHOD

Given an unbalanced equation, balance it by adding the correct coefficients (the numbers that precede the formulas) to each reactant and product. The principal means for accomplishing this in simple equations is by the inspection method. To successfully balance equations by inspection, use the following general guidelines.

1. Change the coefficients of the reactants and products, but never change the subscripts. If a subscript is changed, it alters the identity of that substance. For example, CO is not the same as CO_2.
2. Usually balance the atoms that only appear once in the reactants and products, and then balance those that appear in many compounds. Subsequently, balance metals first, followed by the nonmetals except O and H. Because O and H appear in many compounds, balance them only after balancing all other elements.
3. After finishing, always check to see that both sides of the equation have equal numbers of the same type of atoms.

Problem 4.24   Balance the equation for the formation of phosphoric acid from tetraphosphorus decoxide, P_4O_{10}, and water, H_2O.

$$P_4O_{10} + H_2O \rightarrow H_3PO_4 \text{ (unbalanced)}$$

Solution 4.24 First, balance the P atoms and then proceed to the H and O atoms. After balancing each atom, it is a good practice to underline them, and when all atoms are underlined, the equation should be balanced. Four P atoms are on the left side and only one on the right, so place a 4 in front of H_3PO_4.

$$P_4O_{10} + H_2O \rightarrow 4H_3\underline{P}O_4 \text{ (unbalanced)}$$

Twelve H atoms are on the right side, so place a 6 in front of the H_2O.

$$\underline{P_4}O_{10} + 6\underline{H_2}O \rightarrow 4\underline{H_3P}O_4 \text{ (balanced)}$$

If the H and P atoms are correctly balanced, then the O atoms should already be balanced. The left side has 10 O atoms in the P_4O_{10} and six O atoms in the six molecules of H_2O. Thus, the left side of the equation has a total of 16 O atoms. The right side has four molecules of H_3PO_4 with 16 O atoms. Hence, the equation is balanced.

$$P_4O_{10} + 6H_2O \rightarrow 4H_3PO_4 \text{ (balanced)}$$
$$\text{4 P, 12 H, 16 O} \qquad \text{4 P, 12 H, 16 O}$$

Problem 4.25 Use the inspection method to balance the following equation.

$$B_3N_3H_6 + O_2 \rightarrow N_2O_5 + B_2O_3 + H_2O$$

Solution 4.25 First, balance the B, N, and H atoms before balancing the O atoms. Three B atoms are on the left side and two B atoms are on the right side. To balance the B atoms, calculate the lowest common multiple between 2 and 3, which is 6. Thus, 2 is the coefficient of $B_3N_3H_6$ and 3 is the coefficient of B_2O_3.

$$2\underline{B_3}N_3H_6 + O_2 \rightarrow N_2O_5 + 3\underline{B_2}O_3 + H_2O \text{ (unbalanced)}$$

Six N atoms are on the left and only two N atoms are on the right, hence, place a 3 in front of the N_2O_5.

$$2\underline{B_3}N_3H_6 + O_2 \rightarrow 3\underline{N_2}O_5 + 3\underline{B_2}O_3 + H_2O \text{ (unbalanced)}$$

Continuing, twelve H atoms are on the left and two H atoms are on the right; therefore, place a 6 in front of the H_2O.

$$2\underline{B_3}N_3H_6 + O_2 \rightarrow 3\underline{N_2}O_5 + 3\underline{B_2}O_3 + 6\underline{H_2}O \text{ (unbalanced)}$$

Finally, 30 O atoms are on the right side: 15 in 3 molecules of N_2O_5, 9 in 3 molecules of B_2O_3, and 6 in 6 molecules of H_2O. Two O atoms in O_2 are on the left side. Hence, multiply O_2 by 15 to balance the O atoms.

$$2\underline{B_3}N_3H_6 + 15\underline{O_2} \rightarrow 3\underline{N_2}O_5 + 3\underline{B_2}O_3 + 6\underline{H_2}O \text{ (balanced)}$$

Each side has 6 N atoms, 6 B atoms, 12 H atoms, and 30 O atoms.

Problem 4.26 Balance the following equation which shows the oxidation of ethane, C_2H_6 to CO_2 and H_2O.

$$C_2H_6(g) + O_2(g) \rightarrow CO_2(g) + H_2O(g)$$

Solution 4.26 It is convenient to start with C atoms, proceed to H atoms, and balance O atoms last. Two C atoms are on the left side, and they are balanced by placing 2 as the coefficient of CO_2.

$$\underline{C_2H_6}(g) + O_2(g) \rightarrow \underline{2CO_2}(g) + H_2O(g) \text{ (unbalanced)}$$

Six H atoms in C_2H_6 are balanced by placing a 3 in front of the H_2O.

$$\underline{C_2H_6}(g) + O_2(g) \rightarrow \underline{2CO_2}(g) + \underline{3H_2O}(g) \text{ (unbalanced)}$$

Seven O atoms are found in the products. This time balance the equation using a fractional coefficient. Because 2 O atoms are on the left, ask yourself "what number multiplied by 2 gives 7?" The answer is 7/2 or 3.5; thus, the coefficient is 3.5.

$$\underline{C_2H_6}(g) + \underline{3.5O_2}(g) \rightarrow \underline{2CO_2}(g) + \underline{3H_2O}(g) \text{ (balanced)}$$

A check of the coefficients shows us that 2 C, 6 H, and 7 O atoms are in both the reactants and products; thus, the equation is balanced.

4.4   MOLE AND MASS RELATIONSHIPS IN CHEMICAL REACTIONS

Stoichiometry Defined

Stoichiometry is the study of mass, mole, volume, and energy relationships in chemical reactions.

Information Obtained from a Balanced Equation

A balanced chemical equation provides us with a wealth of information. For example, consider the equation for the combustion of methane, CH_4.

$$CH_4(g) + 2O_2(g) \rightarrow CO_2(g) + 2H_2O(g)$$

Recall that the coefficients in the equation give the ratios in which the reactants combine and the products form. One CH_4 molecule combines with two molecules of O_2 to yield one molecule of CO_2 and two molecules of H_2O. Starting with Avogadro's number of CH_4 molecules, 6.0×10^{23} molecules, $2 \times 6.0 \times 10^{23}$ molecules or 1.2×10^{24} molecules of O_2 react, and 6.0×10^{23} molecules of CO_2 and $2 \times 6.0 \times 10^{23}$ molecules of H_2O form. Consequently, 1.0 mole of CH_4 (16 g) combines with 2.0 moles of O_2 (64 g) and produces 1.0 mole of CO_2 (44 g) and 2.0 moles of H_2O (36 g).

Equation Calculations

The mole ratios from a balanced chemical equation may be used to calculate the masses of reactants that combine or products that form.

Problem 4.27 (a) Calculate the mass of O_2 that combines with 5.60 g CH_4 and the mass of products that form. (b) What mass of CO_2 results? (c) What mass of H_2O results?

$$CH_4(g) + 2O_2(g) \rightarrow CO_2(g) + 2H_2O(g)$$

Solution 4.27

(a) The equation shows that one mole of CH_4 reacts with two moles of O_2. Thus, to solve this stoichiometry problem, convert the mass of CH_4, 5.60 g CH_4, to moles and then use the above conversion factor to calculate the number of moles of O_2. Finally, convert to grams of O_2, using the molar mass of O_2, 32.0 g O_2/mol O_2.

5.60 g CH_4 × 1 mol CH_4/16.0 g CH_4 × 2 mol O_2/1 mol CH_4

$$\times \, 32.0 \text{ g } O_2/1 \text{ mol } O_2 = 22.4 \text{ g } O_2$$

(b) To calculate the mass of CO_2 that results, obtain the mole ratio of mol CH_4 to mol CO_2. One mole of CO_2 forms from one mole of CH_4. In a similar manner, use the factor-label method to calculate the resulting mass of CO_2.

5.60 g CH_4 × 1 mol CH_4/16.0 g CH_4 × 1 mol CO_2/1 mol CH_4

$$\times \, 44.0 \text{ g } CO_2/1 \text{ mol } CO_2 = 15.4 \text{ g } CO_2$$

(c) To compute the mass of H_2O, use the following conversion factor.

$$\frac{2 \text{ mol } H_2O}{1 \text{ mol } CH_4}$$

5.60 g CH_4 × 1 mol CH_4/16.0 g CH_4 × 2 mol H_2O/1 mol CH_4

$$\times \, 18.0 \text{ g } H_2O/1 \text{ mol } H_2O = 12.6 \text{ g } H_2O$$

Problem 4.28   Consider the following reaction in which Cu metal and SO_2 result when copper(I) oxide, Cu_2O, and copper(I) sulfide, Cu_2S, are heated.

$$2Cu_2O + Cu_2S \xrightarrow{\text{heat}} 6Cu + SO_2$$

What mass of Cu can be obtained when 4.58 kg Cu_2O is heated with excess Cu_2S?

Solution 4.28   The equation tells us that 6 moles of Cu metal results for each 2 moles of Cu_2O. Therefore, 3 moles of Cu form for each 1 mole of Cu_2O. Then, apply the factor-label method to solve this problem.

4.58 kg Cu_2O × 1000 g Cu_2O/1 kg Cu_2O × 1 mol Cu_2O/143 g Cu_2O ×

$$3 \text{ mol Cu}/1 \text{ mol } Cu_2O \times 63.5 \text{ g Cu}/1 \text{ mol Cu} = 6.10 \times 10^3 \text{ g Cu}$$

Problem 4.29   Consider the following equation.

$$Na_2CO_3 + Ca(OH)_2 \rightarrow 2NaOH + CaCO_3$$

What mass of Na_2CO_3 reacts with excess $Ca(OH)_2$ to produce 915 g NaOH?

Solution 4.29   First, convert the mass of NaOH in grams to moles and then use the following mole ratio between NaOH and Na_2CO_3, obtained from the equation, to calculate the number of moles of Na_2CO_3.

$$\frac{\text{mol } Na_2CO_3}{\text{mol NaOH}}$$

Then, convert to grams using the molar mass of Na_2CO_3, 106 g Na_2CO_3/mol.

915 g NaOH × 1 mol NaOH/40.0 g NaOH × 1 mol Na_2CO_3/2 mol NaOH

$$\times \ 106 \ g \ Na_2CO_3/1 \ mol \ Na_2CO_3 = 1.21 \times 10^3 g \ Na_2CO_3$$

The answer indicates that 1.21×10^3 g Na_2CO_3, or 1.21 kg Na_2CO_3, is needed to produce 915 g NaOH in the given reaction.

Theoretical and Actual Yields

The mass of product isolated is called the actual yield. Because the actual yield is usually less than the theoretical yield, the percent yield for a reaction is often calculated. The percent yield is the ratio of the actual yield to the theoretical yield multiplied by 100.

$$Percent \ yield = \frac{Actual \ yield}{Theoretical \ yield} \times 100$$

Problem 4.30 A student attempts to synthesize acetylsalicylic acid (aspirin, ASA), $C_9H_8O_4$. The student mixes 10.620 g of salicylic acid (SA), $C_7H_6O_3$, with excess acetic anhydride, $C_4H_6O_3$, in the presence of an acid catalyst, H_2SO_4.

$$\underset{\text{Salicylic acid}}{C_7H_6O_3} \ + \ \underset{\text{Acetic anhydride}}{C_4H_6O_3} \ \overset{H_2SO_4}{\rightarrow} \ \underset{\text{Aspirin}}{C_9H_8O_4} \ + \ \underset{\text{Acetic acid}}{C_2H_4O_2}$$

If the student isolates 7.762 g ASA, what is their percent yield?

Solution 4.30 To calculate the theoretical yield, use the factor-label method to convert the mass of salicylic acid (SA) to moles. Then use the mole ratio of aspirin (ASA) to salicylic acid to calculate the moles of aspirin. Finally, use the molar mass of aspirin, 180.16 g ASA/mol ASA, to calculate the mass of aspirin.

10.620 g SA × 1 mol SA/138.12 g SA × 1 mol ASA/1 mol SA

$$\times \ 180.16 \ g \ ASA/1 \ mol \ ASA = 13.852 \ g \ ASA$$

Then, calculate the percent yield.

$$\%yield = (actual \ yield/theoretical \ yield) \times 100$$
$$= (7.762 \ g \ ASA/13.852 \ g \ ASA) \times 100 = 56.03\%$$

Limiting-Reactant Problems

So far, the assumption is made that sufficient amounts of all other reactants are present to react with the stated amount of a given reactant. Often, the more practical problem is encountered in which the amounts of reactants are not all present in stoichiometric amounts. In these cases, one reactant is consumed before all the others have completely reacted and the reaction stops. No more products form and the amount of products isolated will therefore be limited by the amount of the limiting reactant–the one used up first.

PROCEDURE FOR SOLVING LIMITING-REACTANT PROBLEMS

1. First determine that the problem is a limiting-reactant problem. Limiting-reactant problems can be easily recognized from those solved previously because limiting-reactant problems must give the masses of two or more reactants. In nonlimiting-reagent problems, all other reactants are present in sufficient quantities or in excess.
2. Then, determine which substance is the limiting reactant.

3. Use the number of moles of the limiting reactant to calculate the moles or mass of the product of interest.

Problem 4.31   What mass of HCl can be obtained from 40.3 g of phosgene, $COCl_2$, and 7.49 g of H_2O in the following reaction?

$$COCl_2(g) + H_2O(l) \rightarrow CO_2(g) + 2HCl(g)$$

Solution 4.31   To identify the limiting reactant, first calculate the number of moles of each reactant present.

$$40.3 \text{ g } COCl_2 \times 1 \text{ mol } COCl_2/98.9 \text{ g } COCl_2 = 0.407 \text{ mol } COCl_2$$
$$7.49 \text{ g } H_2O \times 1 \text{ mol } H_2O/18.0 \text{ g } H_2O = 0.416 \text{ mol } H_2O$$

The equation shows that one mole of $COCl_2$ reacts with one mole of H_2O. Thus, after 0.407 moles of $COCl_2$ are consumed, excess H_2O remains (0.416 mol − 0.407 mol = 0.009 mol H_2O in excess). This means that $COCl_2$ is the limiting reactant.

Complete the problem using the limiting reactant.

$$0.407 \text{ mol } COCl_2 \times 2 \text{ mol } HCl/1 \text{ mol } COCl_2 \times 36.5 \text{ g } HCl/1 \text{ mol } HCl = 29.7 \text{ g } HCl$$

The maximum mass of HCl that can be obtained from 40.3 g $COCl_2$ and 7.49 g H_2O is 29.7 g. Note that if you had incorrectly solved this problem using the mass of water H_2O, which is in the reactant in excess, a mass of 30.4 g HCl is obtained. This mass cannot result because of an insufficient amount of $COCl_2$. The reactant in excess always gives a larger calculated value for the mass of product than the limiting reactant.

Problem 4.32   Consider the following equation.

$$2BCl_3 + 3H_2 \rightarrow 2B + 6HCl$$

(a) What mass of boron can be obtained from 11.9 g BCl_3 and 0.297 g H_2? (b) What mass of excess reactant remains after the reaction stops?

Solution 4.32
(a) First, identify the limiting reactant.

$$11.9 \text{ g } BCl_3 \times 1 \text{ mol } BCl_3/117.2 \text{ g } BCl_3 = 0.102 \text{ mol } BCl_3$$
$$0.297 \text{ g } H_2 \times 1 \text{ mol } H_2/2.02 \text{ g } H_2 = 0.147 \text{ mol } H_2$$

Because the reactants do not combine in a 1-to-1 ratio, calculate the number of moles of the second reactant needed to react with the first. Let's calculate the number of moles of H_2 required to react with 0.102 mol BCl_3.

$$0.102 \text{ mol } BCl_3 \times 3 \text{ mol } H_2/2 \text{ mol } BCl_3 = 0.153 \text{ mol } H_2 \text{ needed}$$

This calculation shows that 0.153 mol H_2 is needed to react exactly with 0.102 mol BCl_3. In other words, more H_2 (0.153 mol) is required than is present (0.147 mol). Therefore, the limiting reactant is H_2. If you select H_2 and calculate the number of moles of BCl_3 needed, you discover that only 0.0980 mol BCl_3 is required.

0.147 mol H_2 × 2 mol BCl_3/3 mol H_2 = 0.0980 mol BCl_3 needed

This number of moles is less than the amount present (0.102 mol), which also shows that H_2 is the limiting reactant and BCl_3 is in excess. Then, complete the problem using the limiting reactant.

0.147 mol H_2 × 2 mol B/3 mol H_2 × 10.8 g B/1 mol B = 1.06 g B

(b) To obtain the mass of unreacted BCl_3, calculate the mass of BCl_3 that reacts with the 0.147 mol H_2, and then subtract it from the amount present initially, 11.9 g BCl_3.

0.147 mol H_2 × 2 mol BCl_3/3 mol H_2 × 117.2 g BCl_3/1 mol BCl_3 = 11.5 g BCl_3

Mass of excess BCl_3 = 11.9 g − 11.5 g = 0.4 g BCl_3

Combustion Analysis

Combustion analysis may be used to determine the empirical formulas of carbon compounds. For example, an unknown C, H, and O compound is placed into a furnace and is burned in the presence of excess O_2 gas. The combustion products of the reaction are $CO_2(g)$ and $H_2O(g)$.

C, H, O compound + $O_2(g) \rightarrow CO_2(g) + H_2O(g)$

The gaseous products of this reaction, CO_2 and H_2O, pass through two traps where they are absorbed. One trap removes the $CO_2(g)$ and the other removes the $H_2O(g)$. From the masses of CO_2 and H_2O, the number of moles of C, H, and O and the empirical formula of the compound are calculated.

Problem 4.33 An unknown C, H, and O compound is burned in excess O_2. If a 5.000-g sample of this compound produces 9.613 g CO_2 and 3.374 g H_2O, what is the empirical formula of the compound?

Solution 4.33 After the reaction, all of the C originally in the unknown compound is in the CO_2 and all of the H is in the H_2O. Oxygen in CO_2 and H_2O comes from both the compound and the O_2 used for combustion. Therefore, to obtain the mass of O in the compound, calculate the combined mass of C and H and then subtract it from the total mass of the sample, 5.000 g.

9.613 g CO_2 × 1 mol CO_2/44.01 g CO_2 × 1 mol C/1 mol CO_2 × 12.01 g C/1 mol C = 2.623 g C
3.374 g H_2O × 1 mol H_2O/18.02 g H_2O × 2 mol H/1 mol H_2O × 1.008 g H/1 mol H = 0.3775 g H

Next, calculate the mass of O in the compound. The total mass of the compound is 5.000 g. Thus, subtract the combined mass of C and H from 5.000 g to obtain the mass of O.

Total mass = g C + g H + g O
5.000 g = 2.623 g C + 0.3775 g H + g O
g O = 5.000 g − (2.623 g + 0.3775 g) = 2.000 g O

Then, calculate the number of moles of C, H, and O.

Mol of C = 2.623 g C × 1 mol C/12.01 g C = 0.2184 mol C
Mol of H = 0.3775 g H × 1 mol H/1.008 g H = 0.3745 mol H

$$\text{Mol of O} = 2.000 \text{ g O} \times 1 \text{ mol O}/16.00 \text{ g O} = 0.1250 \text{ mol O}$$

Divide each by the smallest number of mol, 0.1250 mol O.

$$0.2184 \text{ mol C}/0.1250 \text{ mol O} = 1.747 \text{ mol C/mol O}$$
$$0.3745 \text{ mol H}/0.1250 \text{ mol O} = 2.996 \text{ mol H/mol O}$$
$$0.1250 \text{ mol O}/0.1250 \text{ mol O} = 1.000$$

Multiplying each of these by 4 gives the simplest ratio of whole numbers.

$$\text{C } 1.747 \text{ mol C} \times 4 = 6.988 \text{ mol C} = 7 \text{ mol C}$$
$$\text{H } 2.996 \text{ mol H} \times 4 = 11.98 \text{ mol H} = 12 \text{ mol H}$$
$$\text{O } 1.000 \text{ mol O} \times 4 = 4.000 \text{ mol O} = 4 \text{ mol O}$$

The empirical formula of the compound is $C_7H_{12}O_4$.

Mixture Problems

Stoichiometric principles may be used to determine the composition of two-component mixtures that have a common element. For example, the percent composition of a mixture of NaF and KF may be calculated from its total mass and the mass of F. In calculations that have two unknown values, the percent of NaF (% NaF) and KF (% KF), two simultaneous equations must be solved.

Problem 4.34   What is the percent composition of a 3.50-g mixture of NaF and KF that contains 1.30 g F?

Solution 4.34   To obtain the percent of the two fluorides, first write an equation for the masses of NaF, x, and KF, y. The sum of the masses of NaF and KF equals the total mass of the mixture, 3.50 g.

$$x + y = 3.50 \text{ g}$$

A second equation is written in terms of the number of moles of F in the mixture. The moles of F contributed by NaF plus the moles from KF equal the total moles of F in the mixture.

$$\text{mol}_{total} \text{ F} = \text{mol F}_{NaF} + \text{mol F}_{KF}$$

The sample has x g NaF and y g KF. Therefore, the moles of F from NaF is as follows:

$$x \text{ g NaF} \times 1 \text{ mol NaF}/42.0 \text{ g NaF} \times 1 \text{ mol F}/1 \text{ mol NaF} = x/42.0 \text{ mol } F_{NaF}$$

and the moles of F from KF is

$$y \text{ g KF} \times 1 \text{ mol KF}/58.1 \text{ g KF} \times 1 \text{ mol F}/1 \text{ mol KF} = y/58.1 \text{ mol } F_{KF}$$

The total moles of F in the mixture is obtained by converting the mass of F to moles using its molar mass, 19.0 g F/mol.

$$1.30 \text{ g F} \times 1 \text{ mol F}/19.0 \text{ g F} = 0.0684 \text{ mol}_{total} \text{ F}.$$

The second equation becomes the following:

$$x/42.0 + y/58.1 = 0.0684$$
$$\text{mol F}_{NaF} + \text{mol F}_{KF} = \text{moles}_{total} \text{ F}$$

After the first equation is rearranged and y is found, it can be substituted into the second equation so that the value of x can be calculated.

$$x + y = 3.50$$
$$y = 3.50 - x$$
$$(x/42.0) + (3.50 - x)/58.1 = 0.0684$$

The equation can be solved because it has one unknown. Solving this equation for x yields 1.23 g. In other words, the mass of NaF in the mixture is 1.23 g. To get the mass of KF, subtract the mass of NaF from the total mass.

$$\text{Total mass} = 3.50 \text{ g} = \text{mass NaF} + \text{mass of KF}$$
$$\text{mass of KF} = 3.50 \text{ g} - \text{mass of NaF} = 2.27 \text{ g KF}$$

To complete the problem, calculate the percent of each component of the mixture.

$$\% \text{ NaF} = (1.23 \text{ g NaF}/3.50 \text{ g}) \times 100 = 35.1\% \text{ NaF}$$
$$\% \text{ KF} = (2.27 \text{ g KF}/3.50 \text{ g}) \times 100 = 64.9\% \text{ KF}$$

Problem 4.35 A 1.00-g sample of a mixture of KBr and $MgBr_2$ is dissolved in H_2O. To this solution, $AgNO_3(aq)$ is added to precipitate the Br^- as AgBr(s). A precipitate is a solid insoluble substance.

$$Ag^+(aq) + Br^-(aq) \rightarrow AgBr(s)$$

If 1.63 g AgBr is isolated, what is the percent of each component in the mixture?

Solution 4.35 First, write an equation for the total mass of the mixture. If x equals the mass of KBr and y equals the mass of $MgBr_2$, then $x + y = 1.00$ g. The sum of the masses of KBr and $MgBr_2$ equals 1.00 g. Then, write an equation for the total number of moles of bromide ions. The bromide ions, Br^-, in the mixture combine with silver ions, Ag^+, producing solid insoluble AgBr. Thus, the total number of moles Br can be calculated from the mass of AgBr.

$$1.63 \text{ g AgBr} \times 1 \text{ mol AgBr}/188 \text{ g AgBr} \times 1 \text{ mol Br}/1 \text{ mol AgBr} = 8.67 \times 10^{-3} \text{ mol}_{\text{total}} \text{ Br}$$

Next, convert the mass of AgBr to moles using its molar mass, 188 g AgBr/mol. Because one mole of Br is found per mole of AgBr, the number of moles of Br equals the moles of AgBr. Second, calculate the moles of Br in KBr using its molar mass, 119 g KBr/mol, as follows.

$$x \text{ g KBr} \times 1 \text{ mol KBr}/119 \text{ g KBr} \times 1 \text{ mol Br}/1 \text{ mol KBr} = x/119 \text{ mol Br}$$

Obtain the moles of Br in $MgBr_2$ using its molar mass, 184 g $MgBr_2$/mol, and the fact that two moles of Br are in one mole of $MgBr_2$, 2 mol Br/1 mol $MgBr_2$.

$$y \text{ g MgBr}_2 \times 1 \text{ mol MgBr}_2/184 \text{ g MgBr}_2 \times 2 \text{ mol Br}/1 \text{ mol MgBr}_2 = 2y/184 \text{ mol Br}$$

The sum of the moles of Br in each compound equals the total number of moles of Br.

$$\frac{x}{119} + \frac{2y}{184} = 8.67 \times 10^{-3} \text{ mol}_{\text{total}} \text{Br}$$

Solve the first equation for y ($y = 1.00 - x$) and substitute it into the second equation.

$$\frac{x}{119} + \frac{2(1.00 - x)}{184} = 8.67 \, x \, 10^{-3} \text{mol}_{total} \text{Br}$$

Solving this equation gives a value of 0.892 g for x and 0.108 g for y. Thus, the mass of KBr in the sample is 0.892 g and the mass of $MgBr_2$ is 0.108 g.

Finally, calculate the percents of each component of the mixture.

$$\% \, KBr = (0.892 \, g \, KBr/1.00 \, g \, mixture) \times 100 = 89.2\% \, KBr$$
$$\% \, MgBr_2 = (0.108 \, g \, MgBr_2/1.00 \, g \, mixture) \times 100 = 10.8\% \, MgBr_2$$

4.5 MOLARITY

Solutions are homogeneous mixtures of pure substances. The dissolved substance is called the solute. It is usually in smaller amount. The substance that dissolves the solute is the solvent. One of the most important solvents in chemistry is H_2O.

Molarity Defined

Many different units of concentration are used to express the quantity of solute dissolved in a solution. The one used most often in introductory chemistry is molarity. Molarity, M, is the number of moles of solute per liter of solution.

$$\text{Molarity } (M) = \frac{\text{Moles of solute}}{\text{Liters of solution}}$$

How is a 1.0 M solution prepared? To prepare 1.00 L of a 1.00 M solution, add 1.00 mole of the solute to a 1.00 L volumetric flask. Next add about 500 mL of deionized or distilled water and swirl the flask until the solute dissolves. Finally, add enough deionized water to bring the total volume of the solution to exactly 1.00 L, and then shake the flask to obtain a homogenous mixture. An unlimited number of ways exist to prepare a 1.00 M solution.

Calculating the Molarity of a Solution

To calculate the molarity of a given solution, soln, divide the moles of solute by the number of liters of solution.

Problem 4.36   What is the molarity of a solution that has 7.85 g methanol, CH_4O, dissolved in 153 mL of aqueous solution?

Solution 4.36   First, calculate the moles of methanol, CH_4O.

$$7.85 \, g \, CH_4O \times 1 \, mol \, CH_4O/32.0 \, g \, CH_4O = 0.245 \, mol \, CH_4O$$

Next, calculate volume of the methanol solution in liters.

$$153 \, mL \, soln \times 1 \, L \, soln/1000 \, mL \, soln = 0.153 \, L \, soln$$

Finally, calculate the molarity of the solution.

$$M = moles \, CH_4O/L \, soln$$
$$= 0.245 \, mol \, CH_4O/0.153 \, L \, soln = 1.60 \, M \, CH_4O$$

Molarity as a Conversion Factor

It is convenient to think of molarity as the conversion factor of moles of solute to liters of solution.

$$\frac{\text{mol solute}}{\text{L solution}}$$

Problem 4.37 What mass of dissolved NaOH is in 1.00 L of 6.00 M NaOH?

Solution 4.37 A 6.00 M solution of NaOH has 6.00 mol NaOH/1.00 L solution. Thus, use this conversion factor to convert liters to moles. Knowing the molar mass of NaOH, 40.0 g NaOH/mol, the mass of NaOH is calculated as follows.

1.00 L solution × 6.00 mol NaOH/1.00 L solution × 40.0 g NaOH/mol NaOH = 240 g NaOH

Problem 4.38 Calculate the mass of ammonium nitrate, NH_4NO_3, in mg, in 45.1 mL of a 0.119 M aqueous solution.

Solution 4.38 First, convert the volume in milliliters to liters and then use the molarity, 0.119 mol NH_4NO_3/L soln, to obtain the number of moles of NH_4NO_3 in solution. Then calculate the mass in grams of NH_4NO_3 by multiplying by the molar mass of NH_4NO_3, 80.0 g NH_4NO_3/mol. Finally, convert to milligrams, using 1000 mg/g.

45.1 mL soln × 1 L soln/1000 mL × 0.119 mol NH_4NO_3/L soln ×

80.0 g NH_4NO_3/1 mol NH_4NO_3 × 1000 mg/g = 429 mg NH_4NO_3

Problem 4.39 A chemical experiment requires 0.644 M NaOH. What is the maximum volume that can be prepared from 57.6 g NaOH(s)?

Solution 4.39 First, convert the grams of NaOH to moles of NaOH, using 40.0 g NaOH/mol. Then use the molarity, 0.644 mol NaOH/L, to obtain the volume of solution.

57.6 g NaOH × 1 mol NaOH/40.0 g NaOH × 1 L NaOH/0.644 mol NaOH = 2.24 L NaOH

Dilution of Solutions

Often a more concentrated solution must be diluted with solvent to get desired solutions with lower concentrations. The addition of solvent increases the total volume, which decreases the molar concentration of the solute. Always remember that during dilution, the number of moles of solute remains constant. Whenever the solution volume doubles, the concentration becomes half of the original concentration because the same number of moles occupy twice the volume. If the solution volume triples, the molar concentration becomes one-third of its original concentration.

DILUTION CALCULATIONS

To solve dilution problems remember that the number of moles of solute in the concentrated solution (mol_{concd}) equals the number of moles of solute in the diluted solution (mol_{dil}). The moles of solute in the concentrated solution equals the product of the molarity of the concentrated solution (M_{concd}) times its volume (V_{concd}) in L.

$$mol_{concd} = M_{concd} \times V_{concd}$$
$$= (mol_{concd}/L_{concd}) \times L_{concd}$$

Likewise, the moles of solute in the diluted solute equals the product of the molarity of the diluted solution (M_{dil}) times its volume (V_{dil}) in L.

$$mol_{dil} = M_{dil} \times V_{dil}$$
$$= (mol_{dil}/L_{dil}) \times L_{dil}$$

The moles of solute in the concentrated solution equals the moles in the diluted solution; thus,

$$M_{concd}V_{concd} = M_{dil}V_{dil}$$

Problem 4.40   How is 150 mL of 0.250 M HNO_3 prepared from concentrated nitric acid, 15.9 M HNO_3?

Solution 4.40

$$M_{concd}V_{concd} = M_{dil}V_{dil}$$

M_{concd} is 15.9 M HNO_3, V_{dil} is 150 mL, and M_{dil} is 0.250 M HNO_3. To calculate the volume of 15.9 M HNO_3 that must be diluted, rearrange the equation and solve for V_{concd}. Then substitute the known values into the equation as follows.

$$V_{concd} = (M_{dil}V_{dil})/M_{concd}$$
$$= (0.250 \text{ M} \times 150 \text{ mL})/15.9 \text{ M}$$
$$= 2.36 \text{ mL of } 15.9 \text{ M } HNO_3$$

To prepare a 0.250 *M* solution, our calculation tells us to dilute 2.36 mL of 15.9 *M* HNO_3 to 150 mL. Place a small volume of water into a container and dissolve the 2.36 mL of 15.9 *M* HNO_3. Then, add enough water until the total volume is 150 mL and mix thoroughly.

SUMMARY

*T*he mole is the counting unit used by chemists to keep track of atoms, ions, molecules, and formula units. One mole of any substance has the same number of particles as are found in exactly 12 g of ^{12}C. One mole of particles equals 6.022×10^{23} particles, Avogadro's number of particles. One mole of like atoms has a mass equal to their atomic mass in grams, and one mole of molecules has a mass equal to their molecular mass in grams.

The percent composition of a compound gives the mass percents of all elements in the compound. The empirical formula expresses the simplest ratio of whole numbers of the atoms in a compound. The molecular formula is the actual ratio of the atoms in a compound.

Chemical equations are used to show what happens in chemical reactions. The substances initially present in a reaction are the reactants and those that form as a result of the reaction are the products. The coefficients in an equation indicate the mole relationships in which the reactants combine and the products form. The coefficients in an equation are found by balancing it. Equations are balanced, using the inspection method, by equalizing the number of atoms of each type on either side of the equation.

Stoichiometry is the study of mole, mass, volume, and energy relationships in chemical reactions. Balanced equations allow us to make theoretical predictions concerning the amounts of reactants that combine and the amounts of products that form. The mass of a product predicted from stoichiometric principles is called the theoretical yield. The percent yield of a reaction is the ratio of the actual mass *produced to the theoretical yield multiplied times 100. The masses of the products that form depend on the limiting reactant. When the limiting reagent is consumed, the reaction stops.*

Solutions are homogeneous mixtures of pure substances. A solution is composed of a solute, the dissolved substance, and a solvent, the dissolving substance. Molarity is the ratio of the moles of solute per liter of solution.

CHAPTER 4 REVIEW EXERCISE

1. Perform a rough calculation to determine how many centuries it would take exactly one–billion people working 24 hours per day, 365 days per year, to produce exactly one mole of donuts at a rate of 10 donuts per person each second. (HINT: First use conversion factors to calculate how many donuts could be produced per year.)

2. Calculate the number of moles of atoms in the following masses of elements: (a) 5.00 g Ti, (b) 5.00 kg Te, (c) 5.00 mg Ta, (d) 5.0 μg Tl.

3. Calculate the mass of each of the following samples of elements: (a) 0.11 mol Kr, (b) 0.11 Mmol He, (c) 0.11 mmol Ne.

4. Explain why it is incorrect to refer to the "molecular mass" of NaCl.

5. What is the mass of each of the following samples of gold atoms? (a) 3.0×10^{23} atoms Au, (b) 5.40 billion atoms Au, (c) exactly 1 atom Au

6. Find the unknown quantity for each of the following: (a) 5.500 mg vanadium = ? mol, (b) 9.09×10^{23} atoms Hg = ? mol, (c) 0.001099 mol neon = ? g.

7. Calculate the molecular mass to four significant figures for each of the following: (a) $LiClO_3$, (b) $P(SCN)_3$, (c) $Sm_2(MoO_4)_3$, (d) $Na_2B_4O_7 \cdot 10H_2O$

8. How many moles of O atoms are contained in each of the following? (a) 2.00 mol CO_2, (b) 2.00 g P_2O_5, (c) 2.00×10^{22} molecules H_5IO_6

9. Calculate the unknown quantity for each of the following: (a) 3.643 mg SF_6 = ? mol F, (b) 9.99×10^{23} molecules S_2O_3 = ? g S_2O_3, (c) 8.33 mmol C_9H_{20} = ? mol H

10. How many formula units are contained in each of the following samples? (a) 9.34 g $MgSiO_3$, (b) 5.8 kg $Hg_2(NO_2)_2$, (c) 8.7 mg Na_2HPO_4

11. Calculate the mass percent of Ag to three significant figures in each of the following compounds: (a) Ag_2O, (b) $AgIO_3$, (c) Ag_3AsS_3

12. Arrange the following from highest to lowest in percent iron by mass: (a) $FeCl_3$, (b) $Fe(OH)_2$, (c) Fe_3O_4, (d) $Fe_3(PO_4)_2$

13. What are the empirical formulas for each of the following compounds? (a) 70.2% Pb, 8.1% C, and 21.7% O, (b) 46.54% Cu, 11.72% S, and 41.75% F, (c) 6.90% C, 1.15% H, and 91.95% Br

14. After analysis, a 20.0-g sample was found to contain 8.00 g C, 9.35 g N, and the remainder is H. What is the empirical formula of the compound?

15. Analysis of a compound that contains H, O, and Br reveals a 61.50 g-sample contains 0.64 g H and 10.15 g O. If its molecular mass is 96.9, what is its molecular formula?

16. Boranes are B and H compounds. A borane is analyzed and found to contain 11.843 g B and 0.885 g H, and its molecular mass is 232.4. What is the molecular formula of the compound?

17. (a) What mass of sodium phosphate, Na_3PO_4, contains the same number of formula units as are found in 9.971 g of KOH? (b) What mass of sodium phosphate contains the same number of Na atoms as 4.506 g of elemental sodium, Na?

18. Penicillin G is a widely used antibiotic. It has a molecular formula of $C_{16}H_{18}N_2O_4S$. (a) Calculate the mass percent (three significant figures) of C in penicillin. (b) What mass of penicillin contains 1.00 g of carbon? (c) How many carbon atoms are contained in a 1.00-g sample of penicillin?

19. Iodine pentafluoride, IF_5, is a colorless liquid that has a density of 3.252 g/cm³. (a) Calculate the volume of 4.31 mol of IF_5. (b) How many moles of F atoms are contained in 2.65 L of IF_5? (c) What volume of IF_5 contains 4.821×10^{23} atoms of F?

20. The psychoactive chemical in marijuana is composed of 71.23% C, 12.95% H, and 15.81% O. What is the empirical formula of this compound?

21. A compound is found to have the formula XBr_2, in which X is an unknown element. Bromine is found to be 71.55% of the compound. (a) What is the atomic mass of the element? (b) What is the symbol of the element?

22. Nicotine, $C_{10}H_{14}N_2$, is a mild stimulant found in tobacco products. It is a very toxic compound and was once used as a pesticide. (a) What is the empirical formula of nicotine? (b) What is the percent composition of nicotine? (c) If a cigarette has a mass of 1.48 g and it is composed of 0.21% by mass nicotine, how many nicotine molecules are contained in the cigarette?

23. Use the inspection method to balance each of the following unbalanced equations:

    (a) $C_3H_8 + O_2 \rightarrow CO_2 + H_2O$
    (b) $Al + S_8 \rightarrow Al_2S_3$
    (c) $Mg(NO_3)_2 + H_3PO_4 \rightarrow HNO_3 + Mg_3(PO_4)_2$

24. Use the inspection method to balance each of the following chemical equations:

    (a) $Cu + HNO_3 \rightarrow Cu(NO_3)_2 + NO_2 + H_2O$
    (b) $Na_2H_3IO_6 + AgNO_3 \rightarrow Ag_5IO_6 + NaNO_3 + HNO_3$
    (c) $LiBH_4 + NH_4Cl \rightarrow B_3N_3H_6 + H_2 + LiCl$

25. Consider the following equation.

$$CS_2(g) + 3Cl_2(g) \rightarrow CCl_4(l) + S_2Cl_2(g)$$

    (a) How many moles of CCl_4 results when 1.00 g CS_2 reacts with excess Cl_2? (b) How many moles of Cl_2 are needed to react with 1.00 g CS_2? (c) How many moles of CS_2 are need to produce 8.31×10^{23} molecules of CCl_4?

26. An easy way to produce oxygen gas, O_2, in the laboratory is to decompose potassium chlorate, $KClO_3$, as follows.

$$2KClO_3(s) \overset{\Delta}{\underset{MnO_2}{\rightarrow}} 2KCl(s) + 3O_2(g)$$

    (a) What mass of O_2 result when a 5.000-g sample of $KClO_3$ is totally decomposed? (b) What mass of $KClO_3$ must be decomposed to produce 1.250 g O_2? (c) What mass of $KClO_3$ is needed to produce 1.250 g KCl?

27. Mercury metal is liberated from its ore cinnabar, HgS, when it is mixed with lime, CaO, and then heated.
$$4CaO + 4HgS \rightarrow 3CaS + CaSO_4 + Hg$$

The density of Hg is 13.6 g/cm³. (a) What mass of Hg results when 73.4 g HgS combines with excess CaO? (b) What volume of Hg in cm³ results when 73.4 g HgS combines with excess CaO? (c) What mass of HgS must react with excess CaO to produce 1.00 L Hg?

28. Sodium hydrogensulfate, $NaHSO_4$, can be prepared by combining sodium chloride, NaCl, and sulfuric acid, H_2SO_4.
$$NaCl + H_2SO_4 \rightarrow NaHSO_4 + HCl$$

A 12.3-g sample of NaCl is reacted with excess H_2SO_4. The actual yield of $NaHSO_4$ is 18.4 g. (a) What is the theoretical yield for this reaction? (b) What is the percent yield of $NaHSO_4$?

29. Pure boron, B, results when B_2O_3 is heated with Mg.

$$B_2O_3 + 3Mg \xrightarrow{\Delta} 3MgO + 2B$$

When 45.0 g B_2O_3 combines with excess magnesium a yield of 11.1 g B results. (a) Calculate the percent yield for this reaction. (b) What is the yield of B, starting with 45.0 g B_2O_3, if the percent yield is 88.1%?

30. Nitrogen trifluoride, NF_3, results when nitrogen, N_2, and fluorine, F_2, react as follows.

$$N_2 + 3F_2 \rightarrow 2NF_3$$

(a) What is the limiting reactant when 21.6 g N_2 and 85.2 g F_2 react? (b) What mass of NF_3 results from the masses in part (a)? (c) What mass of excess reactant remains after the limiting reactant is consumed?

31. Phosphoric acid, H_3PO_4, can be prepared by the following reaction.

$$PCl_5 + 4H_2O \rightarrow H_3PO_4 + 5HCl$$

   (a) What mass of phosphoric acid can be obtained from 136.8 g PCl_5 and 50.93 g H_2O?
   (b) Calculate the mass of the reactant that remains after the limiting reactant is consumed.

32. A 5.500-g sample of an unknown alcohol, a compound composed of C, H, and O, is combusted and 15.43 g CO_2 and 3.159 g H_2O result. (a) What is the empirical formula of the compound? (b) If the empirical formula is the same as the molecular formula, what is the molar mass of the unknown alcohol?

33. Citric acid occurs in rather high concentrations in citrus fruits and is in all cells of the human body. When a scientist burns a 0.5000-g sample of citric acid in O_2, 0.6872 g CO_2 and 0.1876 g H_2O is isolated. What is the empirical formula of citric acid? b. If the molecular mass of citric acid is 192.1, what is the molecular formula of citric acid?

34. A 15.0-g sample of a mixture of NaCl and NaF is analyzed and is found to contain 6.99 g Na. (a) Calculate the masses of NaCl and NaF in the mixture. (b) Calculate the percent composition of the mixture.

35. A student dissolves a 4.00-g mixture of NaBr and KBr in H_2O and precipitates the Br^- with $AgNO_3$. If the student isolates 7.03 g AgBr, calculate the masses of NaBr and KBr in the mixture.

36. Explain exactly how you would prepare 10.0 L of a 1.39 *M* $CaCl_2$ solution.

37. (a) Calculate the molarity of a $NaNO_3$ solution prepared by dissolving 1.00 g $NaNO_3$ in enough water to give a total volume of 665 mL. (b) Calculate the molarity of a $NaNO_3$ solution prepared by dissolving 5.00 mg $NaNO_3$ in enough water to give a total volume of 1.85 L.

38. (a) What is the molarity of $AgNO_3$ solution in which 0.0225 g $AgNO_3$ is dissolved in enough water to have 125 mL of solution? (b) What is the molarity of a $AgNO_3$ solution in which 1.09 g $AgNO_3$ is dissolved in enough water to have 125 mL of solution?

39. (a) Explain exactly how you would dilute 345 mL of 12.0 *M* HCl to produce a 2.00 *M* HCl solution. (b) Explain exactly how you would dilute 345 mL of 12.0 *M* HCl to produce a 0.100 *M* HCl solution.

40. (a) If you add enough H_2O to dilute 50.0 cm³ of 11.7 *M* KOH solution to a total volume of 375 cm³, what is the molar concentration KOH in the diluted solution? (b) If you add enough H_2O

to dilute 50.0 cm^3 of 11.7 *M* KOH solution to a total volume of 1.00 dm^3, what is the molar concentration KOH in the diluted solution?

41. A cube of NaCl with an edge length of 0.0994 mm is dissolved in 1.25 L of pure water. The density of NaCl is 2.164 g/cm^3. (a) Calculate the concentration of NaCl in this solution in mmol/L. (b) What volume of this salt water contains 1.0×10^{17} dissolved formula units of NaCl?

42. Quinine is a medicine used to treat malaria. It is an alkaloid, a biologically active C, H, O, and N-containing compound, obtained from different varieties of the cinchona tree. A pharmaceutical chemist burns a 7.007-g sample of quinine and produces 19.01 g CO_2 and 4.670 g H_2O. In a different experiment, the chemist analyzes a 4.759-g sample of quinine and finds 410.8 mg N. If the molecular mass of quinine is 324.4, what is the molecular formula of quinine?

ANSWERS TO REVIEW EXERCISE

1. 1.9×10^4 centuries
2. (a) 0.104 mol Ti, (b) 39.2 mol Te, (c) 2.76×10^{-5} mol Ta, (d) 2.45×10^{-8} g Tl
3. (a) 9.2 g Kr, (b) 4.4×10^5 g He, (c) 2.2×10^{-3} g Ne
4. NaCl is composed of formula units
5. (a) 98 g, (b) 1.77×10^{-12} g, (c) 3.27×10^{22} g
6. (a) 1.080×10^{-4} mol V, (b) 1.51 mol Hg, (c) 2.218×10^{-2} g Ne
7. (a) 90.39, (b) 205.2, (c) 780.5, (d) 381.4
8. (a) 4.00 mol O, (b) 7.05×10^{-2} mol O, (c) 0.199 mol O
9. (a) 1.497×10^{-4} mol F, (b) 186 g S_2O_3, (c) 0.167 mol H
10. (a) 5.60×10^{22} formula units $MgSiO_3$, (b) 7.1×10^{24} formula units $Hg_2(NO_2)_2$, (c) 3.7×10^{19} formula units Na_2HPO_4
11. (a) 93.1%, (b) 38.1%, (c) 65.4%
12. Fe_3O_4 (72.36%) > $Fe(OH)_2$ (62.15%) > $Fe_3(PO_4)_2$ (46.87%) > $FeCl_3$(34.43%)
13. (a) PbC_2O_4, (b) Cu_2SF_6, (c) CH_2Br_2
14. H_4CN
15. HBrO
16. $B_{20}H_{16}$
17. (a) 29.13 g Na_3PO_4, (b) 10.71 g Na_3PO_4
18. (a) 57.5% C, (b) 1.74 g penicillin, (c) 2.88×10^{22} atoms C
19. (a) 294 cm^3, (b) 194 mol, (c) 10.93 cm^3
20. $C_6H_{13}O$
21. (a) 63.54%, (b) Cu
22. (a) C_5H_7N, (b) 74.0% C, 8.70% H, 17.3% N, (c) 1.2×10^{19} molecules nicotine
23. (a) $C_3H_8 + 5O_2 \rightarrow 3CO_2 + 4H_2O$
    (b) $16Al + 3S_8 \rightarrow 8Al_2S_3$
    (c) $3Mg(NO_3)_2 + 2H_3PO_4 \rightarrow 6HNO_3 + Mg_3(PO_4)_2$
24. (a) $Cu + 4HNO_3 \rightarrow Cu(NO_3)_2 + 2NO_2 + 2H_2O$
    (b) $Na_2H_3IO_6 + 5AgNO_3 \rightarrow Ag_5IO_6 + 2NaNO_3 + 3HNO_3$
    (c) $3LiBH_4 + 3NH_4Cl \rightarrow B_3N_3H_6 + 9H_2 + 3LiCl$

25. (a) 0.0131 mol CCl_4, (b) 0.0394 mol Cl_2, (c) 1.38 mol CS_2

26. (a) 1.958 g O_2, (b) 3.193 g $KClO_3$, (c) 2.056 g $KClO_3$

27. (a) 15.8 g Hg, (b) 1.16 cm^3, (c) 63.1 kg HgS

28. (a) 25.3 g $NaHSO_4$, (b) 72.8%

29. (a) 79.4%, (b) 12.3 g B

30. (a) F_2, (b) 106 g NF_3, (c) 0.674 g N_2

31. (a) 64.38 g H_3PO_4, (b) 3.58 g H_2O

32. (a) C_6H_6O, (b) 94.12 g/mol

33. (a) $C_6H_8O_7$, (b) $C_6H_8O_7$

34. 7.96 g NaCl, 7.04 g NaF

35. 2.90 g NaBr, 1.10 g KBr

36. Dissolve 1.54 kg $CaCl_2$ in enough water to have a total volume of 10.0 L

37. (a) 0.177 M, (b) 3.18×10^{-5} M

38. (a) 1.05×10^{-3} M, (b) 0.0513 M

39. (a) dilute to 2.07 L, (b) dilute to 41.4 L

40. (a) 1.56 M KOH, (b) 0.585 M KOH

41. (a) 2.91×10^{-5} mmol/L, (b) 5.71 L

42. $C_{20}H_{24}N_2O_2$

5

Introduction to Chemical Reactions

*I*n *this chapter we begin our study of inorganic chemical reactions and solution stoichiometry. The first section introduces four general types of inorganic reactions. The second section covers precipitation reactions–those in which a solid insoluble substance forms. In the final two sections, acid-base and oxidation-reduction reactions are considered.*

5.1 INORGANIC REACTIONS

Classification of Inorganic Reactions

Inorganic reactions may be subdivided into four major types:
1. *Combination reaction* in which two substances combine.

$$A + X \rightarrow AX$$

2. *Decomposition reaction.* It is the reverse of a combination reaction.

$$AX \rightarrow A + X$$

3. *Single replacement reaction.* It occurs when an element replaces another one that is part of a compound.

$$A + BX \rightarrow AX + B$$

4. *Metathesis or double replacement.*

$$AX + BY \rightarrow AY + BX$$

Combination Reactions *(A + X → AX)*

A combination reaction occurs when two substances join and form a compound. The general equation for all combination reactions is

$$A + X \rightarrow AX$$

in which A and X are either elements or compounds and AX is a compound. Some common types of combination reactions include metal oxide formation. A metal oxide forms when a metal undergoes a combination reaction with a nonmetal. For example, when calcium, $Ca(s)$, reacts with oxygen gas, $O_2(g)$, solid calcium oxide, $CaO(s)$, results. Another example is base formation combination reaction. Metal oxides undergo a combination reaction with water to produce bases. A base is a compound that increases the $OH^-(aq)$ ion concentration in aqueous solutions. For example, the base sodium hydroxide, $NaOH$, forms from sodium oxide, $Na_2O(s)$, and $H_2O(l)$. A final example of a combination reaction is acid formation combination reaction. An acid forms from the combination reaction of a nonmetal oxide and water. An acid is a compound that increases the $H^+(aq)$ ion concentration in aqueous solutions. For example, sulfuric acid, H_2SO_4, results when gaseous sulfur trioxide, $SO_3(g)$, and $H_2O(l)$ react.

Problem 5.1   Classify each of the following combination reactions.
- (a) $4Na(g) + O_2(g) \rightarrow 2Na_2O(s)$
- (b) $BaO(s) + H_2O(l) \rightarrow Ba(OH)_2(aq)$
- (c) $CO_2(g) + MgO(s) \rightarrow MgCO_3(s)$

Solution 5.1   (a) metal oxide formation, (b) base formation, (c) salt formation

DECOMPOSITION REACTIONS ($AX \rightarrow A + X$)

A decomposition reaction is the reverse of a combination reaction. In a decomposition reaction, a single compound breaks up and forms two or more substances.

$$AX \rightarrow A + X$$

In this general equation, compound AX decomposes to A and X, which may be either elements or compounds. Usually decomposition reactions require energy sources such as heat or electricity to break the chemical bonds in the reactant. An example of a decomposition reaction is the thermal decomposition of a metallic oxide yields a metal and O_2. If mercury(II) oxide, $HgO(s)$, is heated, then mercury metal, $Hg(l)$, and oxygen gas, $O_2(g)$, result.

$$2HgO(s) \xrightarrow{\Delta} 2Hg(l) + O_2(g)$$

Another example of a decomposition reaction is electrolysis. Electrolysis occurs when an electric current decomposes a compound. For example, water undergoes electrolysis to $H_2(g)$ and $O_2(g)$. Water can also be decomposed to its component elements when heated to a sufficiently high temperature.

$$2H_2O(l) \xrightarrow{elec} 2H_2(g) + O_2(g)$$

Problem 5.2   Classify each of the following decomposition reactions:
- (a) $MgCO_3(s) \rightarrow MgO(s) + CO_2(g)$
- (b) $2KHCO_3(s) \rightarrow K_2CO_3(s) + CO_2(g) + H_2O(g)$

Solution 5.2   (a) decomposition of a carbonate, (b) decomposition of a hydrogencarbonate

Single Replacement Reactions $(A+BX \rightarrow AX+B)$

In single replacement reactions, sometimes called single displacement reactions, a more reactive element displaces a less reactive one in a compound. The general equation for single displacement reactions is

$$A + BX \rightarrow AX + B$$

in which element A displaces element B in the compound BX.

REPLACEMENT OF METAL IONS BY ACTIVE METALS

Many active metals displace less active metals in compounds. If a strip of $Zn(s)$ is placed into a solution of $Cu(NO_3)_2(aq)$, the Zn dissolves and metallic $Cu(s)$ forms.

$$Zn(s) + Cu(NO_3)_2(aq) \rightarrow Zn(NO_3)_2(aq) + Cu(s)$$

REPLACEMENT OF HYDROGEN BY ACTIVE METALS

Very reactive metals can displace hydrogen, H_2, from H_2O. For example, sodium, Na, combines violently with water and liberates H_2.

$$2Na(s) + H_2O(l) \rightarrow 2NaOH(aq) + H_2(g)$$

A large enough sample of Na liberates sufficient heat that ignites the H_2 and causes an explosion. Less reactive metals cannot displace H_2 in water, but can liberate H_2 from acids.

Problem 5.3   What type of single replacement reaction occurs in each of the following?
  (a) $2K(s) + H_2O(l) \rightarrow 2KOH(aq) + H_2(g)$
  (b) $Fe(s) + 2AgNO_3(aq) \rightarrow Fe(NO_3)_2(aq) + 2Ag(s)$

Solution 5.3   (a) an active metal replacing hydrogen, (b) a more active metal replacing a less active one

Metathesis Reactions ($AX + BY \rightarrow AY + BX$)

In metathesis reactions, also called double-replacement reactions, two compounds combine in the following manner.

$$AX + BY \rightarrow AY + BX$$

A from *AX* combines with *Y* and *B* from *BY* combines with *X*, which yields *AY* and *BX*. The positive component of one compound bonds to the negative component of the other.

PRECIPITATION METATHESIS REACTIONS

One of the most common types of metathesis reactions is the precipitation reaction. In this reaction two aqueous solutions of compounds combine and produce a solid insoluble compound–a precipitate. For example, mixing a solution of silver nitrate, $AgNO_3(aq)$, with one of sodium chloride, $NaCl(aq)$, yields a white precipitate of silver chloride, $AgCl(s)$.

$$AgNO_3(aq) + NaCl(aq) \rightarrow AgCl(s) + NaNO_3(aq)$$

GAS-FORMATION METATHESIS REACTIONS

Besides precipitation reactions, another common type of metathesis reaction is a gas-formation reaction. Such reactions occur when various salts react with acids. For example, acids combine with carbonates and hydrogencarbonates and produce carbon dioxide gas, $CO_2(g)$. For example, $SrCO_3$, dissolves in perchloric acid and forms CO_2, H_2O, and $Sr(ClO_4)_2$.

$$SrCO_3(s) + 2HClO_4(aq) \rightarrow CO_2(g) + H_2O(l) + Sr(ClO_4)_2(aq)$$

In the reactions of acids with carbonates or bicarbonates, unstable carbonic acid, $H_2CO_3(aq)$, forms and immediately decomposes to $CO_2(g)$ and $H_2O(l)$.

$$H_2CO_3(aq) \rightarrow CO_2(g) + H_2O(l)$$

NEUTRALIZATION REACTIONS

A neutralization reaction occurs when an acid combines with a base and produces a salt and in most cases water. An example of a neutralization reaction is the one in which hydrochloric acid, $HCl(aq)$, and sodium hydroxide, $NaOH(aq)$, react and produce aqueous sodium chloride, $NaCl(aq)$, and $H_2O(l)$.

$$HCl(aq) + NaOH(aq) \rightarrow NaCl(aq) + H_2O(l)$$

Problem 5.4   What type of metathesis reaction occurs in each of the following?
   (a) $HNO_3(aq) + KCN(s) \rightarrow HCN(g) + KNO_3(aq)$
   (b) $H_2SO_4(aq) + Mg(OH)_2(s) \rightarrow MgSO_4(aq) + 2H_2O(l)$
   (c) $Na_2S(aq) + Cu(NO_3)_2(aq) \rightarrow CuS(s) + 2NaNO_3(aq)$

Solution 5.4   (a) gas-formation metathesis reaction, (b) neutralization reaction, (c) precipitation reaction

Problem 5.5   Classify each of the following reactions.
   (a) $2KClO_3(s) \xrightarrow{\Delta} 2KCl(s) + 3O_2(g)$
   (b) $4Al(s) + 3O_2(g) \rightarrow 2Al_2O_3(s)$
   (c) $2HCl(aq) + K_2CO_3(s) \rightarrow 2KCl(aq) + CO_2(g) + H_2O(l)$
   (d) $2Li(s) + 2HCl(aq) \rightarrow H_2(g) + 2LiCl(aq)$

Solution 5.5   (a) thermal decomposition reaction, (b) combination reaction, (c) gas-formation metathesis reaction, (d) single replacement of hydrogen

5.2   PRECIPITATION REACTIONS

Solute Dissociation

Ionic compounds dissociate in water and form hydrated ions. The general equation for the dissociation of ionic compounds in aqueous solution is

$$M^+X^-(s) \xrightarrow{H_2O} M^+(aq) + X^-(aq)$$

in which M^+ is a metal cation and X^- is a nonmetal anion.

Electrolytes and Nonelectrolytes

Solutes are classified as electrolytes, those that produce ions in solution, and as nonelectrolytes, those that do not produce ions in solution. An example of an electrolyte is hydrogen chloride gas, $HCl(g)$.

$$HCl(g) \xrightarrow{H_2O} H^+(aq) + Cl^-(aq)$$

An example of a nonelectrolyte is sucrose, $C_{12}H_{22}O_{11}$ (also called table sugar). When solid sucrose dissolves in water its crystal structure is destroyed and hydrated sucrose molecules result.

$$C_{12}H_{22}O_{11}(s) \xrightarrow{H_2O} C_{12}H_{22}O_{11}(aq)$$

STRONG AND WEAK ELECTROLYTES

If electrolytes produce many dissolved ions, then they are strong electrolytes. If they produce few dissolved ions, then they are weak electrolytes. Examples of strong electrolytes include $NaCl$, $CaCl_2$, and KNO_3. Each of these compounds dissociates 100% when dissolved in water. Examples of weak electrolytes include $HgCl_2$, $CdBr_2$, and $HC_2H_3O_2$. When these compounds enter solution, they establish an equilibrium between the undissociated compound and its ions. A chemical equilibrium results when the rate or speed of the forward reaction equals the rate of the reverse reaction. In this case, the rate at which the molecules ionize or formula units dissociate equals the rate at which the ions recombine to form the un-ionized compound or formula unit.

Problem 5.6   Write equations for the dissociation of the following strong electrolytes in aqueous solution:

(a) $CaCl_2(s)$
(b) $Fe(NO_3)_3(s)$

Solution 5.6   Because both ionic compounds are strong electrolytes, they dissociate totally to ions. Thus, first calculate the charges on the ions that compose the compound.

(a) In binary ionic compounds, Cl carries a charge of 1− and group 2 (IIA) elements such as Ca have a charge of 2+. Thus, the equation for the dissociation of $CaCl_2$ is

$$CaCl_2(s) \xrightarrow{H_2O} Ca^{2+}(aq) + 2Cl^-(aq)$$

(b) Calculate the charge on the iron ion using the 1− charge on the nitrate ion, NO_3^-. Since the formula has three nitrates, then this is iron(III) nitrate. Hence, Fe^{3+} and NO_3^- enter solution as follows.

$$Fe(NO_3)_3(s) \xrightarrow{H_2O} Fe^{3+}(aq) + 3NO_3^-(aq)$$

Problem 5.7   Write the equation for the dissociation of $Al_2(SO_4)_3(s)$.

Solution 5.7

$$Al_2(SO_4)_3(s) \xrightarrow{H_2O} 2Al^{3+}(aq) + 3SO_4^{2-}(aq)$$

Quantitative Aspects of Electrolyte Solutions

Problem 5.8   What are the molarities of Ca^{2+} and Cl^- in a $CaCl_2$ solution that contains 5.00 mg $CaCl_2$ dissolved in 0.500 L of solution?

Solution 5.8   First, write the equation for the dissociation of $CaCl_2$.

$$CaCl_2 \xrightarrow{H_2O} Ca^{2+}(aq) + 2Cl^-(aq)$$

Next, convert the mass of $CaCl_2$ from mg to g. Then, convert to moles, knowing that the mass of one mole of $CaCl_2$ is 112.1 g/mol. Finally, divide by the total volume, 0.500 L, to obtain the molarity of $CaCl_2$.

$$5.00 \text{ mg } CaCl_2 \times 1 \text{ g}/1000 \text{ mg} \times 1 \text{ mol } CaCl_2/112.1 \text{ g} = 4.46 \times 10^{-5} \text{ mol } CaCl_2$$
$$M_{CaCl_2} = 4.46 \times 10^{-5} \text{ mol } CaCl_2/0.500 \text{ L} = 8.92 \times 10^{-5} \text{ } M$$

The equation shows that for each mole of $CaCl_2$ that dissolves, one mole of Ca^{2+} and two moles of Cl^- result.

$$8.92 \times 10^{-5} \text{ } M \text{ } CaCl_2 \times 1 \text{ mol } Ca^{2+}/1 \text{ mol } CaCl_2 = 8.92 \times 10^{-5} \text{ } M \text{ } Ca^{2+}$$
$$8.92 \times 10^{-5} \text{ } M \text{ } CaCl_2 \times 2 \text{ mol } Cl^-/1 \text{ mol } CaCl_2 = 1.78 \times 10^{-4} \text{ } M \text{ } Cl^-$$

Problem 5.9   What is the molarity of all dissolved ions in a solution prepared by dissolving 1.00 g $NaNO_3$ and 1.00 g $Mg(NO_3)_2$ in enough water to have 1.00 L of solution?

Solution 5.9   First, write the equations for the dissociations of $NaNO_3$ and $Mg(NO_3)_2$.

$$NaNO_3 \rightarrow Na^+ + NO_3^-$$
$$Mg(NO_3)_2 \rightarrow Mg^{2+} + 2NO_3^-$$

Using the molar masses of $NaNO_3$ and $Mg(NO_3)_2$, 85.0 g/mol and 148 g/mol, respectively, convert each to moles.

$$1.00 \text{ g } NaNO_3 \times 1 \text{ mol } NaNO_3/85.0 \text{ g} = 0.0118 \text{ mol } NaNO_3$$
$$1.00 \text{ g } Mg(NO_3)_2 \times 1 \text{ mol } Mg(NO_3)_2/148 \text{ g} = 0.00676 \text{ mol } Mg(NO_3)_2$$

Because they are dissolved in 1.00 L of solution, the moles and molarity values are equal.

$$M_{NaNO_3} = 0.0118 \text{ M}$$
$$M_{Mg(NO_3)_2} = 0.00676 \text{ M}$$

Because one mole of Na^+ and Mg^{2+} are produced per mole of $NaNO_3$ and $Mg(NO_3)_2$, respectively, the molarities of the ions are 0.0118 M Na^+ and 0.006676 M Mg^{2+}. For each mole of $Mg(NO_3)_2$ that dissolves, two moles of NO_3^- enter solution; hence, 0.0135 M is the concentration of NO_3^- from the $Mg(NO_3)_2$. Adding 0.0118 M from $NaNO_3$ gives a total NO_3^- concentration of 0.0253 M.

Solubility and Electrolyte Behavior

The solubility of a substance in water is independent of its electrolyte behavior. Some strong electrolytes are only slightly soluble, and some weak electrolytes are very soluble in water.

Precipitation of Ionic Compounds

Precipitation reactions belong to the general class of reactions called metathesis reactions. Thus, the positive ion from one compound "replaces" the positive ion from the other and vice versa. Let's consider the precipitation reaction that occurs when equal volumes of 0.1 M $KBr(aq)$ and 0.1 M $AgNO_3(aq)$ mix. Because both compounds are strong electrolytes, these solutions contain the dissolved ions that result after each compound dissociates. $K^+(aq)$ and $Br^-(aq)$ are in the KBr solution, and $Ag^+(aq)$ and $NO_3^-(aq)$ are in the $AgNO_3$ solution. After the two solutions are mixed, the cations from one may combine with the anions from the other solution and form a precipitate. In this case, $Ag^+(aq)$ combines with $Br^-(aq)$ and produces a precipitate (an insoluble solid) of $AgBr(s)$.

OVERALL IONIC EQUATIONS

To show what happens during this aqueous reaction, an overall ionic equation is written that shows all of the ions in solution.

$$K^+(aq) + Br^-(aq) + Ag^+(aq) + NO_3^-(aq) \rightarrow AgBr(s) + K^+(aq) + NO_3^-(aq)$$

NET IONIC EQUATIONS

This equation shows us that $K^+(aq)$ and $NO_3^-(aq)$ do not change in the reaction. Such ions are called spectator ions because they do not participate in the reaction. Because they appear in the same form on both sides of the equation, subtract them from both sides so only the reacting species remain. The resulting equation, without the spectator ions, is the net ionic equation.

$$Ag^+(aq) + Br^-(aq) \rightarrow AgBr(s)$$

A net ionic equation shows what change occurs in an aqueous ionic reaction. Net ionic equations are written because they focus our attention on the substances that react, allowing us to see the reaction more clearly.

Solubility of Inorganic Compounds

To predict if a precipitate forms use a solubility table. This table lists the solubilities of various classes of ionic compounds as soluble or insoluble. A soluble compound enters solution and thus does not precipitate. An insoluble compound has a low solubility, in many cases below 0.1 g solute/100 g solvent. Consequently, it forms a precipitate if produced in an aqueous reaction.

Problem 5.10 Use a solubility table to obtain the solubility of the following compounds and state if they precipitate in an aqueous reaction.
(a) Na_2S
(b) Hg_2I_2

Solution 5.10

(a) Na_2S is soluble in water and will not precipitate. In general, sulfides are insoluble compounds, but one of the exceptions is the group 1 (IA) sulfides.
(b) Hg_2I_2 is insoluble and forms a precipitate in aqueous reactions. Unlike all other metallic ions you may have encountered, the mercury(I), Hg_2^{2+}, exists as pairs of metal ions and does not exist as a monatomic ion in aqueous solution.

Problem 5.11 Using a solubility table predict the solubilities and state if the following compounds precipitate from solution:
(a) $KClO_3$
(b) $(NH_4)_2CO_3$

Solution 5.11

(a) $KClO_3$ is soluble and does not precipitate,
(b) $(NH_4)_2CO_3$ is soluble and does not precipitate.

Predicting the Products of a Precipitation Reaction

Problem 5.12 Use the solubility table to predict the products and write the overall and net ionic equations when aqueous solutions of ammonium phosphate and iron(II) nitrate mix.

Solution 5.12 First, translate the compound names to formulas. Ammonium ions have a 1+ charge and phosphate ions have a 3– charge; thus the formula of ammonium phosphate is $(NH_4)_3PO_4$. The iron(II) ion is Fe^{2+} and the nitrate ion is NO_3^-. Thus, the formula of iron(II) nitrate is $Fe(NO_3)_2$.

To predict the products of ionic metathesis reactions, look at the combinations that result when the cation from one solution combines with the anion from the other solution. Then, determine if they precipitate. Ammonium compounds are soluble, but most phosphates are insoluble. Hence, a precipitate results from the combination of $Fe^{2+}(aq)$ and $PO_4^{3-}(aq)$, which gives iron(II) phosphate, $Fe_3(PO_4)_2(s)$.

Next, write and balance the equation with the undissociated compounds and then translate it to the overall and net ionic equations. Thus, the overall equation showing the undissociated compounds is as follows.

$$2(NH_4)_3PO_4(aq) + 3Fe(NO_3)_2(aq) \rightarrow Fe_3(PO_4)_2(s) + 6NH_4NO_3(aq)$$

Translating it to an overall ionic equation it becomes the following.

$$6NH_4^+(aq) + 2PO_4^{3-}(aq) + 3Fe^{2+}(aq) + 6NO_3^-(aq) \rightarrow Fe_3(PO_4)_2(s) + 6NH_4^+(aq) + 6NO_3^-(aq)$$

After removing the spectator ions, $NH_4^+(aq)$ and $NO_3^-(aq)$, the net ionic equation results.

$$3Fe^{2+}(aq) + 2PO_4^{3-}(aq) \rightarrow Fe_3(PO_4)_2(s)$$

Problem 5.13 Write the overall and net ionic reactions for the combination of potassium carbonate and copper(II) bromide solutions.

Solution 5.13 Begin by writing the formulas for the two compounds. Potassium belongs to group 1 (IA) and forms 1+ ions, K^+. The formula for the carbonate ion is CO_3^{2-}. Hence, the formula of potassium carbonate is K_2CO_3. Copper(II) is Cu^{2+} and bromide is Br^-; thus, the formula of copper(II) bromide is $CuBr_2$.

Most carbonates are insoluble and most bromides are soluble. Therefore, the combination of $Cu^{2+}(aq)$ and $CO_3^{2-}(aq)$ gives the precipitate $CuCO_3(s)$. The ions that remain in solution are K^+ and Br^-; thus, $KBr(aq)$ is the second product. The balanced equation is as follows.

$$K_2CO_3(aq) + CuBr_2(aq) \rightarrow CuCO_3(s) + 2KBr(aq)$$

Next, translate to an overall ionic equation. Because K_2CO_3, $CuBr_2$, and KBr are strong electrolytes, write them as dissolved ions.

$$2K^+(aq) + CO_3^{2-}(aq) + Cu^{2+}(aq) + 2Br^-(aq) \rightarrow CuCO_3(s) + 2K^+(aq) + 2Br^-(aq)$$

Translate to a net ionic equation by removing the spectator ions, $K^+(aq)$ and $Br^-(aq)$. The resulting net ionic equation is as follows.

$$Cu^{2+}(aq) + CO_3^{2-}(aq) \rightarrow CuCO_3(s)$$

Problem 5.14 Write the overall and net ionic reactions for the combination of ammonium sulfide and aluminum nitrate solutions.

Solution 5.14

$$6NH_4^+(aq) + 3S^{2-}(aq) + 2Al^{3+}(aq) + 6NO_3^-(aq) \rightarrow Al_2S_3(s) + 6NH_4^+(aq) + 6NO_3^-(aq)$$
$$3S^{2-}(aq) + 2Al^{3+}(aq) \rightarrow Al_2S_3(s)$$

Precipitation Titrations

A common volumetric laboratory method is called a *titration*. In this procedure, a standard solution of known concentration is systematically added to a solution of unknown concentration until the equivalence point is reached. At the equivalence point (also called the stoichiometric point) the number of moles of the unknown solute reacts completely with the standard solution. The concentration or the mass of the unknown solute can be calculated from the volumetric data collected from a titration.

During a precipitation titration, a standard solution of known concentration precipitates the unknown ion from solution.

Problem 5.15 Calculate the mass of Cl^- in a solution that requires 23.5 cm³ of 0.115 M $AgNO_3$ to precipitate all of the dissolved Cl^-.

Solution 5.15

23.5 cm³ soln × 1 L soln/1000 cm³ soln × 0.115 mol $AgNO_3$/L soln

$\times$ 1 mol Cl^-/1 mol $AgNO_3$ × 35.45 g Cl^-/mol Cl^- = 0.0958 g Cl^-

First, convert the volume of $AgNO_3$ to liters so that the moles of $AgNO_3$ present may be calculated from the molarity, 0.115 *M* $AgNO_3$. The equation for the reaction shows the number of moles of $AgNO_3$ equals the moles of Cl^-, 1 mol Cl^-/1 mol $AgNO_3$. Finally, to obtain the mass of Cl^-, multiply by the molar mass of Cl^-, 35.45 g Cl^-/mol.

Problem 5.16 What volume of 0.1000 *M* Na_3PO_4 exactly precipitates the Pb^{2+} in 45.35 mL 0.3441 *M* $Pb(NO_3)_2$?

Solution 5.16 The net ionic equation is as follows.

$$3Pb^{2+}(aq) + 2PO_4^{3-}(aq) \rightarrow Pb_3(PO_4)_2(s)$$

Then calculate the number of moles of Pb^{2+} by multiplying the volume in liters times the molarity, mol Pb^{2+}/L.

$$45.35 \text{ mL } Pb^{2+} \times 1 \text{ L}/1000 \text{ mL} \times 0.3441 \text{ mol } Pb^{2+}/L = 0.01560 \text{ mol } Pb^{2+}$$

The net ionic equation shows us that three moles of Pb^{2+} requires two moles of PO_4^{3-}. Finally, calculate the volume of Na_3PO_4 from its molarity, 0.1000 mol Na_3PO_4/L.

$$0.01560 \text{ mol } Pb^{2+} \times 2 \text{ mol } PO_4^{3-}/3 \text{ mol } Pb^{2+} \times 1 \text{ mol } Na_3PO_4/1 \text{ mol } PO_4^{3-}$$

$$\times 1 \text{ L}/0.1000 \text{ mol } Na_3PO_4 = 0.1040 \text{ L}$$

5.3 ACID-BASE REACTIONS

Properties of Acids and Bases

Acids taste sour while bases taste bitter. Acids change the color of acid-base indicators exactly the opposite to that of bases. For example, acids change the color of litmus, a vegetable dye, from blue to red, while bases change the color of litmus from red to blue. Acids neutralize bases and produce salts. Many acids dissolve metals and release hydrogen gas. Bases produce a slippery feeling on the skin. Both acids and bases may cause inflammations and severe burns if exposed to the skin.

Acids and Bases Defined

Svante Arrhenius proposed the first valid and widely used definitions of acids and bases. An Arrhenius acid is a substance that dissolves in water and increases the hydrogen ion (H^+) concentration. An Arrhenius base is a substance that dissolves in water and increases the hydroxide ion (OH^-) concentration. Thus, any Arrhenius acid may be represented as H*A*. When it enters aqueous solution the acid ionizes and produces hydrogen ions, $H^+(aq)$, and anions, $A^-(aq)$.

$$HA \xrightarrow{H_2O} H^+(aq) + A^-(aq)$$

Common examples of Arrhenius acids include hydrochloric acid, HCl; nitric acid, HNO_3; and sulfuric acid, H_2SO_4.

Some Arrhenius bases may be represented as *M*OH in which *M* is a metal cation. When it dissolves in water, the base dissociates and produces metal cations, $M^+(aq)$, and hydroxide ions, $OH^-(aq)$.

$$MOH \xrightarrow{H_2O} M^+(aq) + OH^-(aq)$$

Common examples of Arrhenius bases are sodium hydroxide, NaOH; potassium hydroxide, KOH; and ammonia, NH_3.

Acid-Base Neutralization

Using the Arrhenius definitions of acids and bases, neutralization is explained in terms of the production of water from the combination of the H^+ from the acid and the OH^- from the base.

$$H^+(aq) + OH^-(aq) \rightarrow H_2O(l)$$

For example, a neutralization reaction occurs when hydrochloric acid, $HCl(aq)$, combines with sodium hydroxide, $NaOH(aq)$, and produces aqueous sodium chloride, $NaCl(aq)$, and water.

$$H^+(aq) + Cl^-(aq) + Na^+(aq) + OH^-(aq) \rightarrow Na^+(aq) + Cl^-(aq) + H_2O(l)$$

Note that the net ionic equation for the reaction of this strong acid and strong base is

$$H^+(aq) + OH^-(aq) \rightarrow H_2O(l)$$

Problem 5.17 Write the overall ionic equation and the net ionic equation for the neutralization of sulfuric acid by potassium hydroxide.

Solution 5.17 The overall ionic equation is

$$2H^+(aq) + SO_4^{2-}(aq) + 2K^+(aq) + 2OH^-(aq) \rightarrow 2K^+(aq) + SO_4^{2-}(aq) + 2H_2O(l)$$

The net ionic equation is
$$H^+(aq) + OH^-(aq) \rightarrow H_2O(l)$$

Acid-Base Titrations

Acid-base titrations are one of the most common titrations performed in chemistry labs. The standard solution in an acid-base titration is often a strong base such as sodium hydroxide, NaOH. Standard base from a buret is carefully added to an acid of unknown concentration until the equivalence point is reached. At the equivalence point in the titration of a strong acid with a strong base, the moles of H^+ equal the moles of OH^-.

The equivalence point of the titration of strong acids and bases is usually detected with the indicator phenolphthalein. Phenolphthalein is colorless in acidic solutions and reddish color in basic solutions. At the equivalence point, a phenolphthalein solution has a pale-pink color.

Problem 5.18 A 25.00-cm^3 sample of sulfuric acid, H_2SO_4, of unknown concentration is titrated with 0.1219 M standard NaOH solution. The equivalence point is reached after 18.73 cm^3 of 0.1219 M NaOH is added. What is the molar concentration of this H_2SO_4 solution?

Solution 5.18 To solve this problem, calculate the moles of sulfuric acid and divide it by the total number of liters of solution. First, write the overall equation for the reaction.

$$H_2SO_4(aq) + 2NaOH(aq) \rightarrow Na_2SO_4(aq) + 2H_2O(l)$$

This equation shows that each mole of H_2SO_4 in the sample reacts with two moles of NaOH. Calculate the moles of H_2SO_4 in the solution by converting the volume of NaOH to liters. Then, multiply it by the molarity of the NaOH solution, 0.1219 mol NaOH/L soln. To obtain the number of moles of H_2SO_4, the equation tells us that for each two moles of NaOH, one mole of H_2SO_4 must be present, 1 mol H_2SO_4/2 mol NaOH.

18.73 cm^3 soln × 1 L soln/1000 cm^3 × 0.1219 mol NaOH/L soln×

1 mol H_2SO_4/2 mol NaOH = 1.142 × 10^{-3} mol H_2SO_4

The molarity of the solution is the moles of solute per liter.

$$M_{H_2SO_4} = \text{moles } H_2SO_4/\text{L soln}$$

Convert 25.00 mL to 0.02500 L and then divide the number of liters into the moles of H_2SO_4, 1.142×10^{-3} mol H_2SO_4.

$$M_{H_2SO_4} = 1.142 \times 10^{-3} \text{ mol } H_2SO_4/0.02500 \text{ L soln}$$
$$= 4.566 \times 10^{-2} M \text{ } H_2SO_4$$

Problem 5.19 A 50.0-mL sample of an unknown phosphoric acid solution, $H_3PO_4(aq)$, is analyzed. When titrated, it takes 39.8 mL 0.0946 M NaOH to completely neutralize the acid. What is the molarity of the phosphoric acid solution?

Solution 5.19 First, write the equation for the reaction.

$$H_3PO_4(aq) + 3NaOH(aq) \rightarrow Na_3PO_4(aq) + 3H_2O(l)$$

Then calculate the number of moles of H_3PO_4.

39.8 cm^3 soln $\times$ 1 L soln/1000 cm^3 $\times$ 0.0946 mol NaOH/L soln

$$\times \text{ 1 mol } H_3PO_4/3 \text{ mol NaOH} = 1.26 \times 10^{-3} \text{ mol } H_3PO_4$$

The molarity of the solution is the moles of solute per liter.

$$M_{H_3PO_4} = \text{moles } H_2SO_4/\text{L soln}$$

Convert the volume 50.0 mL to 0.0500 L and then divide the number of liters into the moles of H_3PO_4, 1.26×10^{-3} mol H_3PO_4.

$$M_{H_3PO_4} = 1.26 \times 10^{-3} \text{ mol } H_2SO_4/0.0500 \text{ L soln}$$
$$= 2.51 \times 10^{-2} M \text{ } H_3PO_4$$

Problem 5.20 A 0.5810-g sample of a soluble unknown solid acid is dissolved in water. The equivalence point is reached after titrating 28.55 mL of 0.1995 M NaOH. If the solid acid has two moles of H^+ per mole of acid, what is the molar mass of the unknown acid?

Solution 5.20 The molar mass, MM, of a compound is the mass of one mole of the acid. Thus, the molar mass is obtained by dividing the moles of acid in the sample into its mass. In such calculations a conversion factor must be included that accounts for the fact that one mole of this acid releases two moles of H^+ ions, 2 mol H^+/1 mol acid.

Begin by calculating the moles of solid acid. To obtain the moles of NaOH, convert the volume of the NaOH solution to liters and multiply by the molarity, 0.1995 mol NaOH/L soln. At the equivalence point the moles of H^+ equals the moles of OH^-, and the moles of solid acid equals half the number of moles of H^+ present, 1 mol acid/2 mol H^+.

28.55 mL soln $\times$ 1 L soln/1000 mL $\times$ 0.1995 mol NaOH/L soln

$$\times \text{ 1 mol } OH^-/1 \text{ mol NaOH} \times 1 \text{ mol } H^+/1 \text{ mol } OH^-$$

$$\times \text{ 1 mol acid/2 mol } H^+ = 2.848 \times 10^{-3} \text{ mol acid}$$

Finally, calculate the molar mass of the acid as follows.

$$MM = \text{g of acid/mol acid}$$
$$= 0.5810 \text{ g acid}/2.848 \times 10^{-3} \text{ mol acid} = 204.0 \text{ g acid/mol}$$

Problem 5.21   Aspirin (acetylsalicylic acid, ASA), $HC_9H_7O_4$, is the most widely used analgesic (painkiller) in the world. A pharmaceutical chemist analyzes the aspirin content of a pain medication. The chemist dissolves 0.155-g sample and titrates it with 17.08 mL 0.0106 M NaOH. What is the percent by mass of aspirin in this pain medication?

Solution 5.21   To calculate the percent aspirin in the sample, divide the mass of aspirin by the mass of the total sample, 0.155 g, and multiply by 100. The mass of ASA is calculated as follows.

17.08 mL $\times$ 1 L/1000 mL $\times$ 0.0106 mol NaOH/L
$$\times \text{ 1 mol } OH^-/\text{1 mol NaOH} \times \text{1 mol ASA/1 mol } OH^-$$
$$\times \text{ 180 g ASA/mol} = 0.0326 \text{ g ASA}$$

Then calculate the percent of ASA in the sample.

$$\%\text{ASA} = (0.0326 \text{ g ASA}/0.155 \text{ g sample}) \times 100 = 21.0\% \text{ ASA}$$

Problem 5.22   A chemist uses solid potassium hydrogen phthalate, KHP, to standardize a NaOH solution. KHP has a molar mass of 204.2 g/mol and releases only one H^+ per formula unit. The chemist finds that it takes 31.07 mL NaOH(aq) to reach the equivalence point for a 1.079-g sample of dissolved KHP. What is the molarity of the NaOH solution?

Solution 5.22   The molarity of the NaOH solution is the number of moles of NaOH per liter of solution. The volume of this solution is known, 31.07 mL or 0.03107 L; hence, the number of moles must be calculated from the mass of KHP neutralized.

1.079 g KHP $\times$ 1 mol KHP/204.2 g $\times$ 1 mol NaOH/1 mol KHP = 5.284×10^{-3} mol NaOH

The molarity is calculated as follows.

$$M = 5.284 \times 10^{-3} \text{ mol NaOH}/0.03107 \text{ L}$$
$$= 0.1701 \text{ M NaOH}$$

5.4   OXIDATION-REDUCTION (REDOX) REACTIONS

Oxidation and Reduction Defined

Oxidation occurs when substances lose electrons. Reduction takes place when substances gain electrons. Thus, oxidation-reduction reactions (also called redox reactions) are electron-transfer reactions. Atoms lose and gain electrons in chemical reactions in order to become more stable.

Example of a Redox Reaction

Consider the reaction in which sodium chloride, NaCl(*s*), results from metallic sodium, Na(*s*), and chlorine gas, $Cl_2(g)$.

$$2Na(s) + Cl_2(g) \rightarrow 2NaCl(s)$$

In this reaction, each sodium atom loses one electron to a chlorine atom producing sodium cations, Na^+, and chloride, Cl^-, anions.

$$Na \rightarrow e^- + Na^+$$
$$Cl + e^- \rightarrow Cl^-$$

Thus, each sodium atom undergoes oxidation and each chlorine atom undergoes reduction. In all oxidation-reduction reactions the electrons lost during oxidation equal those gained during reduction.

Oxidation Numbers

Signed numbers called oxidation numbers, *ON*, also called oxidation states, are used to determine which substances oxidize and reduce. Oxidation numbers are also used to write formulas and predict properties of substances. What is an oxidation number? It is a number assigned to an atom from a set of rules that shows the charge on an ion or the charge an atom appears to have in a covalent molecule. In other words, oxidation numbers indicate if atoms are electron deficient, electron rich, or neutral.

RULES FOR ASSIGNING OXIDATION NUMBERS

The seven rules for assigning oxidation numbers are:

1. The oxidation number for each atom in an element as it exists in nature is 0. Assign 0 for each atom in the following elements: Fe(*s*), Cu(*s*), Pb(*s*), C(*s*), $Br_2(l)$, $P_4(s)$, and $S_8(s)$. This means that the apparent charge on elements is zero.
2. The oxidation number for each monatomic (single atom) ion equals its charge. Thus, the oxidation numbers of Fe^{3+}, S^{2-}, Al^{3+}, and F^- are +3, −2, +3, and −1, respectively. Note that the charge precedes the magnitude in oxidation numbers, exactly the opposite of how charges on ions are written.
3. The oxidation number of H is +1 when bonded to nonmetals and −1 when bonded to metals. Therefore, the oxidation number of H in H_2O, NH_3, or CH_4 is +1 because H bonds to nonmetals in each. When H bonds to metals such as Na or Ca in NaH and CaH_2, its oxidation number is −1.
4. The oxidation number of O in most compounds is −2. In compounds such as CO_2, H_2O, NO_2, P_2O_5, and Na_2O the oxidation number of O is −2. However, assign an oxidation number of −1 to O in peroxides, compounds with two bonded O atoms (–O–O–). For example, in hydrogen peroxide, H_2O_2, and sodium peroxide, Na_2O_2, the oxidation number of O is −1.
5. The oxidation numbers of halogens (group 17 elements) in binary compounds is usually −1. Assign −1 as the oxidation number of F, Cl, Br, or I in all binary compounds except for those in which they bond to O atoms or other halogen atoms. For example, in HCl, NF_3, PBr_3, and CI_4, the oxidation number for each of the halogens is −1.
6. The oxidation numbers of group 1 (IA) and group 2 (IIA) atoms are +1 and +2, respectively. Unlike transition metals, alkali metals, group 1, and alkaline earth metals, group 2, have fixed oxidation states. Assign +1 to Li, Na, K, Rb, Cs, and Fr, and +2 to Be, Mg, Ca, Sr, Ba, and Ra.
7. The sum of the oxidation numbers in a compound equals zero, and the sum of the oxidation numbers in a polyatomic ion, an ion with more than one atom, equals its charge.

Problem 5.23 Determine the oxidation numbers of the atoms in sodium chlorate, $NaClO_3$.

Solution 5.23   The oxidation number of Na is +1 because it is a member of group 1 (Rule 6). Each O atom has an oxidation number of -2 (Rule 4); thus, three O atoms have a total oxidation number of -6 (-2×3). To calculate the oxidation number of Cl, use Rule 7 which states that the sum of the oxidation numbers in a compound equals zero. Hence, the oxidation number of Cl, ON_{Cl}, in $NaClO_3$ is 5.

Problem 5.24   What is the oxidation number of Cr in the dichromate ion, $Cr_2O_7^{2-}$?

Solution 5.24   Each O atom has an oxidation number of -2 and seven O atoms have a total oxidation number of -14. In $Cr_2O_7^{2-}$, the sum of its oxidation numbers equals $-2(ON_{Cr_2O_7^{2-}})$, the charge on dichromate. Hence, the total oxidation number on two Cr atoms is +12 and the oxidation number on one Cr atom is +6.

Problem 5.25   Calculate the oxidation number of Mn in each of the following:
   (a) $MnCl_6^{4-}$
   (b) $Ca(MnO_4)_2$

Solution 5.25
   (a) The sum of the oxidation numbers in this polyatomic ion equals -4, the charge on the $MnCl_6^{4-}$ ion (Rule 7). In many ions and binary compounds, Cl has an oxidation number of -1 (Rule 5), and six Cl atoms have a total oxidation number of -6. Therefore, the oxidation number of Mn is +2 because the sum of +2 and -6 is -4.
   (b) Ca belongs to group 2 (IIA) and has an oxidation number of +2 (Rule 6). Since each O atom has an oxidation number of -2 (Rule 4), the eight O atoms have a total oxidation number of -16. Because $Ca(MnO_4)_2$ is a compound, the sum of its oxidation numbers is 0 (Rule 7). Therefore, the oxidation number for two Mn atoms is +14. Dividing this number by 2 gives the oxidation number for one Mn atom, +7.

Oxidizing and Reducing Agents

Oxidizing agents are reactants in redox reactions that bring about oxidation; thus, they undergo reduction. Reducing agents are reactants that bring about reduction; thus, they undergo oxidation.

Problem 5.26   Consider the single-displacement reaction that occurs when a strip of Cu metal is placed into a $AgNO_3$ solution.

$$Cu(s) + 2AgNO_3(aq) \rightarrow Cu(NO_3)_2(aq) + 2Ag(s)$$

   (a) What substance undergoes oxidation?
   (b) What substance undergoes reduction?
   (c) What are the oxidizing and reducing agents?

Solution 5.26   To identify what has undergone oxidation and reduction, first assign oxidation numbers to all elements. The oxidation number of each atom is written below the symbol.

$$\text{ON per atom} = \underset{0}{Cu(s)} + \underset{+1+5-2}{2AgNO_3(aq)} \rightarrow \underset{+2 \ +5-2}{Cu(NO_3)_2(aq)} + \underset{0}{2Ag(s)}$$

Then, identify which elements change oxidation numbers.
   (a) In this reaction, the Cu changes from 0 to +2. When the oxidation number of an atom increases, it undergoes oxidation because it loses electrons. If atoms lose negative particles such as electrons, then their oxidation number increases.
   (b) The oxidation number of Ag decreases from +1 to 0. Thus, it is reduced because it gains electrons–negative particles. If an atom gains electrons, then its oxidation number decreases.
   (c) $AgNO_3$ pulls electrons from Cu and brings about its oxidation; therefore, $AgNO_3$ is the oxidizing agent. Cu releases electrons and reduces $AgNO_3$; hence, Cu is the reducing agent.

Problem 5.27 Identify the oxidizing and reducing agents and what undergoes oxidation and reduction in the following reaction. This reaction produces electricity in rechargeable nicad batteries.

$$Cd + NiO_2 + 2H_2O \rightarrow Ni(OH)_2 + Cd(OH)_2$$

Solution 5.27 Write the oxidation numbers for each atom in the equation.

$$\underset{ON \text{ per atom} =}{\quad} \underset{0}{Cd} + \underset{+4-2}{NiO_2} + \underset{+1-2}{2H_2O} \rightarrow \underset{+2-2+1}{Ni(OH)_2} + \underset{+2\ -2+1}{Cd(OH)_2}$$

The Cd increases its oxidation number from 0 to +2. Thus, Cd undergoes oxidation and is the reducing agent. Additionally, the Ni in NiO_2 decreases from +4 to +2. Therefore, NiO_2 undergoes reduction and is the oxidizing agent.

Balancing Redox Equations Using the Oxidation-Number Method

Previously, the inspection method has been used to balance equations. However, oxidation-reduction reactions sometimes are almost impossible to balance by inspection. Therefore, another method is needed to balance redox equations.

Employ the following steps to balance redox equations using the oxidation-number method.

1. Write the complete unbalanced equation.
2. Assign oxidation numbers to each element in the equation, and identify the substances that undergo oxidation and reduction.
3. Extract the elements that undergo oxidation and reduction from the equation, and write them with their oxidation numbers separated by arrows. First balance the atoms and then equalize the oxidation numbers by adding electrons to the right side of oxidations and to the left side of reductions.
4. Equalize the electrons released by the oxidation and gained by the reduction.
5. Place these coefficients in the unbalanced equation, balance all other substances by inspection, and check to see if the atoms and charge balance.

Problem 5.28 Balance the following equation using the oxidation-number method, and identify the reactants that undergo oxidation and reduction.

Aqueous iron(III) chloride and hydrogen sulfide react to produce iron(II) chloride, sulfur, and hydrochloric acid.

Solution 5.28

Step 1. First, write the unbalanced equation.

$$FeCl_3 + H_2S \rightarrow FeCl_2 + S + HCl \text{ (unbalanced)}$$

Step 2. Next, assign oxidation numbers to all elements.

$$\underset{+3-1}{FeCl_3} + \underset{+1-2}{H_2S} \rightarrow \underset{+2-1}{FeCl_2} + \underset{0}{S} + \underset{+1-1}{HCl}$$

Fe in $FeCl_3$ reduces $(+3 \rightarrow -2)$ and S in H_2S oxidizes $(-2 \rightarrow 0)$. Thus, $FeCl_3$ is the oxidizing agent and H_2S is the reducing agent.

Step 3. Remove each element from the equation and separate them by an arrow.

$$\underset{-2}{S} \rightarrow \underset{0}{S}$$
$$\underset{+3}{Fe} \rightarrow \underset{+2}{Fe}$$

In both cases, an equal number of atoms is on either side of the arrow. Sulfur undergoes oxidation; thus add two electrons to the right side so that a −2 charge is on either side of the arrow. In a similar manner, equalize the charge by adding one electron to the left side of the Fe equation.

$$\underset{-2}{S} \rightarrow \underset{0}{S} + 2e^- \text{ (oxidation)}$$

$$e^- + \underset{+3}{Fe} \rightarrow \underset{+2}{Fe} \quad \text{(reduction)}$$

Step 4. As written, the oxidation releases two electrons and the reduction takes in one electron; hence, multiply the Fe equation by 2.

$$\underset{-2}{S} \rightarrow \underset{0}{S} + 2e^-$$

$$2\underset{+3}{Fe} + 2e^- \rightarrow 2\underset{+2}{Fe}$$

Therefore, the correct coefficient is 1 for H_2S and S, and is 2 for $FeCl_3$ and $FeCl_2$.

Step 5. Place the coefficients in the unbalanced equation, balance all other substances by inspection, and check to see if the atoms and charge balance.

$$2FeCl_3 + H_2S \rightarrow 2FeCl_2 + S + HCl \text{ (unbalanced)}$$

After the coefficients are placed in front of the substances that undergo oxidation and reduction, HCl is the only remaining compound to balance by inspection. Six Cl are on the left and only five Cl are on the right. Thus, the coefficient of HCl is 2.

$$2FeCl_3 + H_2S \rightarrow 2FeCl_2 + S + 2HCl \text{ (balanced)}$$

Problem 5.29   Balance the following equation using the oxidation-number method.

$$PbS + HNO_3 \rightarrow Pb(NO_3)_2 + NO + S + H_2O \text{ (unbalanced)}$$

Solution 5.29

Steps 1 and 2. Write the unbalanced equation and assign oxidation numbers to all atoms.

$$\underset{+2-2}{PbS} + \underset{+1+5-2}{HNO_3} \rightarrow \underset{+2 \ +5-2}{Pb(NO_3)_2} + \underset{+2-2}{NO} + \underset{0}{S} + \underset{+1-2}{H_2O}$$

Because the oxidation number of the S atom in PbS increases from −2 to 0, PbS undergoes oxidation to free sulfur, S. The N atom in HNO_3 undergoes reduction to NO because the oxidation number of N decreases from +5 to +2. Also note that some of the N atoms in HNO_3 do not reduce–they are in $Pb(NO_3)_2$.

Step 3. Extract the elements from the equation, balance the atoms, and equalize oxidation numbers by adding electrons.

$$\underset{-2}{S} \rightarrow \underset{0}{S} + 2e^- \text{ (oxidation)}$$

$$3e^- + \underset{+5}{N} \rightarrow \underset{+2}{N} \text{ (reduction)}$$

To balance these equations, add two electrons to the right side of the oxidation of sulfur and three electrons to the left side of the reduction of nitrogen.

Step 4. Equalize the number of electrons given off and taken in.

$$3\underset{-2}{S} \rightarrow 3\underset{0}{S} + 6e^-$$

$$6e^- + 2\underset{+5}{N} \rightarrow 2\underset{+2}{N}$$

To equalize the electrons, multiply the first equation by 3 and the second by 2. Thus, six electrons transfer in this redox reaction.

Step 5. Place the coefficients in the unbalanced equation, balance all other substances by inspection, and check to see if the atoms and charge balance. After the coefficients from step 4 are placed into the equation, the following unbalanced equation results.

$$3PbS + HNO_3 \rightarrow 3Pb(NO_3)_2 + 2NO + 3S + H_2O \text{ (unbalanced)}$$

After the remaining atoms are balanced by inspection, the following equation results.

$$3PbS + 8HNO_3 \rightarrow 3Pb(NO_3)_2 + 2NO + 3S + 4H_2O \text{ (balanced)}$$

Balancing Redox Equations Using the Half-Reaction Method

The half-reaction method (also known as the ion-electron method) is most often used to balance equations for reactions that occur in aqueous solutions, especially those that take place in acidic or basic solutions. In this method, separate equations for the oxidation and reduction are written and then balanced. Each of these equations is termed a half-reaction, but would be more accurately called a half equation.

Use the following steps when balancing a redox reaction.

1. Separate the substances that oxidize from those that reduce by writing two half-reactions.
2. Balance the atoms so that the same number of each type of atom is on either side of the half-reactions.
3. Add electrons to the right side of the oxidation half-reaction to balance the charge, and in a similar manner add electrons to the left side of the reduction half-reaction.
4. Equalize the electrons transferred by multiplying the appropriate half-reaction by an integer. In some cases, multiply both by integers to equalize the electrons.
5. Add the two half-reactions, canceling the electrons, and check to see that you have balanced the charge and mass.

Many redox reactions occur in either acidic or basic solutions. If the reaction occurs in an acidic solution, add H^+ and H_2O in Step 2 when balancing the atoms, and if it is in a basic solution, add OH^- and H_2O.

Problem 5.30 Balance the following reaction, in which solid Al oxidizes to aqueous Al^{3+}, and aqueous Ni^{2+} reduces to solid Ni.

$$Al(s) + Ni^{2+}(aq) \rightarrow Ni(s) + Al^{3+}(aq)$$

Solution 5.30 As in the oxidation-number method, use oxidation numbers to separate the substances that undergo oxidation from those that undergo reduction. Al^{3+} forms when Al loses three electrons, and Ni results when Ni^{2+} gains two electrons.

$$Al(s) \rightarrow Al^{3+}(aq) + 3e^-$$
$$2e^- + Ni^{2+}(aq) \rightarrow Ni(s)$$

Equalize the electrons transferred by multiplying the first half-reaction by 2 and the second by 3. To obtain the balanced net ionic equation, add the two half-reactions and cancel the electrons.

$$2Al(s) \rightarrow 2Al^{3+}(aq) + 6e^-$$
$$+6e^- + 3Ni^{2+}(aq) \rightarrow 3Ni(s)$$
$$\overline{2Al(s) + 3Ni^{2+}(aq) \rightarrow 3Ni(s) + 2Al^{3+}(aq)}$$

Problem 5.31 Use the half-reaction method to balance the following equation in which dichromate, $Cr_2O_7^{2-}$, oxidizes iron(II), Fe^{2+} to iron(III), Fe^{3+}.

$$Cr_2O_7^{2-}(aq) + Fe^{2+}(aq) \rightarrow Cr^{3+}(aq) + Fe^{3+}(aq) \text{ (acid)}$$

Solution 5.31

Step 1. Separate the substances that oxidize from those that reduce by writing two half-reactions.

$$Fe^{2+} \rightarrow Fe^{3+}$$
$$Cr_2O_7^{2-} \rightarrow Cr^{3+}$$

If you are unsure of what oxidizes and what reduces, use oxidation numbers to decide. In this reaction Fe^{2+} oxidizes to Fe^{3+}. The oxidation number of Cr in $Cr_2O_7^{2-}$ decreases from +6 to +3 in Cr^{3+}.

Step 2. Next, balance the atoms so that the same number of each type of atom is on either side of the half-reactions. The atoms in the iron half-reaction are balanced; thus, the coefficients remain the same.

$$Fe^{2+} \rightarrow Fe^{3+}$$

In the dichromate half-reaction, the Cr atoms are balanced by placing a 2 in front of Cr^{3+}.

$$Cr_2O_7^{2-} \rightarrow 2Cr^{3+}$$

Because this reaction takes place in an acidic solution, first add enough H_2O molecules to balance the O atoms and add H^+ to balance the H atoms. Seven O atoms are on the left side. Therefore, add seven H_2O molecules to the right side to balance the O atoms.

$$Cr_2O_7^{2-} \rightarrow 2Cr^{3+} + 7H_2O$$

The addition of seven H_2O molecules to the right side adds 14 H atoms, which are balanced by placing 14 H^+ on the left side.

$$14H^+ + Cr_2O_7^{2-} \rightarrow 2Cr^{3+} + 7H_2O$$

Step 3. Add electrons to the right side of the oxidation half-reaction to balance the charge, and in a similar manner add electrons to the left side of the reduction half-reaction. For the iron half-reaction, add one electron to equalize the charge on either side. Thus, this is the oxidation half-reaction.

$$Fe^{2+} \rightarrow Fe^{3+} + e^- \text{ (oxidation)}$$

For the dichromate half-reaction, a total charge of $12+ (14-2)$ is on the right side and only $6+ (2 \times 3+)$ is on the left side. To balance the charge, add six electrons to the left side of the equation.

$$6e^- + 14H^+ + Cr_2O_7^{2-} \rightarrow 2Cr^{3+} + 7H_2O \text{ (reduction)}$$

Step 4. Equalize the electrons transferred by multiplying the appropriate half-reaction by an integer. As written, the oxidation releases one electron and the reduction takes in six electrons. To equalize the electrons, multiply the oxidation half-reaction by 6.

$$6Fe^{2+} \rightarrow 6Fe^{3+} + 6e^-$$
$$6e^- + 14H^+ + Cr_2O_7^{2-} \rightarrow 2Cr^{3+} + 7H_2O$$

Step 5. Add the two half-reactions, canceling the electrons, and check to see that you have balanced the charge and mass. After the two half-reactions are added, the six electrons cancel, yielding the following net ionic equation.

$$6Fe^{2+} + 14H^+ + Cr_2O_7^{2-} \rightarrow 2Cr^{3+} + 6Fe^{3+} + 7H_2O$$

Problem 5.32 Balance the following equation in basic solution using the half-reaction method.

$$S^{2-}(aq) + MnO_4^-(aq) \rightarrow S(s) + MnO_2(s) \text{ (base)}$$

Solution 5.32

1. Separate the substances that oxidize from those that reduce by writing two half-reactions.

$$S^{2-} \rightarrow S$$
$$MnO_4^- \rightarrow MnO_2$$

The S^{2-} oxidizes to S. The Mn in MnO_4^- has an oxidation number of +7 and it decreases to +4 in MnO_2. It is easy to balance the sulfur because it does not involve the addition of H_2O and OH^-. Balance sulfur by adding two electrons to the right side.

$$S^{2-} \rightarrow S + 2e^-$$

The reduction of MnO_4^- to MnO_2 is more complicated.
2. Balance the atoms so that the same number of each type of atom is on either side of the half-reactions. One Mn is on each side; thus, they balance. Now balance the O atoms by adding OH^- and H_2O. Sometimes confusion results as to what side to add the OH^- and H_2O. This problem may be avoided by balancing the equation as if it was in an acidic solution. After adding H^+ and H_2O, add OH^- to each side of the equation to "neutralize" $(H^+ + OH^- \rightarrow H_2O)$ all H^+, and then complete the balancing of the equation as above. The following procedure illustrates this method.

$$4H^+ + MnO_4^- \rightarrow MnO_2 + 2H_2O$$

First, balance the half-reaction with H_2O and H^+ as if it occurs in an acidic solution. Remove the four H^+ by adding four OH^- to both sides of the equation.

$$4H^+ + MnO_4^- \rightarrow MnO_2 + 2H_2O$$
$$+4OH^- \qquad\qquad\qquad 4OH^-$$

$$\overline{}$$

$$4H_2O + MnO_4^- \rightarrow MnO_2 + 4OH^- + 2H_2O$$

After two H_2O molecules are removed from both sides and the charges are balanced, the following equation results.

$$3e^- + 2H_2O + MnO_4^- \rightarrow MnO_2 + 4OH^-$$

3. Equalize the electrons transferred by multiplying the appropriate half-reaction by an integer. The oxidation releases two electrons and the reduction takes in three electrons. Thus, multiply the oxidation half-reaction by three and multiply the reduction half-reaction by two.

$$3S^{2-} \rightarrow 3S + 6e^-$$
$$6e^- + 4H_2O + 2MnO_4^- \rightarrow 2MnO_2 + 8OH^-$$

4. Add the two half-reactions, canceling the electrons, and check to see that you have balanced the charge and mass. After the two half-reactions are added and the six electrons are cancelled, the following balanced equation results.

$$3S^{2-} + 2MnO_4^- + 4H_2O \rightarrow 3S + 2MnO_2 + 8OH^- \text{ (balanced)}$$

Redox Titrations

In redox titrations, strong oxidizing agents such as $K_2Cr_2O_7$ and $KMnO_4$ oxidize substances of interest or strong reducing agents reduce samples. To understand redox titrations, let's consider the oxidation of $Fe^{2+}(aq)$ to $Fe^{3+}(aq)$.

$$Fe^{2+}(aq) \rightarrow Fe^{3+}(aq) + e^-$$

This may be accomplished with an acidic potassium permanganate solution, $KMnO_4(aq)$. The half-reaction for this reduction is as follows.

$$5e^- + 8H^+(aq) + MnO_4^-(aq) \rightarrow Mn^{2+}(aq) + 4H_2O(aq)$$

Thus, the overall ionic equation that occurs is

$$8H^+(aq) + MnO_4^-(aq) + 5Fe^{2+}(aq) \rightarrow 5Fe^{3+}(aq) + Mn^{2+}(aq) + 4H_2O(aq)$$

Potassium permanganate is not only an excellent oxidizing agent, it also detects the equivalence point in a titration because $MnO_4^-(aq)$ is a deep purple color and $Mn^{2+}(aq)$ is almost colorless. Thus, during a redox titration using $KMnO_4$ and a colorless substance, the solution remains colorless as long as the titrated substance remains in solution. However, once it is consumed, the next drop of $KMnO_4$ changes the color of the solution to a persistent pink to purple.

In the redox titration of $Fe^{2+}(aq)$ to $Fe^{3+}(aq)$, a sample that contains Fe^{2+} is dissolved in deionized water in an erlenmeyer flask. Then sulfuric acid, H_2SO_4, is added to provide the proper H^+ ion concentration. When the end point is approached, phosphoric acid is added, H_3PO_4, which combines with the Fe^{3+} and forms a colorless complex ion. The addition of phosphoric acid also makes a sharper end point.

Problem 5.33   A 0.8935-g sample of an iron(II) compound is dissolved in water and is titrated with $KMnO_4(aq)$ to the equivalence point. If this titration requires 17.96 mL of 0.02515 M $KMnO_4$ to reach the pink end point, what is the percent by mass of Fe in the sample?

Solution 5.33   The percent by mass of Fe is calculated in the sample as follows.

$$\%Fe = \frac{g\ Fe}{g\ total} \times 100$$

The mass of the sample, 0.8935 g, is known; thus, the mass of Fe in the sample must be calculated from the titration data. First, calculate the mass of Fe in this sample. As previously discussed, the following reaction occurs when $KMnO_4$ oxidizes Fe^{2+} to Fe^{3+}.

$$8H^+(aq) + MnO_4^-(aq) + 5Fe^{2+}(aq) \rightarrow 5Fe^{3+}(aq) + Mn^{2+}(aq) + 4H_2O(aq)$$

For each added mole of MnO_4^-, five moles of Fe^{2+} oxidize to Fe^{3+}. Thus, the moles of MnO_4^- is calculated from the molarity and volume of $KMnO_4$. Use the above conversion factor to calculate the moles of Fe. Then, the molar mass of Fe, 55.85 g/mol, is used to obtain the mass of Fe.

17.96 mL MnO_4^- $\times$ 1 L MnO_4^-/1000 mL MnO_4^- $\times$ 0.02515 mol MnO_4^-/1 L

$\times$ 5 mol Fe^{2+}/1 mol MnO_4^- $\times$ 55.85 g Fe/1 mol Fe = 0.1261 g Fe

Then, calculate the percent of Fe in the sample

$\%Fe$ = (g Fe/g total) $\times$ 100
= (0.1261 g Fe/0.8935 g sample) $\times$ 100 = 14.11% Fe

SUMMARY

*C*ombination *reactions occur when two or more reactants combine to produce a compound. The reverse of a combination reaction is a decomposition reaction in which a compound breaks up and forms elements and/or compounds. A single replacement reaction occurs when an element replaces another element in a compound. A metathesis reaction is one in which a double replacement occurs.*

Electrolytes are substances that either dissociate or ionize to produce ions in aqueous solutions. The opposite of an electrolyte is a nonelectrolyte–it does not produce dissolved ions. Strong electrolytes almost totally break up and form ions, while weak electrolytes only dissociate to a small extent. Ionic equations are written to show the dissolved ions in aqueous reactions. Removing the ions that do not participate in the reaction from an ionic equation produces the net ionic equation.

Precipitation reactions occur when a solid insoluble substance forms in an aqueous reaction. The products of precipitation reactions are predicted using a table of solubilities. Insoluble substances precipitate and soluble ones do not.

A titration is a volumetric laboratory analysis method in which a standard solution of known concentration is systematically added to a solution of unknown concentration until the equivalence point is reached. The equivalence point is reached when the number of moles of the unknown reacts completely with the standard solution. In a precipitation titration, a precipitate forms in the titration reaction.

Acids are substances that increase the $H^+(aq)$ concentration in water. Bases are substances that increase the $OH^-(aq)$ concentration in water. In neutralization reactions, acids combine with bases and form salts and usually water. In an acid-base titration, a base of known concentration is usually added to an acidic solution of unknown concentration.

Oxidation-reduction reactions are electron-transfer reactions. Substances that lose electrons undergo oxidation. Substances that gain electrons undergo reduction. If a substance undergoes oxidation, it provides the electrons for reduction. Thus, it is a reducing agent. If a substance undergoes reduction, it removes electrons. Therefore, it is an oxidizing agent. A set of signed numbers called oxidation numbers is used to determine if a substance undergoes oxidation or reduction and to help balance some oxidation-reduction equations.

CHAPTER 5 REVIEW EXERCISE

1. To which of the four classes of reactions does each of the following belong?

   (a) $2CO(g) + O_2(g) \rightarrow 2CO_2(g)$
   (b) $Br_2(aq) + 2I^-(aq) \rightarrow 2Br_2(aq) + I_2(aq)$
   (c) $PtO_2(s) \rightarrow Pt(s) + 2O_2(g)$

2. Write a balanced equation that illustrates each of the following: (a) decomposition of a nonmetal oxide, (b) decomposition of a metal oxide, (c) formation of metal oxide, (d) halogenation reaction.

3. Write ionic equations to show the dissociation of each of the following ionic substances in water: (a) $ZnSO_4$, (b) $MgCl_2$, (c) $Al(NO_3)_3$

4. What is the molar concentration of the $Cl^-(aq)$ in 0.0500 M solutions of each of the following? (a) NaCl, (b) $CaCl_2$, (c) $CoCl_3$

5. A solution is prepared by mixing 1.00 L 0.500 M KBr, 1.50 L 0.500 M $MgBr_2$, and 2.00 L 0.500 M $SrBr_2$ and then it is diluted to 10.0 L. (a) What is the molarity of $Br^-(aq)$ in this solution? (b) If enough water is evaporated until the total volume is 2.50 L, what is the concentration of $Br^-(aq)$? (c) If 10.0 mL of the solution in part (b) is diluted to 10.0 L, what is the molar concentration of Br^-?

6. Write the overall and net ionic reactions for the combination of ammonium sulfide and aluminum nitrate solutions.

7. Write the overall and net ionic equations for each of the following:

   (a) mercury(II) bromide(*aq*) + calcium nitrate(*aq*) $\rightarrow$
   (b) sodium phosphate(*aq*) + iron(III) acetate(*aq*) $\rightarrow$

8. A 50.00-cm^3 NaBr solution is titrated to the equivalence point with 41.34 cm^3 0.2071 M $AgNO_3$ and totally precipitates the $Br^-(aq)$. What is the molarity of the NaBr solution?

9. What volume in milliliters of 0.250 M NaOH exactly precipitates the Co^{3+} in 81.2 mL 0.307 M $Co(NO_3)_3$?

10. Calculate the mass of silver iodide, in mg, that results when 24.04 mL 0.2088 M $AgNO_3(aq)$ combines with 10.22 mL 0.1707 M $MgI_2(aq)$.

11. A 50.0-mL sample of an unknown hydrochloric acid solution, HCl(*aq*), is analyzed. When titrated, it takes 39.8 mL 0.0946 M NaOH to reach the end point. What is the molarity of this acid solution?

12. A student dissolves a 1.098-g sample of a solid acid that contains two moles of H^+ per mole of acid in water and titrates it with NaOH. If it takes 29.31 cm^3 of 0.2997 M NaOH to neutralize the acid, what is the molar mass of the student's solid acid?

13. Acetic acid, $HC_2H_3O_2$, is the acidic substance in vinegar. A sample of commercial vinegar is titrated with NaOH to calculate the percent by mass of acetic acid. Initially a 25.00-g

sample of the commercial vinegar is diluted to 100.0 mL. A 28.79-mL sample of 0.2000 M NaOH is required to reach the equivalence point from a 25.00-mL aliquot of this diluted acetic acid. If acetic acid releases one H^+ per molecule, calculate the percent by mass of acetic acid in the commercial vinegar.

14. A 0.500-g impure sample of sodium carbonate is analyzed. If the sample requires 29.08 mL of 0.1499 M HCl to reach the equivalence point, what is the percent by mass of sodium carbonate in the sample?

15. A chemist analyzes a mixture CaO and BaO by reacting the mixture with HCl.

$$CaO(s) + 2HCl(aq) \rightarrow CaCl_2(aq) + H_2O(l)$$
$$BaO(s) + 2HCl(aq) \rightarrow BaCl_2(aq) + H_2O(l)$$

The chemist finds that a 3.90-g sample of the mixture exactly combines with 14.2 mL of 6.00 M HCl(aq). What is the percent composition of the mixture?

16. What is the oxidation number of S in each of the following: (a) SO_2, (b) SO_4^{2-}, (c) $S_2O_3^{2-}$?

17. Identify the oxidizing and reducing agents and what undergoes oxidation and reduction in the following reaction.

$$HCl + HNO_3 \rightarrow NO_2 + \frac{1}{2}Cl_2 + H_2O$$

18. Balance the following equation using the oxidation-number method.

$$As_2O_3 + Cl_2 + H_2O \rightarrow H_3AsO_4 + HCl$$

19. Balance the following equation using the oxidation-number method.

$$KOH + Br_2 \rightarrow KBr + KBrO_3 + H_2O$$

20. Balance the following equation using the oxidation-number method.

$$K_2Cr_2O_7 + HCl \rightarrow KCl + CrCl_3 + H_2O + Cl_2$$

21. Use the half-reaction method to balance the following redox equation that occurs in an acidic solution.
$$MnO_4^- + Cl^- \rightarrow Mn^{2+} + Cl_2 \quad (acid)$$

22. Use the half-reaction method to balance the following redox equation that occurs in an acidic solution.
$$AsH_3 + Ag^+ \rightarrow As_4O_6 + Ag \quad (acid)$$

23. Use the half-reaction method to balance the following redox equation that occurs in a basic solution.
$$Al + H_2O \rightarrow Al(OH)_4^- + H_2 \quad (base)$$

24. Use the half-reaction method to balance the following redox equation that occurs in an basic solution.
$$P_4 \rightarrow PH_3 + HPO_3^{2-}$$

25. Balance the following equation.

$$CrI_3 + H_2O_2 \rightarrow CrO_4^{2-} + IO_4^- + H_2O \quad (base)$$

26. A student dissolves a 1.539-g sample of an iron(II) compound in water and titrates it to the equivalence point with $KMnO_4(aq)$. If 30.07 mL of 0.02663 M $KMnO_4$ is required to reach the pink end point, what is the percent by mass of Fe in the sample?

27. A room has the measurements of 10.0 m × 15.0 m × 3.00 m. What mass of KCN must react with excess hydrochloric acid to produce a lethal dose of $HCN(g)$, 300 mg HCN/kg air. The density of air is 1.18 mg/cm^3

ANSWERS TO REVIEW EXERCISE

1. (a) combination, (b) single replacement, (c) decomposition
2. (a) $2H_2O \rightarrow 2H_2 + O_2$
   (b) $HgO \rightarrow Hg + \frac{1}{2}O_2$
   (c) $2Na + \frac{1}{2}O_2 \rightarrow Na_2O$
   (d) $PbCl_2 + Cl_2 \rightarrow PbCl_4$
3. (a) $ZnSO_4(s) \rightarrow Zn^{2+}(aq) + SO_4^{2-}(aq)$
   (b) $MgCl_2(s) \rightarrow Mg^{2+}(aq) + 2Cl^-(aq)$
   (c) $Al(NO_3)_3(s) \rightarrow Al^{3}+(aq) + 3OH-(aq)$
4. (a) 0.0500 M Cl^-, (b) 0.100 M Cl^-, (c) 0.150 M Cl^-
5. (a) 0.225 M Br^-, (b) 0.900 M Br^-, (c) 0.00900 M Br^-
6. $6NH_4^+(aq) + 3S^{2-}(aq) + 2Al^{3+}(aq) + 6NO_3^-(aq) \rightarrow Al_2S_3(s) + 6NH_4^+(aq) + 6NO_3^-(aq)$
   $3S^{2-}(aq) + 2Al^{3+}(aq) \rightarrow Al_2S_3(s)$
7. (a) no reaction,
   (b) $3Na^+(aq) + PO_4^{3-}(aq) + Fe^{3+}(aq) + 3C_2H_3O_2^-(aq) \rightarrow FePO_4(s)$
   $+ 3Na^+(aq) + 3C_2H_3O_2^-(aq)$
   $PO_4^{3-}(aq) + Fe^{3+}(aq) \rightarrow FePO_4(s)$
8. 0.1712 M NaBr
9. 299 mL 0.250 M NaOH
10. 819.2 mg AgI
11. 0.0753 M HCl
12. 250.0 g/mol
13. 5.528% $HC_2H_3O_2$
14. 46.21%
15. 39.0% CaO, 61.0% BaO
16. (a) +4, (b) +6, (c) +2
17. HCl–oxidation, reducing agent, HNO$_3$–reduction, oxidizing agent
18. $As_2O_3 + 2Cl_2 + 5H_2O \rightarrow 2H_3AsO_4 + 4HCl$
19. $6KOH + 3Br_2 \rightarrow 5KBr + KBrO_3 + 3H_2O$
20. $K_2Cr_2O_7 + 14HCl \rightarrow 2KCl + 2CrCl_3 + 7H_2O + 3Cl_2$
21. $16H^+ + 2MnO_4^- + 10Cl^- \rightarrow 2Mn^{2+} + 5Cl_2 + 8H_2O$
22. $6H_2O + 4AsH_3 + 24Ag^+ \rightarrow 24H^+ + As_4O_6 + 24Ag$
23. $2OH^- + 6H_2O + 2Al \rightarrow 2Al(OH)_4^- + 3H_2$
24. $8OH^- + 4H_2O + 2P_4 \rightarrow 4PH_3 + 4HPO_3^{2-}$
25. $10OH^- + 2CrI_3 + 27H_2O_2 \rightarrow 2CrO_4^{2-} + 6IO_4^- + 32H_2O$
26. 14.53% Fe
27. 384 g KCN

6

Gases

*T*his chapter considers the properties of substances in the gas phase. In Chapter 12, we will complete our discussion of physical states by studying the more condensed states of matter, liquids and solids. In addition, we will also consider the theory that is used to explain the properties of gases—the kinetic-molecular theory.

6.1 INTRODUCTION TO THE GAS PHASE

Properties of Gases

The gas phase is the least dense state of matter, which means that the small particles that compose it (atoms and molecules) are widely separated and exert weak attractive forces on each other. Gases totally fill their containers, and their volumes depend on the pressure exerted on them. They are the most fluid of the three physical states.

Ideal Gases Versus Real Gases

An ideal gas is one that behaves exactly as predicted by the ideal gas laws. One property of ideal gases is that they remain in the gas phase and never change state, regardless of the conditions. To a degree most real gases behave in a manner similar to ideal gases, but not exactly. Real gases most closely resemble ideal gases at higher temperatures and lower pressures.

6.2 GAS PRESSURE

Pressure Defined

Pressure, P, is defined as a force exerted on an area. Gas pressure is the force exerted by a gas on a unit area. Gas pressure results when the particles that make up gases collide with the walls of their container.

Atmospheric Pressure and Barometers

Atmospheric pressure, P_{atm}, is the force of the gases in the atmosphere on a unit area. In other words, atmospheric pressure results from the weight of air on the surface of objects. A barometer is the instrument used to measure atmospheric pressure. Atmospheric pressure exerted on the surface of the Hg supports a 760-mm column of Hg at sea level on an average day.

Gas Pressure and Manometers

Used to measure the pressures of isolated gas samples, mercury manometers are U-shaped glass tubes that contain Hg(*l*). One end of the tube is connected to the vessel that holds the gas of interest and the other end may either be open to the atmosphere or closed and evacuated. To obtain the pressure exerted by a gas sample with an open-end manometer, the difference in height of the Hg columns and the atmospheric pressure is measured.

Units of Gas Pressure

THE SI UNIT OF PRESSURE

In the SI system of units the pascal, Pa, is the unit of pressure. Because pressure is the force per unit area, one pascal is one newton, N, per meter squared, N/m^2. Exerting one newton of force on a one-kilogram mass for one second gives it a speed of one meter/second. A pascal is a very small unit of pressure. Thus, the kilopascal, kPa, is often used for the SI unit of pressure.

NON-SI UNITS OF PRESSURE

Four non-SI units of pressure, including atmospheres, torr, mmHg, and bars are also commonly used. Because at sea level on an average day the atmosphere supports a column of liquid mercury 760 mm high, then one atmosphere, atm, is defined as 760 mmHg. One mmHg equals exactly one torr. Thus, one atmosphere is equivalent to 760 torr. To show the small size of the Pa, one atmosphere equals 101,325 Pa or 101.325 kPa. One bar is equivalent to 100 kPa; therefore, one bar is a unit that is close in magnitude to an atmosphere.

Problem 6.1 Calculate the number of Pa per 1 torr.

Solution 6.1 One atm is equivalent to 101,325 Pa and 760 torr; thus, the number of Pa per torr is calculated as follows.

$$101,325 \text{ Pa/1 atm} \times 1 \text{ atm/760 torr} = 133 \text{ Pa/1 torr}$$

Problem 6.2 A weatherman reports the barometric pressure is 30.2 *in.* of Hg. Convert 30.2 *in.* Hg to: (a) torr, (b) atmospheres, (c) kilopascals, and (d) bars.

Solution 6.2

(a) To change inches of Hg to torr, convert inches to millimeters because one torr is equivalent to one mmHg. One inch is 2.54 cm and there are 10 mm per cm.

$$30.2 \text{ } in. \times 2.54 \text{ cm/}in. \times 10 \text{ mm/cm} \times 1 \text{ torr/1 mmHg} = 767 \text{ torr}$$

(b) 767 torr $\times$ 1 atm/760 torr = 1.01 atm
(c) 1.02×10^5 Pa $\times$ 1 kPa/1000 Pa = 102 kPa
(d) 102 kPa $\times$ 1 bar/100 kPa = 1.02 bar

Problem 6.3 Convert 98.7 kPa to atm, torr, and bars.

Solution 6.3

$$98.7 \text{ kPa} \times 1 \text{ atm/101.3 kPa} = 0.974 \text{ atm}$$
$$0.974 \text{ atm} \times 760 \text{ torr/1 atm} = 740 \text{ torr}$$
$$98.7 \text{ kPa} \times 1 \text{ bar/100 kPa} = 0.987 \text{ bar}$$

6.3 IDEAL GAS LAWS

**Pressure-
Volume
Relationship
(Boyle's Law)**

The volume of an ideal gas is inversely proportional to the applied pressure at constant temperature and number of moles. Robert Boyle (1627–1691) was the scientist who first proposed this relationship. Thus, the inverse relationship of the pressure and volume of an ideal gas is known as Boyle's Law. This law shows us that gases are compressible. Compressibility is a unique property of gases because liquids and solids are essentially incompressible.

MATHEMETICAL EXPRESSIONS OF BOYLE'S LAW

A mathematical equation that expresses Boyle's Law is

$$PV = k \tag{6.1}$$

where P is pressure, V is volume, and k is a proportionality constant. A more useful expression of Boyle's Law is as follows:

$$P_1 V_1 = P_2 V_2 \tag{6.2}$$

where P_1 and V_1 are the initial pressure and volume, respectively, and P_2 and V_2 are the final pressure and volume, respectively.

Problem 6.4   Calculate the final volume of Ne gas when the pressure on 375 mL He is increased from 428 torr to 1657 torr.

Solution 6.4   The initial volume, V_1, is 375 mL and the initial pressure, P_1, is 428 torr. The final pressure, P_2, is 1657 torr.

$$V_2 = V_1(P_1/P_2)$$
$$= 375 \text{ mL } (428 \text{ torr}/1657 \text{ torr}) = 96.9 \text{ mL}$$

**Temperature-
Volume
Relationship
(Charles' Law)**

Charles' Law states that the volume of an ideal gas is directly proportional to its Kelvin temperature at constant pressure and number of moles. A mathematical equation that expresses Charles' Law is

$$\frac{V}{T} = k \tag{6.3}$$

in which V is the volume, T is the Kelvin temperature, and k is a proportionality constant. Such an equation is that of a direct proportion. A more useful Charles' Law expression is as follows:

$$\frac{V_1}{T_1} = \frac{V_2}{T_2} \tag{6.4}$$

where V_1 and T_1 are the initial volume and Kelvin temperature, respectively, and V_2 and T_2 are the final volume and Kelvin temperature, respectively.

Problem 6.5   A 534-L balloon contains an ideal gas at 25.7°C. To what Celsius temperature would you need to cool the balloon to decrease its volume to 488 L?

Solution 6.5   Begin by changing the 25.7°C to 298.9 K. Then, rearrange and solve the Charles' Law equation, Eq. 6.4, for the final temperature, T_2. Then substitute the known values into the equation. This is accomplished as follows:

$$V_1/T_1 = V_2/T_2$$
$$T_2 = T_1(V_2/V_1)$$
$$= 298.9 \text{ K} \times 488 \text{ L}/534 \text{ L}$$
$$= 273 \text{ K} = 0°C$$

Problem 6.6   Calculate the final volume of a 178-mL gas sample of He when the temperature is decreased from 63.5°C to −155.3°C.

Solution 6.6   The initial volume, V_1, is 178 mL and the initial temperature, T_1, is 63.5°C. The final temperature, T_2, is −155.3°C. Begin by converting the Celsius temperatures to kelvins.

$$T_1 = 63.5°C + 273.2 = 336.7 \text{ K}$$
$$T_2 = -155.3°C + 273.2 = 117.9 \text{ K}$$

Then apply Eq. 6.4 to obtain the final volume of He.

$$V_2 = V_1(T_2/T_1)$$
$$= 178 \text{ mL} \times (117.9 \text{ K}/336.7 \text{ K}) = 62.3 \text{ mL}$$

Mole-Volume Relationship (Avogadro's Law)

Avogadro's Law states that the volume of an ideal gas is directly proportional to the number of moles of gas, at constant pressure and temperature. This relationship is called Avogadro's Law to honor Amadeo Avogadro (1776–1856) who first hypothesized that gas samples at the same temperature and pressure had equal numbers of particles. A mathematical expression of Avogadro's Law is

$$\frac{V}{n} = k \tag{6.5}$$

in which V is the volume, n is the number of moles, and k is the proportionality constant. As was derived for Boyle's and Charles' Laws, Avogadro's Law can be expressed in terms of the initial and final volumes and moles.

$$\frac{V_1}{n_1} = \frac{V_2}{n_2} \tag{6.6}$$

In this equation, V_1 and n_1 are the initial conditions and V_2 and n_2 are the final conditions.

Problem 6.7   A 0.105-g sample of He gas enclosed in a cylinder under a piston occupies 668 cm^3 at 25°C. If 0.0310 g He is removed at constant temperature and pressure, what is the new volume of the cylinder?

Solution 6.7   Initially, 0.105 g He is present and after removing 0.031 g, 0.074 g He (0.105 g − 0.0310 g) remains. To obtain the final volume, convert the initial and final masses to moles.

$$n_1 = 0.105 \text{ g He} \times 1 \text{ mol He}/4.00 \text{ g He} = 0.0263 \text{ mol He}$$
$$n_2 = 0.074 \text{ g He} \times 1 \text{ mol He}/4.00 \text{ g He} = 0.018 \text{ mol He}$$

Rearrange Eq. 6.6 and solve for the final volume, V_2, and substitute the known values into the equation.

$$V_1/n_1 = V_2/n_2$$
$$V_2 = V_1 \times n_2/n_1$$
$$= 668 \text{ cm}^3 \times 0.018 \text{ mol He}/0.0263 \text{ mol He} = 4.6 \times 10^2 \text{ cm}^3$$

RESTATEMENT OF AVOGADRO'S LAW

The most important aspect of Avogadro's Law is that the volumes of ideal gases are equal if they contain the same number of moles of particles, at constant temperature and pressure. Therefore, a molar volume, the volume of one mole of gas, may be expressed for any ideal gas at a fixed set of conditions. For convenience, a standard set of conditions of 1.00 atm and 273 K are used for the ideal gas laws. These conditions are known as standard temperature and pressure, STP. At STP conditions, 1.00 mole of an ideal gas occupies 22.4 L (22.4 L/mol).

MOLAR VOLUME AS A CONVERSION FACTOR

The molar volume of an ideal gas, 22.4 L/mol, is a conversion factor that allows us to calculate volume and mole relationships for gases.

Problem 6.8   Calculate the number of moles of Ne gas in a 1.00 L container at 273 K and 1.00 atm (STP).

Solution 6.8

$$n_{Ne} = 1.00 \text{ L} \times 1.00 \text{ mol}/22.4 \text{ L} = 0.0446 \text{ mol}$$

Problem 6.9   What volume does a 8.40-g sample of Ar gas occupy at STP?

Solution 6.9   Knowing that the molar mass of Ar is 40.0 g/mol and that one mole occupies 22.4 L, the problem is solved as follows.

$$V = 8.40 \text{ g Ar} \times 1.00 \text{ mol Ar}/40.0 \text{ g} \times 22.4 \text{ L Ar}/1.00 \text{ mol Ar} = 4.70 \text{ L Ar}$$

Ideal Gas Equation

Boyle's, Charles', and Avogadro's Laws may be combined into one relationship that expresses the pressure, volume, temperature, and moles of an ideal gas. This equation is as follows

$$PV = nRT \tag{6.7}$$

where P is the pressure, V is the volume, n is the number of moles, R is the ideal gas constant, and T is the temperature.

IDEAL GAS CONSTANT

The proportionality constant, R, in Eq. 6.7 is the ideal gas constant. Its numerical value may be calculated from the molar volume of ideal gases.

Problem 6.10   At STP conditions of 1.000 atm and 273.15 K, the volume occupied by 1.000 mole of an ideal gas is 22.414 L. Calculate the value of the ideal gas constant in (L·atm)/(mol·K) and (L·kPA)/(mol·K).

Solution 6.10   Divide both sides of Eq. 6.7 by nT to obtain the following equation and substitute the known values into the equation.

$$R = PV/nT$$
$$= (1.000 \text{ atm} \times 22.414 \text{ L})/(1.000 \text{ mol} \times 273.15 \text{ K}) = 0.08206 \text{ (L·atm)}/\text{(mol·K)}$$

To convert these units to (L·kPa)/(mol·K), multiply by 101.325 kPa/1 atm.

$$R = 0.08206 \text{ (L·atm)}/\text{(mol·K)} \times 101.325 \text{ kPa/atm} = 8.314 \text{ (L·kPa)}/\text{(mol·K)}$$

IDEAL GAS CONSTANT EXPRESSED IN TERMS OF JOULES

When pressure is multiplied by volume, $P \times V$, units of energy result. For example, L multiplied by kPa equals the number of joules of energy. Therefore, the ideal gas constant may be expressed as 8.314 J/(mol K).

Combined Gas Law

All of the ideal gas laws are embodied in the ideal gas equation. If the initial conditions of an ideal gas are P_1, V_1, T_1 and n_1, and the final set of conditions is P_2, V_2, T_2 and n_2, then the following equation is obtained.

$$\frac{P_1 V_1}{T_1 n_1} = \frac{P_2 V_2}{T_2 n_2} \tag{6.8}$$

Problem 6.11   Show that the combined gas law includes Boyle's, Charles', and Avogadro's Laws.

Solution 6.11   If the number of moles and the temperature are constant ($n_1 = n_2$ and $T_1 = T_2$), the n and T terms drop from the equation, yielding the Boyle's Law equation.

$$\frac{P_1 V_1}{\cancel{T_1}\,\cancel{n_1}} = \frac{P_2 V_2}{\cancel{T_2}\,\cancel{n_2}}$$
$$P_1 V_1 = P_2 V_2$$

If the moles and the pressure are constant ($n_1 = n_2$ and $P_1 = P_2$), the n and P terms drop from the equation, leaving the equation for Charles' Law.

$$\frac{P_1 \cancel{V_1}}{T_1 \cancel{n_1}} = \frac{P_2 \cancel{V_2}}{T_2 \cancel{n_2}}$$
$$\frac{V_1}{T_1} = \frac{V_2}{T_2}$$

Holding the pressure and temperature constant ($P_1 = P_2$ and $T_1 = T_2$) yields the equation for Avogadro's Law.

$$\frac{\cancel{P_1} V_1}{\cancel{T_1} n_1} = \frac{\cancel{P_2} V_2}{\cancel{T_2} n_2}$$
$$\frac{V_1}{n_1} = \frac{V_2}{n_2}$$

Simplified Combined Gas Law

Expressing the ideal gas equation as

$$\frac{P_1 V_1}{T_1 n_1} = \frac{P_2 V_2}{T_2 n_2}$$

allows us to calculate the final conditions of an ideal gas, given the initial conditions or vice versa. If the moles of the ideal gas remain constant, the combined gas law equation simplifies to its most common form.

$$\frac{P_1 V_1}{T_1} = \frac{P_2 V_2}{T_2} \tag{6.9}$$

Problem 6.12   A sample of O_2 gas occupies 2.64 L at 93.8 kPa and 267 K. What volume does the O_2 occupy at STP conditions?

Solution 6.12

$$\frac{P_1 V_1}{T_1 \cancel{n_1}} = \frac{P_2 V_2}{T_2 \cancel{n_2}}$$

$$\frac{P_1 V_1}{T_1} = \frac{P_2 V_2}{T_2}$$

Next, rearrange Eq. 6.9 and solve for V_2, the final volume of the O_2. To accomplish this, divide both sides of the equation by P_2 and multiply both sides by T_2. The following equation results after grouping the P and T terms.

$$V_2 = V_1 \left(\frac{P_1}{P_2}\right) \left(\frac{T_2}{T_1}\right)$$

STP conditions for ideal gases are 1 atm or 101.3 kPa and 273 K. Hence, the final pressure, P_2, and temperature, T_2, are 101.3 kPa and 273 K, respectively.

$$V_2 = 2.64 \text{ L} \times 93.8 \text{ kPa}/101.3 \text{ kPa} \times 273 \text{ K}/267 \text{ K} = 2.50 \text{ L } O_2$$

Calculating P, V, n, and T with the Ideal Gas Equation

The ideal gas equation may be used to solve for any of the four variable quantities, knowing the values of the other three variables.

Problem 6.13 Nitrogen gas, N_2, is the most abundant gas in our atmosphere. What pressure in torr does 458 g N_2 exert in a 43.9-L cylinder at 21.9° C?

Solution 6.13 First, solve the ideal gas equation, Eq. 6.7, for the unknown quantity, P.

$$P = nRT/V$$

Before substituting the values into the equation, convert the Celsius temperature to kelvin and the mass of N_2 to moles.

$$K = 21.9°C + 273.2 = 295.1 \text{ K}$$

$$n_{N_2} = 458 \text{ g } N_2 \times 1 \text{ mol } N_2/28.0 \text{ g } N_2 = 16.4 \text{ mol } N_2$$

Finally, substitute the known values into Eq. 6.7 and solve for P. To calculate the pressure in torr, use 0.0821 (L·atm)/(mol·K) as the value for R and then convert the resulting pressure in atmospheres to torr, using 760 torr/atm. Always check to see that all units cancel except the desired units.

$$P = nRT/V$$
$$= (16.4 \text{ mol} \times 0.0821 \text{ L·atm/mol·K} \times 295.1 \text{ K})/43.9 \text{ L}$$
$$= 9.05 \text{ atm}$$
$$= 9.05 \text{ atm} \times 760 \text{ torr/atm} = 6.88 \times 10^3 \text{ torr } N_2$$

Problem 6.14 Chlorine gas, Cl_2, is a toxic greenish gas that has many important industrial uses. A 115.7-L cylinder contains Cl_2 gas at 29.1°C and 251.8 kPa. What is the mass in grams of Cl_2 in the cylinder?

Solution 6.14 To calculate the mass in grams of the Cl_2 in the cylinder, first use the ideal gas equation to find the moles of Cl_2 and then convert to grams, using the molar mass, 70.90 g Cl_2/mol. Begin by solving the ideal gas equation for n.

$$n = PV/RT$$

Because the pressure is given in kPa, use 8.314 (L·kPa)/(mol·K) as the value for R. Before substituting into the equation, convert 29.1°C to 302.3 K.

$$n = PV/RT$$
$$= (251.8 \text{ Pa} \times 115.7 \text{ L})/(8.314 \text{ L·kPa/mol·K} \times 302.3 \text{ K}) = 11.59 \text{ mol Cl}_2$$

Finally, convert the mol Cl_2 to g, using the molar mass of Cl_2, 70.90 g Cl_2/mol.

$$11.59 \text{ mol Cl}_2 \times 70.90 \text{ g Cl}_2/\text{mol Cl}_2 = 821.7 \text{ g Cl}_2$$

USING THE IDEAL GAS EQUATION TO SOLVE FOR MOLAR MASS

The ideal gas equation may be modified to calculate the molar mass of a gas. To calculate the number of moles of an ideal gas, divide its mass, m, in grams by its molar mass (MM), g/mol.

$$n = m/MM$$

Thus, m/MM can be substituted into the ideal gas equation for n.

$$PV = nRT$$
$$PV = \frac{m}{MM}RT$$

and solve the equation for MM

$$MM = \frac{mRT}{PV} \qquad (6.10)$$

Problem 6.15 A 61.5-g sample of an unknown gas occupies 37.2 L at 313 K and 0.924 atm. What is the molar mass of the unknown gas?

Solution 6.15 Substitute the known values into Eq. 6.10 as follows to obtain the molar mass.

$$MM = \frac{gRT}{PV}$$
$$= \frac{61.5 \text{ g} \times 0.0821 \text{ L·atm/mol·K} \times 313 \text{ K}}{0.924 \text{ atm} \times 37.2 \text{ L}} = 46.0 \text{ g/mol}$$

Problem 6.16 An evacuated 94.751-g glass bulb is filled with a colorless gas. The combined mass of the glass bulb and gas is 95.787 g. To obtain the volume of the flask, it is filled with distilled water. The mass of the flask plus the water is 602.2 g. The pressure of the gas is 833.0 torr and its temperature is 15.9°C. If the density of water is 0.99990 g/cm^3 at 15.9°C, calculate the molar mass of the gas.

Solution 6.16 To calculate the molar mass of the gas, substitute into Eq. 6.10. Thus, the mass, volume, pressure, and temperature of the gas are needed. The pressure and temperature are known, but they must be converted to the proper units to use the ideal gas constant. Additionally, the mass and volume of the gas must be calculated.

Begin by calculating the mass of the gas, m. Subtract the mass of the evacuated flask from the mass of the gas plus the flask.

$$m = 95.787 \text{ g} - 94.751 \text{ g} = 1.036 \text{ g}$$

To obtain the volume of the gas, V_{gas}, calculate the volume of flask. The mass of the water needed to fill the flask is obtained by subtracting the mass of the empty flask from the mass of the flask and water. The volume of the water is then calculated from its density. The volume of the gas equals the volume of the water.

$$\text{mass of } H_2O = 602.2 \text{ g} - 94.751 \text{ g} = 507.5 \text{ g}$$
$$V_{gas} = V_{H_2O}$$
$$= 507.5 \text{ g } H_2O \times 1 \text{ mL } H_2O/0.99990 \text{ g } H_2O$$
$$= 507.6 \text{ mL} \times 1 \text{ L}/1000 \text{ mL} = 0.5076 \text{ L}$$

Convert the pressure in torr to atm and the temperature in °C to K.

$$P = 833.0 \text{ torr} \times 1 \text{ atm}/760 \text{ torr} = 1.096 \text{ atm}$$
$$T = 15.9°C + 273.2 = 289.1 \text{ K}$$

Finally, substitute the values into the ideal gas equation and solve for the molar mass.

$$MM = mRT/PV$$
$$= \frac{1.036 \text{ g} \times 0.08206 \text{ L·atm/K·mol} \times 289.1 \text{ K}}{1.096 \text{ atm} \times 0.5076 \text{ L}}$$
$$= 44.18 \text{ g/mol}$$

USING THE IDEAL GAS EQUATION TO SOLVE FOR GAS DENSITY

The density, d, of a gas is the ratio of its mass, m, to volume, V.

$$d = \frac{m}{V}$$

Therefore, m/V can be obtained by multiplying both sides of the equation by P/RT:

$$\frac{P}{RT}MM = \frac{mR\!\!\!/\,T\!\!\!\!/}{R\!\!\!/\,V}\frac{R\!\!\!/}{R\!\!\!/\,T\!\!\!\!/}$$

Thus,

$$d = \frac{m}{V} = \frac{MM \, P}{RT} \tag{6.11}$$

Problem 6.17 Radon gas is a radioactive gas that has been found to cause lung cancer in people. Calculate the density of Rn gas at 298 K and 755 torr.

Solution 6.17 The density of Rn can most easily be found by substituting into Eq. 6.11. Using 0.0821 (L·atm)/(mol·K) as the ideal gas constant means that 755 torr should be converted to atm with the conversion factor 760 torr/1 atm.

$$P = 755 \text{ torr} \times 1 \text{ atm}/760 \text{ torr} = 0.993 \text{ atm}$$

Then, substitute the known values into the equation and solve for density, d.

$$d = MM \, P/RT$$
$$= 222 \text{ g/mol} \times 0.993 \text{ atm}/(0.0821 \text{ L·atm/mol·K} \times 298 \text{ K})$$
$$= 9.01 \text{ g/L}$$

6.4   GASEOUS MIXTURES

Dalton's Law of Partial Pressures

John Dalton was the first scientist to show that the total pressure of a gaseous mixture equals the sum of the partial pressures of each gas in the mixture. Today this statement is called Dalton's Law of Partial Pressures. A partial pressure is the pressure exerted by one gas in a mixture of gases. Mathematically, Dalton's Law is expressed as follows

$$P_{total} = P_1 + P_2 + P_3 + P_4 \cdots \tag{6.12}$$

in which P_{total} is the total pressure and P_1 to P_4 are the partial pressures of the gases in the mixture.

Problem 6.18   People exhale a mixture of $N_2(g)$, $O_2(g)$, $CO_2(g)$, and $H_2O(g)$. If the partial pressures of N_2, O_2, and CO_2 in exhaled air are 565, 120, and 28 torr, respectively, and the total pressure is 760 torr, what is the partial pressure of water vapor, P_{H_2O}, in exhaled air?

Solution 6.18   The total pressure of this gaseous mixture is calculated as follows.

$$P_{total} = P_{N_2} + P_{O_2} + P_{CO_2} + P_{H_2O}$$

Therefore, substitute the known values into the equation and solve for the unknown value, P_{H_2O}.

$$760 \text{ torr} = 565 \text{ torr} + 120 \text{ torr} + 28 \text{ torr} + P_{H_2O}$$
$$P_{H_2O} = 760 \text{ torr} - (565 + 120 + 28) \text{ torr} = 47 \text{ torr}$$

Pressure-Mole Relationship of Gaseous Mixtures

The pressure of a pure gas depends on the moles of gas present. The same is true for a mixture of gases. An increase in the moles of any of the gases in the mixture causes an increase in the total pressure, if the temperature and volume remain constant. This can be expressed as follows

$$P_{total} = \left(\frac{RT}{V}\right) n_{total} \tag{6.13}$$

in which P_{total} is the total pressure of the gaseous mixture, RT/V is a constant, and n_{total} is the total moles of gas particles.

Problem 6.19   A gaseous mixture of 5.07 g Ar and 9.22 g Kr is in a 6.23-L vessel at 283.8 K. What is the total pressure, P_{total}, of the mixture?

Solution 6.19   First, calculate the number of moles of each gas

$$n_{Ar} = 5.07 \text{ g Ar} \times 1 \text{ mol Ar}/39.95 \text{ g} = 0.127 \text{ mol Ar}$$
$$n_{Kr} = 9.22 \text{ g Kr} \times 1 \text{ mol Kr}/83.80 \text{ g} = 0.110 \text{ mol Kr}$$

Then, substitute the known values into the ideal gas equation and solve for P_{total}.

$$P_{total} = [(0.0821 \text{ L·atm/mol·K} \times 283.8 \text{ K})/6.23 \text{ L}] \times (0.127 \text{ mol Ar} + 0.110 \text{ mol Kr})$$
$$= 0.886 \text{ atm}$$

Mole Fractions and Gaseous Mixtures

When working with gaseous mixtures in which the moles of gases are known, it is convenient to calculate the mole fraction, X, of each component before solving for the partial pressures. The mole fraction of a gas, X_{gas}, in a gaseous mixture is the ratio of the moles of that gas, n_{gas}, to the total number of moles, n_{total}.

$$X_{gas} = \frac{n_{gas}}{n_{total}}$$

For example, the mole fractions for N_2 and O_2 in a gaseous mixture of N_2 and O_2 are as follows.

$$X_{N_2} = n_{N_2}/n_{total}$$
$$X_{O_2} = n_{O_2}/n_{total}$$

Because mole fractions are mole ratios, the units cancel. Mole fractions are one of the few unitless numbers that are encountered in beginning chemistry. The sum of the mole fractions for a gaseous mixture is 1 because the sum of the parts equals the whole.

$$X_{N_2} + X_{O_2} = 1$$
$$\frac{n_{N_2}}{n_{total}} + \frac{n_{O_2}}{n_{total}} = 1$$

To calculate the partial pressures of N_2 and O_2 in the mixture, multiply each mole fraction by the total pressure of the mixture.

$$P_{N_2} = X_{N_2} \times P_{total}$$
$$P_{O_2} = X_{O_2} \times P_{total}$$

Therefore the total pressure of the mixture is calculated as follows.

$$P_{total} = P_{N_2} + P_{O_2} = (X_{N_2} \times P_{total}) + (X_{O_2} \times P_{total})$$

Problem 6.20 A mixture of cyclopropane, C_3H_6, and oxygen, O_2, is a general anesthetic in some medical procedures. Calculate the partial pressures of cyclopropane, $P_{C_3H_6}$, and the partial pressure of oxygen, P_{O_2}, in a mixture that has 0.235 mol C_3H_6 and 0.946 mol O_2 in a 8.11-L container at 298.6 K.

Solution 6.20 First, calculate the total pressure, P_{total}, of the mixture of C_3H_6 and O_2.

$$
\begin{aligned}
P_{total} &= RT/V \times n_{total} \\
&= RT/V \times (n_{C_3H_6} + n_{O_2}) \\
&= ((0.08206 \text{ L·atm/mol·K} \times 298.6 \text{ K})/8.11 \text{ L}) \times (0.235 \text{ mol } C_3H_6 + 0.946 \text{ mol } O_2) \\
&= 3.568 \text{ atm}
\end{aligned}
$$

Then, calculate the mole fraction of cyclopropane, $X_{C_3H_6}$.

$$
\begin{aligned}
X_{C_3H_6} &= n_{C_3H_6}/n_{total} \\
&= 0.235 \text{ mol } C_3H_6/(0.235 \text{ mol } C_3H_6 + 0.946 \text{ mol } O_2) = 0.199
\end{aligned}
$$

Finally, calculate the partial pressure of C_3H_6.

$$
\begin{aligned}
P_{C_3H_6} &= X_{C_3H_6} \times P_{total} \\
&= 0.199 \times 3.568 \text{ atm} = 0.710 \text{ atm } C_3H_6
\end{aligned}
$$

In this mixture the partial pressure of C_3H_6 is 0.710 atm. To calculate the partial pressure of O_2 just subtract the partial pressure of C_3H_6 from the total pressure.

$$3.57 \text{ atm} - 0.710 \text{ atm } C_3H_6 = 2.86 \text{ atm } O_2.$$

6.5   GASES IN CHEMICAL REACTIONS

Law of Combining Volumes (Gay-Lussac's Law)

Gay Lussac's Law of Combining Volumes states that the volumes of gases that combine in chemical reactions can be expressed as ratios of whole numbers, if the pressure and temperature remain constant.

Problem 6.21   Consider the following reaction.

$$N_2(g) + 3H_2(g) \rightarrow 2NH_3(g)$$

(a) What is the volume relationships in this reaction? (b) What volume of H_2 is needed to combine exactly with 6.0 L N_2 and what volume of NH_3 results?

Solution 6.21

(a) One volume of N_2 combines with three volumes of H_2 and produces two volumes of NH_3.

(b) Because 3.0 L of H_2 combines with each 1.0 L of N_2, an 18-L sample of H_2 is needed.

$$6.0 \text{ L } N_2 \times 3 \text{ L } H_2/1 \text{ L } N_2 = 18 \text{ L } H_2$$

Similarly, the equation tells us that 2.0 L NH_3 result for each 1.0 L of N_2. Thus, a 12-L sample of NH_3 results.

$$6.0 \text{ L } N_2 \times 2 \text{ L } NH_3/1 \text{ L } N_2 = 12 \text{ L } NH_3$$

Problem 6.22   The complete combustion of butane, C_4H_{10}, produces $CO_2(g)$ and $H_2O(g)$. If the pressure and temperature remain constant, what volumes of $CO_2(g)$ and $H_2O(g)$ form when 4.58 L C_4H_{10} undergoes combustion?

Solution 6.22   A complete combustion reaction requires an ample supply of O_2. Therefore, the balanced equation for the reaction is

$$C_4H_{10}(g) + 13/2O_2(g) \rightarrow 4CO_2(g) + 5H_2O(g)$$

The equation tells us that 4 L CO_2 and 5 L H_2O result per 1 L C_4H_{10} that undergoes combustion. Then, use the factor-label method to calculate the final volumes.

$$4.58 \text{ L } C_4H_{10} \times 4 \text{ L } CO_2/1 \text{ L } C_4H_{10} = 18.3 \text{ L } CO_2$$
$$4.58 \text{ L } C_4H_{10} \times 5 \text{ L } H_2O/1 \text{ L } C_4H_{10} = 22.9 \text{ L } H_2O$$

Monitoring Gas-Phase Reactions

The progress of reactions that consume or produce gases may be monitored by measuring the pressure of the gas or gaseous mixture. Recall that attaching a manometer to the reaction vessel allows us to measure the pressure of the gases produced.

Problem 6.23   Consider the following gas-phase reaction.

$$2CO(g) + O_2(g) \rightarrow 2CO_2(g)$$

(a) What happens to the total pressure as the reaction proceeds? (b) What pressure change occurs when 2.0 atm $CO(g)$ mixes with 1.0 atm $O_2(g)$ and the reaction is stopped after 1.0 atm $CO_2(g)$ forms?

Solution 6.23

    (a) Because three moles of reactant molecules (2 mol CO + 1 mol O_2) produce two moles of product molecules (2 mol CO_2), the total pressure in the reaction vessel decreases as $CO_2(g)$ forms.

    (b) The equation shows that one mole of CO and 0.50 mol $O_2(g)$ produce 1.0 mol $CO_2(g)$. Therefore, the final reaction mixture of gases has 1.0 atm $CO_2(g)$, 1.0 atm $CO(g)$, and 0.50 atm $O_2(g)$, which exerts a total pressure of 2.5 atm.

$$P_{total} = P_{CO} + P_{O_2} + P_{CO_2}$$
$$= 1.0 \text{ atm} + 0.50 \text{ atm} + 1.0 \text{ atm} = 2.5 \text{ atm}$$

The initial pressure is 3.0 atm (2.0 atm + 1.0 atm); hence, a decrease of 0.5 atm occurs when 1.0 atm $CO_2(g)$ forms.

Problem 6.24 $O_2(g)$ and $NO_2(g)$ combine to produce $NO_2(g)$ as follows.

$$2NO(g) + O_2(g) \rightarrow 2NO_2(g)$$

A 1.98-L reaction vessel is filled with a mixture of NO and O_2 to a pressure of 4.33 atm at 310 K. The reaction is allowed to continue until the total pressure decreases to 4.00 atm. (a) What is the final partial pressure of NO_2? (b) What mass of NO_2 is in the final mixture?

Solution 6.24   (a) Because the total pressures are known and not the initial and final partial pressures, algebra is used to calculate the partial pressures. Before the reaction begins, let's represent the initial partial pressures of NO and O_2 as P_{NO} and P_{O_2}, respectively. Before the reaction occurs no NO_2 is present. If $2x$ equals the partial pressure of NO_2 produced in the final mixture, then the final partial pressures of NO and O_2 are $P_{NO} - 2x$ and $P_{O_2} - x$.

	$2N_2 +$	$O_2 \rightarrow$	$2NO_2$
Before reaction	P_{NO}	P_{O_2}	0
After reaction	$P_{NO} - 2x$	$P_{O_2} - x$	$2x$

The stoichiometry of the reaction shows that for each $2x$ atm NO_2 produced, $2x$ atm NO and x atm O_2 are lost because the pressure is directly related to the number of moles.

    The total pressure of the initial gas mixture, 4.33 atm, equals the sum of the partial pressures of the gases.

$$P_{total} = P_{NO} + P_{O_2} + P_{NO_2}$$
$$4.33 \text{ atm} = P_{NO} + P_{O_2} + 0$$

In a similar manner, the total pressure of the final gas mixture, 4.00 atm, equals the sum of the partial pressures.

$$P_{total} = P_{NO} + P_{O_2} + P_{NO_2}$$
$$4.00 \text{ atm} = (P_{NO} - 2x) + (P_{O_2} - x) + 2x = (P_{NO} + P_{O_2}) - x$$

The above equation tells us that the sum of the initial partial pressures of NO and O_2, $P_{NO} + P_{O_2}$, equals 4.33 atm, so it can be substituted into the equation for $P_{NO} + P_{O_2}$.

$$4.00 \text{ atm} = 4.33 \text{ atm} - x$$
$$x = 0.33 \text{ atm}$$

Because the final pressure of NO_2 equals $2x$, the partial pressure of NO_2 is 2×0.33 atm or 0.66 atm. (b) Calculate the mass of NO_2 from the ideal gas equation

$$m = (MM\ PV)/RT$$
$$= \frac{46.0 \text{ g } NO_2/1 \text{ mol } NO_2 \times 0.66 \text{ atm } \times 1.98 \text{ L}}{0.0821 \text{ L·atm/mol·K } \times 3.10 \times 10^2 \text{K}}$$
$$= 2.4 \text{ g } NO_2$$

6.6 KINETIC-MOLECULAR THEORY OF GASES

The kinetic-molecular theory explains the observed behavior of gases in terms of the particles (atoms and molecules) that compose them.

Qualitative Aspects of the Kinetic-Molecular Theory

The kinetic-molecular theory of ideal gases is based on five fundamental assumptions. Each assumption applies to gases at relatively high temperatures and low pressures. The assumptions of the kinetic-molecular theory are listed below.

1. The particles (atoms or molecules) in gases move rapidly and randomly in all directions throughout their volume. Gas particles move in straight lines until they collide with other particles or the walls of their container.
2. The volume occupied by the gas particles is negligible with respect to the volume of the container. A gas consists mainly of empty space.
3. Particles in a gas do not influence other particles except when they collide.
4. Elastic collisions occur among gas particles and the walls of the container. An elastic collision is one in which kinetic energy is not lost. Hence, the total energy of the colliding bodies after the collision equals their total energy before the collision.
5. The average kinetic energy of the molecules in an ideal gas is proportional to their Kelvin temperature. At a specific Kelvin temperature, all gases have the same average kinetic energy.

Quantitative Aspects of the Kinetic-Molecular Theory

MOVEMENT OF IDEAL GAS PARTICLES

Let's consider a gas sample containing N molecules in which each molecule has a mass of m. These gas molecules are introduced into a cubic container that has a volume of l^3, which means that each side of the container has a length of l. To simplify this derivation, let's assume that $\frac{1}{3}$ of the molecules ($\frac{1}{3} N$) move along the x axis, $\frac{1}{3}$ move along the y axis, and the remaining $\frac{1}{3}$ move along the z axis. Actually the molecules move in all possible directions, but our assumption is valid because the motion of molecules is random and no direction is favored over another. Therefore the motions of all molecules have an x, y, and z component, which when taken together gives $\frac{1}{3}$ along the x axis, $\frac{1}{3}$ along the y axis, and $\frac{1}{3}$ along the z axis.

FORCE AND PRESSURE EXERTED BY IDEAL GAS PARTICLES

To obtain the pressure exerted by the gas, the force per unit area (P = force/area), one can calculate the pressure exerted on one wall because a gas exerts an equal pressure on all of its walls. Let us consider the force of impact by a molecule that moves back and forth along the x axis on the designated wall. The force of impact equals the change in momentum, $m\Delta u$, per time interval, Δt.

$$f = \frac{m\Delta u}{\Delta t} \tag{6.14}$$

In Eq. 6.14, Δu is the change in velocity and Δt is the time interval. To obtain the change in momentum, realize that before the molecule collides with the wall it has a velocity of u and after it collides it changes direction by 180° and travels at the same velocity because it undergoes an elastic collision with the wall. Thus, its new velocity is $-u$. If its initial velocity is u and final velocity is $-u$, then its change in velocity, Δu, is $2u$. Hence, the resulting change in momentum ($m\Delta u$) is $m \times 2u$ or $2mu$.

The time interval for the collision is determined from the distance traveled and velocity of the molecule. When a distance is divided by its velocity, the time interval is obtained.

Time interval = distance traveled/velocity

After the molecule hits the wall, it travels a distance of l and hits the other wall and then travels back a distance of l before striking the wall again. Therefore, the distance traveled between impacts with the wall of interest is $2l$. Because its velocity is u, the time interval between collisions is $2l/u$.

To obtain the force of impact, use Eq. 6.14. Divide the change in momentum, $m\Delta u$, by the time interval, $2l/u$.

$$f = m\,\Delta u/\Delta t$$
$$= 2mu/(2l/u) = mu^2/l$$

Because $N/3$ molecules strike the wall, the total force exerted, f_{total}, by the molecules is calculated as follows.

$$f_{total} = \frac{N}{3} \times \frac{mu_a^2}{l}$$

In this expression u_a is the average velocity of the molecules. The average velocity is used because of the wide range of velocities in a gas sample. Some of the molecules have high velocities and others have low velocities, and most travel at velocities near the average.

PRESSURE-VOLUME RELATIONSHIP OF IDEAL GAS PARTICLES

To calculate the pressure, P, exerted by the gas molecules divide the total force of the molecules, f_{total}, ($N/3 \times mu_a^2/l$) by the area of the wall, l^2.

$$P = f_{total}/\text{area}$$
$$= (N/3 \times mu_a^2/l)/l_2 = N/3 \times mu_a^2/l^3$$

In the denominator of the equation is l^3 or the volume, V, of the cube. Therefore, V can be substituted for l^3. Then the equation is rearranged to obtain the product PV.

$$P = N/3 \times mu_a^2/l^3$$
$$= N/3 \times mu_a^2/V$$
$$PV = 1/3\,Nmu_a^2 \tag{6.15}$$

Equation 6.15 begins to look like the ideal gas equation in that the product $P \times V$ equals a constant because the product of N, m, and u_a^2 is a constant, k. Recall that $PV = k$ is one way to express Boyle's Law.

DERIVATION OF THE IDEAL GAS LAW

One form of the ideal gas equation can be derived that relates PV to the average kinetic energy of the molecules, $E_{kinetic}$. Multiplying both sides of Eq. 6.15 by 2/2 gives $PV = 2/3Nmu_a^2$ or $PV = 2/6N \times 1/2mu_a^2$. The average kinetic energy, $E_{kinetic}$, equals $1/2mu_a^2$. Thus, the ideal gas equation may be expressed as follows.

$$PV = 2/3NE_{kinetic} \tag{6.16}$$

The average kinetic energy of the molecules is proportional to the Kelvin temperature; thus,

$$E_{kinetic} = k_1 T$$

The number of molecules in the gas sample, N, is proportional to the moles of molecules, n; therefore,

$$N = k_2 n$$

Substituting these values into our equation gives the following.

$$PV = 2/3(k_2 n)(k_1 T)$$

After grouping our constants the equation becomes

$$PV = (2/3k_1 k_2)nT \tag{6.17}$$

If the ideal gas constant, R, is set to equal the constant $2/3k_1 k_2$, then the most familiar form of the ideal gas equation results.

$$PV = nRT \tag{6.18}$$

This shows that the ideal gas equation can be derived from the assumptions of the kinetic-molecular theory of gases. In other words, the kinetic-molecular theory can adequately explain the behavior of ideal gases.

6.7   MOLECULAR VELOCITIES AND GRAHAM'S LAW OF EFFUSION

Molecular Velocities

The kinetic-molecular theory allows us to calculate the molecule's average velocity in a gas sample. For a one-mole sample of an ideal gas ($n = 1$ mol), the ideal gas equation may be simplified to $PV = 1$ mol $\times RT$ or

$$PV = RT$$

An alternative way to express the ideal gas equation is in terms of the average kinetic energy of the molecules.

$$PV = 1/3N \times mu_a^2$$

In this equation, P is pressure, V is volume, N is the number of molecules, m is the mass of the molecules, and u_a is the average velocity of the molecules. If N equals one mole of molecules, then the product of the mass of one molecule, m, times Avogadro's number gives the molar mass, MM.

$$PV = 1/3 MM u_a^2$$

Because $PV = 1/3 MM u_a^2$ and $PV = RT$, then $1/3 MM u_a^2 = RT$. Solving for the average velocity, u_a, gives Eq. 6.19.

$$u_a = \sqrt{\frac{3RT}{MM}} \tag{6.19}$$

ROOT-MEAN-SQUARE VELOCITY OF GAS PARTICLES

In Eq. 6.19, u_a is the root-mean-square (rms) velocity. It is not just the average velocity of the molecules. What is the difference between the root-mean-square and the average velocity? The average or mean velocity, $u_{average}$, is calculated from the sum of the velocities, $\sum u$, divided by the total number of molecules, N.

$$u_{average} = \sum u/N$$

To find the root-mean-square velocity, u_a, take the square root of the sum of the velocities squared, $\sum u^2$, and divide by the total number of atoms, N.

$$u_a = \sqrt{\frac{\sum u^2}{N}}$$

Values for the rms velocity and the average velocity are not equal. For example, the rms velocity for 8.00, 15.0, 20.0, and 33.0 m/s is 21.1 m/s and the average velocity is 19.0 m/s.

Returning to Eq. 6.19

$$u_a = \sqrt{\frac{3RT}{MM}}$$

at a constant temperature the rms velocity, u_a, depends on the square root of the reciprocal of the molar mass, $1/MM$, of the gas. As the molar mass of the gas increases, the rms velocity decreases.

Problem 6.25   Compare the rms velocities of Kr and Xe molecules at 30.5°C.

Solution 6.25   Use Eq. 6.19 to calculate the rms velocity of molecules. The value of R to substitute into this equation is 8.314 J/(mol·K). Because 1 J equals 1 kg m^2/s^2, the molar mass must be converted to kg/mol so that the units cancel.

First, calculate the molar masses, MM, of Kr and Xe in kg/mol.

$$MM_{Kr} = 83.80 \text{ g Kr/mol} \times 1 \text{ kg/1000 g} = 0.08380 \text{ kg Kr/mol}$$

$$MM_{Xe} = 131.3 \text{ g Xe/mol} \times 1 \text{ kg/1000 g} = 0.1313 \text{ kg Xe/mol}$$

Then, convert the Celsius temperature 30.4°C to 303.6 K. Finally, substitute into Eq. 6.19 and solve for u_a.

$$u_a(Kr) = \sqrt{\frac{3 \times 8.134 \frac{kg\, m^2}{s^2} \times 303.6\, K}{0.08380\, kg/mol}} = 300.6\ m/s$$

$$u_a(Xe) = \sqrt{\frac{3 \times 8.134 \frac{kg\, m^2}{s^2} \times 303.6\, K}{0.1313\, kg/mol}} = 240.2\ m/s$$

Graham's Law
of Effusion

Effusion occurs when a gas leaks out of a container through a small opening into a vacuum. Effusion is closely related to diffusion, which occurs when one gas mixes with another one. The rate of effusion of a gas depends on the rms velocity of the molecules in a gas sample. However, the rms velocity is proportional to the square root of the reciprocal of its molar mass. Therefore, the effusion rate of a gas is proportional to the square root of the reciprocal of its molar mass.

MATHEMATICAL RELATIONSHIP OF GRAHAM'S LAW

Since the effusion rate is directly proportional to the rms velocities of the molecules then Graham's Law may be expressed as follows

$$\frac{rate_x}{rate_y} = \sqrt{\frac{MM_y}{MM_x}} \tag{6.20}$$

in which $rate_x$ and $rate_y$ represent the rates of effusion of x and y, respectively. In other words, Eq. 6.20 states that the ratio of the rates that two gases effuse under the same conditions is inversely proportional to the square root of the ratio of their molar masses.

Problem 6.26   An unknown gas effuses at a rate 0.632 times the rate of O_2. What is the molar mass of the unknown gas?

Solution 6.26   If x represents the unknown gas, then the ratio of the rates of effusion is 0.632 to 1

$$\frac{rate_x}{rate_{O_2}} = \frac{0.632}{1}$$

Substituting this ratio and the molar mass of O_2, 32.0 g/mol, into the Eq. 6.20 gives the following:

$$\frac{rate_x}{rate_{O_2}} = 0.632 = \sqrt{\frac{32.0 \ g/mol}{MM_x}}$$

To clear the square root from the equation, square both sides of the equation to obtain the following.

$$0.632^2 = 0.399 = 32.0 \ g/mol/MM_x$$

After solving for MM_x, we get 80.2 g/mol for the molar mass of x.

$$MM_x = 32.0 \ g/mol/0.399 = 80.2 \ g/mol$$

6.8   DEVIATIONS FROM IDEAL PROPERTIES–REAL GASES

Non-ideal
Properties of
Gases

The relationships and equations for ideal gases work reasonably well if the gases are at a sufficiently high temperature and low pressure. However, at low temperatures and high pressures, the results obtained from the ideal gas equations are not consistent with laboratory measurements.

The van der
Waals Equation

In 1873, the Dutch scientist Johannes van der Waals (1837-1923) modified the ideal gas equation so that it more closely predicts the properties of gases at high pressures and low temperatures. Today the modified form of the ideal gas equation is called the van der Waals equation. It is expressed as follows

$$\left(P_{obs} + a\left(\frac{n}{V}\right)^2\right)(V - nb) = nRT \tag{6.21}$$

where P_{obs} is the observed pressure, V is the volume of the container, n is the number of moles of gas, and a and b are the van der Waals constants that correct for deviations from ideality.

VAN DER WAALS PRESSURE CORRECTION FACTOR, *a*

The pressure correction constant, a, has the units of $L^2 atm/mol^2$. Molecules with larger values of a have stronger intermolecular forces than those with smaller values. In the equation, a is multiplied by $(n/V)^2$, a term related to the concentration (mol/L) of the gas molecules. At higher concentrations, stronger attractive interactions exist among molecules. Gaseous molecules interact and exert a lower pressure than is predicted with the ideal gas equation. Thus, the term $a(n/V)^2$ compensates for the observed decrease in pressure. In other words, the a(n/V)2 term corrects the observed pressure and makes it equal to the ideal pressure, P_{ideal}.

VAN DER WAALS VOLUME CORRECTION FACTOR, *b*

To correct the volume of a real gas, van der Waals introduced the constant b into his equation. Because real gases occupy some of the total volume of the gas, b corrects for this decrease in volume. Larger molecules have larger values for b, and smaller molecules have smaller values for b. Subtracting the term nb removes the portion of the total volume that is not available due to the finite volume of the molecules. Note that b is roughly related to the volume of one mole of the gas after it has liquefied.

Problem 6.27 (a) Use the van der Waals Equation to calculate the pressure exerted by 1.00 mol $CO_2(g)$ at 298 K that occupies 65.4 mL. (b) Compare the pressure predicted by the van der Waals Equation to the pressure obtained from the ideal gas equation for the same conditions and volume. The a and b values for CO_2 are 3.592 $L^2 atm/mol^2$ and 0.0427 L/mol, respectively.

Solution 6.27

(a) Because the value for the moles, n, equals 1.00, the van der Waals Equation is simplified to the following.

$$\left(P_{obs} + \frac{a}{V_2}\right)(V - b) = RT$$

To begin, algebraically rearrange the equation and solve for P. Divide both sides of the equation by $V - b$, and then subtract a/V^2 from both sides. This gives us the following equation.

$$P_{obs} = (RT/(V - b)) - a/V^2$$

Substitute the known values into the equation and solve for P.

$$P_{obs} = 0.08206 \text{ L·atm/mol·K} \times 298 \text{ K}/(0.0654 \text{ L} - 0.0427 \text{ L}))$$
$$-3.592 \text{ L}^2atm/mol^2/(0.0654 \text{ L})2$$

$$= 237 \text{ atm}$$

(b) The ideal gas equation is solved as follows.

$$P_{ideal} = nRT/V$$
$$= (1.00 \text{ mol} \times 0.08206 \text{ L·atm/mol·K} \times 298 \text{ K})/0.0654 \text{ L}$$
$$= 374 \text{ atm}$$

The ideal gas equation does not consider the attractive forces and the decreased volume. Thus, it gives a higher estimate than the van der Waals Equation.

Problem 6.28 (a) Use the ideal gas equation to calculate the volume occupied by 1.00 mol Cl_2 at 273 K and 175 atm. (b) Compare the volume occupied by Cl_2 predicted from the van der Waals Equation to that obtained from the ideal gas equation in part (a).

Solution 6.28

(a) Rearrange the ideal gas equation and substitute the known values into the equation.

$$PV_{ideal} = nRT$$
$$V = nRT/P$$
$$= (1.00 \text{ mol } Cl_2 \times 0.0821 \text{ L·atm/mol·K} \times 273 \text{ K})/175 \text{ atm}$$
$$= 0.128 \text{ L } Cl_2$$

(b) Express the van der Waals Equation as follows for the case when n equals 1 mole.

$$\left(P_{obs} + \frac{a}{V^2}\right)(V - b) = RT$$

The a and b values for Cl_2 are 6.49 L^2 atm/mol^2 and 0.0562 L/mol, respectively. The product RT is a constant that equals 22.4. Thus, the van der Waals Equation becomes

$$(175 \text{ atm} + 6.49 L^2 \text{ atm/mol}^2/V^2)(V \times 0.0562 \text{ L/mol}) = 22.4 \text{ L atm/mol}$$

It is a somewhat laborious task to solve the van der Waals Equation directly because of the V^2 term. However, it can be solved using the method of successive approximations. In this method, first make an initial prediction for the V^2 term and solve the equation for V. Then use the new value for V to calculate a second value of V^2, and so on. With each solution of the equation, the resulting approximated value of V is closer to the actual value of V. Let's begin our successive approximation by using the value predicted from the ideal gas equation, 0.128 L.

$$(175 + 6.49/0.128^2)(V - 0.0562) = 22.4$$
$$V = 0.0954 \text{ L}$$

For this problem, six more steps are needed to obtain the answer of 0.0719 L. As the approximation comes closer to the actual value, the deviation from the previous value becomes smaller. Fewer approximation steps would have been needed, if we had reasoned that the large value of a means that the volume decreases significantly as a result of attractive forces among Cl_2 molecules. Instead, we should have selected a smaller volume as a starting point. Note that the prediction from the ideal gas equation deviates 69.3% from the value predicted by the van der Waals Equation.

SUMMARY

G*as pressures of isolated samples are measured with a manometer and atmospheric pressure with a barometer. Torr, atm, and kPa are the units of gas pressure most often used.*

Boyle's Law states that the volume of an ideal gas is inversely proportional to its pressure at constant temperature and number of moles. Charles' Law states that the volume of a gas is directly proportional to the Kelvin temperature at constant pressure and number of moles. Avogadro's Law states that the volume of a gas is directly proportional to the moles of gas at constant temperature and pressure. Avogadro's Law implies that equal volumes of ideal gases have the same number of particles.

Combining the ideal gas laws gives the ideal gas equation, $PV = nRT$. Dalton's Law applies to mixtures of gases, and states that the total pressure of a gaseous mixture equals the sum of the partial pressures of its components. Finally, Gay-Lussac's Law of Combining Volumes states that the volumes of gases in reactions may be expressed as ratios of whole numbers, at constant temperature and pressure.

The kinetic-molecular theory explains the behavior of ideal gases in terms of the motions of the molecules that compose the gas. Five assumptions of the kinetic-molecular theory explain most of the ideal properties of gases. The essence of these assumptions is that the particles in ideal gases move rapidly and randomly throughout their volume without exerting forces on each other. Gas particles essentially occupy none of the total volume; thus, gases are mainly empty space. Collisions among gas particles and between gas particles and the walls of the container are elastic. A wide range of velocities is found for gas particles at a particular temperature, and the average kinetic energy of the particles is proportional to the Kelvin temperature.

At high temperatures and low pressures, gases exhibit properties that approach those of ideal gases. Ideal properties are those predicted by the ideal gas laws. As the temperature decreases and the pressure increases, the properties of gases deviate from the ideal. The van der Waals Equation is used to predict the properties of real gases.

CHAPTER 6 REVIEW EXERCISE

1. Convert 125.0 kPa to atm, torr, and bars.
2. The density of Hg is 13.6 g/cm^3 and the density of H_2O is 1.00 g/cm^3. What is the height, in m, of a column of H_2O needed to construct a barometer?
3. One bar is equivalent to 1×10^5 Pa (100 kPa). Convert each of the following to bars: (a) 233 kPa, (b) 1.34×10^3 Pa, (c) 1.00 atm
4. If the initial volume of an ideal gas is 39.5 mL at 810 torr, what volume does it occupy at 215 kPa?
5. An ideal gas initially occupies 74.95 mL at 25.3°C. What volume does it occupy at 83.1°C?
6. A sample of He(g) initially occupies 0.260 mL at 10.3°C. (a) At what Celsius temperature does the He occupy twice its initial volume? (b) At what Celsius temperature does the He occupy one-third its initial volume?
7. A student finds that a 0.510-g sample of Ne(g) occupies 495 mL. What volume would the Ne(g) occupy, if the student adds 0.250 g Ne at constant temperature and pressure?
8. Calculate the value of the ideal gas constant in each of the following sets of units. (a) (cm^3 atm)/(mol K), (b) (m^3 kPa)/(mol K), (c) (dm^3 torr)/(mol K)
9. A sample of Ar gas occupies 90.2 mL at STP conditions. What volume does it occupy at 37°C and 691 torr?
10. What volume in mL does a 2.09-g sample of Kr occupy at 925 torr and 333 K?
11. An evacuated 259-mL flask has a mass of 85.917 g. After adding an unknown gas to flask, the mass of the flask plus the unknown gas is 87.624 g. If the pressure exerted by the gas is 1625 torr at 21.1°C, what is its molar mass?
12. A 1.00-g sample of an unknown noble gas is placed into a 1.50 L vessel at 298 K. If the pressure exerted by the gas is 148 torr, identify the noble gas.
13. Calculate the density of nitrous oxide, N_2O, at 100°C and 104 kPa.

14. What is the temperature of a 5.05-g sample of Xe(g) that occupies 950 mL at 775 torr?

15. A 0.379-g sample of an unknown gas occupies 78.2 mL at 749 torr and 2.0°C. What is the molecular mass of the unknown gas?

16. The total pressure of a mixture of He, Ne, and Ar is 425 kPa. If the pressures of He are 1.22 atm and 1.50 atm, respectively, what is the partial pressure of Ar?

17. What pressure does a mixture of 10.0 g CO and 10.0 g CO_2 exert in a 5.00-L container at 273 K?

18. The total pressure of a mixture of Ar, Kr, and Xe is 120.2 kPa. (a) If the partial pressures of Ar and Kr are 634.1 and 93.5 torr, respectively, calculate the partial pressure of Xe. (b) If the volume of their container doubles, what are the partial pressures of the gases and the total pressure in the mixture?

19. A gaseous mixture of CH_4 and C_2H_6 occupies 1.51 L at 298 K. What is the mole fraction of C_2H_6, if this mixture exerts a total pressure of 2.72 atm and 1.3 g CH_4 is in the mixture?

20. Calcium carbide, CaC_2, combines with water and produces acetylene gas, $C_2H_2(g)$.

$$CaC_2(s) + 2H_2O(l) \rightarrow C_2H_2(g) + Ca(OH)_2(aq)$$

If 92.3 mL C_2H_2 is collected over water at 24°C and 751.0 torr, what mass of CaC_2 was present initially? The vapor pressure of water at 24°C is 22.4 torr.

21. The complete combustion of propane, C_3H_8, produces $CO_2(g)$ and $H_2O(g)$. If the pressure and temperature remain constant, what volumes of $CO_2(g)$ and $H_2O(g)$ form when a 5.50-mL sample of C_3H_8 combusts?

22. A student heats $KClO_3$ with MnO_2 and collects the resulting $O_2(g)$ over water. If 197 mL of O_2 is produced at 294 K and 769.1 torr, what mass of $KClO_3$, in mg, initially decomposed? The vapor pressure of water at 294 K is 18.65 torr.

23. $O_2(g)$ and $NO_2(g)$ produce $NO_2(g)$ as follows:

$$2NO(g) + O_2(g) \rightarrow 2NO_2(g)$$

A 5.00-L reaction vessel is filled with a mixture of NO and O_2 to a pressure 2.90 atm at 350 K, and the reaction is allowed to continue until the total pressure decreases to 2.15 atm. What mass of NO_2 is expected in the final mixture?

24. Calculate the root-mean-square velocity of ozone, $O_3(g)$, at 289 K.

25. (a) Calculate the rms velocity of HCl molecules at 20.0°C and compare it to the rms velocity of HCl molecules at 150°C. (b) What is the percent increase in rms velocity for this temperature change?

26. (a) Compare the rate of effusion of N_2 to O_2. (b) Compare the rate of effusion of N_2 to Cl_2. (c) Compare the rate of effusion of N_2 to Xe.

27. An unknown gas effuses at a rate 0.551 times the rate of Cl_2. What is the molar mass of the unknown gas?

28. Compare the rms velocities of Ar and Kr at STP.

29. (a) Use the van der Waals Equation to calculate the pressure exerted by 1.00 mol $CCl_4(g)$ at 300 K that occupies 1.25 mL. (b) Compare the pressure predicted by the van der Waals Equation to the pressure obtained from the ideal gas equation for the same conditions and volume.

30. (a) Calculate the volume occupied by 1.0 mol of Xe at 298 K and 257 atm using the ideal gas equation. (b) Compare the volume occupied by Xe predicted from the van der Waals Equation to that obtained from the ideal gas equation in part (a).

31. (a) A mixture of $NaHCO_3$ and Na_2CO_3 has a mass of 89.1 g. This mixture is added to a solution that contains an excess amount of HCl(aq). If 22.6 L CO_2 at 298 K and 0.990 atm is produced, what is the percent composition of the mixture? (b) A second mixture of $NaHCO_3$ and Na_2CO_3 has a mass of 57.5 g. If 5.00% of the mixture is $NaHCO_3$ and the

remainder is Na_2CO_3, what volume of CO_2 results when the mixture is mixed with excess HCl(*aq*) at 298 K and 0.990 atm?

ANSWERS TO REVIEW EXERCISE

1. 1.234 atm, 937.6 torr, 1.250 bar
2. 10.3 m
3. (a) 2.33 bar, (b) 1.34×10^{-2} bar, (c) 1.01 bar
4. 19.8 mL
5. 89.46 mL
6. (a) 294°C, (b) −178°C
7. 738 mL
8. (a) 82.1 (cm^3 atm)/(mol K), (b) 8.32×10^{-3} (m^3 kPa)/(mol K), (c) 62.4 (dm^3 torr)/(mol K)
9. 113 mL
10. 560 mL Kr
11. 74.48 g/mol
12. Kr
13. 1.48 g/L
14. 33.6°C
15. 111 g/mol
16. 149 kPa Ar
17. 2.62 atm
18. (a) 174.2 torr, (b) $P_{Ar} = 317.1$ torr, $P_{Kr} = 46.8$ torr, $P_{Xe} = 87.1$ torr, $P_{total} = 450.9$ torr
19. $X_{C_2H_6} = 0.52$
20. 0.215 g
21. 16.5 mL $CO_2(g)$, 22.0 mL $H_2O(g)$
22. 659 mg $KClO_3$
23. 12 g NO_2
24. 388 m/s
25. (a) 448 m/s (20.0°C), 538 m/s (110°C), (b) 20.1%
26. (a) 1.07/1, (b) 1.59/1, (c) 2.17/1
27. 234 g/mol
28. 413 m/s (Ar), 285 m/s (Kr)
29. $P_{obs} = 9.08$ atm, $P_{ideal} = 19.7$ atm
30. $V_{ideal} = 0.076$ L, $V = 0.095$ L
31. (a) 33.3% $NaHCO_3$, 66.7% Na_2CO_3, (b) 13.6 L

7

Thermochemistry–the First Law of Thermodynamics

*T*hermodynamics is the study of energy changes and transformations that occur in physical and chemical processes. Thermochemistry is the application of the laws of thermodynamics to chemical processes. In this chapter, we will consider the most fundamental principles of thermochemistry.

7.1 INTRODUCTION TO THERMO-CHEMISTRY

What is the Importance of Thermodynamics?

Thermodynamic principles may be used to decide if a chemical reaction can occur spontaneously under a given set of conditions. If the reaction does occur, thermochemical principles can be used to predict the magnitude of the energy transfer. Moreover, thermodynamic principles are used to predict the extent to which a chemical reaction occurs. One important property of a reaction that cannot be predicted by chemical thermodynamics is the rate, or speed, at which a reaction occurs.

The Laws of Thermo-dynamics

Thermochemistry is based on three fundamental laws of nature. In this chapter, the first law of thermodynamics is considered. One way to state the first law of thermodynamics is that energy cannot be created or destroyed in physical and chemical processes. This statement is also called the Law of Conservation of Energy. To develop an understanding of the second and third laws of thermodynamics as they apply to chemical reactions, you need to learn more about the fundamentals of chemistry. These two laws are discussed in Chapter 18.

7.2   THE LANGUAGE OF THERMODYNAMICS

Thermodynamic Systems

In thermodynamics, the system, sys, is the part of the universe under investigation. Everything else in the universe is in the surroundings, sur. The combination of the system and the surroundings is the universe, uni: Uni = sys + sur

OPEN AND CLOSED SYSTEMS

Thermodynamic systems are classified as either being open or closed. An open system allows both matter and energy transfers into or out of the system. A closed system only allows energy transfers. In other words, closed systems have a constant mass.

ADIABATIC AND ISOTHERMAL SYSTEMS

Systems may also be classified according to the properties of the walls that separate the system from the surroundings. If the walls insulate the system from the surroundings so that no energy transfers, then the system is an adiabatic system. An example of an adiabatic system is a thermos bottle. If the walls of the system allow energy transfers, then the system is an isothermal system. Most of the chemical reactions that we will study are isothermal systems.

Problem 7.1   (a) Explain what happens to the temperature of an isothermal system when heat is produced or absorbed by the system. (b) Compare this to an adiabatic system.

Solution 7.1   (a) If an isothermal system releases heat, then it flows to the surroundings and does not raise the temperature. If an isothermal system absorbs heat, the surroundings replace it. In either case, the overall temperature of an isothermal system remains constant. (b) If an adiabatic system releases or absorbs heat, then the temperature of the system fluctuates accordingly because the heat is trapped in the system.

THE VOLUME OF SYSTEMS

A system with rigid walls maintains a constant volume ($\triangle V = 0$). One with flexible walls has a variable volume ($\triangle V \neq 0$).

PROPERTIES OF THERMODYNAMIC SYSTEMS

Thermodynamic properties are used to describe thermodynamic systems. For example, the pressure, P, volume, V, and temperature, T of a sample of helium gas (the system) can be measured. Almost any measurement that describes the system is a thermodynamic property. The collection of values for the thermodynamic properties of a system is called the thermodynamic state of the system.

STATE FUNCTIONS

State functions are those properties that depend only on the present state of the system without regard to how it was reached–they are path-independent functions. Examples of state functions include temperature, pressure, volume, and energy. In thermodynamics, uppercase letters (e.g., T, P, and V) are used to represent state functions.

Problem 7.2   Use a 5-g sample of H_2O at 25°C in which its temperature is changed to 40°C to explain why temperature is a state function.

Solution 7.2   If 5 g of H_2O at 25°C is initially present and it is heated to 40°C, the temperature change is 15°C. It does not matter if the 5 g H_2O is first cooled to 0°C and then heated to 40°C, or heated to 60°C and then allowed to cool to 40°C. Temperature changes are independent of the path taken to attain the final temperature.

PATH FUNCTIONS

Path-dependent functions, or just path functions, are properties that depend on the path taken from the initial to final state. When you climb from the base to the summit of a mountain, the distance traveled and elapsed time depend of the path taken. Two thermodynamic path functions, heat (q) and work (w) transfers will soon be discussed. In thermodynamics, path-dependent functions are designated with lowercase letters.

7.3   TEMPERATURE, HEAT, WORK, AND INTERNAL ENERGY

Temperature and Thermal Equilibrium

Temperature is a property that tells us about the thermal equilibrium between bodies. Connected bodies are in thermal equilibrium when no heat flows spontaneously between them. For example, if bodies X and Y are in thermal equilibrium with body Z, then objects X and Y are also in thermal equilibrium. Because objects X and Y are in thermal equilibrium, they are at the same temperature.

TEMPERATURE AND HEAT

When two bodies at different temperatures come in contact with each other, heat flows spontaneously between them until they reach a thermal equilibrium. Heat, the form of kinetic energy that is most often detected when bodies at different temperatures contact each other, transfers spontaneously from a hotter to a colder body. Bodies may possess a variety of different types of energies, but they cannot possess heat.

SI and non-SI Units of Heat

The SI unit for heat and other forms of energy is the joule, J. Because one joule (1 newton × 1 meter) is a small unit of energy, the kilojoule, kJ, is most often encountered. The non-SI unit of heat that is commonly used is the calorie. One calorie, cal, was once defined as the heat required to raise the temperature of one gram of water from 14.5°C to 15.5°C. Today, one calorie is defined as exactly 4.184 J.

Problem 7.3   Convert 34.5 kcal to joules and kilojoules.

Solution 7.3   Use the conversion factor 1000 cal/1 kcal to convert to cal, and 4.184 J/1 cal to convert to J. Then convert J to kJ using 1 kJ/1000 J.

$$34.5 \text{ kcal} \times 1000 \text{ cal/1 kcal} \times 4.184 \text{ J/1 cal} = 1.44 \times 10^5 \text{ J}$$
$$1.44 \times 10^5 \text{ J} \times 1 \text{ kJ/1000 J} = 1.44 \times 10^2 \text{ kJ}$$

Calculating Heat Transfers

To calculate the amount of heat transferred, q, the mass of the substance, m, its change in temperature, $\triangle T$ ($T_2 - T_1$), and the specific heat capacity of the substance, c, are measured.

$$q = m\triangle Tc = m(T_2 - T_1)c \tag{7.1}$$

HEAT CAPACITY

Specific heat capacity, or just specific heat, is the heat required to increase the temperature of one gram of substance by one degree Celsius (or one kelvin). The specific heat of a substance is determined experimentally at constant pressure. For energy transfers in chemical reactions, mole relationships are most important. Thus, Eq. 7.1 is modified to include the moles of substance present.

$$q = n\triangle TC \qquad\qquad (7.2)$$

In Eq. 7.2, n is the number of moles of substance, $\triangle T$ is the change in temperature, and C is the molar heat capacity. Molar heat capacity is the heat required to increase the temperature of *one mole* of a substance by one degree Celsius.

Problem 7.4   If 24.2 J is added to a 16.9-g sample of uranium, U, and the temperature increases from 24.6°C to 36.9°C, calculate the molar and specific heat capacity of U.

Solution 7.4   Equation 7.1 gives the relationship between heat transfer, mass, change in temperature, and specific heat.

$$q = m\triangle Tc$$

Thus, the equation may be rearranged and solved for specific heat, c.

$$c = \frac{q}{m\triangle T}$$

To calculate the specific heat of uranium, U, divide the amount of heat transferred, q, by the product of its mass, m, and change in temperature, $\triangle T$, which equals $T_2 - T_1$.

$$c = 24.2 \text{ J}/(16.9 \text{ g U} \times (36.9° - 24.6°\text{C})) = 0.116 \text{ J}/(\text{g} \cdot °\text{C})$$

To calculate the molar heat capacity, convert the mass in grams to moles using the molar mass of U, 238 g/mol.

$$C = 0.116 \text{ J}/(\text{g} \cdot °\text{C}) \times 238 \text{ g U/mol U} = 27.6 \text{ J}/(\text{mol} \cdot °\text{C})$$

Problem 7.5   A 215-g sample of an unknown solid requires 1.448 kJ of heat to raise its temperature from 25.3°C to 44.9°C. Calculate the specific heat capacity of the solid in J/(g·°C).

Solution 7.5   Use the rearranged form of Eq. 7.1 to calculate the specific heat.

$$c = \frac{q}{m\triangle T}$$
$$c = 1.448 \text{ kJ}/(215 \text{ g} \times (44.9°\text{C} - 25.3°\text{C}))$$
$$= 1.448 \text{ kJ}/(215 \text{ g} \times 19.6°\text{C}) = 3.44 \times 10^{-4} \text{ kJ}/(\text{g} \cdot °\text{C})$$

Then convert kJ/(g·°C) to J/(g·°C) using the conversion factor, 1 kJ/1000 J.

$$3.44 \times 10^{-4} \text{ kJ}/(\text{g} \cdot °\text{C}) \times 1000 \text{ J/kJ} = 0.344 \text{ J}/(\text{g} \cdot °\text{C})$$

Problem 7.6   (a) How many joules of heat are needed to raise the temperature of 324 g H_2O from 15.3°C to 67.1°C? (b) How many joules of heat are needed to raise the temperature of 324 g Al from 15.3°C to 67.1°C? The specific heats of H_2O and Al are 4.18 J/(g·°C) and 0.901 J/(g·°C), respectively.

Solution 7.6   Use Eq. 7.1 to calculate the heat transferred.

$$q = m(T_2 - T_1)c$$
$$= 324 \text{ g H}_2\text{O} \times (67.1°\text{C} - 15.3°\text{C}) \times 4.18 \text{ J/(g°C)}$$
$$= 7.02 \times 10^4 \text{ J (70.2 kJ)}$$

Then, calculate the heat transferred to Al.

$$q = m(T_2 - T_1)c$$
$$= 324 \text{ g Al} \times (67.1°\text{C} - 15.3°\text{C}) \times 0.901 \text{ J/(g°C)}$$
$$= 1.51 \times 10^3 \text{ J (1.51 kJ)}$$

SIGN CONVENTIONS FOR HEAT TRANSFERS

The sign of q is used to show the direction of heat transfer. By convention, if q is greater than zero ($q > 0$), meaning that q is positive, then heat transfers from the surroundings to the system. If q is less than zero ($q < 0$), meaning that q is negative, then heat transfers from the system to the surroundings.

ENDOTHERMIC AND EXOTHERMIC CHANGES

If heat enters a system ($q > 0$), then an endothermic change occurs. If heat leaves a system ($q < 0$), then an exothermic change occurs.

Problem 7.7   (a) Explain in terms of q what happens when 100 J of heat is added to a sample of water. (b) Explain in terms of q what happens when water releases 100 J of heat. Label each change as endothermic or exothermic.

Solution 7.7   (a) If 100 J of heat is added to water, then write: $q = +100$ J. This is an endothermic change. (b) If the water cools and transfers 100 J of heat to the surroundings, then write: $q = -100$ J. This is an exothermic change.

Problem 7.8   Calculate the final temperature of water after 50.0 g Cu at 100.0°C is immersed in 125 g H_2O at 25.0°C. The specific heats of Cu and H_2O are 0.385 J/(g°C) and 4.184 J/(g°C), respectively.

Solution 7.8   The heat lost by Cu equals the heat gained by the water. Thus, equate the expressions for the loss of heat by Cu and the gain of heat by the water as follows and solve for the final temperature, T_2.

$$-(m_{\text{Cu}} \times \Delta T_{\text{Cu}} \times c_{\text{Cu}}) = m_{\text{H}_2\text{O}} \times \Delta T_{\text{H}_2\text{O}} \times c_{\text{H}_2\text{O}}$$
$$-(50.0 \text{ g Cu}(T_2 - 100.0°\text{C}) \, 0.385 \text{ J/(g·°C)}) = 125 \text{ g H}_2\text{O} \, (T_2 - 25.0°\text{C}) \times 4.184 \text{ J/(g·°C)}$$
$$T_2 = 27.7°\text{C}$$

Work

Mechanical work, w, is done when an opposing force displaces matter through a distance. The amount of work done is calculated by multiplying the magnitude of the opposing force, f, times the distance, d, displaced.

$$w = f d \tag{7.3}$$

The units of force and distance in the SI system are the newton (N) and meter (m), respectively. Hence, work has the units of newton meters (N·m) which equal the energy unit joules.

SIGN CONVENTION OF WORK

Chemical systems do work on the surroundings when they expand and push on the surroundings. This is called expansion work. When the surroundings do work on the system, the surroundings compress the system. This is called compression work. The same sign convention is used to show the direction of work transfer as is used to show the direction of heat flow. Work done by a system on the surroundings has a negative value ($w < 0$). Work done by the surroundings on a system has a positive value ($w > 0$).

EXPANSION AND COMPRESSION

Expansion work occurs when a gas expands and pushes on a movable wall such as a piston in a cylinder. If the system expands, then its volume increases to V_2. The amount of expansion work done by gas on the piston in the cylinder (the system) equals minus the P times the $\triangle V$:

$$w = -P\triangle V = -P(V_2 - V_1) \tag{7.4}$$

in which P is the pressure on the piston and $\triangle V$ is the volume change, $V_2 - V_1$.

Problem 7.9 Describe what happens to the change in volume, $\triangle V$, and the work done when a chemical system: (a) expands and (b) is compressed.

Solution 7.9 (a) When a system expands, its final volume, V_2, is greater than its initial volume, V_1. Therefore, the $\triangle V$ term is positive ($\triangle V = V_2 - V_1 > 0$). Pressure is always a positive value and can never be negative. Therefore, the sign for work is negative because of the negative sign in the equation. A negative sign means that energy is lost.

(b) When a system is compressed, its final volume, V_2, is less than its initial volume, V_1. Therefore, the $\triangle V$ term is negative ($\triangle V = V_2 - V_1 < 0$). Pressure is always a positive value and can never be negative. Therefore, the sign for work is positive because of the negative sign in the equation. A positive sign means that energy is gained.

Problem 7.10 Calculate the amount of work, in L·atm and J, done on a system that is compressed from 12.5 L to 10.2 L at a constant pressure of 1.0 atm. One L·atm is equivalent to 101.3 J, 101.3 J/L·atm.

Solution 7.10 Use the following equation to calculate the amount of work done on the system.

$$w = -P \times \triangle V$$
$$= -1.0 \text{ atm } (10.2 \text{ L} - 12.5 \text{ L}) = 2.3 \text{ L·atm}$$

Convert to J as follows.
$$2.3 \text{ L·atm} \times 101.3 \text{ J/(L·atm)} = 2.3 \times 10^2 \text{ J}$$

Internal Energy   Bodies can have both kinetic energy ($E_{kinetic}$), energy of motion, and potential or stored energy ($E_{potential}$). In addition, bodies possess internal energy, $E_{internal}$. What is internal energy? Let's consider the example of a rock that falls and hits the ground. As the rock falls, its kinetic energy increases because its velocity increases until it hits the ground, when it stops and no longer possesses kinetic energy. What happens to the kinetic energy of the rock? The energy of motion transfers to the particles that compose the rock and ground and increase their kinetic energies. An increase in the average kinetic energy of the particles could be measured by a small increase in the temperature of the rock and ground. The energy that results from the motion of the particles (atoms and molecules) that make up a system is the internal energy.

THE TOTAL ENERGY, E_{total}, OF A SYSTEM

The total energy, E_{total}, of a body is the sum of the kinetic energy, potential energy, and the internal energy.

$$E_{total} = E_{kinetic} + E_{potential} + E_{internal} \tag{7.5}$$

In thermochemistry, the kinetic and potential energies of the system may be discarded ($E_{kinetic} = E_{potential} = 0$) because chemical systems do not move from place to place and do not have stored energy as a result of their position in a gravitational field. Hence, the total energy of a chemical system equals the internal energy.

CHANGE IN INTERNAL ENERGY, $\triangle E$

No way exists to measure the total or absolute amount of the internal energy, E, of a system. However, the internal energy change, $\triangle E$, that occurs in a body can be measured. The $\triangle E$ for a system equals the difference between the final internal energy, E_2, and the initial internal energy, E_1.

$$\triangle E = E_2 - E_1 \tag{7.6}$$

7.4   THE FIRST LAW OF THERMODYNAMICS

Statement of the First Law of Thermodynamics

The first law of thermodynamics is the Law of Conservation of Energy. It states that energy cannot be created or destroyed under normal chemical conditions. In thermodynamics, the first law is stated as follows: The total energy in the universe is constant.

A mathematical statement of the first law is

$$\triangle E_{sys} + \triangle E_{sur} = 0 \tag{7.7}$$

in which $\triangle E_{sys}$ is the energy change in the system and $\triangle E_{sur}$ is the energy change in the surroundings. This equation shows us that the total energy change in the system, $\triangle E_{sys}$, plus the total energy change in the surroundings, $\triangle E_{sur}$, equals zero.

Rearranging Eq. 7.7, the equation for the first law, by subtracting $\triangle E_{sur}$ from both sides, yields the following equation.

$$\triangle E_{sys} = -\triangle E_{sur} \tag{7.8}$$

This equation shows the signs of $\triangle E_{sys}$ and $\triangle E_{sur}$ differ. This means that the surroundings gains the energy lost by the system or vice versa.

RELATIONSHIP OF q AND w TO $\triangle E_{sys}$

The $\triangle E$ for chemical systems depends on the heat transfer, q, and the work w, done on or by the system. Therefore, the following equation results.

$$\triangle E_{sys} = q + w \tag{7.9}$$

Equation 7.9 states that the energy change for a system equals the sum of the heat transfer and the pressure-volume, PV, work performed by the system.

Problem 7.11   (a) Explain what it means when the q and w of a system are positive values. (b) What are the signs of q, w, and $\triangle E$ of the surroundings of this system?

Solution 7.11   (a) Under these conditions, $\triangle E_{sys}$ is positive.

$$q_{sys} > 0 \text{ and } w_{sys} > 0 \qquad \triangle E_{sys} > 0$$

When the q is positive, heat transfers from the surroundings to the system and increases that system's energy. When w is positive, the surroundings does work on the system and increases the energy of the system. Both $+q$ and $+w$ increase the energy of the system; therefore $\triangle E$ is positive, $\triangle E_{sys} > 0$. (b) When a system gains energy, energy is lost by the surroundings, $\triangle E_{sur} < 0$. This is expressed in the following equation.

$$-\triangle E_{sur} = -q_{sur} + (-w_{sur})$$

Problem 7.12   (a) Calculate the $\triangle E_{sys}$ when the system releases 550 J to the surroundings and the surroundings does 350 J of work on the system. (b) What is $\triangle E_{sur}$?

Solution 7.12   (a) To solve this problem use Eq. 7.9, $\triangle E_{sys} = q + w$. When a system loses 550 J of heat, then $q = -550$ J. When the system has 350 J of work done on it by the surroundings, then $w = +350$ J.

$$\triangle E_{sys} = q + w$$
$$= -550 \text{ J} + (+350 \text{ J}) = -200 \text{ J}$$

(b) Equation 7.7 allows us to calculate $\triangle E_{sur}$.

$$\triangle E_{sys} + \triangle E_{sur} = 0$$
$$\triangle E_{sur} = -\triangle E_{sys}$$
$$= -(-200 \text{ J}) = 200 \text{ J}$$

Problem 7.13   (a) What is the $\triangle E_{sys}$ when the system loses 124 J of heat to the surroundings and the system increases in volume by 0.53 L under a pressure of 1.0 atm? (b) What $\triangle E_{sur}$ accompanies the change in part (a)?

Solution 7.13   (a) Use Eq. 7.9 as follows.

$$\triangle E_{sys} = q + w$$

If the system loses 124 J of heat, then the value of q equals -124 J. Equation 7.3 may be used to calculate the work done by the system on the surroundings as it expands.

$$w = -P\triangle V$$

Because the volume increases, $\triangle V$ equals $+0.53$ L; thus,

$$w = -1.0 \text{ atm} \times +0.53 \text{ L} = -0.53 \text{ L·atm}$$

The units of work in L·atm must be changed, because the joule is the unit for the heat transfer. Hence, knowing that 101.3 J is equivalent to 1 L·atm allows us to change L·atm to joules.

$$w = -0.53 \text{ L·atm} \times 101.3 \text{ J/L·atm} = -54 \text{ J}$$

Then substitute these values into Eq. 7.9.

$$\triangle E_{sys} = -124 \text{ J} + (-54 \text{ J}) = -178 \text{ J}$$

(b) To calculate the $\triangle E_{sur}$, apply Eq. 7.7.

$$\triangle E_{sur} = -\triangle E_{sys}$$
$$= -(-178 \text{ J}) = +178 \text{ J}$$

7.5   ENTHALPY CHANGES IN CHEMICAL REACTIONS

Enthalpy Change

It is convenient to measure the heat transfer of a chemical reaction at constant pressure. Rearranging the first law equation at constant pressure and solving for heat transfer at constant pressure, q_p, gives the following equation.

$$q_p = \triangle E + P\triangle V \tag{7.10}$$

The heat transfer at constant pressure equals the sum of the internal energy change and the pressure-volume work. If the chemical reaction does no work ($P\triangle V = 0$) then q_p equals $\triangle E$.

$$q_p = \triangle E \text{ when } P\triangle V = 0 \tag{7.11}$$

If the chemical reaction does only pressure-volume work or if it does no work, then q_p can be redefined as the state function called the change in enthalpy, $\triangle H$.

$$q_p = \triangle H \tag{7.12}$$

Therefore,

$$\triangle H = \triangle E + P\triangle V \tag{7.13}$$

The enthalpy change, $\triangle H$, is the heat that a chemical reaction transfers at constant pressure.

ENTHALPY CHANGE IS A STATE FUNCTION

The change in enthalpy, $\triangle H$, a state function, equals the difference between the final enthalpy, H_2, and the initial enthalpy, H_1.

$$\triangle H = H_2 - H_1 \tag{7.14}$$

In a chemical reaction, the final enthalpy is the enthalpy of the products and the initial enthalpy is the enthalpy of the reactants; thus,

$$\triangle H = H_{products} - H_{reactants} \tag{7.15}$$

Endothermic and Exothermic Reactions

If the enthalpy of the products is greater than the enthalpy of the reactants, then the value for $\triangle H$ is positive. This means that the products have absorbed heat from the surroundings at constant pressure. A reaction that absorbs heat from the surroundings is an endothermic reaction. If the enthalpy of the products is less than the enthalpy of the reactants, then the value for $\triangle H$ is negative. This means that the reactants lose heat to the surroundings. A reaction that releases heat to the surroundings is an exothermic reaction.

Problem 7.14   Classify each of the following as endothermic or exothermic reactions.
(a) $CaCO_3(s) \rightarrow CaO(s) + CO_2(g)$ $\triangle H = +178$ kJ
(b) $CH_4(g) + 2O_2(g) \rightarrow CO_2(g) + 2H_2O(g)$ $\triangle H = -802$ kJ

Solution 7.14

(a) This is an endothermic reaction, because the enthalpy increases.
(b) This is an exothermic reaction, because the enthalpy decreases.

Problem 7.15 Consider the following reaction.

$$Ag_2O(s) \rightarrow 2Ag(s) + \frac{1}{2}O_2(g) \qquad \triangle H = +31.1 \text{ kJ}$$

What is the $\triangle H$ of the reverse reaction?

Solution 7.15 An important consequence of the first law of thermodynamics is that the reverse of a reaction has a $\triangle H$ of equal magnitude but opposite sign.

$$2Ag(s) + \frac{1}{2}O_2(g) \rightarrow Ag_2O(s) \qquad \triangle H = -31.3 \text{ kJ}$$

Standard Conditions for $\triangle H$

$\triangle H$ is an extensive property which means that it depends on the magnitude of the mass of reactants. It is a common practice to specify the $\triangle H$ in kilojoules, kJ, for the reaction of interest. Because temperature and pressure also can influence the $\triangle H$ for a reaction, thermodynamic tables with enthalpy data must specify the reaction conditions. Most often, thermodynamic data is given at standard conditions of 298.2 K (25.0°C) and 1 atm (101 kPa).

To express an enthalpy change at standard conditions, $\triangle H°$ is written.

Quantitative Energy Effects in Chemical Reactions

The amount of heat transferred for any mass of reactants and products in a given reaction at standard conditions can be calculated from its standard enthalpy change, $\triangle H°$.

Problem 7.16 Consider the complete combustion of propane, $C_3H_8(g)$.

$$C_3H_8(g) + 5O_2(g) \rightarrow 3CO_2(g) + 4H_2O(l) \qquad \triangle H° = -2220 \text{ kJ}$$

(a) How much heat is released per mole of propane? (b) How much energy is produced from the complete combustion of 1.00 kg $C_3H_8(g)$?

Solution 7.16

(a) The $\triangle H°$ for the combustion of propane shows that one mole of C_3H_8 (44.1 g C_3H_8/mol) releases 2220 kJ of heat.
(b) The factor-label method may be used to solve this problem. First, convert the kg of C_3H_8 to g of C_3H_8 and then convert g of C_3H_8 to mol of C_3H_8. Then use the standard enthalpy change to calculate the amount of heat released.

1.00 kg C_3H_8 × 1000 g C_3H_8/1 kg C_3H_8 × 1 mol C_3H_8/44.1 g C_3H_8 × 2220 kJ/mol C_3H_8

$$= 5.03 \times 10^4 \text{ kJ}$$

Problem 7.17 Glucose, $C_6H_{12}O_6(s)$, is one of the principal fuels that biological cells use to produce energy. One mole of glucose releases 2816 kJ of heat when completely burned.

$$C_6H_{12}O_6(s) + 6O_2(g) \rightarrow 6CO_2(g) + 6H_2O(l) \qquad \triangle H° = -2816 \text{ kJ}$$

A nutrition table shows that the recommended energy intake for a male between the ages of 23 and 50 years is 11.3 MJ/day. What mass of glucose produces 11.3 MJ of heat?

Solution 7.17 Use the factor-label method to first convert the number of megajoules, MJ, to kilojoules, kJ. One MJ is equivalent to 1000 kJ. Then, calculate the moles of $C_6H_{12}O_6$ from the enthalpy change, -2816 kJ/mol, and mass of $C_6H_{12}O_6$ from the molar mass of glucose, 180 g $C_6H_{12}O_6$/mol.

$$11.3 \text{ MJ} \times 1000 \text{ kJ/MJ} \times 1 \text{ mol } C_6H_{12}O_6/2816 \text{ kJ} \times 180 \text{ g } C_6H_{12}O_6/\text{mol } C_6H_{12}O_6 = 722 \text{ g } C_6H_{12}O_6$$

Standard Enthalpies of Formation, $\triangle H_f^\circ$

A reaction of interest to thermochemists is the formation of a compound from its elements. The enthalpy change for such a reaction is called the standard molar enthalpy of formation, $\triangle H_f^\circ$. $\triangle H_f^\circ$ is the heat transferred when one mole of a compound forms from its elements at the standard conditions of 298 K and 1 atm. For example, the $\triangle H_f^\circ$ for methane is -74.85 kJ/mol CH_4. Gaseous methane results when solid carbon (graphite) combines with gaseous hydrogen.

$$C(graphite) + 2H_2(g) \rightarrow CH_4(g) \qquad \triangle H_f^\circ = -74.85 \text{ kJ}$$

Problem 7.18 Use data from a table of thermodynamic data to answer the following questions. (a) Write the equation for the formation of gaseous hydrogen fluoride, $HF(g)$. (b) What energy transfer occurs when 1.00 mol $HF(g)$ results? (c) How much heat is required to produce 158 g of $HF(g)$ from the elements?

Solution 7.18

(a) Hydrogen gas, $HF(g)$, results when $H_2(g)$ and $F_2(g)$ combine as follows.

$$\tfrac{1}{2}H_2(g) + \tfrac{1}{2}F_2(g) \rightarrow HF(g)$$

Fractional coefficients for H_2 and F_2 are used so that only one mole of $HF(g)$ results. Standard enthalpies of formation are usually expressed per mole of substance.

(b) The $\triangle H_f^\circ$ for $HF(g)$ is -273 kJ/mol.

$$\tfrac{1}{2}H_2(g) + \tfrac{1}{2}F_2(g) \rightarrow HF(g) \qquad \triangle H_f^\circ = -273 \text{ kJ}$$

This formation of HF from the elements liberates 273 kJ of heat per mole of HF.

(c) First, convert the mass of $HF(g)$ to moles and then use the $\triangle H_f^\circ$ as a conversion factor to calculate the heat released from 158 g $HF(g)$.

$$158 \text{ g HF} \times 1 \text{ mol HF}/20.0\text{g HF} \times 273 \text{ kJ/mol HF} = 2.16 \times 10^3 \text{ kJ}$$

7.6   HESS'S LAW

Calculation of Enthalpy Changes For Chemical Reactions

The enthalpy change for a chemical reaction can be calculated in different ways. Each of them is based on Hess's law. Hess's law states that the enthalpy change for a chemical reaction equals the sum of the enthalpy changes of any set of reactions that can be added to give the overall reaction.

Problem 7.19 Calculate the $\triangle H^\circ$ for the decomposition of hydrogen peroxide, H_2O_2, to water and oxygen gas:

$$2H_2O_2(l) \rightarrow 2H_2O(l) + O_2(g)$$

using the following two equations.

$$H_2O_2(l) \rightarrow H_2(g) + O_2(g) \qquad \triangle H^\circ = +187.8 \text{ kJ}$$
$$H_2(g) + \tfrac{1}{2}O_2(g) \rightarrow H_2O(l) \qquad \triangle H^\circ = -285.8 \text{ kJ}$$

Solution 7.19   In the first equation $H_2O_2(l)$ is a reactant and in the second $H_2O(l)$ is a product. Thus, these equations are added, both $H_2O_2(l)$ and $H_2O(l)$ are on their respective proper sides of the equation–H_2O_2 on the left and H_2O on the right. However in the overall equation, two moles of $H_2O_2(l)$ are in the reactants and two moles of $H_2O(l)$ are in the products. Hence, multiply each equation and the $\triangle H^\circ$ by 2 before adding them.

$$2H_2O_2(l) \rightarrow 2H_2(g) + 2O_2(g) \qquad \triangle H^\circ = +375.6 \text{ kJ}$$
$$\underline{+\ 2H_2(g) + O_2(g) \rightarrow 2H_2O(l) \qquad\qquad \triangle H^\circ = -571.6 \text{ kJ}}$$
$$2H_2O_2(l) \rightarrow 2H_2O(l) + O_2(g) \qquad \triangle H^\circ = -196.0 \text{ kJ}$$

Problem 7.20   Calculate the $\triangle H^\circ$ for the conversion of graphite to diamond

$$C(graphite) \rightarrow C(diamond)$$

given the following two equations

$$C(graphite) + O_2(g) \rightarrow CO_2(g) \qquad \triangle H^\circ = -393.5 \text{ kJ}$$
$$C(diamond) + O_2(g) \rightarrow CO_2(g) \qquad \triangle H^\circ = -395.4 \text{ kJ}$$

Solution 7.20   Reverse the equation for $C(diamond)$ before adding them, so that it is on the right side.

$$C(graphite) + O_2(g) \rightarrow CO_2(g) \qquad\qquad\qquad \triangle H^\circ = -393.5 \text{ kJ}$$
$$\underline{+\ CO_2(g) \rightarrow C(diamond) + O_2(g) \qquad\qquad \triangle H^\circ = +395.4 \text{ kJ}}$$
$$C(graphite) \rightarrow C(diamond) \qquad\qquad\qquad \triangle H^\circ = +1.9 \text{ kJ}$$

Problem 7.21   Calculate the $\triangle H^\circ$ for the reaction of Cu with NF_3

$$Cu(s) + 2NF_3(g) \rightarrow N_2F_4(g) + CuF_2(s)$$

given the following equations

$$CuF_2(s) \rightarrow Cu(s) + F_2(g) \qquad\qquad\qquad \triangle H^\circ = +531.0 \text{ kJ}$$
$$NO(g) + \tfrac{1}{2}F_2 \rightarrow ONF(g) \qquad\qquad\qquad \triangle H^\circ = -156.9 \text{ kJ}$$
$$2NF_3(g) + 2NO(g) \rightarrow N_2F_4(g) + 2ONF(g) \qquad \triangle H^\circ = -82.9 \text{ kJ}$$

Solution 7.21
(a) The first equation is reversed because $CuF_2(s)$ is a product. The second equation is reversed so that $ONF(g)$, $NO(g)$, and $F_2(g)$ cancel when the equations are added. When an equation is reversed, the sign for $\triangle H^\circ$ is changed.

$$Cu(s) + F_2(g) \rightarrow CuF_2(s) \qquad\qquad\qquad \triangle H^\circ = -531.0 \text{ kJ}$$
$$ONF(g) \rightarrow NO(g) + \tfrac{1}{2}F_2 \qquad\qquad\qquad \triangle H^\circ = +156.9 \text{ kJ}$$
$$2NF_3(g) + 2NO(g) \rightarrow N_2F_4(g) + 2ONF(g) \qquad \triangle H^\circ = -82.9 \text{ kJ}$$

(b) Multiply the second equation and its $\triangle H^\circ$ by 2 to cancel unwanted compounds, and add the three equations and three enthalpy changes.

$$Cu(s) + F_2(g) \rightarrow CuF_2(s) \qquad\qquad\qquad \triangle H^\circ = -531.0 \text{ kJ}$$
$$2ONF(g) \rightarrow 2NO(g) + F_2(g) \qquad\qquad\quad \triangle H^\circ = +156.9 \text{ kJ} \times 2 = 313.8 \text{ kJ}$$
$$\underline{+\ 2NF_3(g) + 2NO(g) \rightarrow N_2F_4(g) + 2ONF(g) \quad \triangle H^\circ = -82.9 \text{ kJ}}$$
$$Cu + 2NF_3(g) \rightarrow N_2F_4(g) + CuF_2 \qquad\qquad \triangle H^\circ = -300.1 \text{ kJ}$$

Enthalpy Changes From $\triangle H_f$

Enthalpy changes can be conveniently calculated from standard enthalpies of formation, $\triangle H_f^\circ$. The $\triangle H^\circ$ for a reaction equals the sum of the standard enthalpies of formation of the products minus the sum of the enthalpies of formation of the reactants.

$$\triangle H^\circ = \Sigma \triangle H_f^\circ (\text{products}) - \Sigma \triangle H_f^\circ (\text{reactants}) \qquad (7.16)$$

In this equation the symbol sigma, Σ, means "sum of." $\Sigma \triangle H_f^\circ (\text{products})$ symbolizes the sum of the standard molar enthalpies of formation of the products and $\Sigma \triangle H_f^\circ (\text{reactants})$ indicates the sum the standard molar enthalpies of formation of the reactants. Note that Eq. 7.16 is just another way to express Hess's law.

Problem 7.22

(a) Calculate the enthalpy change to oxidize carbon monoxide, $CO(g)$, to carbon dioxide, $CO_2(g)$ using the equations for the standard molar enthalpies of formation.

$$CO(g) + \tfrac{1}{2}O_2(g) \rightarrow CO_2(g)$$

The $\triangle H_f^\circ$ values for CO and CO_2 are listed below.

$$
\begin{aligned}
C(graphite) + \tfrac{1}{2}O_2(g) &\rightarrow CO(g) & \triangle H_f^\circ &= -110 \text{ kJ} \\
C(graphite) + O_2(g) &\rightarrow CO_2(g) & \triangle H_f^\circ &= -393 \text{ kJ}
\end{aligned}
$$

(b) Use Eq. 7.16 to do this same calculation.

Solution 7.22

(a) Because CO_2 is a product in the desired reaction, it is not changed. However, CO is a reactant in the desired reaction. Hence, its equation is reversed and the sign of $\triangle H_f^\circ$ is changed before the equations are added.

$$
\begin{aligned}
CO(g) &\rightarrow C(graphite) + \tfrac{1}{2}O_2(g) & \triangle H_f^\circ &= 110 \text{ kJ} \\
\underline{C(graphite) + O_2(g) \rightarrow CO_2(g)} & & \underline{\triangle H_f^\circ = -393 \text{ kJ}} \\
CO(g) + \tfrac{1}{2}O_2(g) &\rightarrow CO_2(g) & \triangle H^\circ &= -283 \text{ kJ}
\end{aligned}
$$

(b) Using Eq. 7.16 to obtain the enthalpy change, subtract the sum of all of the $\triangle H_f^\circ$ values for the reactants from the sum of all of the $\triangle H_f^\circ$ values of the products.

$$
\begin{aligned}
\triangle H^\circ &= \Sigma \triangle H_f^\circ (\text{products}) - \Sigma \triangle H_f^\circ (\text{reactants}) \\
&= \triangle H_f^\circ (CO_2) - \triangle H_f^\circ (CO) \\
&= -393 \text{ kJ} - (-110 \text{ kJ}) = -283 \text{ kJ}
\end{aligned}
$$

Problem 7.23

Calculate the $\triangle H^\circ$ for the oxidation reaction of ammonia, $NH_3(g)$, with oxygen, $O_2(g)$, to form $NO(g)$ and $H_2O(g)$.

$$4NH_3(g) + 5O_2(g) \rightarrow 4NO(g) + 6H_2O(g)$$

The $\triangle H_f^\circ$ values for $NH_3(g)$, $O_2(g)$, $NO(g)$, and $H_2O(g)$ are $-46.11, 0.0, 90.25$, and -241.82 kJ/mol, respectively.

Solution 7.23

Apply Hess's law as follows.

$$\triangle H^\circ = \sum \triangle H_f^\circ \text{(products)} - \sum \triangle H_f^\circ \text{(reactants)}$$

$$= (4 \text{ mol } \triangle H_f^\circ (NO) + 6 \text{ mol } \triangle H_f^\circ (H_2O)) - (4 \text{ mol } \triangle H_f^\circ (NH_3) + 5 \text{ mol } \triangle H_f^\circ (O_2))$$

$$= (4 \text{ mol } (90.25 \text{ kJ/mol}) + 6 \text{ mol } (-241.82 \text{ kJ/mol})) - 4 \text{ mol } (-46.11 \text{ kJ/mol})$$

$$= -905.48 \text{ kJ}$$

Problem 7.24   Calculate the $\triangle H^\circ$ for the following reaction.

$$P_4O_{10}(s) + 4HNO_3(l) \rightarrow 4H_3PO_4(l) + 2N_2O_5(g)$$

The enthalpies of formation of $P_4O_{10}(s)$, $HNO_3(l)$, $H_3PO_4(l)$, and $N_2O_5(g)$ are -2984, -174.1, -1267, and 11.3 kJ/mol, respectively.

Solution 7.24

$$\triangle H^\circ = \sum \triangle H_f^\circ \text{(products)} - \sum \triangle H_f^\circ \text{(reactants)}$$

$$= (4 \text{ mol } \triangle H_f^\circ (H_3PO_4) + 2 \text{ mol } \triangle H_f^\circ (N_2O_5)) - (\triangle H_f^\circ (P_4O_{10}) + 4 \text{ mol } \triangle H_f^\circ (HNO_3))$$

$$= (4 \text{ mol } (-1267 \text{ kJ/mol}) + 2 \text{ mol } (-11.3 \text{ kJ/mol})) - (-2984 \text{ kJ/mol} + 4 \text{ mol } (-174.1 \text{ kJ/mol}))$$

$$= -1365 \text{ kJ}$$

Problem 7.25   Consider the following reaction in which calcium carbide, CaC_2, and carbon monoxide are produced from CaO and C.

$$CaO(s) + 3C(s) \rightarrow CaC_2(s) + CO(g)$$

The $\triangle H_f^\circ$ values for CaO, CaC_2, and CO are -635 kJ/mol, -63 kJ/mol, and -111 kJ/mol, respectively. Calculate the heat transfer when 45.0 g CaC_2 result.

Solution 7.25   First use Hess' Law to calculate the $\triangle H^\circ$ for the reaction.

$$\triangle H^\circ = \sum \triangle H_f^\circ \text{(products)} - \sum \triangle H_f^\circ \text{(reactants)}$$

$$= (\triangle H_f^\circ (CaC_2) + \triangle H_f^\circ (CO)) - (\triangle H_f^\circ (CaO))$$

$$= (-63 \text{ kJ} + (-111 \text{ kJ})) - (-635 \text{ kJ}) = +461 \text{ kJ}$$

This means that for each mole of CaC_2 that results 461 kJ must be added. Thus, convert 45.0 g CaC_2 to moles and use the conversion factor 461 kJ/mol CaC_2 to find the heat transferred.

$$45.0 \text{ g } CaC_2 \times 1 \text{ mol } CaC_2/64.1 \text{ g} \times 461 \text{ kJ/mol } CaC_2 = 324 \text{ kJ}$$

Calculation of $\triangle H_f^\circ$

One way to determine the enthalpy of formation of an unknown compound is to burn it in excess oxygen and measure the standard molar enthalpy of combustion, $\triangle H^\circ_{\text{combustion}}$ ($\triangle H_c^\circ$). The standard enthalpy of combustion is the heat liberated per mole of compound at the standard state in a combustion reaction.

Problem 7.26   When benzene, C_6H_6, burns in excess $O_2(g)$, $CO_2(g)$ and $H_2O(g)$ result.

$$C_6H_6(l) + \tfrac{15}{2}O_2(g) \rightarrow 6CO_2(g) + 3H_2O(l)$$

The $\triangle H_c^\circ$ for benzene is -3268 kJ/mol and the $\triangle H_f^\circ$'s for $CO_2(g)$ and $H_2O(l)$ are -394 kJ/mol and -286 kJ/mol, respectively. Calculate the $\triangle H_f^\circ$ for liquid benzene, $C_6H_6(l)$.

Solution 7.26   The Hess's law equation for the combustion of benzene is as follows.

$$\triangle H_c^\circ(C_6H_6) = (6 \text{ mol } \triangle H_f^\circ(CO_2) + 3 \text{ mol } \triangle H_f^\circ(H_2O)) - (\triangle H_f^\circ(C_6H_6))$$

A term for O_2 has not been included in the equation because the $\triangle H_f^\circ$ for O_2 is 0 and thus makes no contribution to this calculation. Substitute the known values into the equation and solve for the $\triangle H_f^\circ(C_6H_6)$, the unknown value.

$$-3268 \text{ kJ} = (6 \text{ mol } (-394 \text{ kJ/mol}) + 3 \text{ mol } (-286 \text{ kJ/mol}) - \triangle H_f^\circ(C_6H_6)$$

$$\triangle H_f^\circ(C_6H_6) = -46 \text{ kJ/mol}$$

7.7   CALORIMETRY

Measurement of Enthalpy Changes

Calorimetry is the experimental procedure for measuring heat transfers. A calorimeter is the instrument used to measure these heat transfers. To measure enthalpy changes of chemical reactions, q_p, chemists use a calorimeter in which a constant pressure is maintained.

If an exothermic reaction occurs in a calorimeter, then the heat liberated increases the temperature of the calorimeter and solution in which the reaction occurs. The First Law tells us that the heat absorbed by the solution, q_{soln}, and calorimeter, $q_{calorimeter}$, equals the heat released by the reaction, q_{rxn}.

$$q_{rxn} + q_{soln} + q_{calorimeter} = 0$$

$$q_{rxn} = -(q_{soln} + q_{calorimeter})$$

The heat absorbed by the solution is calculated from the change in temperature, $\triangle T$, of the solution, mass of the solution, m_{soln}, and specific heat of the solution, c_{soln} (J/g·°C).

$$q_{soln} = m_{soln} \triangle T \, c_{soln}$$

The heat absorbed by the calorimeter is calculated from the $\triangle T$ of the calorimeter, which is the same $\triangle T$ as the solution because they are in thermal equilibrium, and the heat capacity of the calorimeter, $C_{calorimeter}$ (J/°C). The heat capacity of the calorimeter is obtained experimentally when it is calibrated.

Problem 7.27   A calorimeter is calibrated by adding 60.0 g H_2O at 48.9°C to 60.0 g H_2O at 26.2°C in the calorimeter. The final temperature of the H_2O after mixing is 36.2°C. If the specific heat of H_2O is 4.18 J/(g·°C), what is the heat capacity, C, for the calorimeter?

Solution 7.27   First, calculate the heat lost by the hot H_2O and the heat gained by the cold H_2O and the calorimeter. The cold H_2O (26.2°C) and calorimeter absorb the heat lost by the hot H_2O (48.9°C).

$$q_{hot \, H_2O} + q_{cold \, H_2O} + q_{calorimeter} = 0$$

$$q_{hot \, H_2O} = -(q_{cold \, H_2O} + q_{calorimeter})$$

The heat lost by the hot H_2O is calculated as follows.

$$q_{hot \, H_2O} = m_{hot \, H_2O} \triangle T_{hot \, H_2O} c_{H_2O}$$

$$= 60.0 \text{ g } (36.2°C - 48.9°C) \, 4.18 \text{ J/(g·°C)} = -3.19 \times 10^3 \text{ J}$$

The heat gained by the cold H_2O is calculated as follows.

$$q_{cold\ H_2O} = m_{cold\ H_2O}\Delta T_{cold\ H_2O}c_{H_2O}$$
$$= 60.0\ g\ (36.2°C - 26.2°C) \times 4.18\ J/(g·°C) = 2.51 \times 10^3\ J$$

The heat gained by the calorimeter equals the ΔT of the calorimeter times the heat capacity of the calorimeter, $C_{calorimeter}$.

$$q_{calorimeter} = \Delta T_{calorimeter} \times C_{calorimeter}$$

Because the cold H_2O is in the calorimeter, the change in temperature of the calorimeter is the same as that of the cold H_2O.

$$q_{calorimeter} = (36.2°C - 26.2°C) \times C_{calorimeter} = 10.0°C \times C_{calorimeter}$$

Then, calculate $C_{calorimeter}$ as follows.

$$q_{hot\ H_2O} + q_{cold\ H_2O} + q_{calorimeter} = 0$$
$$-3.19 \times 10^3\ J + 2.51 \times 10^3\ J + (10.0°C \times C_{calorimeter}) = 0$$

$$10.0°C \times C_{calorimeter} = 6.80 \times 10^2\ J$$
$$C_{calorimeter} = 6.80 \times 10^2\ J/10.0°C = 68\ J/°C$$

Using Calorimetry to Measure Enthalpies of Solution

The enthalpy of solution, $\Delta H°_{soln}$, is the heat transferred when one mole of substance dissolves in a solvent such as water. For example, NaOH dissociates in H_2O and produces an aqueous solution of $Na^+(aq)$ and OH^- (aq).

$$NaOH \xrightarrow{H_2O} Na^+(aq) + OH^-\ (aq)$$

The energy released per mole of NaOH is the enthalpy of solution.

Problem 7.28   A calorimeter with a heat capacity of 53.2 J/°C is used to measure the enthalpy of solution of NaOH, $\Delta H°_{soln}$(NaOH). Initially, 125 g of H_2O at 24.7°C is poured into the calorimeter. After adding 5.51 g NaOH to the water, the temperature of the NaOH solution rises to 37.2°C. If the specific heat of the NaOH solution is 3.59 J/(g·°C), what is the $\Delta H°_{soln}$(NaOH) in kJ/mol?

Solution 7.28   The heat released when the NaOH dissolves, q, plus the heat absorbed by the NaOH solution ($q_{NaOH(aq)}$) and calorimeter ($q_{calorimeter}$) equal zero.

$$q + q_{NaOH(aq)} + q_{calorimeter} = 0$$

Thus after the equation is rearranged, the heat released by the NaOH may be expressed as follows.

$$q = -(q_{NaOH(aq)} + q_{calorimeter})$$

After obtaining the value for q in J, convert it to kJ. Then divide by the number of moles of NaOH dissolved to obtain the $\Delta H°_{soln}$(NaOH). First, calculate the heat absorbed by the NaOH solution.

$$q_{NaOH(aq)} = m_{soln} \times \Delta T \times c_{NaOH(aq)}$$
$$= (125\ g\ H_2O + 5.51\ g\ NaOH) \times (37.2°C - 24.7°C) \times 3.59\ J/(g°C)$$
$$= 5.86 \times 10^3\ J$$

Calculate the heat absorbed by the calorimeter.

$$q_{calorimeter} = \triangle T_{calorimeter} C_{calorimeter}$$
$$= (37.2°C - 24.7°C)\ 23.5\ J/°C = 294\ J$$

Then, calculate the heat released when NaOH dissolves.

$$q = -(q_{NaOH(aq)} + q_{calorimeter})$$
$$= -(5860\ J + 294\ J) = -6.15 \times 10^3\ J$$

Finally, calculate $\triangle H°_{soln}(NaOH)$ as follows

$$-6.15 \times 10^3\ J \times 1\ kJ/1000\ J = -6.15\ kJ$$
$$5.51\ g\ NaOH \times 1\ mol\ NaOH/40.0\ g\ NaOH = 0.138\ mol$$
$$\triangle H°_{soln}(NaOH) = -6.15\ kJ/0.138\ mol$$
$$= -44.6\ kJ/mol\ NaOH$$

SUMMARY

*T*hermodynamics is the study of energy and energy transformations. Thermochemistry is the area of thermodynamics concerned mainly with energy changes in chemical reactions.

In thermodynamics, the system is the part of the universe under investigation and everything else is considered the surroundings. The properties of thermodynamic systems are classified as either state functions or path dependent functions. A state function depends only on the initial and final state and is independent of the path taken to reach the final state. A path-dependent function depends on the path taken from the initial to final state. An isothermal system can transfer heat across its walls and thus maintains a constant temperature. An insulated system is called an adiabatic system.

Temperature is a measure of the average kinetic energy of the molecules that make up a system. Heat is a form of kinetic energy that moves from the boundary of a hot object to a colder one. Heat capacity is the heat required to increase the temperature of a substance by $1°C$. Molar heat capacity is the heat required to raise one mole of a substance by $1°C$. Specific heat capacity is the heat required to raise 1 g of substance by $1°C$.

A body can possess kinetic energy, potential energy, and internal energy. The internal energy results from the energy possessed by the particles that compose a body. A change in internal energy, $\triangle E$, depends on the heat transfer, q, and work, w, done on or by the system. The sum of q plus w equals the internal energy change for a system.

A statement of the first law of thermodynamics is that the energy in the universe is constant. This means that if the system loses energy that energy enters the surroundings, and if the system gains energy such energy comes from the surroundings. A mathematical statement of the first law is $\triangle E_{sys} + \triangle E_{sur} = 0$

Hess's law states that the enthalpy change for a chemical reaction equals the sum of the enthalpy changes of any set of reactions that can be added to give the overall reaction. One of the most common ways to calculate the $\triangle H°$ for a reaction is to use standard enthalpies of formation, $\triangle H°_f$. A standard enthalpy of formation is the heat transferred when one mole of a compound forms from its elements at standard conditions (1 atm and 298 K). The $\triangle H°$ for a reaction equals the sum of the standard enthalpies of formation of the products minus the sum of the standard enthalpies of formation of the reactants.

Calorimetry is the procedure for finding the heat transfer in a chemical reaction. A calorimeter is the device used to measure heat transfers. Calorimeters are used to measure the heat transfer at constant pressure, q_p, or the heat transfer at constant volume, q_v.

CHAPTER 7 REVIEW EXERCISE

1. When 266 J of heat is added to a 55.7-g sample of an unknown metal, the temperature increases from 30.5°C to 42.9°C. Calculate the specific heat capacity of the unknown substance.

2. Compare the amount of heat that is needed to raise 5.2 kg Au and 5.2 kg H_2O from 298 K to 310 K. The specific heats of gold and water are 0.130 J/(g·°C) and 4.18 J/(g·°C), respectively.

3. What is the final temperature when 75.0 g H_2O at 95.3°C mixes thoroughly with 50.0 g H_2O at 3.5°C?

4. Calculate the ΔE_{sys} and ΔE_{sur} when the system absorbs 37 J of heat and does 39 J of work on the surroundings.

5. A system is compressed 3.16 L by the surroundings under a constant pressure of 10.0 atm, and the system releases 1.9 kJ of heat to the surroundings. What is ΔE_{sys} and ΔE_{sur}?

6. The formation of two moles of NO(g) from nitrogen, N_2, and oxygen, O_2 requires the addition of 180.5 kJ at standard conditions. (a) Write the equation for the formation of NO. (b) What is the $\Delta H°$ for the reaction? (c) Is this reaction an endothermic reaction or an exothermic reaction?

7. How many kJ of heat are needed to decompose 5.04 g $CaCO_3(s)$ to CaO(s) and $CO_2(g)$ in the following reaction?

$$CaCO_3(s) \rightarrow CaO(s) + CO_2(g) \quad \Delta H° = +178 \text{ kJ}$$

8. Welders use oxyacetylene torches to cut and weld metals. Acetylene, C_2H_2, and O_2 combine and produce CO_2, H_2O, and a large quantity of energy.

$$C_2H_2(g) + 5/2O_2(g) \rightarrow 2CO_2(g) + H_2O(g) \quad \Delta H° = -1.30 \times 10^3 \text{ kJ}$$

(a) If 14.51 g C_2H_2 reacts with 46.2 g O_2, how much heat results? (b) What masses of acetylene and oxygen are needed to increase the temperature of 5.00 kg $H_2O(l)$ from 25.0°C to 60.0°C? Assume that 75.0% of the heat from the reaction transfers to the water.

9. (a) Write the equation for the formation of hydrogen sulfide, $H_2S(g)$. (b) What energy transfer occurs when 1.00 mol $H_2S(g)$ results? (c) How much heat is needed to produce 3.03 g of $H_2S(g)$ from the elements?

10. Use Hess's law to calculate the $\Delta H°$ for the following reaction:

$$N_2O_4(g) \rightarrow 2NO_2(g)$$

from the following equations:

$$
\begin{array}{ll}
NO_2(g) \rightarrow \frac{1}{2}N_2(g) + O_2(g) & \Delta H° = -33.9 \text{ kJ} \\
N_2(g) + 2O_2(g) \rightarrow N_2O_4(g) & \Delta H° = 9.7 \text{ kJ}
\end{array}
$$

11. Given the following equations:

$$
\begin{array}{ll}
H_2(g) + Cl_2(g) \rightarrow 2HCl(g) & \Delta H° = -185 \text{ kJ} \\
H_2(g) + \frac{1}{2}O_2(g) \rightarrow H_2O(g) & \Delta H° = -242 \text{ kJ}
\end{array}
$$

calculate the $\triangle H°$ for

$$4HCl(g) + O_2(g) \rightarrow 2Cl_2(g) + 2H_2O(g)$$

12. Calculate the $\triangle H°$ for the following reaction

$$N_2H_4(l) + 2H_2O_2(l) \rightarrow N_2(g) + 4H_2O(g)$$

The enthalpies of formation for $N_2H_4(l)$, $H_2O_2(g)$, $N_2(g)$, and $H_2O(g)$ are 50.6, −187.8, 0.0, and −241.8 kJ/mol, respectively.

13. Consider the following equation:

$$PF_5(g) \rightarrow PF_3(g) + F_2(g)$$

The $\triangle H°$ for this reaction is 658.2 kJ. If the $\triangle H_f°$ of PF_5 is −1578 kJ/mol, calculate the $\triangle H_f°$ of PF_3.

14. A student calibrates a calorimeter by adding 100.0 g H_2O at 88.1°C to 100.0 g H_2O at 24.8°C in the calorimeter. The final temperature of the H_2O after mixing is 34.3°C. If the specific heat of H_2O is 4.18 J/(g·°C), what is the heat capacity, C, for the calorimeter?

15. A student uses a calorimeter with a heat capacity of 97.3 J/°C to measure the enthalpy of solution of $NaClO_4$, $\triangle H_{soln}°(NaClO_4)$. Initially the student pours 175 g of H_2O at 22.0°C into the calorimeter. After the student adds 8.08 g $NaClO_4$ to the water, the temperature of the $NaClO_4$ solution lowers to 20.7°C. If the specific heat of the $NaClO_4$ solution is 4.0 J/(g·°C), what is the $\triangle H_{soln}°(NaClO_4)$ in kJ/mol?

16. A student places a mixture of methane, $CH_4(g)$ and $O_2(g)$ in a cylinder under a piston. Initially, the volume of the cylinder is 575 cm³. The mixture is then ignited. If the reaction produces 1.95 kJ of energy, and all of the energy is converted to work, what will be the final volume of the cylinder under a constant pressure of 1.15 atm?

17. Benzene, C_6H_6, is a liquid that has a density of 0.88 g/cm³ and octane, C_8H_{18}, is a liquid that has a density of 1.40 g/cm³. The $\triangle H_f°$ for benzene and octane are −49.1 kJ/mol and −283.4 kJ/mol, respectively. (a) Calculate the enthalpy of combustion, $\triangle H_c°$, per cm³ for benzene and octane. (b) Which of these compounds is a better fuel with respect to the amount of energy produced per cm³?

18. The molar enthalpy of combustion for naphthalene, $C_{10}H_8$, is −5154 kJ. If 29.7 g of naphthalene is burned and all of the heat transfers to ice, $H_2O(s)$, at 0.0°C, calculate the mass of ice in kg that could be converted to $H_2O(l)$ at 0.0°C. The amount of heat required to melt one mole of ice to $H_2O(l)$ at 0.0°C is 6.010 kJ/mol (the molar enthalpy of fusion of ice).

19. A 5.00-L calorimeter, with a combined heat capacity of 16.2 kJ/°C, contains a mixture of CH_4 and O_2 at 298 K and 760 torr. This mixture was allowed to react at constant pressure as follows:

$$CH_4(g) + 2O_2(g) \rightarrow CO_2(g) + 2H_2O(g) \quad \triangle H° = -801 \text{ kJ}$$

The increase in temperature of the calorimeter and contents is found to be 2.52 °C. What is the mole fraction of CH_4 in the initial mixture?

ANSWERS TO REVIEW EXERCISE

1. 0.385 J/(g·°C)
2. 8.11 kJ for Au, 2.6×10^2 kJ for H_2O

3. 58.6°C

4. $\triangle E_{sys} = -2$ J, $\triangle E_{sur} = +2$ J

5. $\triangle E_{sys} = +1.3$ kJ, $\triangle E_{sur} = -1.3$ kJ

6. (a) $N_2(g) + O_2(g) \rightarrow 2NO(g)$, (b) $\triangle H° = +180.5$ kJ, (c) endothermic

7. 8.96 kJ

8. (a) 725 kJ, (b) 19.5 g C_2H_2, 60.1 g O_2

9. (a) $H_2(g) + S(s) \rightarrow H_2S(g)$, (b) $\triangle H_f° = -20.6$ kJ, (c) 1.84 kJ

10. 58.1 kJ

11. -114 kJ

12. -642.2 kJ

13. -919.8 kJ/mol

14. 1.9 kJ/°C

15. 14 kJ/mol

16. 17.3 L

17. (a) 34 kJ/cm^3 C_6H_6, 62 kJ/cm^3 C_8H_{18}, (b) C_8H_{18}

18. 3.58 kg H_2O

19. 0.250

8

The Electronic Structure
of Atoms

The arrangement of electrons, the electron configuration, in an atom determines its properties. Therefore, it is important to have a thorough understanding of how the electrons are arranged in atoms. The theory that explains electron configurations is called the quantum theory.

8.1   ELECTROMAGNETIC RADIATION AND QUANTUM THEORY

What is the Quantum Theory?

Quantum theory explains the properties and behavior of small particles such as electrons. This theory was proposed and developed at the beginning of the twentieth century when scientists discovered that the principles of physics developed before 1900 (classical physics) could not explain adequately the properties and behavior of small particles or the interaction of electromagnetic radiation with matter.

Electromagnetic Waves

A moving wave is a disturbance that travels through a medium or through empty space. In addition, there are stationary or standing waves that do not move through a medium. They will be discussed in Section 8.3.

Radiation propagates through space as vibrating electric and magnetic fields that are at right angles to each other. These waves are called electromagnetic radiation. Examples of electromagnetic waves are radio waves, infrared radiation (IR), visible light, and ultraviolet radiation (UV). All electromagnetic waves travel through space with a velocity of 2.998×10^8 m/s (the velocity of light).

WAVELENGTH

The three main characteristics of waves are wavelength, frequency, and amplitude. Wavelength, λ (Greek lowercase lambda), is the distance from one peak on a wave to the next peak. One cycle of a wave is the segment between the two peaks or any other two equivalent points that define the wavelength. Wavelength has the units of length such as m, mm, nm, and pm.

FREQUENCY

The frequency, ν, (the Greek letter nu) of a wave is the number of cycles that pass a point in a time interval–usually one second. The SI unit for frequency is the hertz, Hz. One hertz is one cycle/s or, 1/s (s^{-1}).

AMPLITUDE

The amplitude of a wave is its height measured from the line that cuts the wave in half–the axis of propagation. More simply, the amplitude is the size of the wave.

RELATIONSHIP OF WAVELENGTH AND FREQUENCY

Wavelength, λ, is inversely related to frequency, ν. The proportionality constant that links the wavelength and frequency of electromagnetic waves is the velocity of light, c, which equals 2.998×10^8 m/s in a vacuum.

$$\lambda\nu = c \qquad (8.1)$$

Knowing the wavelength, the equation is rearranged and solved for frequency.

$$\nu = c/\lambda \qquad (8.2)$$

Problem 8.1   Electromagnetic waves A and B have wavelengths of 5.39×10^{-8} m and 10.5 m, respectively. Compare the frequencies of waves A and B.

Solution 8.1   To calculate the frequency of A, divide its wavelength, λ, in meters into the speed of light, 2.998×10^8 m/s.

$$\nu = c/\lambda$$
$$= (2.998 \times 10^8 \text{ m/s})/5.39 \times 10^{-8}\text{m} = 5.56 \times 10^{15} \text{ s}^{-1}$$

Before substituting into the equation, convert the wavelength of B from nm to meters or the units will not cancel.

$$10.5 \text{ nm } \times 1 \text{ m}/1 \times 10^9 \text{ nm } = 1.05 \times 10^{-8} \text{ m}$$
$$\nu = c/\lambda$$
$$= (2.998 \times 10^8 \text{ m/s})/1.05 \times 10^{-8} \text{ m}$$
$$= 2.86 \times 10^{16} \text{ s}^{-1}$$

Because the wavelength of A is longer than that of B, the frequency of A, 5.56×10^{15} s^{-1}, is lower than that of B, 2.86×10^{16} s^{-1}.

Types of Electromagnetic Radiation

The electromagnetic spectrum consists of radio waves, microwaves, infrared (IR), visible light, ultraviolet (UV), x-rays, and gamma rays. Radio waves have the longest wavelength, and gamma rays have the shortest wavelength.

Problem 8.2   Blue light that is emitted by heating CuCl has a frequency of $6.6 \times 10^{14} s^{-1}$. Calculate the wavelength of this light in nm.

Solution 8.2

$$\lambda = c/\nu$$
$$= 3.0 \times 10^8 \text{ m/s}/6.6 \times 10^{14} \text{s}^{-1} = 4.5 \times 10^{-7} \text{ m}$$
$$= 4.5 \times 10^{-7} \text{ m} \times 10^9 \text{ nm/m} = 4.5 \times 10^2 \text{ nm}$$

Quantum Theory

Despite the evidence for the wave nature of light, at the beginning of the twentieth century experimental evidence revealed that electromagnetic radiation, under certain circumstances, had both wave and particle properties.

QUANTA AND PLANCK'S THEORY

In 1900, Max Planck (1885–1947) proposed a theoretical explanation of the properties of light emitted when bodies are heated to high temperatures. He showed that atoms, when heated, can either emit or absorb a certain minimum energy or some integral multiple of that energy. This idea was contrary to the belief of classical physicists who thought that atoms could emit or absorb energy over a continuous range. Scientists termed this fixed amount of energy a quantum (plural, *quanta*), a word derived from the Latin word that means how much. Therefore, Planck presented the idea that the absorption or emission of energy is quantized.

MATHEMATICAL EXPRESSIONS OF PLANCK'S THEORY

Mathematically, Planck presented his explanation as follows:

$$\triangle E = nh\nu \tag{8.3}$$

in which $\triangle E$ is the change in energy, n is a positive integer such as 1, 2, 3, 4, etc., h is a proportionality constant called Planck's constant, and ν is the lowest possible frequency absorbed or emitted by an atom.

In its most general form, Planck presented his quantum theory as follows:

$$\triangle E = h\nu \tag{8.4}$$

in which $\triangle E$ is the energy emitted or absorbed, ν is the frequency of light, and h is Planck's constant. The value of Planck's constant is 6.626×10^{-34} J s. This equation can also be expressed in terms of wavelength. Recall that $\nu = c/\lambda$; therefore, c/λ can be substituted into the equation for ν.

$$\triangle E = \frac{hc}{\lambda} \tag{8.5}$$

Problem 8.3   When sodium is heated, it releases light with many different wavelengths. One of these waves has a wavelength of 589 nm. (a) Calculate the change in energy associated, $\triangle E$, with one quantum of this light. (b) Calculate the $\triangle E$ in kJ/mol.

Solution 8.3   (a) To solve this problem use Eq. 8.5. First, convert the wavelength of the light emitted by Na from nm to m because the value for c is 3.00×10^8 m/s.

$$589 \text{ nm} \times 1 \text{ m}/1 \times 10^9 \text{ nm} = 5.89 \times 10^{-7} \text{ m}$$

Substituting the known values into Eq. 8.5 gives us the following.

$$\Delta E = hc/\lambda$$
$$= (6.63 \times 10^{-34} \text{ J s} \times 3.00 \times 10^8 \text{ m/s})/5.89 \times 10^{-7} \text{ m}$$
$$= 3.38 \times 10^{-19} \text{ J/quantum}$$

(b) Use the conversion factors 1 kJ/1000 J and 6.02×10^{23} quanta/mol to convert to kJ/mol.

$$\Delta E = 3.38 \times 10^{-19} \text{ J} \times 1 \text{ kJ}/1000 \text{ J} \times 6.02 \times 10^{23} \text{ quanta/mol}$$
$$= 203 \text{ kJ/mol}$$

Problem 8.4   How many quanta with a wavelength of 656 nm (red visible light) produce 1.00 kJ of energy?

Solution 8.4   To solve this problem first determine the number of kJ/ quantum. To accomplish this, convert the wavelength 656 nm to 6.56×10^{-7} m. Substitute into Eq. 8.5 and determine the kJ/quantum.

$$\Delta E = hc/\lambda$$
$$= (6.63 \times 10^{-34} \text{ J s} \times 3.00 \times 10^8 \text{ m/s})/6.56 \times 10^{-7} \text{ m}$$
$$= 3.03 \times 10^{-19} \text{ J/ quantum}$$
$$= 3.03 \times 10^{-19} \text{ J/ quantum} \times 1 \text{ kJ}/1000 \text{ J} = 3.03 \times 10^{-22} \text{ kJ/ quantum}$$

Finally, divide the number of kJ/ quantum into the total energy, 1.00 kJ.

$$\text{No. of quanta} = 1.00 \text{ kJ}/3.03 \times 10^{-22} \text{ kJ/ quantum} = 3.30 \times 10^{21} \text{ quanta}$$

Problem 8.5   To remove one electron from a Na atom, 8.22×10^{-19} J of energy is needed. This is called the first ionization energy of Na. Calculate the maximum wavelength in nm needed to remove an electron from a sodium atom.

Solution 8.5

$$\Delta E = hc/\lambda$$
$$\lambda = hc/\Delta E$$
$$= (6.63 \times 10^{-34} \text{ J s} \times 3.00 \times 10^8 \text{ m/s})/8.22 \times 10^{-19} \text{ J}$$
$$= 2.42 \times 10^{-7} \text{ m}$$
$$= 2.42 \times 10^{-7} \text{ m} \times 10^9 \text{ nm/m} = 242 \text{ nm}$$

Einstein and The Photoelectric Effect

In 1905, Albert Einstein (1879–1955) applied quantum theory to solve another of the problems that perplexed physicists at the turn of the twentieth century. Einstein proposed an explanation for a phenomenon known as the photoelectric effect. The photoelectric effect occurs when a beam of electromagnetic radiation (e.g., visible light or uv) strikes the surface of metals and ejects electrons. An electron absorbs enough energy from the light to overcome the forces that bind it to the atom.

Einstein explained the experimental results of the photoelectric effect by suggesting that electromagnetic radiation is composed of very small "particles" or "packets" of energy called photons (quanta of light). These photons have energies, E_{photon}, equal to $h\nu$. Einstein showed that the total energy of a light beam equals the sum of the energies of the large number of photons that make up the beam. Therefore, when light hits a metal, many photons collide with the metal's electrons, transferring totally their energies to them. When this happens, the photons no longer exist–the electrons absorb the photons. If the energy of a photon, $h\nu$, exceeds the energy that binds an electron to the atom, $E_{binding}$, then the photon ejects the electron from the metal. The kinetic energy ($E_{kinetic} = \frac{1}{2}mv^2$) of an ejected electron is the difference between the initial energy of the photon (E_{photon}) and the binding energy of the electron ($E_{binding}$).

$$E_{photon} = E_{binding} + E_{kinetic} \tag{8.6}$$
$$E_{kinetic} = E_{photon} - E_{binding}$$
$$\frac{1}{2}mv^2 = h\nu - E_{binding}$$

Problem 8.6 Calculate the kinetic energy of an electron, $E_{kinetic}$, emitted in a photoelectric effect experiment in which light with a frequency of $6.0 \times 10^{16}\,s^{-1}$ removes electrons from a metal that has a threshold frequency of $2.0 \times 10^{16}\,s^{-1}$.

Solution 8.6

$$E_{kinetic} = E_{photon} - E_{binding}$$
$$= h\nu_{photon} - h\nu_{binding}$$
$$= h(\nu_{photon} - \nu_{binding})$$
$$= 6.63 \times 10^{-34}\,J\,s(6.0 \times 10^{16}\,s^{-1} - 2.0 \times 10^{16}\,s^{-1})$$
$$= 2.65 \times 10^{-17}\,J$$

Problem 8.7 The binding energy, $E_{binding}$, for platinum, Pt, is $9.0 \times 10^{-19}\,J$. What is the maximum kinetic energy of the electrons ejected from Pt using ultraviolet light with a wavelength of 39.0 nm?

Solution 8.7 Begin by changing the wavelength of the light from nm to m. Then, calculate the frequency of the light.

$$39.0\,nm \times 1\,m/10^9\,nm = 3.90 \times 10^{-8}\,m$$
$$\nu = c/\lambda$$
$$= 3.00 \times 10^8\,m/s/3.90 \times 10^{-8}\,m$$
$$= 7.69 \times 10^{15}\,s^{-1}$$

Next, use Eq. 8.5 to calculate the maximum kinetic energy of the electrons.

$$E_{kinetic} = E_{photon} - E_{binding}$$
$$= h\nu_{photon} - E_{binding}$$
$$= (6.63 \times 10^{-34}\,J\,s \times 7.69 \times 10^{15}\,s^{-1}) - 9.0 \times 10^{-19}\,J$$
$$= 5.10 \times 10^{-18}\,J - 9.0 \times 10^{-19}\,J = 4.20 \times 10^{-18}\,J$$

Wave-Particle Duality

The wave and particle nature of light is a complementary picture of the same physical phenomenon. Light should be viewed as both a wave and a particle because neither the wave nor the particle description of light can completely describe all aspects of its behavior. Scientists call this nature of light wave-particle duality.

8.2 ATOMIC SPECTRA AND THE BOHR MODEL OF THE ATOM

Spectroscopy

The study of the properties of light from the emission (or absorption) of energy from matter is called spectroscopy. Light is analyzed using a spectroscope or spectrometer. Light enters this optical instrument through a slit and passes through either a prism or diffraction grating. Both the prism and diffraction grating disperse the light into wavelengths of which it is composed.

Line and Continuous Spectra

Light emitted by different gases each produce their own distinct pattern of colors. Some spectra consist of individual lines at specific frequencies separated by dark regions. These are called line spectra. Others lack the dark regions and have a continuous range of frequencies in their spectra. They are termed continuous spectra. One of the outcomes of early spectroscopy experiments was that each substance has its own characteristic spectrum.

The Hydrogen Spectrum

The Swiss scientist Johann Balmer (1825–1898) proposed a mathematical equation that can be used to calculate the wavelengths of the lines in the visible spectrum of hydrogen. One way to express Balmer's equation is as follows.

$$\frac{1}{\lambda} = 1.097 \times 10^7 \left(\frac{1}{2^2} - \frac{1}{n^2} \right) \qquad (n > 2) \qquad (8.7)$$

In Eqn 8.7, n is an integer with a value greater than 2, λ is the wavelength in m, and $1.097 \times 10^7 \text{ m}^{-1}$ is a constant (the Rydberg constant).

Problem 8.8 (a) Use the Balmer Equation to calculate the wavelength in nm when $n = 3$, the longest wavelength in the visible H spectrum. (b) What trend in wavelength is found as the n value increases?

Solution 8.8 (a) Substitute 3 for n into the Balmer Equation as follows.

$$1/\lambda = 1.097 \times 10^7 \text{ m}^{-1} \, (\tfrac{1}{2}^2 - 1/n^2)$$
$$= 1.097 \times 10^7 \text{ m}^{-1}(1/4 - 1/3^2)$$
$$= 1.524 \times 10^6 \text{ m}^{-1}$$
$$\lambda = 1/1.524 \times 10^6 \text{ m}^{-1}$$
$$\lambda = 6.563 \times 10^{-7} \text{ m} \times 1 \times 10^9 \text{ nm/m} = 656.3 \text{ nm}$$

The answer, 656.3 nm, is a red line in the spectrum of hydrogen.

(b) Substituting the n values equal to 4, 5, and 6 gives the wavelengths for three shorter wavelength lines in the visible spectrum of hydrogen–green, blue, and violet lines. These lines in the visible spectrum of hydrogen are called the Balmer Series.

Basic Postulates of the Bohr Model of the Hydrogen Atom

In 1913, the Danish scientist Neils Bohr (1885–1962) proposed a model of the H atom that incorporated the principles of quantum theory to account for the lines in the hydrogen spectrum.

ENERGY LEVELS IN THE BOHR ATOM

Bohr calculated the energy associated with each orbit. He assigned a value of 0.0 J to an electron that was totally removed from the nucleus. As the nucleus attracts the electron, the electron loses energy and moves to lower energy orbits until it finally reaches the ground state, the lowest allowable energy orbit. Bohr found that the energies of the orbits could be calculated as follows:

$$E_n = \frac{-Rhc}{n^2} \tag{8.8}$$

where E_n is the energy of an electron in the nth orbit, R is the Rydberg constant (named after J. R. Rydberg (1854–1919)) and has a value of 1.097×10^7 m^{-1}, h is Planck's constant, c is the velocity of light, and n is the principal quantum number. Because R, h, and c are constants, they can be converted to a single constant, R_H, as follows.

$$R_H = Rhc$$
$$= 1.097 \times 10^7 \text{ m}^{-1} \times 6.626 \times 10^{-34} \text{ J s} \times 2.998 \times 10^8 \text{ m/s}$$
$$= 2.179 \times 10^{-18} \text{ J}$$

Thus, Bohr's Equation simplifies to Eqn 8.9.

$$E_n = \frac{-R_H}{n^2} \tag{8.9}$$

Problem 8.9   Calculate the energies of electrons in the first two orbits of the Bohr atom, and explain their meaning.

Solution 8.9   An electron in the ground state ($n = 1$) has an energy of -2.179×10^{-18} J. This number is calculated by dividing 1^2 into the value of R_H.

$$E_n = -R_H/n^2$$
$$E_1 = -2.179 \times 10^{-18} \text{ J}/1^2 = -2.179 \times 10^{-18} \text{ J}$$

An electron in the first excited state ($n = 2$) has an energy equivalent to -5.448×10^{-19} J ($E_2 = -2.179 \times 10^{-18}$ J$/2^2$). The energy of an electron in the second orbit is less negative than one in the first orbit.

FREQUENCY OF LIGHT RELEASED IN THE BOHR ATOM

Equation 8.9 can be used to derive equations that give the change in energy, $\triangle E$, and frequency of light released and the change of energy as a function of the electron transition. They are expressed as follows.

$$\triangle E = R_H \left(\frac{1}{n_i^2} - \frac{1}{n_f^2} \right) \tag{8.10}$$

$$\nu = \frac{R_H}{h} \left(\frac{1}{n_i^2} - \frac{1}{n_f^2} \right) \tag{8.11}$$

Problem 8.10   An electron in a H atom moves from $n = 2$ to $n = 1$. Calculate the frequency in Hz (s^{-1}) of the photon released as a result of this electron transition.

Solution 8.10   To solve this problem, substitute the known values into Eq. 8.11. For this electron transition n_f is 1 and n_i is 2, and the values of R_H and h are 2.179×10^{-18} J and 6.626×10^{-34} J s, respectively.

$$\nu = R_H/h(1/n_i^2 - 1/n_f^2)$$
$$= 2.179 \times 10^{-18} \text{ J}/6.626 \times 10^{-34} \text{ J s}(\tfrac{1}{2}^2 - 1/1^2)$$
$$= -2.466 \times 10^{15} \text{ Hz}$$

Problem 8.11 If enough energy is added to an atom, it ionizes and produces a cation. When an electron is removed from a gaseous H atom, a gaseous H ion results, $H^+(g)$. The minimum energy needed to remove an electron from a neutral gaseous atom is called the first ionization energy. Calculate the first ionization energy for a H atom, assuming the electron is initially in the ground state.

Solution 8.11

To ionize the electron in a H atom, energy must be added to move the electron from $n = 1$ to $n = \infty$. An electron totally removed from an atom is in the infinite energy level, $n = \infty$. Therefore, substitute the known values, 1 and ∞, into Eq. 8.10.

$$\triangle E = R_H(1/n_i^2 - 1/n_f^2)$$
$$= 2.179 \times 10^{-18} \text{ J} (1/1^2 - 1/\infty^2)$$

Because the denominator of the $1/\infty^2$ is very large, its reciprocal is essentially zero; thus, the equation becomes

$$= 2.179 \times 10^{-18} \text{ J} (1 - 0)$$
$$= 2.179 \times 10^{-18} \text{ J}$$

8.3   WAVE PROPERTIES OF MATTER

Wave Mechanics

Heisenberg and Schrödinger, independent of each other, proposed mathematical explanations that allow us to understand the nature of electrons in atoms. Today, this approach is called wave, or quantum, mechanics.

THE DE BROGLIE HYPOTHESIS

In 1923, the French scientist Louis de Broglie (1892–1987) proposed a change in the way that scientists view small particles of matter such as electrons. He showed that electrons and other bodies have a dual nature–they are matter-waves or wave-particles.

Mathematically, the de Broglie's Hypothesis is stated as follows

$$\lambda = \frac{h}{mv} \tag{8.12}$$

in which λ is the wavelength of a body, h is Planck's constant, m is its mass, and v is its velocity. This equation allows us to calculate the wavelength of an electron, or any moving body, that travels at constant velocity.

Problem 8.12   (a) What is the wavelength of an electron that has a velocity of 5.0×10^5 m/s? The mass of an electron is 9.1×10^{-31} kg. (b) What is the wavelength of a 1.0-kg mass that has a velocity of 1.0 m/s? Explain the results.

Solution 8.12

(a) The wavelength of the electron is calculated as follows.

$$\lambda = h/(mv)$$
$$= 6.6 \times 10^{-34} \text{ J s}/(9.1 \times 10^{-31} \text{ kg} \times 5.0 \times 10^5 \text{ m/s})$$
$$= 1.5 \times 10^{-8} \text{ m (15 nm)}$$

This wavelength, 1.5×10^{-8} m, is well within the range that can be measured.

(b) The wavelength of the 1.0 kg body moving a 1.0 m/s is calculated as follows.

$$\lambda = h/(mv)$$
$$= 6.6 \times 10^{-34} \text{ J s}/(1.0 \text{ kg} \times 1.0 \text{ m/s}) = 6.6 \times 10^{-34} \text{ m}$$

Such an infinitesimal wavelength is too small to detect. Hence, only very low-mass particles such as electrons, protons, and neutrons, have detectable wave properties.

MATTER-WAVES

Matter-waves are waves that do not move throughout a medium or space. They are now considered because matter-waves are associated with electrons that are restricted to atoms. Matter-waves are often called stationary or standing waves. Stationary waves are quantized. This means that some values are allowed and others are forbidden. Their wavelengths are restricted to certain values given by the following equation:

$$\lambda = \frac{2r}{n} \qquad (8.13)$$

where r is the radius of the orbit, n is a positive integer, and λ is the wavelength of the matter-wave.

A wave that does not fit into an atom interferes with itself and causes some of the wave to cancel. The canceling of one wave by another is called destructive interference of waves. Destructive interference of the wave prevents the electron associated with this matter-wave from existing in this state.

The Uncertainty Principle Defined

If the electron exhibits wave properties, what is the possibility of identifying its exact location at a particular instant? Because a wave spreads out in space, it is impossible to pinpoint its exact location. At best, only amplitude of the wave at a specific point in space can be measured. In 1927, Werner Heisenberg (1901–1976) solved this perplexing problem when he proposed one of the most controversial principles of the twentieth century, the uncertainty principle. A statement of Heisenberg's Uncertainty Principle is that the position and the momentum (mass × velocity) of an electron cannot be precisely measured simultaneously.

THE UNCERTAINTY PRINCIPLE–MATHEMATICAL DEFINITION

One way to write a mathematical statement of the uncertainty principle is:

$$\triangle x \cdot \triangle p \geq h/4\pi \qquad (8.14)$$

where $\triangle x$ is the uncertainty in the measurement of the position of an electron, $\triangle p$ is the uncertainty in measurement of the momentum of an electron, and h is Planck's constant. The Heisenberg equation states that the uncertainty in the position of a particle multiplied by the uncertainty in the momentum must be greater than or equal to $h/4\pi$.

Problem 8.13   (a) If the uncertainty in measuring the position of an electron moving along the x axis is 1.0×10^{-3} nm, what is the uncertainty in its velocity? For purposes of comparison, note that the diameter of a H atom, the smallest atom, is 0.08 nm. (b) If the uncertainty in measuring the position of a 0.35-kg ball is 0.1 cm along the x axis, what is the uncertainty in its velocity? Explain the results.

Solution 8.13

(a) The mathematical expression for the uncertainty principle is as follows (Eq. 8.14).

$$\triangle x \cdot \triangle p \geq h/4\pi$$

Because $\triangle p$ equals $\triangle(mv)$ and the mass of the electron is constant then

$$\triangle x \cdot m \triangle v \geq h/4\pi$$

Rearranging the equation and solving for the uncertainty in velocity, $\triangle v$, gives the following equation:

$$\triangle v = \frac{h}{m \triangle x\, 4\pi}$$

The mass of the electron is 9.11×10^{-31} kg, h is 6.626×10^{-34} J s (kg m^2 s/s^2), π is 3.14, and the uncertainty of the position of the electron is 1.0×10^{-3} nm, which must be converted to 1.0×10^{-12} m. Hence, substitute these values into the equation as follows and solve for $\triangle v$.

$$\triangle v = \frac{6.626 \times 10^{-34} \text{ J s}}{9.11 \times 10^{-31} \text{ kg} \times 1 \times 10^{-12} \text{ m} \times 4 \times 3.14}$$

$$= 5.8 \times 10^{7} \text{ m/s}$$

Our result shows that the small uncertainty in position, 1×10^{-12} m, gives us a large uncertainty in velocity, 5.8×10^{7} m/s. To put this in perspective, the velocity of light is 3×10^{8} m/s. Thus, our uncertainty is about 20% the velocity of light–a large uncertainty.

(b) For the ball, use the same equation, but substitute 0.35 kg for the mass of the ball and convert 0.10 cm to 1.0×10^{-3} m.

$$\triangle v = \frac{6.626 \times 10^{-34} \text{ J s}}{0.35 \text{ kg} \times 1 \times 10^{-3} \text{ m} \times 4 \times 3.14} = 1.5 \times 10^{-31} \text{ m/s}$$

The uncertainty in velocity for the ball is 1.5×10^{-31} m/s. Such a small uncertainty is not detectable. Therefore, there is essentially no uncertainty in the velocity of the ball. It's velocity is known to the limit of the measuring device.

The Schrödinger Equation

The Austrian physicist Erwin Schrödinger (1887–1961) extended the ideas proposed by de Broglie to explain the behavior of the electron in a H atom. Schrödinger expressed his results in the form of a complex equation now known as the Schrödinger equation. The Schrödinger equation for just one dimension may be expressed as follows:

$$-\left(\frac{h^2}{8\pi^2 m}\right) \frac{d^2\psi}{dx^2} + V\psi = E\psi \tag{8.16}$$

where h is Planck's constant, m is the mass of the electron, x is the displacement of the electron along the x axis, V is the potential energy of the electron, E is the total energy of the electron, and ψ (the Greek lowercase letter psi) is the wave function.

MEANING OF THE SCHRÖDINGER EQUATION

To understand the solutions of the Schrödinger Equation recall that only certain wavelengths of stationary waves can be found. Schrödinger showed that only certain wave functions, ψ, can be associated with the matter-waves of electrons. Each of the wave functions designates an allowable energy state for the electron in the atom. Once again, the most fundamental principle of quantum theory applies–the energy of the electron is quantized because only certain matter-waves can be assigned to an electron in an atom.

THE WAVE FUNCTION AND ORBITALS

The actual physical meaning of the wave function, ψ, has little importance to us. However, the square of the electron's wave function, ψ^2, at a specific point in the atom, gives the probability density, which is the probability (the likelihood) of locating the electron at that point in space. Keep in mind that the uncertainty principle tells us that if the Schrödinger Equation gives us the energy of the electron with minimal uncertainty, then there must be a large uncertainty in the position of the electron. Thus, we can only predict the probability of locating an electron at a certain location in the atom when in a specific energy state. The wave functions for each of these allowed energy states are called orbitals.

8.4 QUANTUM NUMBERS AND ATOMIC ORBITALS

Principal Quantum Number, n

The principal quantum number, n, is related to the total energy for an electron. This is the same quantum number encountered in the Bohr model. It can have all positive integral values from 1 to infinity. An electron in the lowest energy level has a principal quantum number of 1. As the value of n increases, the average distance from the nucleus increases. An electron with a n value of 2 is, on an average, farther from the nucleus then an electron whose n value is 1.

In multielectron atoms, electrons with the same principal quantum number are said to be in the same electron shell. A number is assigned to the electron shell that equals the principal quantum number.

Azimuthal or Angular Momentum Quantum Number, l

The azimuthal quantum number, l, defines the sublevel of an electron in an energy level. The values of the azimuthal quantum number depend on the value of the principal quantum number. It can have all integral values from 0 to $n - 1$. In multielectron atoms, electrons with the same azimuthal quantum number, l, are said to be in the same electron subshell.

Problem 8.14   What l values are associated with $n = 1, 2,$ and 3? What do these values mean?

Solution 8.14   When n equals 1, the only allowable value of l is 0, which is $n - 1\,(1 - 1 = 0)$. This means that the first energy level ($n = 1$) can only have one sublevel. When n equals 2, l can have the values 0 and 1. This means that the second energy level has two sublevels. When n equals 3, l can have three values, 0, 1, and 2, indicating that three sublevels make up the third energy level.

SUBSHELLS

The number of subshells in a shell equals the principal quantum number, n. For example, the fourth shell has four subshells because the allowable l quantum numbers are 0, 1, 2, and 3. Letters that were once designations for spectral lines are used to identify the subshells. The letter s identifies orbitals with $l = 0$, p identifies those with $l = 1$, d designates orbitals with $l = 2$, and f designates those with $l = 3$.

Magnetic Quantum Number, m_l

The magnetic quantum number, m_l, determines the number of different orbitals within a subshell. The allowed values of the magnetic quantum number depend on the value of l and can have all integral values between $+l$, 0, and $-l$. The only value that m_l can have is 0 when l equals 0. This means that the s subshell has only one orbital. When l equals 1 (the p subshell), the allowed m_l values are $+1$, 0, and -1. Three values for the m_l quantum number means that three orbitals make up the p subshell.

A mathematical formula may be used to calculate the number of orbitals within a subshell. Each subshell can have $2l + 1$ orbitals. The d subshell ($l = 2$) has $2 \times 2 + 1$ or 5 orbitals with m_l quantum numbers equal to $+2$, $+1$, 0, -1, and -2. A similar calculation shows that the f subshell ($l = 3$) has seven orbitals ($m_l = +3$, $+2$, $+1$, 0, -1, -2, -3).

Shapes and Locations of Atomic Orbitals

Let's consider the lowest energy electron in a H atom, $n = 1$ and $l = 0$. An electron probability density map is drawn to show the shape of this orbital. To obtain such a map, the Schrödinger Equation is solved to obtain the wave function. Then the value of ψ^2 is calculated at a fixed point in the atom. Doing this thousands of times results in a spherical distribution for the lowest-energy electron.

THE s SUBLEVEL

On average, an electron in the lower energy 1s orbital lies closer to the nucleus than an electron in the 2s or 3s. A diagram of the 2s reveals two regions of significant electron density separated by a region of zero electron density at about distance of 0.11 nm. This region is a node, the place where an electron cannot be found. The distribution for the 3s shows two nodes that separate three regions of significant electron density. Each of the boundary surfaces of these s orbitals is that of a sphere. The s orbital has spherical symmetry—a symmetrical distribution. The radius of the sphere depends on the value of n.

THE p SUBLEVEL

The distribution for the lowest energy p orbitals ($n = 2, l = 1$) is different from that of s orbitals. Each p orbital lies along an axis. Hence, they are known as the p_x, p_y, and p_z. Unlike the s orbital, the p orbitals are directional, which means that the probability of finding an electron depends on the direction considered. For example, an electron in the p_x orbital has a very low probability of being found along either the y or z axes because it is most probably located somewhere along the x axis. Another important characteristic of p orbitals is that they have two unconnected lobes. Between the two lobes is a region of space called a nodal plane where ψ^2 is zero.

THE d SUBLEVEL

The boundary surfaces of d orbitals ($n = 3, l = 2$) are more complex distributions than either the s or p orbitals. Three of the five d orbitals—the d_{xy}, d_{yz}, and d_{xz}—have four lobes each located in a plane between the axes. One of the d orbitals, $d_{x^2 - y^2}$, has four lobes located in a plane aligned with the x and y axes. The final d orbital, the d_{z^2}, has two lobes with a doughnut-shaped surface between the lobes. Note that two nodal planes ($l = 2$) are between the lobes of the d orbitals.

THE *f* SUBLEVEL

The *f* sublevel has seven *f* orbitals ($l = 3$). Each of the *f* orbitals has a rather complex distribution that is difficult to represent in two dimensions. Three nodal planes separate the eight lobes of high electron density in *f* orbitals. The *f* orbital distributions are not as important to understand because they generally do not participate in the formation of chemical bonds in simple molecules.

Spin Quantum Number, m_s

A fourth quantum number is needed to designate an electron in an orbital. This quantum number is termed the spin quantum number, m_s. In the 1920s, scientists proposed the idea of electron spin when they discovered that electrons interacted with magnetic fields as if they were tiny magnets. Charged bodies such as the electron produce a magnetic field when they spin. An electron that spins in one direction generates a magnetic field that is equal in magnitude but opposite to one that spins in the opposite direction. Therefore, the electron can only have two orientations with respect to a magnetic field; i.e., electron spin is quantized. The values $+\frac{1}{2}$ and $-\frac{1}{2}$ are assigned for the spin quantum number, m_s, and they correspond to the two possible orientations an electron can have in a magnetic field.

Problem 8.15 What do each of the following mean? (a) $n = 4$, (b) $n = 2$, $l = 1$, (c) $n = 3$, $l = 2$, $m_l = 0$

Solution 8.15

(a) The n quantum number represents the energy level; thus, $n = 4$ represents the fourth energy level.
(b) The l quantum number represents a sublevel in an energy level. When $l = 1$, the p sublevel is indicated; thus, $n = 2$, $l = 1$ represents p sublevel in the second energy level.
(c) The m_l quantum number represents a specific orbital in a sublevel; thus, $n = 3$, $l = 2$, $m_l = 0$, represents a specific orbital in the d sublevel of the third energy level.

Problem 8.16 (a) What possible values can l have when $n = 4$? (b) What possible values can m_l have when $l = 4$? Explain each answer.

Solution 8.16

(a) The l quantum number can have all integer values up to $n - 1$. Thus, when $n = 4$, the possible l values are 0, 1, 2, and 3. This means that the fourth energy level can be divided into four sublevels ($s, p, d,$ and f).
(b) The m_l quantum number can have all integer values between $+l$ and $-l$. Hence, when $l = 4$, the possible values of m_l are +4, +3, +2, +1, 0, −1, −2, −3, and −4. This is a total of 9 orbitals. The letter designation for the sublevel when $l = 4$ is the g sublevel. This shows that the g sublevel has 9 orbitals. This level is not occupied in the ground state of atoms.

Problem 8.17 What is the maximum number of electrons in an atom that can have the following quantum numbers? (a) $n = 2$, (b) $n = 4$, $m_s = +\frac{1}{2}$

Solution 8.17

(a) When $n = 2$, the l values can be 0 or 1. This means the second energy level has both s and p sublevels. The s subshell holds a maximum of two electrons and the p holds a maximum of six electrons; therefore, a total of eight electrons can have $n = 2$.
(b) The fourth energy level, $n = 4$, can hold a maximum of 32 electrons in the $s, p, d,$ and f subshells. However, only half will have a spin quantum number of $+\frac{1}{2}$; hence, a maximum of 16 electrons can have $n = 4$, $m_s = +\frac{1}{2}$.

8.5   ELECTRON CONFIGURATIONS
OF ATOMS

The designation of the distribution of electrons in electron shells and orbitals is called electron configuration.

Representing Electron Configurations

The population of orbitals can be specified in two different ways. First, write the principal quantum number, n, and the letter that corresponds to the subshell, l, with a superscript that shows the number of electrons in the subshell. For example, the one electron in the lowest energy subshell of H is expressed $1s^1$.

Or, an orbital diagram can be drawn that shows the occupancy of electrons by using arrows inside a box or circle. An arrow that points to the top of the page represents an electron that behaves as if it spins in one direction. An arrow that points to the bottom of the page represents an electron with the opposite spin properties. For example, a $1s$ orbital with two electrons is represented as follows.

$$\boxed{\uparrow\downarrow}$$
$$1s$$

The Aufbau Principle

The Aufbau Principle states that electrons fill lower-energy orbitals before higher-energy orbitals. Therefore, when writing the electron configuration that best approximates the ground state for an atom, place the number of electrons that equals the atomic number in the lowest possible energy orbitals available.

Writing Electron Configurations of Atoms

How are the ground state electron configurations for the atoms written? To accomplish this, let's begin with H, the simplest atom, and then proceed to the atom with one more electron, He. The next atom has the same electrons as the one before, plus one more. According to the Aufbau Principle, this electron fills the lowest energy orbital.

THE PERIODIC TABLE AND ELECTRON CONFIGURATIONS

It is important to recognize that the periodic table is organized according to the arrangement of electrons in atoms. During the discussion of the electron configurations of specific atoms follow along on a periodic table. In the outermost shells of the elements in groups 1 (IA) and 2 (IIA), the s subshell fills. The outer p subshell fills in the elements in groups 13 (IIIA) to 18 (VIIIA), the outer d subshell fills in the transition elements (groups 3 to 12), and the outer f subshell fills in the lanthanide and actinide series. Following the periodic table in order of atomic number shows the order in which the subshells fill.

Problem 8.18   (a) Write the electron configuration and orbital diagram for the one electron in a H atom. (b) Write the set of four quantum that represents this electron.

Solution 8.18

(a) The lowest energy orbital in H is the $1s$. Thus, the electron configuration and orbital diagram for hydrogen are as follows.

$$\text{H} \quad 1s^1 \quad \boxed{\uparrow}$$
$$1s$$

(b) The set of four quantum numbers associated with H's electron is

$$n = 1, \; l = 0, \; m_l = 0, \; m_s = +\tfrac{1}{2}$$

Even though $+\frac{1}{2}$ is written for the m_S quantum number, $-\frac{1}{2}$ could have been used because the electron can have an apparent spin in either direction.

Pauli Exclusion Principle

The Pauli Exclusion Principle states that no two electrons in an atom can have the same set of four quantum numbers: n, l, m_l, and m_S. This leads to an important conclusion about the electrons in an atom–orbitals can hold a maximum of two electrons and they must have opposite spins.

Problem 8.19   Using quantum numbers, show how the two electrons in He illustrate the Pauli Exclusion Principle.

Solution 8.19   The first electron in He occupies the $1s$ orbital. Thus, it has the following set of quantum numbers.

$$n = 1,\ l = 0,\ m_l = 0,\ m_S = +\frac{1}{2}$$

According to the Pauli Exclusion Principle, He's second electron must have a different set of quantum numbers. Because it has same values for n, l, and m_l, it must have a different value for m_S. Thus, the quantum numbers for He's second electron is

$$n = 1,\ l = 0,\ m_l = 0,\ m_S = -\frac{1}{2}$$

If two electrons have the same n, l, and m_l, then the only two possibilities for m_S are $\pm\frac{1}{2}$.

PAIRED AND UNPAIRED SPINS OF ELECTRONS

An orbital can hold a maximum of two electrons. These two electrons must have opposite spin properties. Stated differently, two electrons in an orbital have paired spins. Thus, the electron configuration and orbital diagram for helium are as follows.

$$\text{He } 1s^2 \quad \boxed{\uparrow\downarrow}$$
$$1s$$

The one electron in the $1s$ orbital of H is said to be unpaired.

ELECTRON CONFIGURATIONS OF LI THROUGH NE

Lithium Configuration. Lithium has three electrons and the first two are in the lower energy $1s$ orbital. Its third electron occupies the $2s$ orbital because it is the next lowest energy orbital. Hence, the electron configuration and orbital diagram for Li are as follows.

$$\text{Li } 1s^2\,2s^1 \quad \boxed{\uparrow\downarrow} \quad \boxed{\uparrow}$$
$$1s \qquad 2s$$

Because the outer electron of Li is in the $2s$ orbital, its set of quantum numbers are $n = 2$, $l = 0$, $m_l = 0$, $m_S = +\frac{1}{2}$.

Beryllium Configuration. A second electron may occupy the $2s$ orbital. Hence, the electron configuration and the orbital diagram for Be, the atom with four electrons, are as follows.

$$\text{Be } 1s^2\,2s^2 \quad \boxed{\uparrow\downarrow} \quad \boxed{\uparrow\downarrow}$$
$$1s \qquad 2s$$

According to the Pauli Exclusion Principle, the second electron in the $2s$ orbital must have the of quantum numbers of $n = 2$, $l = 0$, $m_l = 0$, $m_S = -\frac{1}{2}$. Electrons in both the $1s$ and $2s$ are paired in Be.

Boron Configuration. Boron has five electrons and is the first atom with an electron in the $2p$ subshell, the lowest energy subshell after the $1s$ and $2s$. Therefore the electron configuration and orbital diagram for B are

B $1s^2 2s^2 2p^1$ [↑↓] [↑↓] [↑] [ ] [ ]
$\quad\quad\quad\quad\quad\quad$ $1s$ $\quad$ $2s$ $\quad$ $2p_x$ $2p_y$ $2p_z$

Boron has two electrons in the $1s$, two electrons in the $2s$, and one electron in the $2p_x$–the $2p$ orbital oriented along the x axis. Arbitrarily, the outermost electron of B was placed in the $2p_x$ orbital. However, this electron could have been placed in either the $2p_y$ or $2p_z$ because the three $2p$ orbitals are of equal energy. Orbitals with the same energy are termed degenerate orbitals. The set of quantum numbers for the $2p$ electron in B is $n = 2$, $l = 1$, $m_l = +1$, $m_s = +\frac{1}{2}$.

Carbon Configuration. Carbon has six electrons, which means that two of its electrons are in the $2p$ subshell. Two possibilities exist for the location of the second $2p$ electron: in the p orbital that holds the first electron, or in an empty p orbital.

Hund's Rule. Hund's Rule is used to decide what orbital this electron will occupy. Hund's Rule states that the most stable arrangement of electrons in a subshell is the one that has the greatest number of unpaired electrons with parallel spins. Having parallel spins means that the electrons spin in the same direction.

Therefore, the electron configuration and orbital diagram for C are as follows.

C $1s^2 2s^2 2p^2$ [↑↓] [↑↓] [↑] [↑] [ ]
$\quad\quad\quad\quad\quad\quad$ $1s$ $\quad$ $2s$ $\quad$ $2p_x$ $2p_y$ $2p_z$

The set of four quantum numbers for the $2p_y$ in C is $n = 2$, $l = 1$, $m_l = 0$, $m_s = +\frac{1}{2}$. Note that the only change in quantum numbers is the value of m_l, which means the electron is in a different orbital than the other $2p$ electron. Because both electrons have the same spin quantum number, they have parallel spins.

Nitrogen Configuration. When applying Hund's Rule to a N atom, which has seven electrons, the following electron configuration and orbital diagram are obtained.

N $1s^2 2s^2 2p^3$ [↑↓] [↑↓] [↑] [↑] [↑]
$\quad\quad\quad\quad\quad\quad$ $1s$ $\quad$ $2s$ $\quad$ $2p_x$ $2p_y$ $2p_z$

The set of four quantum numbers for the $2p_z$ in N is $n = 2$, $l = 1$, $m_l = -1$, $m_s = +\frac{1}{2}$. Each of the three $2p$ electrons in a N atom is in a different $2p$ orbital. Each of these electron has the same spin orientation.

Oxygen Configuration. Oxygen has eight electrons, four of which are in the $2p$ subshell. Thus, O is the first atom to have paired electrons in the $2p$. The electron configuration and orbital diagram for O are

O $1s^2 2s^2 2p^4$ [↑↓] [↑↓] [↑↓] [↑] [↑]
$\quad\quad\quad\quad\quad\quad$ $1s$ $\quad$ $2s$ $\quad$ $2p_x$ $2p_y$ $2p_z$

The set of quantum numbers for this electron, which pairs with an electron in the $2p_x$, is $n = 2$, $l = 1$, $m_l = +1$, $m_s = -\frac{1}{2}$. It has the same first three quantum numbers as the other electrons in the $2p_x$ but has the opposite spin quantum number, $m_s = -\frac{1}{2}$.

Fluorine and Neon Configurations. Fluorine has five and Ne has six electrons in the $2p$ subshell. Their electron configurations and orbital diagrams are as follows.

F $1s^2 2s^2 2p^5$ [↑↓] [↑↓] [↑↓] [↑↓] [↑]
$\quad\quad\quad\quad\quad\quad$ $1s$ $\quad$ $2s$ $\quad$ $2p_x$ $2p_y$ $2p_z$

Ne $\quad 1s^2\,2s^2\,2p^6$

$\uparrow\downarrow$	$\uparrow\downarrow$	$\uparrow\downarrow$	$\uparrow\downarrow$	$\uparrow\downarrow$
$1s$	$2s$	$2p_x$	$2p_y$	$2p_z$

Neon has filled $2p$ orbitals. Because the $n = 2$ shell has only two subshells, s and p, no more electrons can fill orbitals in this shell.

Valence Configuration. The electrons in the highest-energy subshell are termed the valence electrons. The valence electrons in the atoms Li to Ne are in the $2s$ and $2p$ subshells. Valence electrons are always in the s and p orbitals. Electrons in d and f subshells are not valence electrons because they are inner-level electrons.

Problem 8.20 (a) Write the electron configuration for Na. (b) Write the set of quantum numbers that corresponds to the highest-energy electron in Na.

Solution 8.20

(a) Sodium has 11 electrons of which 10 have the same configuration as Ne. To simplify the writing of electron configurations, it is common practice to write the symbol for neon in brackets, [Ne], to represent the filled noble gas (group 18 or VIIIA) inner core of electrons, $1s^2\,2s^2\,2p^6$. The highest energy electron in Na is the $3s^1$. Thus, the electron configuration for Na may be expressed as follows.

$$\text{Na [Ne] } 3s^1$$

The $3s^1$ is the valence electron for Na.

(b) The quantum numbers that describe the $3s^1$ are $n = 3$, $l = 0$, $m_l = 0$, and $m_s = +\frac{1}{2}$.

ELECTRON CONFIGURATION OF Al THROUGH Ar

In the next six elements, Al to Ar, the $3p$ subshell fills in a manner similar to the $2p$. The outer shell of Al has $3s^2\,3p^1$. The number of electrons in the $3p$ increases by one until Ar is reached with a $3s^2\,3p^6$ configuration.

THE $4s$ FILLS BEFORE THE $3d$

Following the periodic table readily shows that the $4s$ fills before the $3d$. Potassium, K, is a member of group 1 (IA), all of which have outer electrons in the s subshell. Hence, the electron configurations for potassium and calcium are K [Ar] $4s^1$ and Ca [Ar] $4s^2$.

THE "IRREGULAR" FILLING OF THE $3d$

The $3d$ fills after the $4s$ subshell. Scandium, Sc, is the first element with an electron in the $3d$ subshell. The $3d$ does not fill regularly from $3d^1$ to $3d^{10}$. Instead, the $3d$ fills as might be predicted until Cr is reached. Chromium, Cr, has a $3d^5\,4s^1$ configuration rather than the expected $3d^4\,4s^2$ configuration. Continuing from Mn to Ni, a regular filling of the $3d$ subshell is observed. However, in Cu atoms the energy of the $3d$ subshell is lower than that of the $4s$ subshell. Thus, the configuration for Cu is [Ar] $3d^{10}\,4s^1$. Other examples of the stabilization associated with a completely filled subshell will be encountered. Finally, Zn has both a filled $3d$ and $4s$ (Zn [Ar] $3d^{10}\,4s^2$).

Problem 8.21 (a) What sublevel fills after the $3d$? (b) What is the electron configuration of Kr?

Solution 8.21

(a) After the $3d$ subshell, the $4p$ subshell fills, starting with Ga and ending at Kr.
(b) Krypton, Kr, (Z = 36) is the first element to have a complete $4p$ configuration. Its configuration is [Ar] $3d^{10}\,4s^2\,4p^6$.

How Do the Remaining Subshells Fill? The 5*s* fills before the 4*d*. This is exactly what happens when *n* = 4. In a similar manner, the 5*s* fills in Sr and then the 4*d* fills from Y to Cd. The irregularities in filling the 4*d* differ from those of the 3*d*. Then the 5*p* fills from In to Xe. Xenon's configuration is [Kr] $4d^{10} 5s^2 5p^6$. After the 5*p* subshell, the 6*s* subshell fills.

Then, the 4*f* fills. The 4*f* subshell holds 14 electrons and fills irregularly because of the large number of electrons in each atom. In addition, the 4*f* and 5*d* subshells have about the same energy in these atoms. The group of elements, Ce to Lu, in which the 4*f* subshell fills is known as the lanthanide series because they follow lanthanum (Z = 57) on the periodic table. After the 4*f* fills, the 5*d* subshell fills from Hf to Hg, and then the 6*p* fills from Tl to Rn. The electron configuration of radon is [Xe] $4f^{14} 5d^{10} 6s^2 6p^6$.

The 7*s* is the next subshell to fill followed by the 5*f*. The group of fourteen elements, from Th to Lw, in which the 5*f* subshell fills is termed the actinide series, and they lie directly below the elements in the lanthanide series. Following the actinides are the last known elements. They have electrons filling the 6*d* subshell.

Problem 8.22 Write the outer-level and complete electronic configuration for strontium, Sr.

Solution 8.22 First, find Sr on the periodic table. It has 38 electrons, is in the fifth period, and is a member of group IIA. All elements in group IIA have an outer electronic configuration of two electrons in the *s* orbital, s^2. Then, follow the periodic table in order of increasing atomic number. Hence, the inner-level electronic configuration of Sr is the same as Kr (Z = 36). The electronic configuration of Kr is $1s^2 2s^2 2p^6 3s^2 3p^6 3d^{10} 4s^2 4p^6$. To this add the two outer level electrons, $5s^2$, to give the complete configuration for Sr is $1s^2 2s^2 2p^6 3s^2 3p^6 3d^{10} 4s^2 4p^6 5s^2$.

Problem 8.23 (a) Write the complete and abbreviated electron configurations, showing the order in which the electrons fill, for radium, Ra. (b) Write the set of four quantum numbers for the outermost electrons of Ra.

Solution 8.23

    (a) A Ra atom (Z = 88) has 88 electrons. Therefore, to determine the order in which the subshells fill refer to the periodic table and follow in order of increasing atomic number. The complete configuration for Rn is $1s^2 2s^2 2p^6 3s^2 3p^6 4s^2 3d^{10} 4p^6 5s^2 4d^{10} 5p^6 6s^2 4f^{14} 5d^{10} 5p^6 7s^2$. The abbreviated form of the electron configuration of Ra is [Rn] $7s^2$

    (b) Because the outermost electrons are in the 7*s* subshell, the first three quantum numbers are *n* = 7, *l* = 0, and m_l = 0. The *n* quantum number tells us the electrons are in the seventh shell, and both *l* = 0 and m_l = 0 designates an *s* orbital. Because these electrons must have apparent spins in opposite directions, their m_s values are $\pm \frac{1}{2}$.

Problem 8.24 What elements have the following electron configurations?

    (a) $1s^2 2s^2 2p^6 3s^2 3p^6 4s^2 3d^{10} 4p^6 5s^2 4d^{10}$

    (b) $1s^2 2s^2 2p^6 3s^2 3p^6 4s^2 3d^{10} 4p^6 5s^2 4d^{10} 5p^6 6s^2 4f^{14} 5d^2$

Solution 8.24 (a) The first element to have a filled $4d^{10}$ is Cd, (b) The first element after the lanthanide series is Hf which has the [Xe] $5d^2 6s^2$ configuration.

Problem 8.25 Write the electron configurations for the atoms that have the following atomic numbers: (a) 25, (b) 50, (c) 75

Solution 8.25

    (a) The electron configuration of element 25, Mn, is $1s^2 2s^2 2p^6 3s^2 3p^6 3d^5 4s^2$.

    (b) The electron configuration of element 50, Sn, is $1s^2 2s^2 2p^6 3s^2 3p^6 3d^{10} 4s^2 4p^6 4d^{10} 5s^2 5p^2$.

Problem 8.26   How many unpaired electrons are found in each of the following atoms? (a) Cd, (b) V

Solution 8.26

 (a) The configuration of Cd is [Kr] $4d^{10}\,5s^2$. All the electrons are paired because all of the orbitals are filled; therefore, Cd has no unpaired electrons.

 (b) The electron configuration of V is [Ar] $3d^3\,4s^2$. All the electrons are paired in the $4s$ and the inner-level electrons. Applying Hund's Rule tells us that the three electrons in the $3d$ are unpaired.

Problem 8.27   (a) Which atom has the electron configuration [Kr] $4d^{10}\,5s^1\,5p^4$? (b) Discuss the electron configuration for this atom.

Solution 8.27

 (a) The number of electrons in this atom is 51; thus, this is the element antimony, Sb.

 (b) This configuration is not the ground state configuration of [Kr] $4d^{10}\,5s^2\,5p^3$; hence, it represents an excited state for Sb. A lower-energy $5s$ electron has been excited to the higher-energy $5p$ orbital.

SUMMARY

Quantum theory was first proposed to explain the light released when bodies are heated. The fundamental principle of quantum theory is that the energy released or absorbed by small particles is in discrete units called quanta. A quantum is a discrete packet of energy. One of the first scientists to apply quantum theory was Einstein when he presented an explanation for the photoelectric effect, which occurs when light hits the surface of a metal and ejects electrons.

Diffracting the light emitted by a gas in discharge tubes produces a line spectrum, with specific wavelengths separated by dark regions, or a continuous spectrum, with a wide range of wavelengths. Analysis of the line spectrum of hydrogen by Balmer revealed that a mathematical equation can be written to predict the wavelengths of the lines in the visible region as a function of integer values.

Bohr used some of the principles of quantum theory to develop a model of the atom that could explain the spectrum of hydrogen. His model of the H atom placed the electron in certain energy states (stationary states). When in these states, the H atom could not emit or absorb energy. Bohr stated that the H atom only emits or absorbs energy when it moves from one stationary state to another. Scientists describe the frequency of the quanta released by using Planck's Equation, $\triangle E = h\nu$. Bohr also thought that the electron in a H atom traveled in concentric circular orbits around the nucleus. Scientists replaced the Bohr model because it could only explain single-electron systems and new scientific evidence showed that some parts of the basic postulates of the Bohr theory were incorrect.

de Broglie proposed that electrons exhibit wave properties. Heisenberg gave us the uncertainty principle, which states that the uncertainty in momentum times the uncertainty in the position of an electron must be equal to or greater than $h/4\pi$. This means that the momentum and position of the electron cannot be precisely measured simultaneously. As a result of the uncertainty principle, scientists can only consider the regions in space in an atom where an electron has a high probability of being found. Schrödinger showed that only certain wave functions, ψ, could be associated with the electron's matter-wave. Each of the wave functions designated an allowable energy for the electron in the atom. The wave functions for each of the allowed energy states are called orbitals. Three quantum numbers are used to describe the locations of orbitals. Another quantum number is used to describe the orientation of an electron.

The electron configuration is a description of the distribution of electrons in energy levels, subshells, and orbitals. The Aufbau Principle tells us that electrons fill the lowest energy orbitals before they fill higher energy orbitals. As electrons fill orbitals they obey Hund's Rule which states that the most stable arrangement of electrons in a subshell is the one that has the greatest number of unpaired electrons with parallel spins.

CHAPTER 8 REVIEW EXERCISE

1. Calculate the wavelength in nm of an electromagnetic wave that has a frequency of 7.00×10^{14} Hz.

2. One of the principal wavelengths associated with the spectrum of Cd is at 2288 Å. If one angstrom, Å, is equivalent to 1×10^{-10} m, calculate the energy associated with one quantum of this light.

3. Calculate the frequency in Hz of light released when an electron in a H atom drops from $n = 6$ to $n = 3$.

4. The average distance from the earth to the sun is 9.29×10^7 miles. (a) How long does it take for light to travel from the earth to the sun? (b) If the wavelength of light is 525 nm, how many wave cycles are between the earth and the sun?

5. The threshold frequency to remove an electron from Au is 1.15×10^{15} s^{-1}. (a) Calculate the binding energy in J for an electron in Au? (b) What is the binding energy per mol of Au electrons?

6. The binding energy for electrons in Hg is 430 kJ/mol e$^-$. (a) What is the binding energy in J per e$^-$? (b) What is the threshold frequency of electrons in Hg? (c) What is the energy of the ejected electrons when photons with a frequency of 1.43×10^{16} s^{-1} strike Hg?

7. (a) Use the Balmer Equation to calculate the wavelengths and frequencies of lines in the hydrogen spectra that correspond to n values equal to 7 and 8. (b) What n value gives a frequency of 8.00×10^{14} s^{-1} in the Balmer Equation?

8. Calculate the ionization energy for a H atom in which its electron is initially in $n = 4$.

9. Bohr derived the following equation to calculate the distance, r, an orbit was from the nucleus:

$$r = \frac{nh}{2\pi mv}$$

in which n is the principal quantum number, h is Planck's constant, m is the electron's mass, and v is its velocity. This distance, r, is known as the Bohr radius. If the velocity of the electron is 5.0×10^5 m/s, what is the Bohr radius for the ground state orbit in a H atom?

10. (a) Calculate the wavelength, λ, and frequency, ν, of the wave associated with a proton ($m_{p^+} = 1.673 \times 10^{-24}$ g) that travels at 1.5×10^6 m/s. (b) Compare the wavelength and frequency of the proton's wave with that of an electron at the same velocity.

11. Calculate the uncertainty in the position along the x axis of an electron that has an uncertainty in velocity of 7.5×10^5 m/s.

12. (a) What values can the l quantum number have for each of the following: $n = 2$, $n = 3$, and $n = 4$? (b) Write the letter notation for each subshell in part (a).

13. Write a set of quantum numbers that is equivalent to each of the following: (a) $2p_x$ orbital (b) $4d$ subshell (c) $6s$ subshell (d) three of the orbitals in the $4f$ subshell.

14. Write the complete electron configuration, showing the order in which the electrons fill, for tellurium, Te, and the quantum numbers for its outermost electrons.

15. Which of the following sets of quantum numbers are not allowable? If they are not allowable, explain why not.

    (a) $n = 3, l = 3, m_l = +1, m_s = +\frac{1}{2}$
    (b) $n = 2, l = 1, m_l = -2, m_s = -\frac{1}{2}$
    (c) $n = 5, l = 3, m_l = +1, m_s = +\frac{1}{2}$
    (d) $n = 2, l = 0, m_l = 0, m_s = -\frac{1}{2}$

16. Write the ground state electron configurations for each of the following: (a) Al (b) Sn (c) Zr.

17. How many unpaired electrons are in each of the following atoms? (a) Ca (b) Fe (c) Se (d) Cd

18. The binding energies for the most loosely-held electrons in Ni and K are 5.0 and 2.2 eV, respectively. One eV is equivalent to 1.60×10^{-19} J. (a) Show the calculations that determines if light with a wavelength of 385 nm can cause the photoelectric effect to be observed in these metals. (b) If so, what is the velocity of the electrons emitted?

19. When an atom is ionized, the highest energy electron leaves first. Write the electron configurations for the following cations. (a) Li^+, (b) Al^{3+}, (c) Ag^+, (d) Fe^{3+}

ANSWERS TO REVIEW EXERCISE

1. 428 nm

2. 8.682×10^{-19} J

3. -2.740×10^{14} Hz

4. (a) 8.30 min, (b) 2.84×10^{17} wave cycles

5. (a) 7.62×10^{-19} J/e$^-$, (b) 459 kJ/mol e$^-$

6. (a) 7.14×10^{-19} J/e$^-$, (b) 1.08×10^{15} s^{-1}, (c) 8.76×10^{-18} J

7. (a) $n = 7$ $\lambda = 3.97 \times 10^{-7}$ m, $\nu = 7.56 \times 10^{14}$ s^{-1}; $n = 8$ $\lambda = 3.89 \times 10^{14}$ m, $\nu = 7.71 \times 10^{14}$ s^{-1}; (b) 12

8. 1.362×10^{-19} J

9. $r_1 = 2.3 \times 10^{-10}$ m

10. (a) $\lambda(p^+) = 2.6 \times 10^{-13}$ m, $\nu(p^+) = 1.1 \times 10^{21}$ s^{-1}, (b) $\lambda(e^-) = 4.8 \times 10^{-10}$ m, $\nu(e^-) = 6.2 \times 10^{17}$ s^{-1}

11. 7.7×10^{-11} m

12. $n = 2, l = 0$ (s), 1 (p); $n = 3, l = 0$ (s), 1 (p), 2 (d); $n = 4, l = 0$ (s), 1 (p), 2 (d), 3 (f)

13. (a) $n = 2, l = 1, m_l = +1$ (or any allowable value), (b) $n = 4, l = 2$, (c) $n = 6, l = 0$, (d) $n = 4, l = 3, m_l =$ any three allowable values

14. $1s^2 2s^2 2p^6 3s^2 3p^6 3d^{10} 4s^2 4p^6 4d^{10} 5s^2 5p^4$
    $n = 5, l = 1, m_l = +1, m_s = +\frac{1}{2}$
    $n = 5, l = 1, m_l = 0, m_s = +\frac{1}{2}$
    $n = 5, l = 1, m_l = -1, m_s = +\frac{1}{2}$
    $n = 5, l = 1, m_l = +14, m_s = -\frac{1}{2}$

15. (a) the highest l value when $n = 3$ is $l = 2$, (b) when $l = 1$ the only allowable values are +1, 0, and -1

16. (a) [Ne $3s^2 3p^1$], (b) [Kr] $4d^{10} 5s^2 5p^2$, (c) [Kr] $4d^2 5s^2$]

17. (a) 0, (b) 4, (c) 2, (d) 0

18. (a) $E_{photon} = 5.16 \times 10^{-19}$ J, $E_{binding}(Ni) = 8.0 \times 10^{-19}$ J, $E_{binding}(K) = 3.5 \times 10^{-19}$ J, (b) 6.0×10^5 m/s for e^- ejected from K

19. (a) $1s^2$, (b) $1s^2\,2s^2\,2p^6$, (c) [Kr] $4d^{10}$, d. [Ar] $3d^5$

9
Periodic Properties of Elements and Atoms

Nineteenth-century scientists such as Lothar Meyer and Dimitri Mendeleev recognized that if the elements were placed in order of atomic mass (they did not know about atomic numbers) various properties of atoms recurred at regular intervals. Both Meyer and Mendeleev proposed periodic tables that placed elements with similar properties in the same group. Today, we know that these recurring properties result from the fact that the elements in the same chemical group have the same valence electron configuration that only differs by energy level. In this chapter, the periodic properties of elements and atoms are considered.

9.1 THE PERIODIC LAW

The Periodic Law states that the properties of the elements are periodic functions of their atomic number. In other words, if the elements are listed in order of their atomic numbers, regular patterns of chemical and physical properties are found.

Metals

Most metals are solid elements with a silvery gray color. They usually have high melting and boiling points. Metals share a set of common properties. They have a high average density, and are excellent conductors of heat and electricity. They are malleable, which means they can be hammered into various shapes and foils. Metals are also ductile–the ability to be drawn into wires.

Nonmetals

In many cases, nonmetals possess properties that are opposite to those of metals. Most nonmetals are liquids and gases, not solids. On average, the melting points, boiling points, densities, and electric and heat conductivities of nonmetals are lower than those of metals. Nonmetals are neither malleable nor ductile.

Organization of the Periodic Table

On most periodic tables a zigzag line separates the metals on the left from the nonmetals on the right. The elements that are intermediate between metals and nonmetals, metalloids, border this line.

Problem 9.1   What is the trend in metallic and nonmetallic properties in period 3?

Solution 9.1   The trend in metallic and nonmetallic properties in period 3 is similar to that found in period 2. Na, Mg, and Al possess metallic properties; Si is a metalloid; and P, S, Cl and Ar are nonmetals.

Problem 9.2   Classify each of the following elements as metals, nonmetals, and metalloids: (a) Ti, (b) Se, (c) As, (d) Sn

Solution 9.2   (a) metal, (b) nonmetal, (c) metalloid, (d) metal

Problem 9.3   Consider the elements Ni, P, V, and O. (a) Which of these elements are malleable? (b) Which of these elements are good conductors of electricity? (c) Which of these elements have low boiling points? (d) Which of these elements have the lowest densities?

Solution 9.3
- (a) Ni and V are metals; thus, they are malleable.
- (b) Being metals, Ni and V are good conductors of electricity.
- (c) P and O have the low boiling points because they are nonmetals. O has the lowest boiling point because it is a gas at room temperature.
- (d) Being nonmetals, P and O have low densities.

Chemical Properties of Metals and Nonmetals

Representative metals (metals in groups 1 and 2) have few valence electrons; hence, they tend to lose these electrons during chemical changes. When this occurs, they form cations that have the same configurations as noble gases. In contrast, nonmetals have more complete valence levels and tend to gain electrons, with the exception of the noble gases. After gaining electrons, they form anions that have the same configurations as noble gases. Ions that have the same electronic configurations as noble gases are said to be isoelectronic to noble gases.

Problem 9.4   (a) Write an equation that shows the formation of the Ca^{2+} cation from Ca. (b) What are the electron configurations of Ca and Ca^{2+}?

Solution 9.4
- (a) $Ca \rightarrow Ca^{2+} + 2e^-$
- (b) The configuration of Ca is $1s^2\,2s^2\,2p^6\,3s^2\,3p^6\,4s^2$. The configuration of Ca^{2+} is isoelectronic to Ar $(1s^2\,2s^2\,2p^6\,3s^2\,3p^6)$.

Problem 9.5   (a) Write an equation that shows the formation of the P^{3-} from P. (b) What is the electron configuration of P^{3-} and what noble gas is it isoelectronic to?

Solution 9.5
- (a) $P + 3e^- \rightarrow P^{3-}$
- (b) The configuration of P^{3-} is isoelectronic to Ar $(1s^2\,2s^2\,2p^6\,3s^2\,3p^6)$.

9.2   PERIODIC TRENDS IN IONIZATION ENERGIES

First Ionization Energy

The first ionization energy, I_1, of an atom is the minimum energy to remove the most loosely-held electron from the ground state of a gaseous atom. If the first ionization energy is transferred to an atom, then the electron with the highest total energy (the outermost electron) is removed from the atom. When this occurs, the atom is ionized.

Problem 9.6   The first ionization energy of Na is 0.496 MJ/mol. (a) Explain what happens when the first ionization energy is added to a Na atom. (b) Write an equation that shows this change.

Solution 9.6

(a) The first ionization energy removes the outermost $3s^1$ electron, and a sodium ion, Na^+, results that is isoelectronic to Ne.

(b) The following equation illustrates the change:

$$Na(g) \rightarrow e^- + Na^+(g) \qquad I_1 = +0.496 \text{ MJ/mol}$$

Ionization is an Endothermic Process

Energy must always be added to an atom to remove an electron. Hence, ionization is an endothermic process ($I_1 > 0$). Adding the first ionization energy to an atom overcomes the attractive force between the protons in the nucleus and the most loosely-held electron.

Periodic Trends in First Ionization Energies

Two periodic trends can be found in first ionization energies. Generally, the first ionization energy increases going from left to right in a period, and decreases going from top to bottom in a group. Elements in the lower-left corner of the periodic table, group 1 (IA) and 2 (IIA) metals, have the lowest first ionization energies, and those in the upper-right corner, group 17 (VIIA) and 18 (VIIIA) nonmetals, have the highest first ionization energies. Within a period, the smallest amount of energy is needed to remove an electron from an alkali metal atom. The most energy is required to remove an electron from a noble gas atom.

Problem 9.7   Using only a periodic table, predict which of the following elements has the highest and lowest first ionization energies: S, Cl, Se, Br.

Solution 9.7   Begin by locating the atoms on the periodic table. Both S and Se are group 16 members and Cl and Br are group 17 members. S and Cl belong to period 3 and Se and Br belong to period 4. First ionization energies generally increase across a period and decrease within a chemical group. Thus, Cl has the highest first ionization energy (1.2 MJ/mol) because it is farther to the right in the period and has a lower-atomic mass. Selenium, Se, has the lowest first ionization energy (0.94 MJ/mol) of this group because it is closest to the left side of the periodic table and is the higher-atomic mass member of group 16.

Factors that Influence First Ionization Energies

Two factors principally determine the magnitude of the first ionization energy: effective nuclear charge and distance from the nucleus to the outermost electron. The attractive force exerted by the nucleus on the electrons depends on the nuclear charge (proportional to the number of p^+). An atom that has a higher nuclear charge should have a stronger force of attraction for the outermost electron than one with a lower nuclear charge. Additionally, the inner electrons shield (block) some of the force of attraction from the outer electrons.

Effective Nuclear Charge and Shielding in Period 3

Three subshells, s, p, and d, exist when $n = 3$. The probability distribution of the $3s$ is closer to the nucleus than those of the $3p$ or $3d$. Thus, electrons in the $1s$, $2s$, and $2p$ orbitals shield the electrons in the $3s$ less effectively than they do the electrons in the $3p$ and $3d$. This means that the $3s$ has a greater effective nuclear charge, Z_{eff}, than the other third level electrons. Electrons with higher values for their Z_{eff} are held tighter than those with lower values. Hence, the $3s$ electrons are at a lower energy level than those with smaller Z_{eff} values. A similar argument could be used to show that electrons in the $3p$ subshell have a higher Z_{eff} than those in $3d$. Therefore, the electrons in the $3p$ subshell are at a lower energy than those in the $3d$ subshell.

Distance and Nuclear Attraction

Besides the effective nuclear charge, the force of attraction by the nucleus on the outermost electron depends on the distance that separates them. The electrostatic force of attraction follows an inverse square relationship $(F \alpha 1/r^2)$. Accordingly, the nucleus attracts an electron in a higher-energy subshell with less force than one in a lower-energy subshell because on the average the higher-energy electron is farther from the nucleus.

Problem 9.8   Use the period 2 atoms to show the relationship between the magnitude of the first ionization energy and effective nuclear charge and shielding.

Solution 9.8   First ionization energies generally increase going from left to right across a period of representative elements because the effective nuclear charges increase. Only the $1s^2$ shields the outer-level electrons. Thus, electron shielding remains constant across the second period. However, the effective nuclear charge increases because the number of protons in the nucleus increases across a period.

Problem 9.9   A regular increase in the first ionization energies across a period is not found. Boron (Z = 5) has a lower first ionization energy than Be (Z = 4), and O (Z = 8) has a lower first ionization energy than N (Z = 7). How can these apparent anomalies be explained?

Solution 9.9

(a) The outer configuration for Be is $2s^2$, and the outer configuration of B, $2s^2 2p^1$. On the average, an electron in a $2p$ orbital tends to be farther from the nucleus than an electron in a $2s$ orbital. The farther the electron is from the nucleus, the weaker the force of attraction by the nucleus. In addition, the $2s$ electrons shield nuclear charge from the $2p$ electron. Hence, the first ionization energy decreases going from Be to B.

(b) Nitrogen has an outer-level configuration of $2s^2 2p^3$, and O has $2s^2 2p^4$. According to Hund's rule, the three outer electrons in N are in three different orbitals, the $2p_x$, $2p_y$, and $2p_z$. Atoms with half-filled subshells tend to be relatively stable because of minimized interelectron repulsions as a result of not having paired electrons in the $2p$ subshell. This is not true for O atoms because two electrons are paired in one of the $2p$ orbitals of O, which means greater interelectron repulsions than in N. Even though the nuclear charge increases, less energy is needed to remove one of the paired electrons from O to produce the following more stable configuration in which the electrons are not paired.

First Ionization Energies of Atoms with d Electrons

The $3d$ subshell fills in the first transition series atoms, Sc to Zn. A relatively small increase in ionization energies is observed going from Sc to Zn when compared to the increase across the representative elements. How can this be explained? Electrons in lower-energy subshells help shield nuclear charge from those in higher-energy subshells. Hence, electrons that enter the $3d$ subshell shield nuclear charge from the electrons in the $4s$ subshell and partially counterbalance the increase in nuclear charge going from Sc (Z = 21) to Zn (Z = 30). Therefore, only a small increase in ionization energy is observed.

IONIZATION OF TRANSITION METALS

Usually when atoms in the first transition series ionize, the resulting cations have no electrons in the $4s$ subshell. This means that the higher-energy $4s$ electrons are ionized before the lower energy $3d$ electrons. This is also true of the second and third transition series.

Problem 9.10   Write an equation that shows the ionization of Ni to Ni^{2+}. Show the valence configurations of Ni and Ni^{2+}.

Solution 9.10   The following equation shows the ionization of a Ni to Ni^{2+}. The two electrons removed come from the $4s$ subshell.

$$Ni\ (3d^8\ 4s^2) \rightarrow 2e^- + Ni^{2+}\ (3d^8\ 4s^0)$$

Second Ionization Energies

The second ionization energy, I_2, is the minimum energy required to remove the most loosely-held electron from a monopositive gaseous cation, $A^+(g)$. For example, the second ionization energy for Na is 4.56 MJ/mol.

$$Na^+(g) \rightarrow Na^{2+}(g) + e^- \qquad I_2 = 4.56\ \text{MJ/mol}$$

Third and Higher-Order Ionization Energies

The third ionization energy of an atom, I_3, is the minimum energy to remove the most loosely held electron from a gaseous dipositive cation, $A^{2+}(g)$. The fourth ionization energy, I_4, is the minimum energy needed to remove the most loosely held electron from a gaseous tripositive cation, $A^{3+}(g)$. Addition of the third ionization energy removes an electron from an atom that has lost two electrons, and the addition of the fourth ionization energy removes an electron from an atom that has lost three electrons. The third and fourth ionization energies of Na are 6.91 and 9.54 MJ/mol, respectively.

$$Na^{2+}(g) \rightarrow \quad Na^{3+}(g) + e^- \qquad I_3 = 6.91\ \text{MJ/mol}$$
$$Na^{3+}(g) \rightarrow \quad Na^{4+}(g) + e^- \qquad I_4 = 9.54\ \text{MJ/mol}$$

MAGNITUDES OF HIGHER-ORDER IONIZATION ENERGIES

In general, the second ionization energy is higher than the first, and the third ionization energy is higher than the second, and so on. The higher the positive charge on an ion, the more difficult it is to remove an electron.

Trends in Second Ionization Energies

The highest first ionization energy in a period is that of the noble gas. In the third period, the noble gas is Ar, which has a first ionization energy, I_1, of 1.52 MJ/mol. The second ionization energy of Na, 4.56 MJ/mol, is the highest second ionization energy of the period 3 atoms. This value is more than double the magnitude of those of most of the period 3 atoms. What could account for this? If an electron is removed from Na, then a Na^+ ion results that is isoelectronic to Ne, $2s^2\ 2p^6$. Isoelectronic species have the same number of electrons. Thus, adding the second ionization energy to Na^+ causes it to lose its stable noble gas configuration. For all periods, the group 1 (IA) elements have the highest second ionization energies.

Problem 9.11   Which group has the highest third ionization energies?

Solution 9.11   More energy is always needed to remove an electron from the stable noble gas electron configuration than any other configuration. Group 2 (IIA) atoms have the highest values for their third ionization energies. In period 3, Mg has the highest third ionization energy because a Mg^{2+} ion has the same stable electron configuration as Ne, $2s^2\ 2p^6$s.

Problem 9.12   Which of the following elements has the highest third ionization energy: Na, Mg, K, or Ca?

Solution 9.12   Na and K are group 1 members and Mg and Ca are group 2 members. Recall that the atom in which an electron is removed from the noble gas configuration requires the largest amount of energy. The third ionization energy removes the most loosely-held electron from a dipositive cation. Therefore, the ionization energies of Mg and Ca, the group 2 members, are higher than Na and K, respectively, because Mg^{2+} and Ca^{2+} have noble gas configurations. Finally, Mg^{2+} should have a higher third ionization energy than Ca^{2+} because the outermost electrons are in a lower energy shell than those of Ca^{2+}. Thus, Mg^{2+} has the highest third ionization energy.

9.3   PERIODIC TRENDS IN ELECTRON AFFINITY

Electron affinity is a measure of the energy transferred when an electron is added to a gaseous atom. Specifically, electron affinity, $\triangle H_{EA}$, is the enthalpy change when an electron is added to a gaseous atom, A, or ion.

$$A(g) + e^- \rightarrow A^-(g) \qquad \triangle H_{EA} = \text{electron affinity}$$

Unlike ionization energies that are always endothermic, the first electron affinities can be either exothermic or endothermic.

Electron Affinities of Nonmetals

The electron affinities for nonmetals such as the halogens (group 17) and chalcogens (group 16) are exothermic. When a H atom accepts an electron, it obtains the stable noble gas electron configuration and thus releases energy. For example, the electron affinity of F is −322 kJ/mol. This large negative first electron affinity is the result of the high effective nuclear charge of F atoms. Not only can a F atom hold its electrons tightly, it can also attract an electron from another atom and hold it tightly.

Problem 9.13   Explain why the electron affinities of noble gases have positive values.

Solution 9.13   Because energy is required to add an electron to noble gases, the values of their first electron affinities are positive. For example, +29 kJ/mol must be added to $Ne(g)$ to form a Ne anion, $Ne^-(g)$. Noble gases have little tendency to accept electrons because they have complete outer energy levels. Addition of an electron to a noble gas produces a highly unstable noble gas anion, that is isoelectronic to the alkali metal in the next period.

Electron Affinities of Metals

Metals, especially those in group 2 (IIA), also have little tendency to accept electrons. Thus, their electron affinities are smaller negative numbers than those of the nonmetals or they have positive values. The large positive first electron affinities of the group 2 (IIA) elements shows that they have little tendency to form anions because it adds an electron to the higher-energy p subshell. Alkali metals, group 1 (IA), have negative values for their first electron affinities because their half-filled s orbitals can accept one electron.

General Trends in Electron Affinities

A decrease occurs across a period from group 2 (IIA) to group 17 (VIIA) with a significant increase at group 18 VIIIA) elements. No general trends exist within a chemical group.

Electron Affinities and Ionization Energies

Trends in the magnitudes of electron affinities parallel those of ionization energies. Electron affinity is defined as the enthalpy change when an electron is added to a gaseous atom such as Br.

$$Br(g) + e^- \rightarrow Br^-(g) \qquad \triangle H = -325 \text{ kJ/mol}$$

Reversing this equation gives the following:

$$Br^-(g) \rightarrow Br(g) + e^- \quad \triangle H = +325 \text{ kJ/mol}$$

The reversed equation shows us that the energy to remove an electron from a bromide ion is +325 kJ/mol. Many atoms with high first ionization energies, such as the halogens, have high negative first electron affinities. Metals that have low ionization energies tend to have smaller negative or positive electron affinities.

Problem 9.14 Predict which of the following has the most positive and most negative first electron affinity: Br, Sr, Kr.

Solution 9.14 Bromine, strontium, and krypton belong to groups 17, 2, and 18, respectively. Group 2 (IIA) members, alkaline earth metals, tend to have the most positive first electron affinities; therefore, Sr has the most positive electron affinity of these three atoms. Group 17 (VIIA) members, halogens, have the most negative values; thus, Br has the most negative value.

9.4 PERIODIC TRENDS IN ATOMIC SIZES

Sizes of Atoms

Measuring the size of an atom is not an easy task because atoms do not have definite boundaries such as baseballs. Another problem in measuring atomic sizes is that atoms do not usually exist as separate, isolated units. This means that the size of an atom depends on the atoms that surround it. Thus, indirect methods are used to estimate the sizes of atoms. The distance from the nucleus to region populated by the outermost electrons is called atomic size (also called atomic radius).

APPROXIMATING SIZES OF ATOMS

The sizes of metallic elements are approximated by knowing that metal atoms are in a three-dimensional network. Hence, the atomic size of a metal atom is estimated to be one-half the distance between the nuclei of adjacent atoms. If an atom forms a chemical bond with itself, it produces a covalent diatomic molecule. Thus, the atomic size of such an atom is half the distance between the nuclei in a covalent diatomic molecule.

Problem 9.15 The distance between nuclei in I_2 molecules is 0.266 nm. What is the covalent radius of I atoms?

Solution 9.15 The covalent radius of an I atom is 0.133 nm, one-half the distance between the I nuclei. Note that this is not a good method for estimating the size of an atom because the distance between the two nuclei depends on many factors and the atoms overlap to some degree.

TRENDS IN THE SIZES OF ATOMS

Atoms decrease in size going from left to right across a period and increase in size going from top to bottom in a chemical group.

Problem 9.16 Explain the trends in sizes of atoms within (a) periods and (b) groups.

Solution 9.16

(a) Effective nuclear charge increases across a period. Thus, the force of attraction on the electrons increases from left to right across a period. This means that the outermost electrons are pulled closer to the nucleus resulting in a smaller size.

(b) Within a chemical group, the size increases because the next member of the group has outer electrons in a higher energy shell. Electrons in higher-energy shells are farther from the nucleus on an average than those in lower energy shells. Consequently, the attractive force on higher-energy electrons decreases.

Trends in the Sizes of Transition Metals

Similar to the trends in ionization energies, the changes in the properties across the transition elements are much less than those of the representative elements. In this case, the decrease in the size of transition elements is smaller than that for the representative elements because the added inner level d electrons shield nuclear charge from the outer-level s electrons. A similar gradual decrease in atomic size occurs across the inner transition elements in which the $4f$ and $5f$ subshells fill. The decrease in radius across the lanthanide elements, Ce to Lu, is called the lanthanide contraction.

Problem 9.17 The inner cores of d^{10} and f^{14} electrons affect the size and properties of elements that directly follow the transition elements and inner transition elements. Explain why the radius of an Al atom ($Z = 13$), a group 13 element, is larger than that of a Ga atom ($Z = 31$).

Solution 9.17 This might be somewhat of a surprise because a Ga atom with an outer electron in the $4p$ subshell might be expected to be larger than an Al atom with an outer electron in the $3p$ subshell. This apparent anomaly may be explained in terms of the incomplete shielding of the d^{10} electrons. Due to the more elongated shape of d orbitals, electrons in the d subshell do not shield as effectively as s or p electrons. Incomplete shielding results in a higher effective nuclear charge, which means a stronger force of attraction on the $4p$ electrons.

Ionic Radii

The ionic radii increase in a group and decrease in a period. For nonmetal ions, the group 15 (VA) anions are the largest because they carry a 3− charge and have the smallest effective nuclear charges among nonmetals. Halide ions, group 17 (VIIA) anions are the smallest because they only carry a 1− charge and have a higher effective nuclear charge. The sizes of metal ions decrease as the charge increases. Subsequently, group 1 metal ions with a single positive charge are larger than the group 2 metals in the same period with a double positive charge.

Problem 9.18 (a) Which of following is the largest atom: Rb, Sr, Cs, Ba? (b) Which of the following is the smallest ion: O^{2-}, F^-, Na^+, Mg^{2+}?

Solution 9.18

(a) Rb and Cs are members of group 1, and Sr and Ba are members of group 2. Larger atoms are farther to the left within a period and have higher energy outer-level electrons in a group. Therefore, Cs is the largest of this group.

(b) When nonmetal atoms such as O and F take in electrons, their ionic radii increase. When metal atoms such as Na and Mg lose electrons, their ionic radii decrease. Because these ions are isoelectronic to Ne, the cations should be smaller than the anions. Because Mg loses two electrons and Na only loses one electron, the size of Mg^{2+} should be smaller than Na^+ as a result of having a higher effective nuclear charge.

9.5 PERIODIC TRENDS IN ELECTRO-NEGATIVITY

Electronegativity is the power an atom has to attract electrons in a chemical bond. Atoms with high electronegativities have a greater capacity to attract electrons in chemical bonds than those with smaller electronegativities. More compact atoms, those with high effective nuclear charges, tend to have higher electronegativities. More diffuse atoms, those with lower effective nuclear charges, tend to have lower electronegativities. In other words, excluding the noble gases, nonmetals have high electronegativities and metals have low electronegativities.

Trends in Electro- negativities

Electronegativity trends are similar to those of ionization energies and electron affinities. Going left to right across a period, the electronegativities of the elements increase, excluding the noble gases. Within a chemical group, the electronegativities decrease. Consequently, elements located in the upper right-hand corner of the periodic table (F, O, N, and Cl) are the most electronegative elements and have the greatest power to attract electrons in chemical bonds. Elements in the lower left-hand corner (Fr, Cs, Ba, and Ra) are the least electronegative and have the smallest power to attract electrons when bonded.

Problem 9.19 Using only a periodic table, rank the following elements from lowest to highest electronegativity: Ca, Mg, O, and S.

Solution 9.19 The first two elements are group 2 (IIA) metals; thus, their electronegativities are lower than the group 16 (VIA) nonmetals, O and S. Within a group the electronegativity decreases from top to bottom; therefore, the electronegativity of Mg is higher than Ca, and that of O is higher than S. Hence, the ranking of electronegativities from lowest to highest is: $Ca < Mg < S < O$.

9.6 PERIODIC TRENDS IN MAGNETIC PROPERTIES

Diamagnetism and Paramagnetism

Spinning charged bodies like electrons produce a magnetic field. Consequently, atoms exhibit magnetic properties and act as if they are tiny magnets. When a body is in a magnetic field it is either attracted, repelled, or unaffected. If a magnetic field does not attract or weakly repels a particle, then it is classified as a diamagnetic species. If the field attracts a particle, then it is a paramagnetic species.

Differences in Diamagnetic and Paramagnetic Species

A diamagnetic atom or ion has all paired electrons ($\uparrow\downarrow$). A paramagnetic atom or ion has one or more unpaired electrons ($\uparrow$). In diamagnetic species, the magnetic field of one electron in an orbital cancels that of the second electron in the orbital because they spin in opposite directions. This is not the case for paramagnetic species because the magnetic field associated with the unpaired electron is not canceled and thus may be attracted by the external magnetic field. The attractive force on paramagnetic species by the magnetic field increases with increasing number of unpaired electrons.

Problem 9.20 (a) Predict and discuss the magnetic property of Ne. (b) Are Na^+ and Mg^{2+} diamagnetic or paramagnetic? Explain.

Solution 9.20
  (a) Noble gases ($ns^2\ np^6$) are diamagnetic because they have a filled outer s and p orbitals, which means their electrons are paired. Hence, Ne is diamagnetic.
  (b) All ions isoelectronic to noble gases are also diamagnetic. Therefore, Na^+ and Mg^{2+} are diamagnetic because they are isoelectronic to Ne, $1s^2\ 2s^2\ 2p^6$.

Magnetic Properties of Transition Metals

After transition metals ionize, the resulting cations have electron configurations in which the electrons are in the lower-energy d subshell. For example, the electron configuration of Cu is $1s^2\ 2s^2\ 2p^6\ 3s^2\ 3p^6\ 3d^{10}\ 4s^1$. If it loses one electron, a copper(I) ion, Cu^+, results. The following electron configuration for Cu^+ is $1s^2\ 2s^2\ 2p^6\ 3s^2\ 3p^6\ 3d^{10}$. It is diamagnetic because of its paired electrons. The Cu^+ ion has a pseudonoble gas configuration because of its complete $n = 3$ shell. All transition metal ions with pseudonoble gas configurations are diamagnetic; e.g., Ag^+, Zn^{2+}, Hg^{2+}, and Cd^{2+}.

Problem 9.21 Is cobalt(III), Co^{3+}, a diamagnetic or paramagnetic ion?

Solution 9.21 Cobalt(III), Co^{3+}, is a paramagnetic cation. Co has an electron configuration of $1s^2\ 2s^2\ 2p^6\ 3s^2\ 3p^6\ 3d^7\ 4s^2$. Removing three electrons from a Co atom, produces a Co^{3+} ion which has an electron configuration of $1s^2\ 2s^2\ 2p^6\ 3s^2\ 3p^6\ 3d^6$. Applying Hund's rule tells us that Co^{3+} has four unpaired and two paired $3d$ electrons. The unpaired electrons in Co^{3+} gives it paramagnetic properties.

Problem 9.22 For each of the following determine if they are diamagnetic or paramagnetic species: (a) I^-, (b) Ag^+.

Solution 9.22

(a) I^- is isoelectronic to Xe. Because it has a noble gas configuration with all paired electrons, I^- is diamagnetic. All the halide ions are diamagnetic.

(b) After a Ag atom loses an electron it has the electron configuration of $[Kr]\ 4d^{10}$. Because it has an inner core configuration of Kr and a filled $4d$, it is diamagnetic.

Problem 9.23 Use orbital diagrams to determine if each of the following ions are diamagnetic or paramagnetic species: (a) Fe^{3+}, (b) Ni^{2+}

Solution 9.23

(a) The electron configuration of Fe^{3+} is $[Ar]\ 3d^5$. Hund's Rule tells us that the five electrons in the $3d$ are in different orbitals.

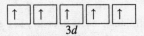
$3d$

Thus, these electrons have parallel spins. Fe^{3+} is paramagnetic.

(b) The electron configuration of Ni^{2+} is $[Ar]\ 3d^8$. The eight electrons in the $3d$ are distributed as follows:

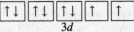
$3d$

Because Ni^{2+} has two unpaired electrons, it is paramagnetic.

PREDICTION OF PROPERTIES

Knowledge of the periodic properties of the elements allows us to predict the properties of elements that have not been measured experimentally or that have not yet been discovered. The key to predicting properties of elements is to identify the location of the element on the periodic table. Once the location is known, determine its electron configuration, its period, its group, and if it is a metal, nonmetal, or metalloid.

Problem 9.24 Using the periodic table, predict each of the following properties of element 38: (a) metal or nonmetal, (b) solid, liquid, or gas, (c) good or bad conductor of heat and electricity, (d) relative first ionization energy, (e) relative atomic size, (f) charge on its ions, (g) formula of its chloride, (h) If the melting points of Ca and Ba are 845°C and 725°C, respectively, estimate the melting point of Sr. (i) If the first ionization energies of Ca and Ba are 0.590 MJ/mol and 0.503 MJ/mol, respectively, estimate the first ionization energy of Sr.

Solution 9.24 Element 38 is strontium, Sr. It belongs to the alkaline earth metals, group 2 (IIA), and is a member of period 5. All members of group 2 (IIA) have an outer electron configuration of s^2; specifically, Sr has an outer configuration of $5s^2$.

(a) Because all of the other members of group 2 (IIA) are metals, we should expect that Sr exhibits metallic properties.
(b) Metals are usually solids at room temperature.
(c) Metals are good conductors of heat and electricity.
(d) Sr atoms should have the lowest first ionization energy of period 5, except for Rb. Metals have low first ionization energies.
(e) Sr should have a relatively large atomic size because the effective nuclear charge is rather small in group 2 (IIA) elements.
(f) When Sr forms an ion, it loses two electrons to obtain the stable noble gas configuration of Kr. ($Sr \rightarrow 2e^- + Sr^{2+}$)
(g) Because Sr ions have a 2+ charge, the formulas of its chloride, is $SrCl_2$.
(h) The average value for the melting points of Ca and Ba, 785°C, is not far from the actual value of 770°C.
(i) Taking the average value of the first ionization energies of Ca and Ba gives 0.546 MJ/mol for the predicted first ionization energy of Sr. The actual value is 0.550 MJ/mol.

Problem 9.25 Predict each of the following properties of the yet to be discovered element 118: (a) physical state, (b) If Xe and Rn, have normal boiling points of $-107°C$ and $-62°C$, respectively, predict its normal boiling point, (c) valence electron configuration, (d) relative first ionization energy, (e) relative atomic size, (f) relative electron affinity, (g) relative electronegativity, (h) stability of its nucleus

Solution 9.25 To begin, identify the chemical group and period to which element 118 belongs. Element 118 belongs to the noble gases in period 7.
(a) All of the group 18 (VIIIA) elements are gases at 25°C; hence, element 118 is probably a gas.
(b) An increase of 50 to 60°C above the boiling point of Rn gives a boiling point somewhat below 0.0°C for element 118.
(c) Element 118 is expected to have an outer-level electron configuration of $7s^2\, 7p^6$.
(d) Because the first ionization energy decreases within a group and increases in a period, element 118 should have the lowest first ionization energy of the noble gases and the highest ionization energy in period 7.
(e) Element 118 should be largest atom in group VIIIA (18) and the smallest in period 7.
(f) The electron affinity of element 118 should be a rather large positive number. This is true for the other noble gases.
(g) Element 118 should have a small capacity to attract electrons in chemical bonds–a low electronegativity.
(h) All elements beyond the actinide series are highly radioactive; hence, element 118 should be intensely radioactive with short-lived atoms.

Problem 9.26 Consider the atoms Si, P, S, and Cl. (a) Which is the most nonmetallic? (b) Which has the highest ionization energy? (c) Which is the largest atom?

Solution 9.26 Si, P, S, and Cl belong to the third period of the periodic table.
(a) Metallic character decreases or nonmetallic character increases from left to right across the periodic table. Accordingly, Cl, a halogen, is the most nonmetallic atom of this group.
(b) First ionization energies increase from left to right across a period; hence, Cl has the highest ionization energy of the four atoms.
(c) Atomic sizes decrease across a period; therefore, Si is the largest atom.

Problem 9.27 Predict the atomic size and boiling point of krypton given the following data.

	Atomic size, nm	Boiling point, °C
Neon, Ne	0.065	−246
Argon, Ar	0.095	−186
Xenon, Xe	0.130	−108

Solution 9.27   Kr is a member of the noble gases (group VIIIA). Its atomic mass is greater than Ar and less than xenon; thus, its atomic size and boiling point should be intermediate between the values of Ar and Xe. To make good predictions, follow the trends within the group.

(a) Atomic size increases within a group, which means that the atomic size of Kr is larger than that of Ar but smaller than Xe. An increase of 0.030 nm is observed from Ne to Ar. However, the same increase is not expected from Ar to Kr because such an increase gives a value (0.125 nm) almost identical in size to Xe. A better estimate might be the average value of Ar and Xe ((0.095 + 0.130)/2), which gives 0.113 nm. The actual value for Kr is 0.110 nm.

(b) The boiling points of the noble gases increase. Subsequently, the boiling point of Kr is larger than Ar but smaller than Xe. Taking the average value of the boiling points of Ar and Xe, gives a reasonable prediction. The average value of −186°C and −108°C is −147°C. This is fairly close to the actual value of −153°C.

SUMMARY

*T*he Periodic Law states that if the elements are arranged according to their atomic numbers then their properties recur periodically.

The first ionization energy of an atom is the minimum energy needed to remove the most loosely held electron from a gaseous atom. From left to right across a period the first ionization energies show an irregular increase, and within a group, from top to bottom, the first ionization energies decrease.

The electron affinity of an atom is the enthalpy change, △H, when an electron is added to a gaseous atom. Atoms that accept electrons have larger negative first electron affinities than those that do not readily accept electrons. Nonmetals tend to have larger negative first electron affinities than metals.

Proceeding across a period from left to right the size of atoms decreases, and going from top to bottom in a chemical group the size of atoms increases. The ionic radius of a metal cation is smaller than the size of the atom because the outer-level electrons are removed. However, the ionic radius of a nonmetallic anion is larger than the size of the atom because electrons are added to the outer level.

Electronegativity is a measure of the power of atoms to attract electrons in chemical bonds. The Pauling electronegativity scale ranges from 0 to 4, in which F is the most electronegative atom. Within a period, electronegativity values increase (excluding the noble gases), and within a group the values decrease.

The magnetic properties of atoms and ions result from their electron configuration. Elements are either classified as diamagnetic or paramagnetic. A diamagnetic species is weakly repelled by magnetic fields because its electrons are paired. A paramagnetic species is attracted by magnetic fields because it has one or more unpaired electrons.

CHAPTER 9 REVIEW EXERCISE

1. Consider the following properties of hypothetical elements *A* and *B*, and classify each as a metal, nonmetal, or metalloid: (a) Element *A* boils at −195.8°C, has a density of 1.3 g/L,

and is a colorless gas at room temperature. (b) Element B boils at $3200°C$, has a density of 10 g/cm^3, and is a good conducting solid.

2. (a) Which of the following has the highest and lowest first ionization energies: C, N, Si, P? (b) Which of the following has the highest fourth ionization energy: Be, B, C, N?

3. Predict which of the following has the most positive and most negative first electron affinity: S, Ar, Na.

4. Predict the smallest and largest atoms from the following group: P, Cl, Na, Sr.

5. For each of the following determine if they are diamagnetic or paramagnetic species: (a) F, (b) O^{2-}, (c) Sc^{3+}, (d) Zn^{2+}, e. Au^{3+}

6. For each of the following properties, compare element 31, gallium (Ga) to element 16, sulfur (S): (a) boiling and melting points (b) thermal conductivity (c) first ionization energy (d) atomic size

7. Which of the following atoms has the highest second ionization energy: Rb, Sr, In, Sn?

8. (a) Calculate the energy in kJ required to totally ionize 1.00 g of gaseous iodine, I, atoms. (b) Calculate the energy in kJ required to ionize 1.00 g of gaseous xenon, Xe, atoms. The ionization energies of I and Xe are 1.01 MJ/mol and 1.17 MJ/mol, respectively.

9. For each of the following groups of elements, select the one with the largest negative electron affinity. (a) O, Ca, Na, Al, (b) C, Cl, O, S

10. From each of the following groups select the atoms or ions with the largest and smallest radii: (a) Ca, Sr, Mg, Ba, (b) Si, P, S, Cl, (c) N^{3-}, O^{2-}, F^-

11. From the following groups of atoms, select the one with the highest electronegativity: (a) N, O, P, S, (b) Li, Be, Na, Mg, (c) Ar, Si, S, Mg

12. How many unpaired electrons do each of the following have? (a) N, (b) Ar, (c) Ag, (d) Mn

13. Classify each of the following ions as paramagnetic or diamagnetic: (a) Sr^{2+}, (b) Fe^{3+}, (c) Ga^{3+}, (d) Au^{3+}

14. Consider the period 2 elements to answer the following questions: (a) Which elements are metallic? (b) Which element is composed of the largest atoms? (c) Which elements do not conduct an electric current? (d) Which has the highest first ionization energy? (e) Which has the highest second ionization energy? (f) Which has the highest positive electron affinity? (g) Which is most electronegative?

15. Arrange the following in order of increasing atomic size: Cl, Cl^-, Cl^+.

16. The densities of Ne, Ar, and Kr at $0°C$ are 0.900, 1.78, and 3.75 g/L, respectively. Predict the density of Xe at the same conditions.

17. Write the symbol for the element that best fits the description: (a) lowest ionization energy on the periodic table, (b) largest atomic size on the periodic table, (c) smallest chalcogen, (d) atom that forms a 2− ion that is isoelectronic to Kr, (e) metalloid that belongs to the chalcogens, (f) group 15 (VA) element with the highest density, (g) largest alkaline earth metal, (h) smallest member of the lanthanide series, (i) transition element that has a completely filled $5d$ sublevel, (j) metallic members of group IIIA.

18. Predict the value for the first ionization energy of antimony, Sb, given the values of the ionization energies for all other members of group VA. Their ionization energies in kJ/mol are: N, 1400; P, 1062; As; 944, and Bi, 703.

19. The ionic radii of V^{2+}, V^{3+}, and V^{5+} are 0.088, 0.074, and 0.059 nm, respectively. Predict the ionic radius of V^{4+} ion. (b) Compare your predicted value to the actual value which is 0.063 nm.

ANSWERS TO REVIEW EXERCISE

1. (a) nonmetal, (b) metal
2. (a) highest = N, lowest = Si, (b) B

3. most positive = Ar, most negative = S
4. smallest = Cl, largest = Sr
5. (a) paramagnetic, (b) diamagnetic, (c) diamagnetic, (d) diamagnetic, (e) paramagnetic
6. (a) Ga has higher melting and boiling points than S. (b) Ga is a better thermal conductor than S. (c) Ga has a lower first ionization energy than S. (d) Ga is composed of larger atoms than S.
7. Rb
8. (a) 7.96 kJ/g, (b) 8.91 kJ/g
9. (a) O, (b) Cl
10. (a) largest = Ba, smallest = Mg; (b) largest = Si, smallest = Cl; (c) largest = N^{3-}, smallest = F^-
11. (a) O, (b) Li, (c) S
12. (a) 3, (b) 0, (c) 1, (d) 5
13. (a) diamagnetic, (b) paramagnetic, (c) diamagnetic, (d) paramagnetic
14. (a) Li, Be, (b) Li, (c) N, O, F, Ne, (d) Ne, (e) Li, (f) Be, (g) F
15. $Cl^+ < Cl < Cl^-$
16. A 1.97 g/L increase from Ar to Kr could be used; thus, add this to the density of Kr, which gives 5.72 g/L. The actual value is 5.86 g/L.
17. (a) Fr, (b) Fr, (c) O, (d) Se, (e) Te, (f) Bi, (g) Ra, (h) Lu, (i) Hg, (j) Al to Tl
18. The average value of As and Bi is 823 kJ. The actual value is 832 kJ/mol
19. Using the average value of V^{3+} and V^{5+} gives a value of 0.066, which is fairly close to the measured value.

10

Chemical Bonding: Fundamental Concepts

A chemical bond is the force of attraction that one atom (or ion) has for another atom (or ion). The principal "driving force" for atoms to combine and form molecules is the release of energy by atoms as they achieve lower energy states. The two principal types of bonds discussed in this chapter are ionic and covalent bonds.

10.1   INTRODUCTION TO CHEMICAL BONDING

Ionic or Electrovalent Bonds

Ionic bonds, also called electrovalent bonds, most commonly result when one or more electrons transfer from a metal to a nonmetal. When this occurs the metal atom becomes a cation and the nonmetal atom becomes an anion. Ionic bonds are the electrostatic forces of attraction among the resulting positive and negative ions.

Covalent Bonds

A covalent bond results when the orbitals of two nonmetal atoms overlap and the nuclei of the atoms attract the electrons in the overlapping region. This is called electron sharing.

Bonding Theories

The valence bond and molecular orbital theories are most often used to explain the properties and formation of chemical bonds. The valence bond theory primarily considers the interactions of the electrons in the outer shell, the valence electrons, in the formation of bonds. The molecular orbital theory considers the energies of all the electrons in the atoms that form chemical bonds. Scientists use both theories to explain chemical bonds and molecular structures because neither can explain adequately the bonds in all chemical species.

Lewis Symbols and Lewis Formulas

The valence electron configurations of the atoms are often shown using Lewis symbols and Lewis structures. To write the Lewis symbol of an atom, place as many dots around its symbol as there are valence electrons. For example, one way to write the Lewis symbol of N is $:\text{N}\cdot$. Five dots are placed around the symbol of nitrogen because it has five valence electrons, $2s^2 2p^3$. All the other members of group 15 (VA) also have five electrons in their outermost shell.

Problem 10.1   Write the Lewis symbols for all of the group 1 (IA) and group 2 (IIA) metals.

Solution 10.1   Members of group 1 (IA) have one valence electron and thus have one dot in their Lewis symbols: Li·, Na·, K·, Rb·, Cs·, Fr·. Group 2 (IIA) atoms have two valence electrons; therefore, their Lewis symbols have two dots: Be:, Mg:, Ca:, Sr:, Ba:, Ra:.

10.2   IONIC BONDS

Formation of Ionic Bonds

One way that an ionic bond can form is through the transfer of electrons from a metal to a nonmetal. For example, when sodium vapor, Na(g), and chlorine gas, $Cl_2(g)$, mix, the binary ionic compound sodium chloride, NaCl, results.

$$Na(g) + \tfrac{1}{2}Cl_2(g) \longrightarrow NaCl(s)$$

Sodium and chlorine are both reactive elements. However, after they combine, a stable ionic compound forms that has little tendency to react.

STABILITY OF NaCl(s)

The electron configurations for Na and Cl are as follows.

$$Na \quad 1s^2 2s^2 2p^6 3s^1$$
$$Cl \quad 1s^2 2s^2 2p^6 3s^2 3p^5$$

Na belongs to group 1 (IA) and has a low first ionization energy and a low first electron affinity. Chlorine belongs to group 17 (VIIA) and has a high first ionization energy and a high first electron affinity. Therefore, when a Cl atom encounters a Na atom, the nucleus of the Cl atom attracts the loosely-held outer electron of Na.

$$Na \cdot + :\ddot{C}l: \longrightarrow Na^+[:\ddot{C}l:]^-$$

In this reaction the Na atom loses its outer $3s^1$ electron and produces a sodium ion, Na^+, which is isoelectronic (the same electron configuration) to Ne. The Cl atom gains this electron and produces a chloride ion, Cl^-, which is isoelectronic to Ar. Both ions obtain stable noble gas configurations. After the formation of the sodium cation, Na^+, and the chloride anion, Cl^-, they attract each other and form an ionic bond. When bonds form, energy is released. This release of energy is the principal driving force in the formation of ionic compounds.

Octet Rule

Binary ionic compounds of representative elements result when electrons transfer from a metal to a nonmetal so the resulting ions become isoelectronic to a noble gas. This statement is most often called the Octet Rule (also called the Noble Gas Rule). It is termed the Octet Rule because noble gases, excluding He, have eight valence electrons. Be careful when applying the Octet Rule because some atoms in molecules cannot obtain noble gas configurations.

Problem 10.2   (a) Show the electron transfer and Lewis structure for the resulting compound when Ba and S atoms react. (b) What noble gases are the resulting ions isoelectronic to?

Solution 10.2

(a) A Ba atom (group 2 (IIA)) combines with a S atom (group 16 (VIA)) and transfers two electrons in the formation of barium sulfide, BaS.

$$\text{Ba:} + \text{:}\ddot{\text{S}}\text{:} \longrightarrow \text{Ba}^{2+} \, [\text{:}\ddot{\underset{..}{\text{S}}}\text{:}]^{2-}$$

Metals in group 2 (IIA) must lose two electrons and nonmetals in group 17 (VIA) atoms must gain two electrons to obtain a noble gas configuration.

(b) Ba and S become isoelectronic to Xe and Ar, respectively.

Problem 10.3   (a) Show the electron transfer and Lewis structure for the resulting compound when Mg and I atoms react. (b) What noble gases are the resulting ions isoelectronic to?

Solution 10.3

(a) When Mg atoms (group 2 (IIA)) combine with I atoms (group 17 (VIIA)), Mg loses two electrons and each I gains one electron to obtain noble gas configurations. Therefore, one Mg atom combines with two I atoms.

$$\text{:}\ddot{\underset{..}{\text{I}}}\cdot + \text{Mg:} + \text{:}\ddot{\underset{..}{\text{I}}}\cdot \longrightarrow \text{Mg}^{2+} \, 2[\text{:}\ddot{\underset{..}{\text{I}}}\text{:}]^{-}$$

(b) Mg^{2+} is isoelectronic to Ne, and I^{-} is isoelectronic to Xe.

Problem 10.4   Describe the ionic bond in the compound that results when Al and O react.

Solution 10.4   Al has three valence electrons, and O has six valence electrons. Hence, Al must lose three electrons and O must gain two electrons to achieve a noble gas configuration. To obtain the formula of the resulting compound, calculate the lowest common multiple between three and two–6. Hence, six electrons transfer between two Al atoms and three O atoms so that all of the ions become isoelectronic to Ne.

Transition Elements and the Formation of Ionic Bonds

Transition elements, such as the group 3 (IIIB) elements, lose three electrons to become isoelectronic to a noble gas. For example, Sc loses three electrons and produces Sc^{3+} ions, which are isoelectronic to Ar. However, most of the transition elements would have to lose a large number of electrons to obtain a noble gas configuration. For example, Zn with an outer configuration of $3d^{10} \, 4s^2$ must lose 12 electrons to obtain the Ar configuration. This does not occur because of the extremely large energy requirement.

PSEUDONOBLE GAS CONFIGURATIONS

Zinc and some other transition elements can form stable ions that have pseudonoble gas configurations. When Zn loses two electrons, it leaves the filled $3d^{10}$, which is a stable configuration. Therefore, when Zn and the other group 12 (IIB) elements combine with nonmetals they obtain a 2+ charge. For example, the oxide of Zn has the formula of ZnO because one Zn atom loses two electrons to an O atom.

CHARGES OF TRANSITION METAL IONS

No simple relationship exists to predict the charges on the ions of the metals in groups 4 (IVB) to 10 (VIIIB). Many of these metals form two or more ions of which one has a 2+ charge. For example, Fe forms ions with 2+ and 3+ charges. When Fe forms a 2+ ion, it loses two electrons and obtains a $3d^6$ configuration. When Fe forms a 3+ ion, it loses three electrons giving it a $3d^5$ configuration.

Problem 10.5 Write equations that show the ionization of Cu to Cu^+ and Cu^{2+}. Show the electron configuration of all species.

Solution 10.5

$$Cu\ ([Ar]\ 3d^{10}4s^1) \longrightarrow 2e^- + Cu^+\ ([Ar]\ 3d^{10})$$
$$Cu\ ([Ar]\ 3d^{10}4s^1) \longrightarrow 3e^- + Cu^{2+}\ ([Ar]\ 3d^9)$$

Energy Considerations in the Formation of Ionic Bonds

To understand completely why ionic bonds form, the energy changes that occur must be considered. Let us use NaCl as our model ionic compound. To remove an electron from a gaseous Na atom, the first ionization energy, 496 kJ/mol, must be added.

$$Na(g) \longrightarrow Na^+(g) + e^- \quad I_1 = +496\ kJ$$

Whenever an electron is removed from an atom, energy must be added–an endothermic process. When an electron is added to a gaseous Cl atom, the first electron affinity, −348 kJ/mol, is released.

$$Cl(g) + e^- \longrightarrow Cl^-(g) \quad \Delta H_{EA} = -348\ kJ$$

All halogens have large negative first electron affinities. A negative first electron affinity means that the atom releases energy–an exothermic process.

Hess's Law allows us to calculate the overall energy change. Adding the first ionization energy of Na to the first electron affinity of Cl gives the overall energy change.

$$Na(g) \longrightarrow Na^+(g) + e^- \qquad I_1 = +496\ kJ$$
$$\underline{Cl(g) + e^- \longrightarrow Cl^- \qquad \Delta H_{EA} = -348\ kJ}$$
$$Na(g) + Cl^-(g) \longrightarrow Na^+(g) + Cl^-(g) \qquad \Delta H = +147\ kJ$$

The answer shows that +147 kJ/mol is needed to produce gaseous Na^+ cations and Cl^- anions. In other words, an endothermic change occurs that requires 147 kJ/mol. Why is the formation of Na^+ and Cl^- energetically unfavorable? The addition of the ionization energy of Na is greater in magnitude than the energy liberated when an electron is added to a Cl atom. Such is the case for the formation of any pair of gaseous metallic and halide ions.

Why does sodium chloride form at all if it is not favored energetically? So far, the fact that $Na^+(g)$ ions attract $Cl^-(g)$ ions and form ionic bonds has been overlooked. Whenever a chemical bond forms, energy is released. In this case, $Na^+(g)$ and $Cl^-(g)$ combine to form the $Na^+Cl^-(g)$ ion pair and release 450 kJ/mol. Add this to the equation for the formation of $Na^+(g)$ and $Cl^-(g)$ shows that the overall energy change is −303 kJ/mol.

$$Na(g) + Cl(g) \longrightarrow Na^+(g) + Cl^-(g) \qquad \Delta H = +147\ kJ$$
$$\underline{Na^+(g) + Cl^-(g) \longrightarrow Na^+Cl^-(g) \qquad \Delta H = -450\ kJ}$$
$$Na(g) + Cl(g) \longrightarrow Na^+Cl^-(g) \qquad \Delta H = -303\ kJ$$

Thus the large quantity of energy released when the ions combine to produce the ion pair exceeds the energy absorbed in the formation of the ions from the atoms.

Problem 10.6 Use the following thermodynamic data to calculate the enthalpy change for the formation of solid lithium fluoride, $LiF(s)$, from $Li(s)$ and $F_2(g)$:

$$Li(s) + \tfrac{1}{2}F_2(g) \longrightarrow LiF(s)$$

1. Enthalpy of sublimation of Li(*s*):

$$Li(s) \longrightarrow Li(g) \qquad \triangle H° = 155 \text{ kJ}$$

2. Dissociation energy of $\frac{1}{2}F_2(g)$ to F atoms:

$$\frac{1}{2}F_2(g) \longrightarrow F(g) \qquad \triangle H° = 75 \text{ kJ}$$

3. First ionization energy of Li:

$$Li(g) \longrightarrow e^- + Li^+(g) \qquad \triangle H° = 520 \text{ kJ}$$

4. First electron affinity of F:

$$F(g) + e^- \longrightarrow F^-(g) \qquad \triangle H° = -333 \text{ kJ}$$

5. Lattice energy of LiF:

$$Li^+(g) + F^-(g) \longrightarrow LiF(s) \qquad \triangle H° = -1012 \text{ kJ}$$

Solution 10.6   Therefore, add the above equations as follows to obtain the overall enthalpy change.

$$
\begin{array}{ll}
Li(s) \longrightarrow Li(g) & \triangle H° = 155 \text{ kJ} \\
\frac{1}{2}F_2(g) \longrightarrow F(g) & \triangle H° = 75 \text{ kJ} \\
Li(g) \longrightarrow e^- + Li^+(g) & \triangle H° = 520 \text{ kJ} \\
F(g) + e^- \longrightarrow F^-(g) & \triangle H° = -333 \text{ kJ} \\
\underline{Li^+(g) + F^-(g) \longrightarrow LiF(s)} & \underline{\triangle H° = -1012 \text{ kJ}} \\
Li(s) + \frac{1}{2}F_2(g) \longrightarrow LiF(s) & \triangle H° = -595 \text{ kJ}
\end{array}
$$

Ionic Structures and Lattice Energy

At 25°C, ionic compounds are crystalline solids. The structure of a crystalline ionic solid is an ordered network of alternating cations and anions. If enough energy is added to an ionic solid, all of the ionic bonds break and the ions enter the gas phase. For example, 786 kJ/mol is needed to break the bonds in NaCl(*s*). The energy required to change one mole of an ionic compound to isolated gaseous ions is the lattice energy. Another way to think of the lattice energy is the energy released when gaseous ions combine to form an ionic solid. For the case of Na^+ and Cl^-, −786 kJ/mol is released. Note that $Na^+(g)$ and $Cl^-(g)$ release more energy when they combine to form NaCl(*s*) (−786 kJ/mol) than they do when they form a gaseous ion pair, $Na^+Cl^-(g)$, (−450 kJ/mol). Solid sodium chloride, NaCl(*s*), has many more ionic bonds than gaseous ion pairs, $Na^+Cl^-(g)$. Thus, the formation of solid sodium chloride liberates more energy than the formation of gaseous ion pairs.

Problem 10.7   The lattice energy of K_2S is 2052 kJ/mol. Calculate the amount of heat in kJ needed to convert 1.00 g $K_2S(s)$ to a vapor.

Solution 10.7   Convert the mass of K_2S to moles and use the lattice energy to find the energy.

$$1.00 \text{ g } K_2S \times 1 \text{ mol } K_2S/110.3 \text{ g} \times 2052 \text{ kJ/mol } K_2S = 18.6 \text{ kJ}$$

FACTORS THAT INFLUENCE LATTICE ENERGIES

Lattice energies depend mainly on the type of crystal structure, the distance between ions, and the magnitude of the charges on the ions. By far the most important factor that influences the lattice energy of an ionic compound is the magnitude of the charges on the ions.

Problem 10.8 Explain in terms of the ions' charges why the lattice energy of NaF, 933 kJ/mol, is significantly smaller than that of MgF_2, 2910 kJ/mol.

Solution 10.8 In NaF, the charges on the ions are 1+ and 1−. In MgF_2, the charges are 2+ and 1−. Higher charges means the bond has a higher energy. Therefore, the force of attraction between ions is greater in MgF_2 than in NaF.

Problem 10.9 Which of the following cesium compounds have the lowest and highest lattice energies?

CsF   CsCl   CsBr   CsI

Solution 10.9 Both the Cs^+ cation and the halide anions, X^-, have 1+ and 1− as their respective charges. Therefore, the charge on the ions is not a factor that determines the magnitude of the lattice energy. Another factor to consider is the lengths of the bonds. Essentially, the size of the Cs^+ cation is fixed but the size of the halide ions vary. F^- is the smallest and I^- is the largest. The longest bonds are in CsI and the shortest are in CsF. Hence, the lowest lattice energy is for CsI and the highest for CsF. As the distance between ions increases, the strength of the bond decreases. This is verified by considered the experimentally determined values: CsF, 744 kJ/mol; CsCl, 630 kJ/mol; CsBr, 600 kJ/mol; and CsI, 584 kJ/mol.

Properties of Ionic Compounds

Ionic compounds are hard but brittle crystalline solids with relatively high melting and boiling points. They generally have low electrical conductivities as solids, but are good electric conductors in the liquid (molten) state. Ionic compounds, themselves, do not conduct an electric current because the ions are tightly held in the network of positive and negative ions. However, melting ionic compounds breaks some of the ionic bonds, liberating charged particles, cations and anions, which are free to flow in an electric field.

10.3 COVALENT COMPOUNDS AND COVALENT BONDS

Properties of Covalent Compounds

Covalent compounds result when two or more nonmetals combine. Water, H_2O; ammonia, NH_3; ethyl alcohol (ethanol), C_2H_6O; and carbon dioxide, CO_2, are just a few examples of covalent compounds. The properties of covalent compounds differ from those of ionic compounds. Covalent compounds may be solids, liquids, or gases. Typical covalent compounds generally have lower melting and boiling points than ionic compounds with similar molecular masses. The densities of covalent compounds are usually less than those of ionic compounds.

Covalent Bonds and Overlapping Orbitals

A covalent bond results when two or more electrons pair are shared between two nonmetal atoms. Sharing of electrons occurs when the outer-shell orbital from one atom overlaps with one from another atom. In the overlapping orbitals, two or more electrons are attracted by the nuclei of both nonmetal atoms. The force of attraction by nonmetallic nuclei for the electrons in overlapping orbitals is a covalent bond.

Formation of Covalent Bonds

Let's consider the simplest covalent molecule, diatomic hydrogen, H_2. A H atom has one electron in the $1s$ orbital. Thus, when one H atom combines with another, the resulting H_2 molecule has two electrons.

$$H\cdot + \cdot H \longrightarrow H\text{:}H$$

The two nuclei of the H atoms share these two electrons. Each H nucleus attracts the region where the $1s$ orbitals from each atom overlap. Another way to show the shared pair of electrons is to draw a dash that designates a single covalent bond.

$$H\text{:}H = H–H$$

Each H atom in the diatomic H_2 molecule achieves the noble gas configuration of He ($1s^2$).

ENERGY CONSIDERATIONS IN THE FORMATION OF THE H–H BOND

When widely separated, the two H atoms do not interact. Hence, this is the zero point for their potential energy. As the two H atoms approach each other, their $1s$ orbitals begin to overlap at about 250 pm. At this point, the energy of the H atom begins to decrease because of the attractive forces of the nuclei for the increased electron density in the overlapping regions. The energy continues to decrease until the internuclear distance reaches the energy minimum of -432 kJ/mol at about 74 pm.

10.4   COVALENT BONDS IN DIATOMIC MOLECULES

Single Covalent Bonds

A single bond consists of a pair of shared electrons. For example, each of the molecules that composes the halogens (group 17 (VIIA)) exists at 25°C as a diatomic molecule with a single covalent bond. Halogen atoms have the configuration of $ns^2\ np^5$ and must overlap with an orbital that has one electron to achieve the noble gas configuration of ns^2np^6. Lewis structures show us how halogen atoms, X, combine to produce a single covalent bond.

$$:\ddot{X}\cdot + \cdot\ddot{X}: \longrightarrow :\ddot{X}:\ddot{X}: \text{ or } :\ddot{X} - \ddot{X}:$$

The Lewis structures for the diatomic halogen molecules are as follows.

$$:\ddot{F}\text{:}\ddot{F}: \qquad :\ddot{Cl}\text{:}\ddot{Cl}: \qquad :\ddot{Br}\text{:}\ddot{Br}: \qquad :\ddot{I}\text{:}\ddot{I}: \qquad :\ddot{At}\text{:}\ddot{At}:$$

Multiple Covalent Bonds

Many atoms share more than one electron to become isoelectronic to noble gases. Four electrons are shared in a double covalent bond, and six electrons are shared in a triple covalent bond.

Problem 10.10   (a) Write an equation that shows how two N atoms bond. (b) What type of bond is found between the N atom?

Solution 10.10   Nitrogen is a member of group 15 (VA), and has five outer electrons ($2s^2 2p^3$). Therefore, a N atom gains the stability of a noble gas configuration, if it shares three electrons from another N atom.

$$:\dot{N}\cdot + \cdot\dot{N}: \longrightarrow :N\text{::}N: \text{ or } :N \equiv N:$$

Hence, diatomic nitrogen molecules, N_2, have six shared electrons between the two N nuclei, or a triple covalent bond.

Bond Order

Bond order is defined as the number of covalent bonds (shared electron pairs) between two atoms. Bond orders usually are in a range from 0 to 4. Sometimes the values for bond orders are fractional. For example, the bond order in O_3 is 1.5. Bond orders are related to bond distances and the energies needed to cleave bonds.

Bond Distances and Bond Energies

Each bond may be characterized by the average distance between the two nuclei that attract the overlapping electrons. This is the bond distance or bond length. A bond distance is an average distance because covalent bonds are not static: the atoms in a bond vibrate back and forth.

Problem 10.11 (a) Consider F_2 and Cl_2 that have bond distance of 142 pm and 199 pm, respectively. Why is the bond distance in F_2 shorter than that in Cl_2? (b) What should be true about the bond distances of Br_2 and I_2 compared to F_2 and Cl_2?

Solution 10.11

(a) In F_2, the $2p$ orbitals from each F atom overlap, and in Cl_2 the $3p$ orbitals overlap. Because the $2p$ is on an average closer to the nucleus than the $3p$, the average bond distance in F_2 is shorter than that of Cl_2.

(b) As might be predicted, the bond distances of Br_2, 228 pm, and I_2, 267 pm, are longer than those of F_2 and Cl_2.

RELATIONSHIP BETWEEN BOND DISTANCES AND BOND ORDERS

As the number of shared electrons increases between two nuclei, the force of attraction of the nuclei for the overlapping orbitals increases and the bond distance decreases.

RELATIONSHIP BETWEEN BOND DISTANCES AND BOND ENERGIES

Bond distances are also related to bond energies. A bond energy (D_0) is the average energy required to dissociate a bond at absolute zero. The average bond energy of the H—H single bond is 432 kJ/mol. When 432 kJ is added to one mole of H_2 molecules, two moles of H atoms result.

$$H_2(g) + 432 \text{ kJ} \longrightarrow 2H \cdot (g)$$

Stronger bonds have higher bond energies and weaker bonds have lower bond energies.

Problem 10.12 Predict the trends in bond distances and bond energies for the carbon halogen bonds: C—F, C—Cl, C—Br, and C—I.

Solution 10.12 The shortest bond results when C bonds with F, a member of the same period as C; thus, it has the most effective overlap and the highest bond energy, 485 kJ/mol. A C—Cl bond is longer, 177 pm, than a C—F bond because the valence electrons in Cl are in the $n = 3$ shell. Hence, the C—Cl bond energy, 327 kJ/mol, is smaller than that for C—F. A similar trend is found with C—Br and C—I, which have bond lengths of 0.194 and 214 pm and bond energies of 285 and 213 kJ/mol, respectively.

Problem 10.13 Arrange the following bonds in increasing order, lowest to highest, of bond distance and bond energies: N=N, N≡N, C=C, C≡C.

Table 10.1   *Selected Bond Lengths and Average Bond Energies*

Bond	Bond Length, pm	Bond Energy, kJ/mol
H−H	74.2	432
H−C	109	413
H−O	96	463
H−N	101	391
H−S	134	349
H−F	91.8	565
H−Cl	127	431
H−Br	141	363
H−I	161	295
C−C	154	348
C=C	134	614
C≡C	120	835
C−F	135	485
C−Cl	177	327
C−Br	194	285
C−I	214	213
C−O	143	358
C=O	120	799
C≡O	113	1072
C−N	147	305
C=N	–	615
C≡N	116	887
Si−Si	235	222
Si−O	166	368
Si−F	157	565
Si−Cl	202	381
Si−Br	216	310
Si−I	244	234

(*continued*)

Solution 10.13

(a) Triple bonds are shorter than double bonds due to the greater electrostatic attractive forces. Hence, N≡N and C≡C are shorter than N=N and C=C. Because N and C are in the second period, the atomic radius of N is smaller than that of C because sizes of atoms decrease across a period. Therefore, N≡N is shorter than C≡C and N=N is shorter than C=C. This means that the shortest bond distance is N≡N followed by C≡C. The next in the series is N=N and the longest is C=C.

(b) Bond energy is indirectly related to the bond distance. Shorter bonds have higher bond energies than longer bonds. Thus, the order of bond energies is opposite that of bond distances.

Problem 10.14   The methane molecule, CH_4, has four C−H single bonds.

The enthalpy change needed to break all of the C−H bonds in methane is 1652 kJ/mol.

$$CH_4(g) \longrightarrow C(g) + 4H(g) \qquad \triangle H = +1652 \text{ kJ}$$

Table 10.1   (continued)

Bond	Bond Length, pm	Bond Energy, kJ/mol
N–N	145	160
N=N	125	418
N≡N	110	942
N–O	140	201
N=O	121	607
N–F	136	272
N–Cl	175	200
O–O	149	142
O=O	121	494
O–F	142	190
F–F	142	155
Cl–Cl	199	240
Br–Br	228	190
I–I	267	149
S–H	131	347
S–F	168	327
S–Cl	203	253
S–Br	218	218
S–S	208	266
S=O	143	323
S=S	189	418

Calculate the average bond energy.

Solution 10.14   Because methane has four C–H bonds, the average C–H bond energy is 413.0 kJ/mol.

$$D_{C–H} = 1652 \text{ kJ}/4 = 413.0 \text{ kJ}$$

Bond Energies and Thermodynamics

Average bond energies are used to estimate enthalpy changes, ΔH, for chemical reactions. The ΔH for a reaction equals the sum of the average bond energies of the reactants, $\Sigma D_{reactants}$, minus the sum of the average bond energies of the products, $\Sigma D_{products}$.

$$\Delta H = \Sigma D_{reactants} - \Sigma D_{products} \tag{10.1}$$

In reactions, bonds break in the reactants and form in the products. Thus, the sum of the bond energies of the reactants, $\Sigma D_{reactants}$, is the total energy needed to break bonds. The sum of the bond energies of the products, $\Sigma D_{products}$, is the energy liberated as bonds form.

Problem 10.15   Consider the reaction in which H_2 and F_2 to produce two HF molecules.

$$H_2(g) + F_2(g) \longrightarrow 2HF(g)$$

(a) What bonds break and form in this reaction?   (b) If the bond energies of H–H and F–F are 432 kJ/mol and 155 kJ/mol, respectively, calculate the total energy needed to break the bonds in this reaction. (c) If the bond energy of H—F is 565 kJ/mol, calculate the energy released when bonds form in this reaction. (d) What is the $\triangle H°$ for this reaction?

Solution 10.15

(a) The bonds in H_2 and F_2 break and two HF bonds form.

(b) A total of 587 kJ ($\Sigma D_{reactants} = 432$ kJ + 155 kJ) is needed to break the bonds in the reactants.

(c) In the products, two H—F bonds form and release energy. Because the bond energy of a H—F single bond is 565 kJ/mol, then the formation of two moles of HF liberates 2×565 kJ/mol or 1130 kJ ($\Sigma D_{products}$).

(d) To calculate the overall enthalpy change, $\triangle H$, subtract the sum of the bond energies of the products, $\Sigma D_{products}$, from the sum of the bond energies of the reactants, $\Sigma D_{reactants}$.

$$\triangle H = \Sigma D_{reactants} - \Sigma D_{products}$$
$$= 587 \text{ kJ} - 1130 \text{ kJ} = -543 \text{ kJ}$$

Problem 10.16

(a) Use the average bond energies from Table 10.1 to calculate the $\triangle H$ for the hydrogenation of acetylene, HC≡CH, to produce ethane, C_2H_6.

$$2H_2(g) + HC≡CH(g) \longrightarrow C_2H_6(g)$$

(b) Compare the value obtained in part (a) with the value obtained using Hess's Law.

Solution 10.16

(a) First, calculate the sum of the bond energies of the reactants, $\Sigma D_{reactants}$. In the reactants, two H—H single bonds ($D_{H-H} = 432$ kJ/mol) and one C-C triple bond ($D_{C≡C} = 835$ kJ/mol) break.

$$\Sigma D_{reactants} = 2D_{H-H} + D_{C-C}$$
$$= (2 \text{ mol} \times 432 \text{ kJ/mol}) + 835 \text{ kJ} = 1699 \text{ kJ}$$

Then, calculate the sum of the bond energies of the products, $\Sigma D_{products}$. In the products four C—H single bonds ($D_{C-H} = 413$ kJ/mol) and one C—C single bond ($D_{C-C} = 348$ kJ/mol) form.

$$\Sigma D_{products} = 4D_{C-H} + D_{C-C}$$
$$= (4 \text{ mol} \times 413 \text{ kJ/mol}) + 348 \text{ kJ} = 2000 \text{ kJ}$$

Finally, subtract the bond energies of the products from that of the reactants.

$$\triangle H = \Sigma D_{reactants} - \Sigma D_{products}$$
$$= 1699 \text{ kJ} - 2000 \text{ kJ} = -301 \text{ kJ}$$

(b) To apply Hess's Law add the standard enthalpies of formation, $\triangle H_f°$ of the products and subtract the sum of the enthalpies of formation of the reactants.

$$\triangle H = \Sigma \triangle H_f°(\text{products}) - \Sigma \triangle H_f°(\text{reactants})$$

The $\triangle H_f^\circ$ for C_2H_6 is -84.7 kJ/mol, 227 kJ/mol for C_2H_2, and 0 kJ/mol for H_2. Thus, the $\triangle H^\circ$ is calculated as follows.

$$\triangle H^\circ = \triangle H_f^\circ(C_2H_6) - [\triangle H_f^\circ(C_2H_2) + \triangle H_f^\circ(H_2)]$$
$$= -84.7 \text{ kJ} - (227 \text{ kJ} + 0 \text{ kJ}) = -312 \text{ kJ}$$

Heteronuclear Diatomic Molecules

Most of the examples considered to this point are homonuclear diatomic molecules, those with the same bonded atoms. Now we turn our attention to heteronuclear diatomic molecules—covalent diatomic molecules with two different atoms. For example, HCl results when the $1s$ orbital from a H atom overlaps with the $3p$ orbital of a Cl atom. A single covalent bond results because each atom shares one electron from the other atom and both obtain a noble gas configuration.

Nonpolar Covalent Bonds

The atoms in homonuclear diatomic molecules share their electron pair equally because both atoms have the same electronegativity. Covalent bonds that result from identical atoms or two different atoms with the same electronegativity are nonpolar covalent bonds. Such bonds do not have a charge separation because the atoms share the electrons equally. H_2, F_2, O_2, and N_2 are examples of molecules with nonpolar covalent bonds.

Polar Covalent Bonds

If two atoms with different electronegativities bond, one attracts the shared electron pair more strongly than the other. Such is the case in HCl. The electronegativities of H and Cl are 2.2 and 3.0, respectively. Thus, the Cl atom exerts a greater force of attraction on the shared electron pair than does H. This means that the electron density associated with the shared electrons is larger in the Cl atom than it is in the H atom. As a result of having "extra" electron density, the F atom in HF is more negative than the H atom. Hence, the HCl molecule has a separation of charge. The pair of separated equal and opposite charges is called a dipole. To designate the more negative end of the molecular dipole write the symbol lowercase delta, δ, with a negative sign, $\delta-$, which means "partially negative." To designate the more positive end of the dipole write $\delta+$, which means, "partially positive."

$$\overset{\delta+}{H}\text{---}\overset{\delta-}{Cl}$$

Problem 10.17   Discuss the bonding and polarity of the iodine monofluoride, IF, molecule. The electronegativities of I and F are 2.2 and 4.0, respectively.

Solution 10.17   Because both I and F are group 17 (VIIA) elements, each shares one electron to become isoelectronic to a noble gas.

$$:\overset{..}{\underset{..}{I}}\text{---}\overset{..}{\underset{..}{F}}:$$

Because the electronegativity of F, 4.0, is higher than that of I, 2.2, the F end of the molecule is more negative (partially negative) with respect to the I end of the molecule (partially positive).

DIPOLE MOMENTS

The dipole moment, μ, is the measure of molecular polarity. It is found by multiplying the partial charge, q, (either $\delta+$ or the absolute value of $\delta-$) times the distance, d, that separates the charges.

$$\mu = qd \tag{10.2}$$

The most commonly used unit of dipole moment is the debye, D, in which one D equals 3.34×10^{-30} C m (C is the charge in coulombs and m is the distance in meters separating the nuclei). Nonpolar covalent molecules do not have a charge separation, hence they do not have a dipole moment, $\mu = 0$ D. The magnitudes of the dipole moments of polar covalent molecules are greater than zero.

Problem 10.18   The dipole moments for HF and HCl are as follows.

$$HF \qquad HCl$$
$$\mu = 1.91\,D \qquad \mu = 1.07\,D$$

Explain why the dipole moment of HCl is smaller than that of HF.

Solution 10.18   The decrease in dipole moments in the hydrogen halides is the result of the decrease in the electronegativity differences, ΔEN. The ΔENs for HF and HCl are 1.8 and 0.8, respectively. Therefore, the charge separation in HF is significantly larger than that in HCl. Because the magnitudes of the partial charges in HF are greater than those in HCl, the dipole moment of HF is much larger than that of HCl even though the distance that separates the charges in HCl is greater than the distance in HF.

Covalent and Ionic Character

Nonpolar molecules are purely covalent because they do not have a charge separation. Consequently, they have 0% ionic character and 100% covalent character. As the separation of charge approaches the charges in ionic compounds, the ionic character increases and the covalent character decreases. The percent ionic character is calculated from electronegativity differences, ΔEN.

Problem 10.19   The dipole moment of HCl is 1.08 D and the bond distance is 1.27×10^{-10} m. If one debye, D, is 3.34×10^{-30} C m, calculate the percent ionic character of HCl.

Solution 10.19   If an HCl molecule was a purely ionic, H^+Cl^-, the charge on the H atom is 1.60×10^{-19} C (the charge of a proton) and the bond distance of a HCl molecule is 1.27×10^{-10} m. Therefore, the theoretical dipole moment in debyes, μ, for the hypothetical H^+Cl^- molecule is calculated as follows.

$$\mu = qd$$
$$= 1.60 \times 10^{-19}\,C \times 1.27 \times 10^{-10}\,m \times 1\,D/3.34 \times 10^{-30}\,C\,m$$
$$= 6.08\,D$$

If HCl was purely ionic, it would have a dipole moment of 6.08 D. The actual dipole moment of HCl is 1.07 D. Therefore, divide the experimental value by the theoretical ionic value and multiplying by 100 to estimate the percent ionic character.

$$\% \text{ ionic character} = \frac{\text{actual experimental dipole moment}}{\text{theoretical ionic dipole moment}} \times 100 \qquad (10.3)$$
$$= (1.07\,D/6.08\,D) \times 100 = 17.6\%$$

Problem 10.20   The bond distance in lithium hydride, LiH, is 160 pm, and its dipole moment is 5.89 D. If one debye, D, is 3.34×10^{-30} C m, calculate the percent ionic character of LiH.

Solution 10.20   First, calculate the hypothetical dipole moment for Li^+H^-. To calculate the dipole moment multiply the charge of the ions in C by the distance that separates them in meters, d (Eq. 10.2). The charge on a proton, which equals the charge on the Li^+ ion, is 1.60×10^{-19} C. The bond distance is given in pm; thus, convert the 160 pm to 1.6×10^{-10} m. If the charge in C is multiplied by the distance in m, the dipole moment is in units of C m. Hence, it can be converted to D by using the conversion factor, $1\,D/3.34 \times 10^{-30}$ C m.

$$\mu = qd$$
$$= 1.60 \times 10^{-19}\,C \times 1.60 \times 10^{-10}\,m \times 1\,D/3.34 \times 10^{-30}\,C\,m$$
$$= 7.66\,D$$

Then, calculate the percent ionic character. The actual experimental value for the dipole moment of LiH is 5.89 D and the theoretical ionic dipole moment is 7.66 D. Therefore, to calculate the percent ionic character use Eq. 10.3 as follows.

$$\% \text{ ionic character} = \frac{\text{actual experimental dipole moment}}{\text{theoretical ionic dipole moment}} \times 100$$

$$= (5.89 \text{ D}/7.66 \text{ D}) \times 100 = 76.9\%$$

10.5 COVALENT BONDS IN POLYATOMIC MOLECULES

Writing Lewis Structures for Simple Polyatomic Molecules

Use the following steps to write the Lewis structures for simple covalent molecules in which all the atoms obey the Octet Rule.

1. Find the number of valence electrons in all atoms in the molecule or ion.
2. Identify the central atom and draw the skeleton structure of the molecule.

   (a) A central atom must have the capacity to bond to more than one atom. Therefore, H and F can never be central atoms because when they bond to one other atom they obtain a stable noble gas configuration.

   (b) In numerous molecules, the central atom is the one with the lowest electronegativity, which is usually the one written first in the molecular formulas of most binary compounds. For example, in NF_3, SF_2, and CCl_4 the central atoms are N, S, and C, respectively.

   (c) Oxygen atoms are rarely central atoms. When two or more O atoms are in the formula, they most often bond to the central atom and not to each other. However, occasionally the unstable O–O single bond in peroxides is encountered; e.g., H_2O_2 (H–O–O–H).

   (d) In compounds with H, O, and some other nonmetal, the H atoms most often bond to the O atoms and not to the nonmetal. For example, acids such as nitric acid, HNO_3; sulfuric acid, H_2SO_4; and phosphoric acid, H_3PO_4, have molecules in which all of the H atoms bond to O atoms. The nonmetals excluding H and O (N, S, and P in these examples) are the central atoms.

3. Determine the number of electrons that remain to be placed into the Lewis structure. Count the number of electrons in the skeleton structure from Step 2. Each dash represents a single covalent bond with two shared electrons. Subtract the number of electrons in the formula from the total number of valence electrons in Step 1. This number tells how many electrons remain to be placed into the structure.
4. Determine the number of electrons required to complete the noble gas configurations for each atom in the molecule.
5. Compare the number of electrons needed to complete the noble gas configurations of each atom (Step 3) with the number of electrons that remain to be placed into the formula (Step 2).

   (a) If the numbers are equal, the molecule has all single covalent bonds. Therefore, place the correct number of electrons around each atom to obtain the noble gas configuration.

   (b) When more electrons are needed to complete the noble gas configuration than are available, the Lewis structure contains one or more multiple bonds. If two more electrons are needed than are available in Step 2, the molecule has a double bond. If four more electrons are needed than are available in Step 2, the molecule has either two double bonds or one triple bond. Only certain atoms form multiple bonds. For example, H and F can only bond to one electron so they do not form multiple bonds. C, N, O, and S are the atoms that most commonly form multiple bonds. C and N can form single, double, or triple bonds. O and S usually form single and double bonds.

Use the above information to identify the atoms that form multiple bonds and place the appropriate number of electrons between them. Finally, distribute the remaining electrons around all other atoms in such a way to complete their noble gas configurations.

6. After writing the Lewis structure, check to see that each atom has a noble gas configuration. Also check to determine if that the number of valence electrons from the first step are in the structure.

Problem 10.21 (a) Draw the Lewis structure for a phosphorus trifluoride, PF_3, molecule. (b) Describe the bonding in a PF_3 molecule.

Solution 10.21
(a) Follow the six-step method to obtain the Lewis structure.

(a) This molecule has 26 valence electrons (5+21).

(b) Draw the skeleton structure. An F atom cannot be the central atom because it only bonds to one other atom. Hence, P, the atom listed first in the formula, is the central atom in PF_3. The skeleton structure of PF_3 is

$$F— P—F$$
$$\mid$$
$$F$$

(c) Six electrons are in the skeleton structure because it has three single bonds. Step 1 shows a total of 26 e^-. Therefore, 20 e^- (26 e^- − 6 e^- = 20 e^-) remain to be placed into the Lewis structure.

(d) Each F needs six additional electrons to obtain a noble gas configuration, resulting in a total of 18 e^- for the F atoms. Phosphorus only needs two electrons because it already has six electrons. Hence, 20 electrons (18 e^- + 2 e^- = 20 e^-) are needed to complete the noble gas configurations of the four atoms in PF_3.

(e) A total of 20 electrons is needed to complete the noble gas configurations. Step 3 shows us that 20 electrons remain to be add to the structure. Because the number of electrons that remains equals the number needed, the Lewis structure has all single covalent bonds. Place the remaining electrons into the structure so each atom achieves a noble gas configuration.

$$:\!F — P — F\!:$$
$$\mid$$
$$:\!F\!:$$

(f) This structure is correct because each atom has eight valence electrons, and it has a total of 26 electrons.

(b) This Lewis structure shows us that the PF_3 molecule have three P–F single covalent bonds. In addition, the central P atom has a pair of electrons that is not bonded to another atom. A pair of electrons that does not bond to an atom is called either lone pair electrons or nonbonded electrons.

Problem 10.22 Draw the Lewis structure for a nitric acid molecule, HNO_3.

Solution 10.22

1. The total number of valence electrons in HNO_3 is 24 (1+5+18).
2. H is never a central atom and O is rarely a central atom; thus, N is the central atom. When a molecule contains H, O and another nonmetal, the H most often bonds to an O atom. Hence, the skeleton structure for HNO_3 becomes.

$$O-N-O-H$$
$$|$$
$$O$$

3. Eight electrons are in the skeleton structure because of its four bonds. The first step revealed a total of 24 electrons. Therefore, 16 electrons ($24\,e^- - 8\,e^- = 16\,e^-$) remain to add to the Lewis structure.
4. The two O atoms not bonded to H atoms require six electrons apiece, and the O atom bonded to the H atom needs four electrons. Hence, the O atoms need 16 electrons ($12\,e^- + 4\,e^- = 16\,e^-$). Two electrons are needed to complete the noble gas configuration for N. The H atom requires no electrons because it already has two electrons. Thus, 18 electrons are needed to complete the Lewis structure of HNO_3.
5. Two more electrons are needed than are available. This means that the HNO_3 structure has a double bond. Therefore, place a double bond between the O and N atoms and then complete the noble gas configurations of all atoms.

$$:\ddot{O}=N-\ddot{O}-H$$
$$|$$
$$:\ddot{O}:$$

This is the not the only way to place the electrons in the Lewis structure of HNO_3. Some molecules have more than one Lewis structure. These molecules are considered in Section 10.6.

6. The structure is correct because each atom has a noble gas configuration, and the structure has a total of 24 electrons.

Problem 10.23 Write the Lewis structure for the oxalate anion, $C_2O_4^{2-}$.

Solution 10.23

1. Thirty-four valence electrons are in the oxalate ion (8+24+2).
2. The two C atoms are the central atoms because O is rarely the central atom. Thus, the skeleton structure is

$$O-C-C-O$$
$$|\quad|$$
$$O\quad O$$

3. Ten electrons are in the skeleton structure because it has five bonds. The first step reveals a total of 34 electrons. Therefore, 24 electrons ($34\,e^- - 10\,e^- = 24\,e^-$) remain to be placed into the Lewis structure.
4. The four O atoms need 24 electrons because each requires six more electrons. The two C atoms need four electrons because each requires two electrons. Consequently, a total of 28 electrons ($24\,e^- + 4\,e^- = 28\,e^-$) are required for the structure.
5. Four more electrons are needed than are available. This means that the oxalate ion has either a triple bond or two double bonds. A triple bond cannot form in the molecule because O atoms cannot share three electrons and obtain a noble gas configuration. Also the two C

atoms are already bonded to two atoms. Therefore, the oxalate ion has two C-O double bonds.

$$\left[\ddot{\underset{..}{O}} = C - C = \ddot{\underset{..}{O}} \atop {\underset{:\ddot{O}:}{|} \quad \underset{:\ddot{O}:}{|}} \right]^{2-}$$

6. Our structure is correct because each atom has eight outer electrons and the structure has a total of 34 electrons.

Formal Charges and Lewis Structures

The arrangement of the atoms in a molecule is not always obvious. For example, two different Lewis structures of hydrogen cyanide, HCN, obey all of the stated rules.

$$H-C\equiv N: \quad \text{or} \quad H-N\equiv C:$$
$$\text{I} \qquad\qquad \text{II}$$

Which of these two structures, I or II, is the one in nature? To make such a decision, a system of formal charges is used to identify the more plausible structure.

Formal charges are not actual electric charges such as those in ionic compounds, but are a means for keeping track of the valence electrons of atoms in covalent structures. Formal charges are used because theoretical calculations indicate that the distribution of valence electrons in a molecule tends to be that which effectively gives each atom in the molecule the same number of outer-level electrons as it has in an isolated atom. To calculate the formal charge, *FC*, for an atom use the following formula.

$$FC = \text{outer-level electrons} - (\text{nonbonding electrons} + \tfrac{1}{2} \text{ bonding electrons}) \qquad (10.4)$$

FORMAL CHARGE VALUES

If the formal charge of an atom is zero, it has the same number of outer electrons in the molecule as it has in a nonbonded atom. An atom with a positive formal charge has fewer outer electrons and one with a negative formal charge has more outer electrons than the nonbonded atom.

It is important to note that the sum of formal charges in a molecule equals zero because it is neutral and carries no charge. The sum of the formal charges on an ion equals its charge.

Problem 10.24 Calculate the formal charges on the three atoms in structures I and II of the proposed structures of hydrogen cyanide, H–C≡N: and H–N≡C:, respectively. Compare the results and select the more plausible structure.

Solution 10.24
(a) H–C≡N:

FC = valence electrons − (nonbonding electron + $\tfrac{1}{2}$ bonding electrons)

$$FC_H = 1 - (0 + \tfrac{1}{2}(2)) = 0$$
$$FC_C = 4 - (0 + \tfrac{1}{2}(8)) = 0$$
$$FC_N = 5 - (2 + \tfrac{1}{2}(6)) = 0$$

In all cases, the formal charges equal zero. Because each atom has a formal charge of 0, they have the same number of valence electrons in the molecule as in the individual atoms. Note that the sum of the formal charges equals zero because HCN is a molecule.

(b) H–N≡C:

$$FC_H = 1 - (0 + \tfrac{1}{2}(2)) = \;\; 0$$
$$FC_C = 4 - (2 + \tfrac{1}{2}(6)) = -1$$
$$FC_N = 5 - (0 + \tfrac{1}{2}(8)) = +1$$

In general, the Lewis structure of a molecule that has atoms with no formal charges is a more plausible structure than those with positive and negative formal charges. Therefore, structure I is a better prediction for the molecular structure of hydrogen cyanide than is structure II. In nature, hydrogen cyanide molecules exist as $H–C\equiv N:$.

Problem 10.25   (a) Draw two different Lewis structures for formaldehyde, CH_2O. (b) Use formal charges to decide which of these structures is the more plausible structure.

Solution 10.25

(a) Using the rules for drawing Lewis structures gives the following structures.

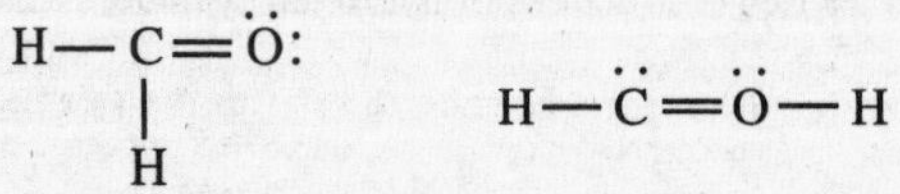

$$H—C\!\!=\!\!\ddot{O}:$$
$$|$$
$$H$$
$$I$$

$$H—\overset{..}{\underset{..}{C}}\!\!=\!\!\overset{..}{\underset{..}{O}}—H$$
$$II$$

In structure I, C is the central atom to which two H atoms and one O atom bond. In structure II, one H and one O atom bond to the central C atom and the second H bonds to the O atom.

(b) Calculate the formal charges on each atom in structures I and II.

The formal charges on the atoms in structure I is as follows:

$$FC_H = 1 - (0 + \tfrac{1}{2}(2)) = 0$$
$$FC_C = 4 - (0 + \tfrac{1}{2}(8)) = 0$$
$$FC_O = 6 - (4 + \tfrac{1}{2}(4)) = 0$$

The formal charges on the atoms in structure II is as follows:

$$FC_H = 1 - (0 + \tfrac{1}{2}(2)) = 0$$
$$FC_C = 4 - (2 + \tfrac{1}{2}(6)) = -1$$
$$FC_O = 6 - (2 + \tfrac{1}{2}(6)) = +1$$

In structure II a formal negative charge is on the C atom and a formal positive charge is on the very electronegative O atom. More electronegative atoms tend to have negative formal charges and not positive ones. Nevertheless, all atoms in structure I have formal charges of zero. Therefore, structure I is the more plausible structure and corresponds to the actual bonding in the formaldehyde molecule.

10.6   RESONANCE

What is Resonance?

Some molecules do not have a unique Lewis structure. Instead, two or more Lewis structures can be written for these molecules. Ozone, O_3, is an example of such a molecule. Two different Lewis structures can be written for O_3 that only differ in the placement of the electrons.

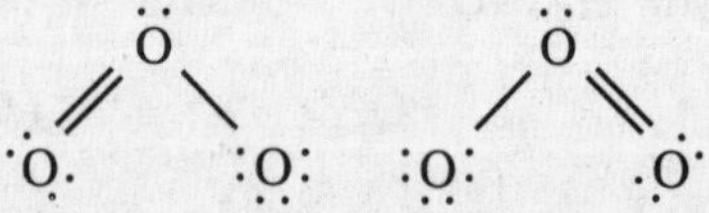

$$\ddot{O}$$
I   II

Both structures show a double bond and a single bond. However, the bonds are in different positions. In structure I, the double bond is between the first two O atoms and in structure II it is between the second two O atoms. Which of these Lewis structures corresponds to the actual structure of the ozone molecule? Each of these proposed Lewis structures shows that the two O–O distances should be different. Recall that a O–O double bond is shorter than an O–O single bond. However, the actual experimentally determined structure of O_3 shows that both O–O bond distances (128 pm) are equal. Moreover, the experimental O–O bond distance is intermediate between that for the O–O double bond (121 pm in O2) and an O-O single bond (0.149 in H–O–O–H). Clearly neither structure I nor II alone is an adequate representation of the bonding in O_3. This dilemma is resolved by saying that a better representation is the average of structures I and II. This may be shown in the following way:

in which the double headed arrow means the average of the structures shown. This predicts an average bond order of 1.5, the average of a single bond (bond order = 1) and a double bond (bond order = 2).

RESONANCE AND DELOCALIZATION OF ELECTRONS

In molecules that exhibit resonance, such as O_3, the electrons in multiple bonds are delocalized. The second bond of the double bond shown in structures I and II of O_3 is not localized between two O atoms. Instead, it is spread out or delocalized over the entire molecule. Half of the electron density of that bond is between each O–O bond. The actual structure of ozone is often expressed as in the following structure.

The dashed lines represents partial bonds that have a bond order of 0.5.

Contributing Structures and Resonance

Molecules exhibit resonance whenever more than one correct Lewis structure can be written that differ only in the placement of electrons. Each Lewis structure that differs with respect to the placement of the electrons in a molecule is called a contributing or resonance structure. The average of all of the valid contributing structures most closely corresponds to the actual structure of the molecule. Each contributing structure is separated with a double headed arrow ($\leftrightarrow$).

Problem 10.26

(a) Draw four contributing structures for carbon dioxide, CO_2.
(b) Assign formal charges to the atoms in these contributing structures and predict which are the most plausible ones.

Solution 10.26

(a) Following the rules for writing Lewis structures gives the following contributing structures.

$$:\ddot{O}=C=\ddot{O}: \quad \leftrightarrow \quad :O\equiv C-\ddot{O}: \quad \leftrightarrow \quad :\ddot{O}-C\equiv O: \quad \leftrightarrow \quad :\ddot{O}-C-\ddot{O}:$$

$$\text{I} \qquad\qquad \text{II} \qquad\qquad \text{III} \qquad\qquad \text{IV}$$

(b) Following the rules for formal charges gives the following results.

$$:\overset{0}{\underset{}{\text{O}}}=\overset{0}{\underset{}{\text{C}}}=\overset{0}{\underset{}{\text{O}}}: \quad \leftrightarrow \quad :\overset{+}{\text{O}}\equiv\overset{0}{\text{C}}-\overset{-}{\underset{}{\text{O}}}: \quad \leftrightarrow \quad :\overset{-}{\underset{}{\text{O}}}-\overset{0}{\text{C}}\equiv\overset{+}{\text{O}}: \quad \leftrightarrow \quad :\overset{-}{\underset{}{\text{O}}}-\overset{2+}{\text{C}}-\overset{-}{\underset{}{\text{O}}}:$$

$$\text{I} \qquad\qquad\qquad \text{II} \qquad\qquad\qquad \text{III} \qquad\qquad\qquad \text{IV}$$

Each atom in structure I has a formal charge of 0. Thus, structure I is predicted to be the contributing structure that is most important. Structures II and III are less important because each has an electronegative O atom with a formal positive charge. Structure IV is least important because of the high formal charge on the C atom. Thus, the C–O bond in CO_2 should have the characteristics of a C–O double bond, and should not resemble either a C–O single or triple bond. Experimental data supports this prediction.

10.7   MOLECULES THAT DO NOT OBEY THE OCTET RULE

Incomplete Octets

Some covalently bonded atoms have less than eight electrons. For example, in the gas phase the covalent molecule BeH_2 has been observed. Because Be is a group 2 (IIA) element, it only has two valence electrons ($2s^2$). These electrons form covalent bonds with H, giving the following structure in which the Be atom only has four valence electrons.

$$\text{H–Be–H}$$

Problem 10.27   (a) Write the Lewis structure of boron trifluoride and show that the B atom has an incomplete octet. (b) Explain why BF_3 a reactive molecule.

Solution 10.27

(a) The Lewis structure that best represents BF_3 shows that each of the three outer electrons of B ($2s^2 2p^1$) shares one electron from F, which results in six valence electrons.

$$:\ddot{\text{F}} - \text{B} - \ddot{\text{F}}:$$
$$|$$
$$:\ddot{\text{F}}:$$

(b) BF_3 is a thermodynamically stable molecule; however, it is reactive and tends to combine with any chemical species that can donate two additional electrons, allowing it to achieve the more stable noble gas configuration.

Expanded Octets

Some molecules have a central atom with more than eight electrons. These molecules are said to have an expanded octet. A good example is sulfur hexafluoride, SF_6.

$$\begin{array}{c} :\!\ddot{F}\!: \\ :\!\ddot{F}\!\diagdown \!\mid\! \diagup\!\ddot{F}\!: \\ S \\ :\!\ddot{F}\!\diagup\!\mid\!\diagdown\!\ddot{F}\!: \\ :\!\ddot{F}\!: \end{array}$$

This Lewis structure shows that the S atom in SF_6 has 12 outer-level electrons, four more than the noble gas configuration of S.

Problem 10.28   Draw the Lewis structures for phosphorus pentafluoride, PF_5; iodine trichloride, ICl_3; and xenon difluoride, XeF_2, and determine the number of electrons around the central atom.

Solution 10.28   The Lewis structures for PF_5, ICl_3, and XeF_2 are as follows.

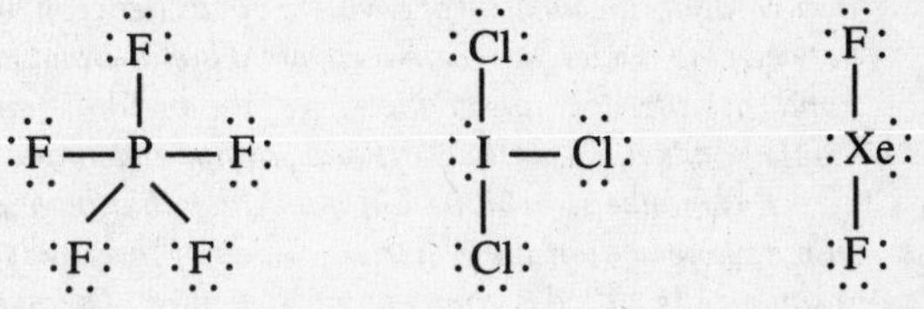

The central atoms in each of these has 10 valence electrons.

Problem 10.29   (a) Draw the Lewis structure for XeF_4 and determine the number of valence electrons on Xe. (b) How many bonds and lone pairs are found on the Xe atom?

Solution 10.29

(a) Xe is a noble gas that already has eight valence electrons. If it bonds with four F atoms it must have a total of 12 valence electrons. Therefore the Lewis structure for XeF_4 is as follows.

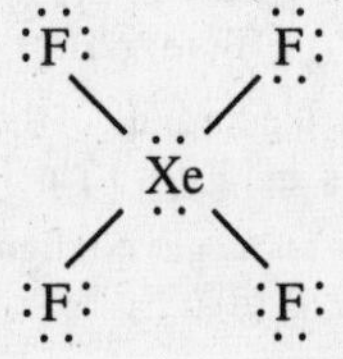

(b) This Lewis structure shows that XeF_4 has four Xe-F bonds and the Xe has two lone pairs.

SUMMARY

*C*hemical bonds are the forces of attraction among atoms and ions. Ionic bonds result when one or more electrons transfer between atoms or groups of atoms. The resulting cations and anions attract each other as a result of their opposite charges. The force of attraction between oppositely charged ions is an ionic bond. In the formation of an ionic bond, atoms of representative elements obtain a stable noble gas electron configuration. Few transition elements can obtain a noble gas configuration. However, some obtain a pseudonoble gas configuration.

Ions in an ionic compound are in a specific crystal structure, which is a regular network of alternating cations and anions. The energy needed to dissociate the crystal lattice structure is the lattice energy. Ionic compounds that have ions with higher charges that are closely packed tend to have higher lattice energies than those with lower charges that are more widely separated.

Covalent bonds result when one or more of the outer orbitals of one nonmetal atom overlaps with one or more outer orbitals from another nonmetal atom. The nuclei from the atoms that form a covalent bond attract the electrons in the region of the overlapping orbitals and produce the covalent bond. The electrons in overlapping orbitals are termed shared electrons.

If nonmetallic atoms with the same electronegativity bond, they form nonpolar covalent bonds in which the atoms share the electrons equally. If atoms with different electronegativities bond, they form polar covalent bonds in which the atoms do not share the electrons equally. Polar diatomic molecules have dipole moments greater than zero, and nonpolar diatomic molecules have zero dipole moments. The dipole moment, μ, of a molecule is calculated from the product of its partial charges and distance that separates them.

Covalent bonds may be characterized by their bond orders, bond distances, and bond energies. Bond order is the number of covalent bonds between two atoms. Bond distance is the average distance between the nuclei that form a covalent bond. Bond energy is the energy needed to cleave a covalent bond. As the bond order increases, the bond distance decreases, and the bond energy increases. Triple bonds are usually short and strong, and single bonds are usually long and weak.

Resonance is exhibited in molecules that have more than one Lewis structure that differ only in the placement of the electrons. Each of the Lewis structures written for a molecule that exhibits resonance is called a contributing structure. The average of all of the most important contributing structures best approximates the actual bonding in the molecule.

While most molecules obey the Octet Rule, many molecules have atoms that do not achieve noble gas configurations. These molecules are generally less stable than similar molecules that have atoms with noble gas configurations.

CHAPTER 10 REVIEW EXERCISE

1. Classify each of the following compounds as ionic or covalent: (a) N_2O_4, (b) CS_2, (c) RbF, (d) $V(OH)_2$, (e) NBr_3

2. Write the formula of the ionic compound that results from each of the following pairs of atoms: (a) Cs and F, (b) Li and O, (c) Al and S

3. What noble gas configurations do the ions achieve in each of the following? (a) LiCl, (b) BaS, (c) Fr_3P, (d) YF_3

4. Show the electron transfer and the resulting Lewis structure of the ionic combines from the following metals and nonmetals. (a) K and O, (b) Mg and P

5. Show the electron transfer and the resulting Lewis structure of the ionic combines from the following metals and nonmetals: (a) Ba and I, (b) Sr and S

6. Use the following thermodynamic data to calculate the enthalpy change for the formation of solid magnesium chloride, $MgCl_2(s)$, from $Mg(s)$ and $Cl_2(g)$:

$$Mg(s) + Cl_2(g) \longrightarrow MgCl_2(s)$$

(a) Enthalpy of sublimation of $Mg(s)$:

$$Mg(s) \longrightarrow Mg(g) \qquad \triangle H^\circ = 150 \text{ kJ}$$

(b) Dissociation energy of $Cl_2(g)$ to 2Cl atoms:

$$Cl_2(g) \longrightarrow 2Cl(g) \qquad \triangle H° = 243 \text{ kJ}$$

(c) First ionization energy of Mg:

$$Mg(g) \longrightarrow e^- + Mg^+(g) \qquad \triangle H° = 738 \text{ kJ}$$

(d) Second ionization energy of Mg:

$$Mg^+(g) \longrightarrow e^- + Mg^{2+}(g) \qquad \triangle H° = 1450 \text{ kJ}$$

(e) First electron affinity of Cl_2:

$$Cl_2(g) + e^- \longrightarrow 2Cl^-(g) \qquad \triangle H° = -698 \text{ kJ}$$

(f) Lattice energy of $MgCl_2$:

$$Mg^{2+}(g) + 2Cl^-(g) \longrightarrow MgCl_2(s) \qquad \triangle H° = -2525 \text{ kJ}$$

7. Which of the following has the lowest and highest lattice energies: LiF, NaF, KF, or RbF?

8. Arrange the following bonds in increasing order, lowest to highest, of bond distance and bond energies: N≡N, C=O, and F–O.

9. Arrange the following bonds from least polar to most polar: (a) C–F, (b) O–F, (c) Cl–F, (d) Br–F, (e) P–F

10. (a) Use bond energies to calculate the $\triangle H$ for the following reaction:

$$N_2(g) + 3H_2(g) \longrightarrow 2NH_3(g)$$

(b) What is the $\triangle H$ value using Hess's Law?

11. The dipole moment of HBr is 0.778 D and the bond distance is 141 pm. Calculate the percent ionic character of HBr.

12. Draw the Lewis structure for CF_4.

13. Draw the Lewis structure for CS_2.

14. Draw the Lewis structure of the hydrogen sulfate ion, HSO_4^-.

15. (a) Draw two different Lewis structures for CNBr. (b) Calculate the formal charges on all atoms in each structure, and decide which is the more plausible structure

16. (a) Draw three contributing structures for nitrous oxide, N_2O. The skeleton structure of N_2O is N–N–O. (b) Assign formal charges to the atoms in these contributing structures and predict which are the most plausible ones.

17. Draw the Lewis structure for krypton difluoride.

18. Calculate the formal charges on the C atoms in each of the following: (a) CO_2, (b) CO, (c) CO_3^{2-}, (d) CN^-, (e) CH_2

19. How many valence electrons are around the central atoms of each of the following molecules? (a) BCl_3, (b) AlF_6^-, (c) BrF_3, (d) SF_4, (e) XeF_6

20. Which of the following structures can exhibit resonance? (a) HCN, (b) BF_4^-, (c) SF_2, (d) XeO_3, (e) NO_3^-

ANSWERS TO REVIEW EXERCISE

1. (a) covalent, (b) covalent, (c) ionic, (d) ionic, (e) covalent

2. (a) CsF, (b) Li_2O, (c) Al_2S_3

3. (a) Li^+ = He, Cl^- = Ar; (b) Ba^{2+} = Xe, S^{2-} = Ar; (c) Fr^+ = Rn, P^{3-} = Ar; (d) Y^{3+} = Kr, F^- = Ne

4. (a) $2K \cdot +:\ddot{O}: \longrightarrow 2K^+[:\ddot{O}:]^{2-}$

   (b) $3Mg: + 2 :\ddot{P}: \longrightarrow 3Mg^{2+}2[:\ddot{P}:]^{3-}$

5. (a) $Ba: + 2 :\ddot{I}: \longrightarrow Ba^{2+}2[:\ddot{I}:]^-$ (b) $Sr: + :\ddot{S}: \longrightarrow Sr^{2+} [:\ddot{S}:]^{2-}$

6. -642 kJ

7. lowest = RbF, highest = LiF

8. bond distance N≡N < C=O < F–O; bond energy O–F < C=O < N≡N

9. O–F < Cl–F < Br–F < C–F < P–F

10. (a) -93.0 kJ/mol, (b) -92 kJ/mol

11. % ionic character = 11.5%

12.
$$:\ddot{F}: - \underset{\underset{:\ddot{F}:}{|}}{\overset{\overset{:\ddot{F}:}{|}}{C}} - :\ddot{F}:$$

13. $:\ddot{S}=C=\ddot{S}:$

14.
$$\left[H-\ddot{\underset{..}{O}}-\underset{\underset{:\ddot{O}:}{|}}{\overset{\overset{:\ddot{O}:}{|}}{S}}-\ddot{\underset{..}{O}}: \right]^-$$

15. 1. $:N≡C-\ddot{B}r:$, each of its atoms has a zero formal charge, more plausible; 2. $:C≡N-\ddot{B}r:$, the formal charges on C and N are -1 and $+1$, respectively, less plausible.

16. (a) I = $\ddot{N} = N = \ddot{O}$, II = $:N ≡ N-\ddot{O}:$, III = $:\ddot{N}-N ≡ O:$

$$\underset{\text{I}}{:\overset{-}{\ddot{N}}=\overset{+}{N}=\overset{0}{\ddot{O}}} \quad \leftrightarrow \quad \underset{\text{II}}{:\overset{0}{N}≡\overset{+}{N}-\overset{-}{\ddot{O}}:} \quad \leftrightarrow \quad \underset{\text{III}}{:\overset{-2}{\ddot{N}}-\overset{+}{N}≡\overset{+}{O}:}$$

   (b) Structures I and II are more plausible and make a greater contribution to the actual structure than III, which has a formal charge of -2 on a N atom.

17. $\ddot{F}-\ddot{K}r-\ddot{F}:$

18. (a) 0, (b) -1, (c) 0, (d) -1, (e) $+2$

19. (a) 6, (b) 12, (c) 10, (d) 10, (e) 14

20. XeO_3, and NO_3^-

11

Chemical Bonding: Shapes of Molecules and Molecular Orbitals

In Chapter 10, we considered the most fundamental principles of chemical bonding. In this chapter, we further develop these principles by first considering molecular geometry, the shapes of molecules. Additionally, we will consider the basic principles of the Valence Bond Theory and hybrid orbitals, and the Molecular Orbital Theory and molecular orbitals.

11.1   SHAPES OF MOLECULES

Valence Shell Electron Pair Repulsion (VSEPR) Method

Each molecule has a three-dimensional shape called its molecular geometry. The shape taken by a molecule results from a balance between the attractive and repulsive forces that occur among the various components of the molecule. The approximate geometry of a molecule can be predicted from its Lewis structure and the application of the Valence Shell Electron Pair Repulsion method, often called the VSEPR method.

Using the VSEPR Method

First, write the Lewis structure of the molecule and determine the number of pairs of valence electrons (bonding and nonbonding electrons) on the central atom. In the VSEPR method, the predicted molecular geometry corresponds to that arrangement of valence electron pairs that maximizes their separation from each other. These electrons repel each other and position themselves as far away from each other as possible.

AB_2 GEOMETRY

A molecule with the general formula of AB_2 has A as its central atom. The A atom is bonded to two B atoms and has no lone pairs. Molecules of this type are linear and have a BAB bond angle of $180°$. The two B atoms are at a maximum angle from each other in linear geometry. Thus, the two bonding pairs of electrons minimize their repulsive forces. An example of such a molecule is $BeCl_2(g)$: Cl—Be—Cl

AB_3 GEOMETRY

If a central atom, A, has three bonded groups, B, and no lone pair electrons (E_0), the maximum angle between the B atoms that minimizes the electron repulsions is 120°. Therefore the three B atoms are equidistant from each other in one plane around the central A atom. This is called the trigonal planar molecular geometry. An example of a molecule with trigonal planar geometry is boron trichloride, BCl_3.

AB_2E GEOMETRY

Three electron pairs (two bonding pairs and one lone pair) are at a maximum distance from each other when they are in the same plane and separated by a 120° angle. Molecules with the general formula of AB_2E have angular or V-shaped geometry because the lone pair is not included in the description of the molecular geometry. An example of a molecule with angular geometry that results from two bonding electron pairs and one lone pair on the central atom is sulfur dioxide, SO_2. Note that in the VSEPR method multiple bonds are treated the same way as single bonds.

Lone-Pair and Bonding-Pair Interactions

The actual angle between the O atoms in SO_2 is slightly less than 120° (119.5°) because of the repulsions of the bonding pairs by the more diffuse lone pair. Lone-pair electrons are more spread out than bonding-pair electrons because the lone pairs are only held by one nucleus. A bonding pair is more compact due to the attractive forces of the two nuclei on either side of the electron pair. Because lone pairs are more diffuse than bonding pairs, the repulsive forces between lone pairs, lp, and bonding pairs, bp, are greater than those between two bonding pairs. Additionally, the repulsive forces between two lone pairs is greater than lone pair- bonding pair repulsions.

lp-lp repulsive forces > lp-bp repulsive forces > bp-bp repulsive forces

AB_4 GEOMETRY

Molecules that have a central atom, A, with four bonded atoms, B, and no lone pairs, AB_4, exhibit tetrahedral geometry in which all of the bond angles are 109.5°. Tetrahedral geometry refers to the shape of a tetrahedron, a solid geometric figure that has four faces of equal area. Methane, CH_4, molecules exhibit tetrahedral geometry.

Problem 11.1   (a) What is the shape of the carbon tetrachloride, CCl_4, molecule? (b) What is polarity of the CCl_4 molecule? Explain.

Solution 11.1

(a) The CCl_4 molecule has a central C atom with four bonding pairs and zero lone pairs. Thus, CCl_4 is a tetrahedral molecule.

(b) The Cl atoms in CCl_4 are evenly distributed around the central C atoms. Experimentally, the dipole moment of CCl_4 is zero. Therefore, it is a nonpolar molecule, even though all of its bonds are polar. The four dipoles cancel as a result of the symmetrical tetrahedral arrangement of the Cl atoms.

AB_3E GEOMETRY

Molecules with three bonding pairs and one lone pair, AB_3E, also have a tetrahedral arrangement of the four electron pairs around the central atom. Because the lone pair is not considered in the description of the geometry of the molecule, AB_3E molecules is trigonal pyramidal (pronounced pi·ram´e·dal) molecular geometry. Trigonal pyramidal geometry is a pyramid with a triangular base. Three bonded atoms form a triangle on the opposite side of the molecule from the lone pair. An example of such a molecule is ammonia, NH_3.

Problem 11.2 (a) Predict the bond angle between H atoms in the ammonia molecule. (b) Compare this prediction to the experimentally determined bond angle of 107°. Explain.

Solution 11.2

(a) One might predict that the bond angle between H atoms in ammonia is 109.5° because it is the maximum angle when four electron pairs surround a central atom.

(b) Lone pair-bonding pair repulsion is greater than bonding pair-bonding pair repulsion. Therefore, repulsion of the bonding pairs by the lone pair depresses the angle by 2.5°.

AB_2E_2 GEOMETRY

Water, H_2O, is an example of a molecule with the general formula of AB_2E_2. In these molecules, two bonding and two lone pairs surround the central atom. Once again, four electrons pairs are distributed tetrahedrally around the O atom. Because water molecules only have two bonds, its geometry is called angular or V-shaped. Repulsion of the two bonding pairs by the two lone pairs depresses the angle between the H atoms even more than the one lone pair in ammonia. The bond angle in H_2O is 104.5°, depressed 5.0° from the theoretical angle of 109.5°.

Problem 11.3 (a) Predict the shape and polarity of a carbon dioxide, CO_2, molecule. (b) Discuss the polarity and dipole moment of CO_2.

Solution 11.3

(a) First, write the Lewis structure for CO_2.

$$\ddot{O} = C = \ddot{O}$$

Carbon dioxide

The central C atom has two double bonds, each of which is treated in the same manner as a single bond in the VSEPR method. Whenever the central atom has two bonds and no lone pairs, the molecule has a linear geometry.

(b) Because the electronegativity of an O atom is higher than that of C atom, both C—O double bonds are polar. However, the bond dipoles point in opposite directions as a result of their linear arrangement and thus cancel each other. Therefore, a CO_2 molecule is a nonpolar molecule whose dipole moment equals zero ($\mu = 0$).

Problem 11.4 (a) Predict the shape of a phosphorus trichloride, PCl_3, molecule. (b) Discuss the polarity of PCl_3. (c) What are the approximate bond angles in PCl_3?

Solution 11.4

(a) The Lewis structure for PCl_3 shows that the central P atom has three bonding pairs and one lone pair. Molecules that have central atoms with three bonding pairs and one lone pair have a trigonal pyramidal molecular geometry.

(b) Each of the P—Cl bonds in PCl_3 is polar, and the three Cl atoms are located on one side of the P atom. Hence, PCl_3 is a polar covalent molecule; i.e., it has a nonzero dipole moment ($\mu > 0$).

(c) The VSEPR method does not allow us to predict exactly what Cl—P—Cl bond angles are in PCl_3, but we would expect them to be less than 109.5°.

Problem 11.5 (a) Describe the molecular geometry of the methanol, CH_3OH, molecule. (b) Discuss the polarity of this molecule.

Solution 11.5 (a) The Lewis structure shows that the C atom has four bonding and no lone pairs, and O has two bonding and two lone pairs. Both C and O atoms have tetrahedral arrangements of electron pairs, but C has a tetrahedral geometry with four bonded atoms and O has an angular geometry of two bonded atoms and two lone pairs.

Methanol is a polar molecule with a rather large dipole moment because the electronegative O atom pulls electron density from both the H and C atoms.

Problem 11.6 What is the molecular geometry of the carbonate ion, CO_3^{2-}?

Solution 11.6 (a) One of the contributing structures for the carbonate ion is as follows.

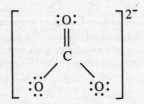

The Lewis structure shows that the central C atom has three bonds to the O atoms and no lone pairs. The VSEPR method predicts that the three O atoms are separated at a maximum angle of 120°. Thus, the carbonate ion has trigonal planar geometry. This agrees with the experimentally determined structure of the carbonate ion.

Molecular Geometries of Molecules with Expanded Octets

A central atom with an expanded octet is most often surrounded by either 10 or 12 electrons—5 or 6 electron pairs.

AB_5 GEOMETRY

When five pairs of electrons surround a central atom, the molecular geometry that minimizes the repulsive forces is a trigonal bipyramid. In a trigonal bipyramid, three of the bonded groups occupy the central equatorial plane separated by 120°. The remaining two bonded atoms are in the axial positions perpendicular to the equatorial plane. This is the first molecular geometry that we have encountered in which all the bonds angles are not equivalent. An example of such a molecule is phosphorus pentafluoride, PF_5.

AB_4E GEOMETRY

Experimental evidence indicates that lone-pair electrons in molecules with five electron pairs on the central atom occupy the equatorial positions and not the axial positions. For example, the molecular geometry of sulfur tetrafluoride, SF_4 (AB_4E), is termed "see-saw" or "distorted" tetrahedral because the lone pair occupies one of the equatorial positions.

Problem 11.7 In the SF_4 molecule, a bond angle of 101.4° instead of 120°, is found between the two equatorial F atoms, and 86.5°, instead of 90°, is found between the axial and equatorial F atoms. What could account for these differences?

Solution 11.7 The presence of a lone pair in an equatorial position distorts the bond angles in the trigonal bipyramidal geometry of the electron pairs. The placement of the lone pair in the equatorial position produces two lone pair-bonding pair repulsions at 90°. If the lone pair was in the axial position, three lone pair-bonding pair repulsions at 90° result. Hence, placement of the lone pair in the equatorial position minimizes the repulsion energy of the molecule.

AB_3E_2 GEOMETRY

The two lone pairs in AB_3E_2 molecules occupy the equatorial region of the molecule. Therefore, the molecular geometry of these molecules is T-shaped. Chlorine trifluoride, ClF_3, is an example of a T-shaped molecule. The actual bond angle between the F atoms is $87.5°$ because the two lone pairs on the Cl depress the angle.

AB_2E_3 GEOMETRY

Xenon difluoride, XeF_2, is an example of a molecule with the formula AB_2E_3. It is a linear molecule because the three lone pairs occupy the three equatorial positions which leaves a $180°$ bond angle between the F atoms.

AB_6 GEOMETRY

In AB_6 molecules, six electron pairs surround a central atom. These molecules have an octahedral geometry. An example of such a molecule is sulfur hexafluoride, SF_6. It has six F atoms bonded symmetrically to the central S atom. Each bond angle in SF_6 is $90°$.

AB_5E GEOMETRY

Introduction of a lone pair into the octahedral geometry of electron pairs (AB_5E) produces the tetragonal pyramidal or square pyramidal geometry. An example of such a molecule is bromine pentafluoride, BrF_5. Do not confuse a tetragonal pyramid that has five faces with a trigonal pyramid with four faces.

AB_4E_4 GEOMETRY

If two lone pairs are in the octahedral geometry of electron pairs, a square planar molecule results because the lone pairs are most widely separated when they are $180°$ from each other. Xenon tetrafluoride, XeF_4, has the general formula of AB_4E_2 and is a square planar molecule

Problem 11.8   (a) Draw the Lewis structure of selenium hexafluoride, SeF_6. (b) What is the molecular geometry of SeF_6? (c) Is SeF_6 a polar or nonpolar molecule?

Solution 11.8

(a) The Lewis structure shows that SeF_6 has a central Se atom with six bonding pairs.

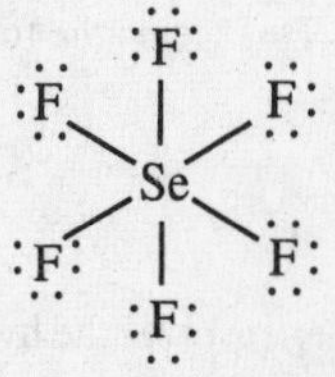

(b) A molecule with six bonding pairs has the octahedral molecular geometry.
(c) Because the geometry of the molecule is symmetrical, the polar bonds cancel. Therefore, SeF_6 molecules are nonpolar and have a dipole moment that equals zero ($\mu = 0$).

Problem 11.9   Predict the molecular geometries for each of the following molecules: (a) ClF_5, (b) BrF_3, (c) PF_2Cl_2Br, (d) TeF_6

Solution 11.9

(a) The ClF_5 molecule has the general formula of AB_5E; thus, it has square pyramidal geometry.
(b) The BrF_3 molecule has the general formula of AB_3E_2; thus, it has T-shaped geometry.

(c) The PF_2Cl_2Br molecule has the general formula AB_5; thus, it has trigonal bipyramidal geometry.

(d) The TeF_6 molecule has the general formula AB_6; thus, it has octahedral geometry.

11.2 VALENCE BOND THEORY AND THE HYBRIDIZATION OF ATOMIC ORBITALS

Even though the VSEPR method allows us to easily predict the shapes of molecules, it does not permit us to understand how bonds result and how the properties of molecules relate to the orbitals that form bonds.

Hybridization of Atomic Orbitals

In the Valence Bond Theory, the interaction of valence electrons during bonding changes the characteristics of the atomic orbitals, producing hybrid orbitals. Hybridization is a mathematical process by which atomic orbitals (orbitals in isolated atoms) are changed to hybrid orbitals (orbitals in molecules). Hybridization of orbitals may be viewed as a mathematical blending of the wave functions associated with valence atomic orbitals to produce orbitals in molecules; i.e., hybrid orbitals. In the Valence Bond Theory, valence atomic orbitals are mathematically combined to produce hybrid orbitals with the proper characteristics to bond with other atoms. In addition, hybrid orbitals give the molecule its experimentally observed properties.

Bonding in Methane, CH_4

The ground-state electron configuration of the central C atom, $1s^2 2s^2 2p^2$. From the ground-state electron configuration of C, it might be predicted that a C atom bonds to two H atoms instead of four H atoms because only the two unpaired electrons in the $2p$ could overlap with the $1s$ orbitals from H atoms. A C atom can bond to two H atoms, but it produces a very unstable molecular species called methylene, CH_2, which contains a C atom with only six valence electrons. This indicates to us that the ground-state electron configuration of C cannot explain adequately the bonding in CH_4. Consequently, the electron orbitals of C that overlap with orbitals of H in CH_4 cannot be the same as the ground state orbitals on C.

sp^3 Hybrid Orbitals

Mathematically, the hybrid orbitals of C in CH_4 are generated by first promoting an electron from the $2s$ to the $2p$. Promotion involves moving an electron from the lower energy $2s$ to the higher energy $2p$. This yields the following configuration.

The next step involves the hybridization (mathematical blending) of the $2s$ with the three $2p$ orbitals.

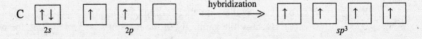

Four degenerate hybrid orbitals result that have energies intermediate between the energy of the $2s$ and the $2p$. Because three $2p$ orbitals hybridize with only one $2s$, the energy and characteristics of the four sp^3 hybrid orbitals more closely resemble the $2p$ than the $2s$. They are called sp^3 hybrid orbitals because one s and three p orbitals hybridize.

Characteristics of sp^3 Hybrid Orbitals

Each sp^3 orbital has two lobes, one elongated lobe that overlaps with other orbitals, and a small lobe that usually does not form bonds. The sp^3 hybrid orbital more closely resembles a p rather than a *s* atomic orbital. As a result of the shape of the sp^3 orbital distribution, it more readily overlaps with other orbitals than either *s* or *p* orbitals. The main lobes of the four sp^3 hybrid orbitals point to the corners of a tetrahedron. The angle between them is 109.5°, the same angle predicted by the VSEPR method. Therefore, the molecular geometry associated with sp^3 hybrid orbitals bonded to four atoms is tetrahedral.

Problem 11.10   Use sp^3 hybrid orbitals to explain the bonding in the NH_3 molecule.

Solution 11.10   The ground-state electron configuration of N is $1s^2 2s^2 2p^3$ and after hybridization of the *s* and three *p* orbitals, one filled and three half-filled sp^3 hybrid orbitals result.

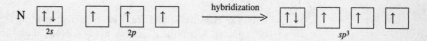

Each of the three unpaired electrons in the sp^3 hybrid orbitals of N overlap with an electron in the $1s$ orbital of a H atom. The remaining electron pair in the sp^3 hybrid orbitals is the lone pair on the N atom. Because the angle between sp^3 hybrid orbitals is 109.5° and the lone pair depresses the angle somewhat, the 107° bond angle in ammonia can be readily explained.

Problem 11.11   Show that sp^3 hybrid orbitals can describe the bonding of the O atom in the water molecule.

Solution 11.11   The ground-state configuration of O is $1s^2 2s^2 2p^6$, and after hybridization two filled and two half-filled sp^3 hybrid orbitals result.

Thus, two $1s$ orbitals from two H atoms overlap with the half-filled sp^3 orbitals to produce the two bonds in water. The two remaining filled sp^3 orbitals are lone pairs on the O atom. The angular geometry of water and its 104.5° bond angles result from the depression by the two lone pairs of the 109.5° angles found between sp^3 orbitals.

*sp*² *Hybrid Orbitals*

In molecules such as BF_3, with only six electrons in the valence shell of B, a different blend of orbitals is needed to explain the bonding. The ground-state electron configuration of B is $1s^2 2s^2 2p^1$, and after promotion of one electron from the $2s$ to the $2p$, three unpaired electrons are available for bonding, one in the *s* and two in the *p* orbitals.

For B in BF_3, the *s* with two *p* orbitals are hybridized to produce a set of three sp^2 hybrid orbitals.

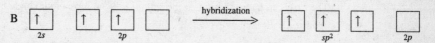

Besides the three sp^2 hybrid orbitals an empty unhybridized $2p$ orbital remains.

CHARACTERISTICS OF sp² HYBRID ORBITALS

Each sp^2 orbital has the same general shape as an sp^3 hybrid orbital. However, the three sp^2 orbitals point to the corners of an equilateral triangle, which means that a 120° angle separates them. The unhybridized $2p$ orbital is perpendicular to the plane of the three sp^2 orbitals—one of its lobes is above and the other is below the plane of the atoms.

Problem 11.12 Boron trifluoride, BF_3, has an electron-deficient B atom. When a F^- ion bonds to the BF_3 molecule the tetrafluroborate ion, BF_4^-, results. (a) Write an equation for this reaction. (b) Describe the change in hybridization and molecular geometry that occurs in this reaction.

Solution 11.12

(a) $BF_3 + F^- \rightarrow BF_4^-$

(b) Initially, the hybridization of the B atom in BF_3 is sp^2 and the geometry of the orbitals is trigonal planar. When the F^- bonds to the B atom, the hybridization changes to sp^3 with its associated tetrahedral geometry.

sp Hybrid Orbitals

If the central atom only bonds to two atoms and has no lone pairs, the structure is explained by sp hybrid orbitals. These orbitals result from the blending of one s and one p orbital. Beryllium chloride, $BeCl_2$, is an example of a molecule that has sp hybrid orbitals. Beryllium has the ground-state electron configuration of $1s^2 2s^2$. From this configuration, one might predict that Be does not bond with Cl. However, if one electron is promoted from the $2s$ to the $2p$, and these two orbitals are hybridized, two sp hybrid orbitals result. In addition, two $2p$ orbitals remain unhybridized

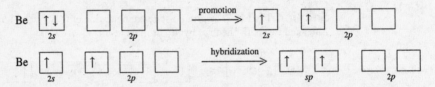

Because the repulsions are minimized when sp hybrid orbitals point in opposite directions, this gives a molecule with sp hybrid orbitals a linear geometry. Hence, the geometry of the $BeCl_2$ is linear with a 180° bond angle. The unhybridized $2p$ orbitals are perpendicular to each other and to the sp hybrid orbitals. Many molecules and ions have atoms with sp hybrid orbitals, especially those with triple bonds.

Problem 11.13 Show the promotion and hybridization of the central Si atom in silicon tetrachloride, $SiCl_4$.

Solution 11.13 The Lewis structure for $SiCl_4$ is as follows.

$$
\begin{array}{c}
:\ddot{Cl}: \\
| \\
Si \\
:\ddot{Cl} \diagup \,|\, \diagdown \ddot{Cl}: \\
:\ddot{Cl}:
\end{array}
$$

The Lewis structure shows that the central Si atom forms four single bonds with the Cl atoms. The valence electron configuration of Si is $3s^2\, 3p^2$.

Si [↑↓] (3s) [↑] [↑] [ ] (3p)

Thus, like C, one electron is promoted from the 3s to the 3p.

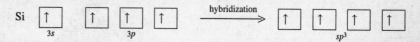

Finally, the one 3s and the three 3p orbitals are hybridized to give three equivalent sp^3 hybrid orbitals.

Si [↑] 3s [↑] [↑] [↑] 3p → hybridization → [↑] [↑] [↑] [↑] sp^3

Hybrid Orbitals in Molecules with Multiple Bonds

Hybrid orbitals can also explain the properties of multiple bonds—double bonds and triple bonds.

PROPERTIES OF DOUBLE BONDS

A double covalent bond between two atoms, A, consists of a strong sigma bond, σ, and a weaker pi bond, π. A σ bond results when the ends of orbitals overlap and the region of maximum electron density is along the internuclear axis, the line that connects the two nuclei. Such a bond is usually strong because of the high electron density that occupies the region between the two positively charged nuclei. The weaker π bond results from the sideways overlap of atomic orbitals. When orbitals overlap sideways the regions of maximum electron density are above and below the internuclear axis, which results in a weaker force of attraction between the two nuclei when compared to σ bonds.

Problem 11.14 (a) Draw the Lewis structure for ethylene, C_2H_4. (b) Explain why sp^3 hybrid orbitals cannot explain the structure of ethylene. (c) Show that sp^2 hybrid orbitals can explain the structure of ethylene. (d) How does the π bond form, and where is it compared to the σ bonds?

Solution 11.14
(a)

$$\begin{array}{cc} H & H \\ \diagdown & \diagup \\ C = C \\ \diagup & \diagdown \\ H & H \end{array}$$

(b) The bonding in C_2H_4 cannot be explained with sp^3 hybrid orbitals. The sideways overlapping p orbitals and the 120° H—C—H bond angles cannot be generated. Thus, sp^3 hybrid orbitals do not participate in the formation of double bonds.

(c) With sp^2 hybrid orbitals, an unhybridized p orbital remains on each C atom to produce the π bond. In addition, the σ bonds of sp^2 hybrid orbitals are separated by 120°. Thus, an electron can be promoted from the ground-state electron configuration of C to the p orbital and then one s and two p orbitals are hybridized, leaving an unhybridized 2p.

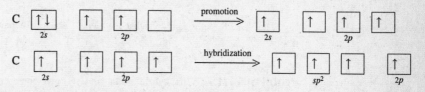

The end of one lobe of the sp^2 hybrid orbitals from one C atom overlaps with the end of the lobe of an sp^2 orbital from another C atom and produces the σ bond of the C—C double bond. The 1s orbitals from four H atoms overlap with the remaining lobes of the sp^2 hybrid orbitals from the two C atoms.

(d) Each C atom has one electron in the unhybridized $2p$ orbital. Hence, these two orbitals can overlap sideways to produce the π bond.

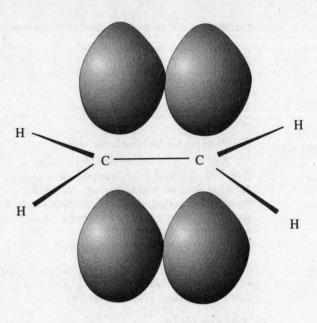

Because the geometry of the sp^2 hybrid orbitals is trigonal planar, the six atoms in C_2H_4 are in the same plane and the π bond extends above and below the plane.

PROPERTIES OF TRIPLE BONDS

A triple bond consists of one σ and two π bonds. To illustrate a molecule with a triple bond, let's consider acetylene, C_2H_2.

$$H—C \equiv C—H$$

Acetylene

The VSEPR method predicts that acetylene is linear, which means that the H—C—C bond angle is $180°$.

Problem 11.15   What hybrid orbitals in C_2H_2 give one σ and two π bonds?

Solution 11.15   To produce two π bonds, the C atoms in C_2H_2 require two unhybridized p orbitals. Therefore, these C atoms use sp hybrid orbitals. Each C atom in C_2H_2 forms σ bonds with a H atom and C atom, and the two perpendicular unhybridized p orbitals overlap sideways to produce the two π bonds:

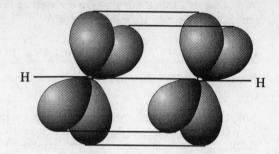

Experimental evidence shows that molecules such a C_2H_2 that have sp hybrid orbitals are linear, as the VSEPR method predicts. One π bond is perpendicular to the axis that runs through the atoms in C_2H_2 and the other π bond is perpendicular to both of them.

Hybrid Orbitals in Molecules with Expanded Octets

To explain the bonding in such molecules, additional orbitals are needed to accommodate the extra electrons. In the Valence Bond Theory, d orbitals hybridize with s and p orbitals to give the desired number of bonding orbitals and lone pairs. These d orbitals are in atoms located in the third period and beyond. Period 2 atoms do not have d orbitals in the second energy level; hence, they never have expanded octets.

CENTRAL ATOMS WITH 10 VALENCE ELECTRONS

Problem 11.16   Use d hybrid orbitals to explain the bonding in phosphorus pentachloride, PCl_5.

Solution 11.16 PCl_5 has a central P atom that has five single bonds to Cl atoms. Phosphorus has an outer electron configuration of $3s^2 3p^3 3d^0$. From this configuration, it might be predicted that a P atom could only bond to three Cl atoms. However, if an electron is promoted from the $3s$ to one of the empty $3d$ orbitals, and a s, three p, and one d orbitals are hybridized, five sp^3d hybrid orbitals (some people refer to these orbitals as dsp^3 hybrid orbitals) are obtained.

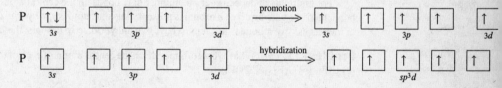

The five sp^3d hybrid orbitals produce a trigonal bipyramidal geometry in which 120° separates the three lobes around the central plane of the molecule, and one lobe is above and the other is below this plane.

Problem 11.17   Show that the Xe atom in xenon difluoride, XeF_2, uses sp^3d hybrid orbitals.

Solution 11.17   Xe, a noble gas, has eight valence electrons. Promoting one electron from the $5p$ to the $5d$ orbital and hybridizing the five orbitals gives the following.

Xe $\boxed{\uparrow\downarrow}$ $\boxed{\uparrow\downarrow}$ $\boxed{\uparrow\downarrow}$ $\boxed{\uparrow}$ $\boxed{\uparrow}$
sp^3d

Two of the sp^3d hybrid orbitals have one electron that can each overlap with a F atom, and the remaining six electrons are in three lone pairs.

CENTRAL ATOMS WITH 12 VALENCE ELECTRONS

Problem 11.18   Show that chlorine pentafluoride, ClF_5, is another example of a molecule with sp^3d^2 hybrid orbitals.

Solution 11.18   Chlorine is a halogen with a valence configuration of $3s^2 3p^5$. If two electrons are promoted from the $3p$ to the $3d$, six sp^3d^2 hybrid orbitals result. One of the sp^3d^2 hybrid orbitals is full (a lone pair) and the other five orbitals overlap with those from five F atoms.

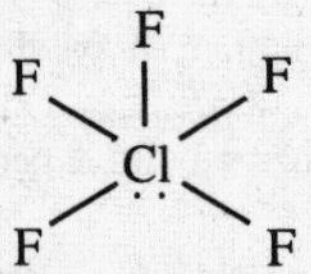

Chlorine pentafluoride

Molecules with sp^3d^2 hybrid orbitals containing one lone pair exhibit tetragonal pyramidal geometry with 90° bond angles.

Predicting the Hybrid Orbitals of Central Atoms

To predict the structure and properties of molecules in the Valence Bond Theory, it is important to identify the hybrid orbitals of bonded atoms. Whenever the hybrid orbitals associated with an atom must be identified, begin by writing the Lewis structure of the molecule. From the Lewis structure, the number of bonding and nonbonding electron pairs around the central atom are obtained. Also the Lewis structure shows if the molecule has one or more multiple bonds. If the molecule does not have multiple bonds, first determine the number of bonding and lone pairs on the central atom. Two bonding orbitals and no lone pairs on the central atom means it has sp hybrids. Three bonding pairs or two bonding pairs and one lone pair on the central atom means it has sp^2 hybrid orbitals. A total of four bonding and/or lone pairs on the central atom results in sp^3 hybrid orbitals. Similarly, sp^3d hybrid orbitals have five electron pairs on the central atom, and, finally, sp^3d^2 hybrid orbitals have six electron pairs on the central atom.

For multiple bonds, consider the number of π bonds on the central atom. If this atom has one π bond, then one unhybridized p orbital is present; thus, the atom is sp^2 hybridized. Whenever the atom of interest has two π bonds, then it must have two unhybridized p orbitals; therefore, it is sp hybridized.

Problem 11.19   What hybrid orbitals are on the central atoms of each of the following molecules? (a) ClF_3, (b) C_2F_2, (c) $COCl_2$

Solution 11.19

(a) The Lewis structure for ClF_3 shows that the central Cl atom has five pairs of electrons, three bonding pairs and two lone pairs. The combination of five bonding and lone-pair electrons indicates that five orbitals must be available on the Cl atom. Hence, the only hybrid orbitals that allow for ten electrons around the central atom are sp^3d.

(b) The Lewis structure of C_2F_2 shows that a triple covalent bond holds the two central C atoms.

$$F—C \equiv C—F$$

To form a triple bond, each C atom must have two unhybridized p orbitals for the formation of the two π bonds. Only when C forms sp hybrid orbitals does it have the two unhybridized orbitals for the triple bond. No other hybrid orbitals can explain the formation of a triple bond between C atoms.

(c) Phosgene, $COCl_2$, molecules have the following Lewis structure.

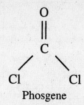

Phosgene

The Lewis structure shows that the C—O bond is a double bond and the C—Cl bonds are single bonds. Thus, the C atom has three σ bonds and one π bond. A π bond requires an unhybridized p orbital. Therefore, the C atom has sp^2 hybrid orbitals to form the three σ bonds and the remaining unhybridized p overlaps with a p orbital from the O atom.

11.3   MOLECULAR ORBITAL THEORY

Introduction to the Molecular Orbital Theory

The Molecular Orbital Theory is an alternative bonding theory that can describe many of the properties not explained by the valence bond theory. Molecular orbitals generated from the molecular orbital theory result from combinations of occupied atomic orbitals (not just the outer-level orbitals as in the valence bond theory). Molecular orbitals obey Hund's Rule, the Aufbau Principle, and Pauli's Exclusion Principle. In other words, molecular orbitals are treated in the same way as atomic orbitals.

Formation of Bonding Molecular Orbitals

Let's first consider the simplest molecule, diatomic hydrogen, H_2. Each H atom has one electron in the $1s$ orbital. The $1s$ orbital can be described by the wave function, psi (ψ_{1s}). The wave functions from each H atom can be combined in two ways. In other words, two atomic orbitals produce two molecular orbitals. First, the two wave functions are added to produce a bonding molecular orbital, ψ_b.

$$\psi_b = \psi_{1s} + \psi_{1s}$$

A bonding molecular orbital results when the wave functions reinforce each other and produce a molecular orbital in which a high electron density is found between the two H nuclei. Bonding molecular orbitals are always lower in energy than the atomic orbitals from which they were formed because of the effective overlap and the resulting attractive forces.

Formation of Antibonding Molecular Orbitals

A second way to combine the wave functions is to subtract one from the other to produce an antibonding orbital, ψ_a.

$$\psi_a = \psi_{1s} - \psi_{1s}$$

An antibonding orbital results when the wave functions cancel each other and produce a molecular orbital that has a node, a region with no electron density, between the two nuclei. Most of the electron density in an antibonding orbital is on opposite sides of the nuclei. Antibonding orbitals are always higher in energy than the atomic orbitals from which they are formed because of the repulsion of the two nuclei that results from the low electron density between them.

Molecular Orbital Diagrams

A diagram is written that shows the energy relationships of the bonding and antibonding molecular orbitals in H_2. Figure 11.1 shows the atomic orbitals of H_2 on opposite sides of the two molecular orbitals. Notice that the increase in energy of the antibonding molecular orbital, E_2, equals the decrease in energy of the bonding molecular orbital, E_1. The sum of the energies of the bonding and antibonding orbitals equals the energy of the atomic orbitals. The bonding orbital is symbolized as σ_{1s}

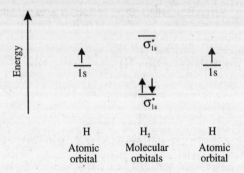

Fig. 11.1   *Atomic Orbitals of H_2 on Opposite Sides of the Two Molecular Orbitals*

and the antibonding orbital as σ_{1s}^*. A σ_{1s} orbital is a sigma bond between two $1s$ orbitals. Recall that σ bonds have electron density concentrated along the internuclear axis. The asterisk in σ_{1s}^* represents an antibonding orbital.

Molecular Orbital Diagram for H_2

The MO energy diagram shows the formation of the bond in H_2 (Fig. 11.1). Each H atom has one $1s$ electron, which is placed into the diagram with the same spin. When these two H atoms bond, the electrons pair (following Pauli's Exclusion Principle) and occupy the lower energy σ_{1s} molecular orbital. Therefore, the molecular orbital configuration for H_2 is $(\sigma_{1s})^2$. A H_2 molecule has two electrons in a lower energy orbital than the orbitals in isolated H atoms.

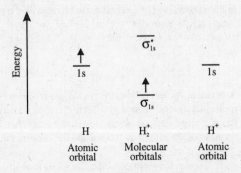

Fig. 11.2   *MO Diagram of H_2^+*

Bond Orders and Molecular Orbital Diagrams

The bond order of H_2 is calculated directly from the MO energy-level diagram. The bond order of a molecule equals one-half the difference between the number of electrons in bonding orbitals and the number of electrons in antibonding orbitals.

$$\text{Bond order} = \tfrac{1}{2}(\text{bonding electrons} - \text{antibonding electrons})$$

In H_2, two electrons are in bonding orbitals and none are in antibonding orbitals. Hence, the bond order in H_2 is one.

$$\text{Bond order}_{H_2} = \tfrac{1}{2}(2 - 0) = 1$$

Problem 11.20   If an electron is removed from a diatomic hydrogen molecule, a molecular hydrogen cation, H_2^+, results. (a) Write a molecular orbital diagram for H_2^+. (b) Calculate the bond order of H_2^+. (c) Compare the bond in H_2^+ with that in H_2.

Solution 11.20

(a) Figure 11.2 shows the MO diagram of H_2^+. Think of the formation of H_2^+ as the result of combining a H atom, with one electron and a H cation, H^+, with zero electrons.

(b) H_2^+ only has one electron in the σ_{1s}, which results in a bond order of 0.5, half of a covalent bond (Bond order$_{H_2^+}$ = $\frac{1}{2}(1 - 0) = 0.5$).

(c) A bond order of 0.5 in H_2^+ is consistent with the experimentally determined values of bond distance (0.106 nm) and bond energy (270 kJ/mol). This bond is longer and weaker than the bond in H_2.

Problem 11.21   (a) Use an MO energy diagram to show why He_2 does not exist. (b) What is the bond order of He_2?

Solution 11.21

(a) Each He atom has two electrons in the $1s$ orbital. In the formation of the molecular orbitals in He_2, two electrons occupy the lower energy σ_{1s} and two electrons occupy the higher energy σ_{1s}^*. Thus, diatomic He has an MO configuration of $(\sigma_{1s})^2 (\sigma_{1s}^*)^2$. The stability gained by placing two electrons in a bonding molecular orbital is canceled by the two electrons in the antibonding orbital. Hence, two isolated He atoms are equal in energy with a He_2 molecule and no driving force exists for molecule formation.

(b) The bond order in He_2 is 0 (Bond order$_{He_2}$ = $\frac{1}{2}(2 - 2) = 0$).

Molecular Orbitals in the Second Period Homonuclear Diatomic Molecules

MOLECULAR ORBITALS IN DILITHIUM, Li₂

Lithium (Z = 3) is the first member of the second period and has an electron configuration of $1s^2 2s^1$. When two Li atoms bond to yield dilithium, Li_2, they form four molecular orbitals with six electrons (Fig. 11.3). Combining the two 1s atomic orbitals produces the σ_{1s} and σ_{1s}^*, and combining the two 2s atomic orbitals produces the σ_{2s} and σ_{2s}^*. The four 1s electrons from both Li atoms fill the

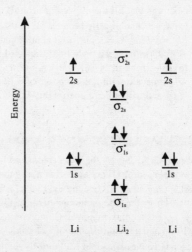

Fig. 11.3

σ_{1s} and σ_{1s}^*, and the two $2s$ electrons fill the σ_{2s} to produce a molecular orbital configuration of $(\sigma_{1s})^2$ $(\sigma_{1s}^*)^2$. Four electrons occupy bonding orbitals and two electrons occupy antibonding orbitals. Thus, the bond order for Li_2 is 1 (Bond order$_{Li_2}$ = $\frac{1}{2}(4-2) = 1$). Dilithium is a molecule found in the gas phase that has a bond energy of 105 kJ/mol and a bond distance of 267 pm.

Problem 11.22 Use an MO diagram to show why Be_2 does not exist.

Solution 11.22 Beryllium ($Z = 4$) has an electron configuration of $1s^2 2s^2$. An MO diagram for Be_2 is the same as the one for Li_2 because the same atomic orbitals interact. Because two Be atoms add eight electrons and fill the four molecular orbitals, $(\sigma_{1s})^2$, $(\sigma_{1s}^*)^2$, $(\sigma_{2s})^2$, $(\sigma_{2s}^*)^2$. Be_2 does not exist because it has filled molecular orbitals—such as was found in He_2. The bond order of Be_2 is zero (Bond order$_{Be_2}$ = $\frac{1}{2}(4-4) = 0$).

MOLECULAR ORBITALS IN DIBORON, B_2

Boron ($Z = 5$) is the first element to have an electron in the $2p$ subshell. Therefore when two B atoms combine to produce B_2, the $2p$ orbitals from one atom combine with the three $2p$ orbitals from the other and produce six molecular orbitals. Figure 11.4 shows an MO diagram for the combinations of $2p$ orbitals. Three of the molecular orbitals, one σ_{2p} and two π_{2p}, are bonding molecular orbitals, and one σ_{2p}^* and two π_{2p}^*, are antibonding orbitals. The σ_{2p} and σ_{2p}^* molecular orbitals result when one lobe of the $2p_x$ overlaps with the other $2p_x$ along the internuclear axis. The π_{2p} and π_{2p}^* orbitals result when the remaining two $2p$ orbitals, $2p_y$ and $2p_z$, overlap sideways.

What is the order in which the molecular orbitals from the $2p$ fill? The first four electrons fill the two lowest energy π_{2p} orbitals before filling the slightly higher energy σ_{2p} orbital. After the bonding orbitals fill, then the antibonding orbitals, π_{2p}^* and σ_{2p}^*, fill. In B_2, electrons fill the σ_{1s}, σ_{1s}^*, σ_{2p}, and σ_{2p}^* orbitals. Each B atom contributes one electron to a π_{2p} orbital because electrons enter empty degenerate orbitals before half-filled orbitals—Hund's Rule. Calculating the bond order for B_2 shows that it has a single covalent bond (bond order$_{B_2}$ = $\frac{1}{2}(6-4) = 1$). These predicted values agree with the experimentally measured properties.

Problem 11.23 Draw MO diagrams for (a) C_2 and (b) N_2. For each, determine the bond order and predict if they are diamagnetic or paramagnetic.

Solution 11.23 Figure 11.5 shows the molecular orbital diagrams of C_2 and N_2. C_2 has a total of 12 electrons that fill the molecular orbitals through the π_{2p}.

(a) C_2 is diamagnetic because all of its electrons are paired. Its bond order of 2 [bond order$_{C_2}$ = $\frac{1}{2}(8-4) = 2$] is in good agreement with its experimentally determined bond energy of 628 kJ/mol and its bond distance of 131 pm.

(b) Electrons in N_2 fill the π_{2p} and σ_{2p} molecular orbitals, which results in a diamagnetic molecule with a bond order of 3 [bond order$_{N_2}$ = $\frac{1}{2}(10-4) = 3$]. N_2 has a strong triple bond with a bond energy of 941 kJ/mol and a bond distance of 110 pm.

MOLECULAR ORBITALS IN O_2 AND F_2

For B_2, C_2, and N_2 the π_{2p} orbitals are lower in energy than the σ_{2p} orbitals. However for O_2 and F_2, the σ_{2p} orbitals are lower in energy than π_{2p} orbitals (Fig. 11.6). In an O_2 molecule, the two highest energy electrons occupy the two π_{2p}^*. Hund's rule tells us that these electrons are in different orbitals. Therefore, the paramagnetism of O_2 can readily be explained using the molecular orbital theory. O_2 has a bond order of 2 (bond order$_{O_2}$ = $\frac{1}{2}(10-6) = 2$), which results in a bond energy of 498 kJ/mol and a bond distance of 121 pm.

F_2 has 18 electrons that fill all of the molecular orbitals except the σ_{2p}^*. Because of their paired electrons, F_2 molecules are diamagnetic. Its bond order is 1 (bond order$_{F_2}$ = $\frac{1}{2}(10-8) = 1$) because

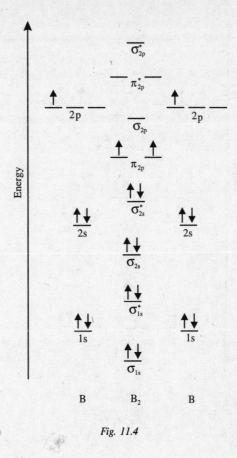

Fig. 11.4

two more electrons are in antibonding orbitals compared to O_2. F_2 has a bond energy of 15 kJ/mol and a bond distance of 142 pm.

Problem 11.24   Use the molecular orbital theory to explain the nonexistence of diatomic Ne, Ne_2. Write the complete MO configuration of Ne_2.

Solution 11.24   The 20 electrons from two Ne atoms fill the available bonding and antibonding molecular orbitals.

$$Ne_2 \, (\sigma_{1s})^2 (\sigma_{1s}^*)^2 (\sigma_{2s})^2 (\sigma_{2s}^*)^2 (\sigma_{2p})^2 (\pi_{2p})^4 (\pi_{2p}^*)^4 (\sigma_{2p}^*)^2$$

Therefore, the bonded atoms have no net stabilization when compared to isolated Ne atoms, resulting in a bond order of zero (bond order$_{Ne_2}$ = $\frac{1}{2}(10 - 10) = 0$).

Problem 11.25   (a) Write the valence molecular-orbital configuration for Cl_2. (b) What is the C—Cl bond order? (c) Describe the magnetic property of Cl_2.

Solution 11.25   (a) The valence electron configuration for Cl is $3s^2 3p^5$. Thus, the molecular

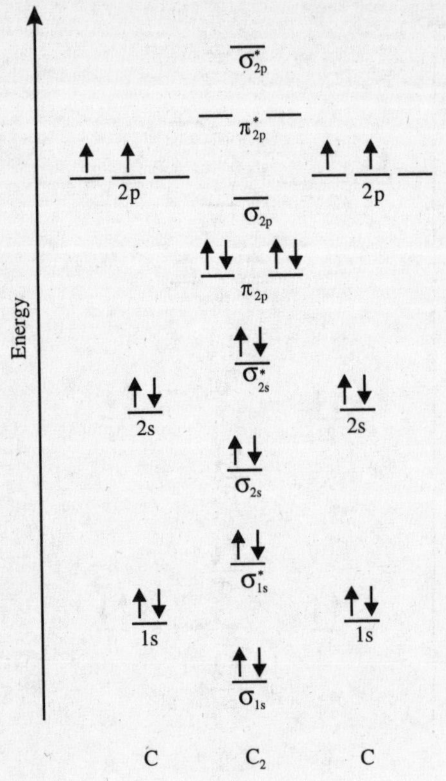

Fig. 11.5a

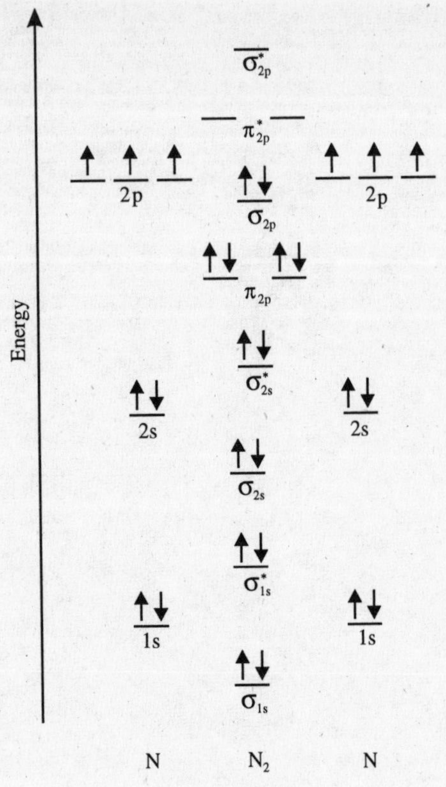

Fig. 11.5b

orbitals in Cl_2 result from combinations of the $3s$ and $3p$ atomic orbitals. These atomic orbitals produce molecular orbitals in a manner similar to F_2. The two $3s$ orbitals produce the σ_{3s} and σ_{3s}^*. The $3p_x$, $3p_y$, and $3p_z$ produce the σ_{3p}, π_{3p}, π_{3p}^*, and σ_{3p}^* molecular orbitals. Because each Cl atom has seven valence electrons, the molecular orbitals contain 14 electrons. Thus, the valence molecular configuration of Cl_2 is $Cl_2(\sigma_{3s})^2(\sigma_{3s}^*)^2(\sigma_{3p})^2(\pi_{3p})^4(\pi_{3p}^*)^4$. (b) Because the number of antibonding and bonding electrons are equal in the inner-level electrons, the bond order can be calculated using only the valence electrons. Thus

$$\text{Bond order}_{Cl_2} = (\text{bonding e}^- - \text{antibonding e}^-)/2$$
$$= (8-6)/2 = 1$$

(c) Because all its electrons are paired, Cl_2 is a diamagnetic molecule.

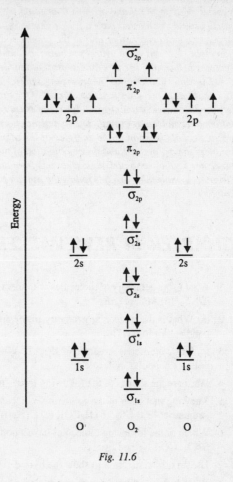

Fig. 11.6

SUMMARY

Molecular geometries are predicted by using the Valence Shell Electron Pair Repulsion (VSEPR) method. This method is based on the fact that the electron pairs on the central atom repel each other so they are as far as possible from each other. A molecule that has a central atom with two bonding and no lone pairs has a linear geometry because the bonding orbitals are at a maximum distance from each other when the bond angle is 180°. Three electron pairs on the central atom have trigonal planar geometry. Four electron pairs have tetrahedral geometry, five pairs have trigonal bipyramidal geometry, and six pairs have octahedral geometry. Lone pairs on the central atoms depress the bonding angles from their theoretical maximum values.

Valence Bond Theory explains the formation of bonds and molecular geometry in terms of hybrid orbitals on the central atom. A hybrid orbital results when two or more atomic orbitals are combined mathematically. If one s orbital and three p hybridize, four degenerate sp^3 hybrid orbitals result that have tetrahedral geometry. If one s and two p orbitals hybridize, three degenerate sp^2 hybrid orbitals result that have trigonal planar geometry. In addition, an unhybridized p orbital is located perpendicular to the plane of the sp^2 orbitals. When an s orbital hybridizes with a p orbital, sp hybrid orbitals result that have a linear geometry. Additionally, two p orbitals remain unhybridized perpendicular to each other and to the other bonds. Molecules that have central atoms with more than eight electrons have hybrid orbitals that combine s, p, and d orbitals. Central atoms with 10 electrons principally use sp^3d and central atoms with 12 electrons mainly use sp^3d^2 hybrid orbitals.

The Molecular Orbital Theory explains the formation of bonds in terms of the linear mathematical combinations of the wave functions for all of the atomic orbitals. When two atomic orbitals combine they produce two molecular orbitals—a lower energy bonding molecular orbital and a higher energy antibonding molecular orbital. The sum of the energies of the bonding and the antibonding molecular orbitals equals the sum of the energies of the atomic orbitals. The combination of two 1s orbitals produces the σ_{1s} and σ_{1s}^* and the combination of two 2s orbitals produces the σ_{2s} and σ_{2s}^*. To obtain molecular orbital configurations, electrons from atomic orbitals are placed into molecular orbitals. Electrons in molecular orbitals follow the Aufbau Principle, Pauli's Exclusion Principle, and Hund's Rule.

CHAPTER 11 REVIEW EXERCISE

1. What is the geometry of molecules with the following general formulas? (a) AB_3, (b) AB_3E, (c) AB_3E_2, (d) AB_6, (e) AB_2

2. (a) What is the molecular geometry of the ammonium ion, NH_4^+? (b) What are the H—N—H bond angles in NH_4^+?

3. (a) Draw the Lewis structure of IF_5. (b) What is the molecular geometry of IF_5? (c) Is IF_5 a polar or nonpolar molecule?

4. What are the shapes of the following ions? (a) ICl_2^-, (b) ICl_4^-, (c) PF_6^-, (d) IF_4^+

5. Knowing that each of the following molecules have multiple bonds, what are their molecular geometries? (a) CS_2, (b) H_2CO_3, (c) C_3H_4, (d) SO_2

6. Which of the following molecules have a nonzero dipole moments? $SiHCl_3$, SF_4, SO_3, CH_2F_2, S_2Cl_2, CO_2, N_2F_4, PF_5

7. Use an orbital diagram to show the hybridization of the P atom in phosphine, PH_3.

8. What hybrid orbitals are on the central atoms of each of the following molecules? (a) O_3, (b) BrF_3, (c) HCN

9. (a) Draw the Lewis structure for carbon disulfide, CS_2. (b) What hybrid orbitals does C use in CS_2. (c) How many σ and π bonds are in CS_2?, (d) What is the molecular geometry of CS_2? (e) What hybrid orbitals does the S atom use in this molecule?

10. What hybrid orbitals are on the central atoms of each of the following ions? (a) NH_4^+, (b) CO_3^{2-}, (c) NH_2^-, (d) ICl_4^-, (e) ClO_3^-, (f) $IO_2F_2^-$

11. How many σ and π bonds are in each of the following? (a) CH_2O, (b) NOF, (c) N_2F_2, (d) C_2H_2, (e) NCO^-

12. What is the hybridization for each atom in the following molecules? (a) N≡C–C≡N, (b) H_2C=CHCH=CH_2, (c) H_2C=C=O, (d) HC≡C–CH=CH–C≡N?

13. (a) Write the valence molecular-orbital configuration for S_2. (b) What is the S–S bond order? (c) Describe the magnetic property of S_2.

14. (a) Write the molecular-orbital order configuration for the molecular oxygen cation, O_2^+. (b) What is the bond order for this ion? (c) Compare the bond order of O_2^+ to the bond order of O_2. (d)

Which of these two chemical species should have the highest bond energy? (e) Which of these two should have the shortest bond distance?

15. (a) Write the molecular-orbital configurations for N_2, N_2^+, and N_2^-. (b) What are the bond order for these three species?

ANSWERS TO REVIEW EXERCISE

1. (a) trigonal planar, (b) trigonal pyramidal, (c) T-shaped, (d) octahedral, (e) linear

2. (a) tetrahedral, (b) 109.5°

3. (a) The I atom has five single bonds to F atoms and one lone pair. (b) square pyramidal, (c) polar

4. (a) linear, (b) square planar, (c) octahedral, (d) see-saw

5. (a) linear, (b) trigonal planar, (c) linear, (d) angular

6. $SiHCl_3$, SF_4, CH_2F_2, S_2Cl_2, N_2F_4

7.

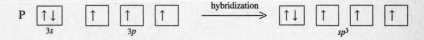

8. (a) sp^2, (b) sp^3d, (c) sp

9. (a) $:\ddot{S}=C=\ddot{S}:$ (b) sp, (c) 2 σ bonds and 2π bonds, (d) linear, (e) sp^2

10. (a) sp^3, (b) sp^2, (c) sp^3, (d) sp^3d^2, (e) sp^3, (f) sp^3d

11. (a) $\sigma = 3$, $\pi = 1$; (b) $\sigma = 5$, $\pi = 0$; (c) $\sigma = 3$, $\pi = 2$, (d) $\sigma = 2$, $\pi = 2$

12. (a) C and N = sp, (b) C = sp^2, (c) central C = sp, other C and O = sp^2, (d) triple bonded C atoms and N = sp, double bonded C = sp^2

13. (a) $(\sigma_{3s})^2 (\sigma_{3s}^*)^2 (\sigma_{3p})^2 (\pi_{3p})^4 (\pi_{3p}^*)^2$, (b) 2, (c) paramagnetic

14. (a) $(\sigma_{1s})^2 (\sigma_{1s}^*)^2 (\sigma_{2s})^2 (\sigma_{2s}^*)^2 (\sigma_{2p})^2 (\pi_{2p})^4 (\pi_{2p}^*)^1$ (b) 2.5, (c) The bond order of O_2^+ is higher than that of O_2 because an electron is removed from an antibonding orbital. (d) O_2^+, (e) O_2^+

15. (a) $N_2 = (\sigma_{1s})^2 (\sigma_{1s}^*)^2 (\sigma_{2s})^2 (\sigma_{2s}^*)^2 (\sigma_{2p})^2 (\pi_{2p})^4$, $N_2^+ = (\sigma_{1s})^2 (\sigma_{1s}^*)^2 (\sigma_{2s})^2 (\sigma_{2s}^*)^2 (\sigma_{2p})^2 (\pi_{2p})^3$, $N_2^- = (\sigma_{1s})^2 (\sigma_{1s}^*)^2 (\sigma_{2s})^2 (\sigma_{2s}^*)^2 (\sigma_{2p})^2 (\pi_{2p})^4 (\pi_{2p}^*)^1$; (b) $N_2 = 3$, $N_2^+ = 2.5$, $N_2^- = 2.5$

12

Liquids and Solids

*L*iquids and solids are the condensed phases of matter. Their properties are very different from those of gases because of the attractive forces between particles of which they are composed. To begin our study of liquids and solids, we will consider the intermolecular forces in liquids.

12.1 INTERMOLECULAR FORCES IN LIQUIDS

Intermolecular forces are the attractive forces that bind particles in the liquid state. The three principal intermolecular forces found among the particles in the liquid state are dipole-dipole interactions, hydrogen bonds, and London dispersion forces.

Dipole-Dipole Interactions

Dipole-dipole interactions are in most liquids composed of polar covalent molecules. As one polar molecule approaches another, the partial negative end of one attracts the partial positive end of the other. In liquids, the more positive ends of molecules align with the more negative ends of other molecules. However, at room conditions (298 K and 1 atm) an orderly regular pattern does not exist, because the kinetic energies of the molecules are too large relative to the energy of attraction to keep the molecules fixed in such an arrangement.

STRENGTH OF DIPOLE-DIPOLE INTERACTIONS

Dipole-dipole interactions are rather weak forces. Two principal factors contribute to their weakness: the small partial charges in polar covalent molecules and the short range of the dipole-dipole interactions. The energy of interaction (the potential energy) of two ions depends on the magnitude of the charges (q_1 and q_2) and the distance, d, that separates them.

$$E \propto \frac{-q_1 q_2}{d} \tag{12.1}$$

For dipole-dipole interactions the values of q are small compared to the full positive and negative charges on ions. Unlike positive and negative ions in which the attractive energy is proportional to $1/d$, the attractive energy for dipole-dipole interactions is proportional to $1/d^6$ for polar rotating molecules ($1/d^3$ for stationary polar molecules).

Problem 12.1   (a) If the value for the attractive energy between two dipoles is 1 unit when d is 1, what is the attractive energy when the distance doubles and triples for polar rotating molecules? (b) What does this mean about the strength of dipole-dipole interactions?

Solution 12.1

  (a) The attractive energy drops to $1/2^6$ or 0.02 when d is 2; it becomes $1/3^6$ or 0.001 when d is 3.

  (b) Only when d is very small will significant dipole-dipole interactions exist between polar molecules.

Hydrogen Bonds

Hydrogen bonds are a special type of dipole-dipole interactions. They are the strongest interactions among molecules in common liquids. Hydrogen bonds only exist among molecules in which a H atom bonds to F, O, or N–the three most electronegative atoms. When the most electronegative atoms withdraw electron density from a H atom, the small highly-charged H nucleus (a proton) is all that remains. Thus, F–H, O–H, and N–H are very polar (high percent ionic character) and have large dipole moments.

Problem 12.2   Liquid hydrogen fluoride, HF(l), is a hydrogen-bonded liquid. Show how a hydrogen bond forms in HF(l).

Solution 12.2   The hydrogen bond in liquid hydrogen fluoride, HF(l), results when the electronegative F atom from one HF molecule attracts and bonds to the electropositive H atom from another HF molecule.

$$\overset{\delta+}{H}-\overset{\delta-}{F}\cdots\overset{\delta+}{H}-\overset{\delta-}{F}$$

hydrogen bond

Hence, a hydrogen bond is a link formed by a H atom between two highly electronegative atoms.

THE HYDROGEN BONDS IN WATER

The more positive H atom in H_2O attracts a lone-pair electron on the more negative O atom from another water molecule. Each water molecule can form a maximum of four hydrogen bonds with other water molecules. Hence, a network of water molecules results from the hydrogen bonds. Because water molecules can form an extensive network of hydrogen bonds, liquid water has an extremely high boiling point (100°C at 1 atm).

London Dispersion Forces

London dispersion forces (dispersion forces or London forces, for short) are the weakest intermolecular attractive forces because they result from nonpolar interactions. On average, the electrons are evenly distributed within a nonpolar molecule (or atom). However, when they interact with the electrons from another nonpolar molecule, the electron distribution distorts briefly and produces a temporary dipole. Widely separated nonpolar molecules do not interact, but when they are close to each other the electrons in one molecule repel the electrons in the other and produce an instantaneous dipole, which in turn induces a dipole in the first molecule. During this time, the nucleus from one molecule attracts the electrons from the other. London forces exist only during the brief interval when these molecules are close to each other.

POLARIZABILITY

The degree to which the electron density in an atom or molecule is distorted is called polarizability. Polarizable atoms and molecules form instantaneous dipoles more easily and, therefore, greater forces of attraction result between them.

Problem 12.3   (a) Compare the polarizability of the electrons in I_2 and F_2. (b) Predict which of these halogens has a higher boiling point. Explain.

Solution 12.3   (a) The valence electrons in I_2 are more polarizable than those in F_2 because the I nucleus has a weaker force of attraction for its valence electrons than a F nucleus has for its outermost electrons. (b) The strength of London forces increases as the number of electrons increases; thus, the boiling point of I_2 is higher than that of F_2.

Problem 12.4   The following molecule are pentane and neopentane (2, 2-dimethylpropane), two molecules with the same molecular formula, C_5H_{12}.

$$CH_3CH_2CH_2CH_2CH_3 \qquad CH_3-\underset{\underset{CH_3}{|}}{\overset{\overset{CH_3}{|}}{C}}-CH_3$$

Pentane   Neopentane

The normal boiling points of pentane and neopentane are 36.2°C and 9.5°C, respectively. In terms of intermolecular forces, explain the differences in boiling points.

Solution 12.4   Because both are nonpolar molecules with the same molecular mass, the difference in boiling points may be attributed to their respective molecular geometries. The structure of a pentane molecule is an unbranched chain of five C atoms, whereas neopentane molecules are branched chains with two C atoms bonded to the second C of a three-carbon chain. The elongated pentane molecules have more points of contact with each other than the compact neopentane molecules. Therefore, stronger London forces exist among pentane molecules than neopentane molecules. In general, the greater the contact between molecules the stronger the London dispersion forces.

Problem 12.5   (a) Discuss the type and strength of intermolecular forces found among the molecules in HCl, HBr, and HI. (b) The boiling points of HCl, HBr, and HI are −85.0°C, −66.7°C, and −35.4°C at 1 atm, respectively. Considering the intermolecular forces, explain the increasing trend in boiling point.

Solution 12.5   (a) These hydrogen halides are composed of polar molecules. Therefore, they have dipole-dipole forces among their molecules. HCl has the strongest dipole-dipole forces of the three because Cl has the highest electronegativity, which makes it the most polar molecule. (b) Exactly the reverse of this increasing trend is expected if the boiling points are predicted based solely on the dipole-dipole interactions. Going from HCl to HI, the number of polarizable electrons increases, which increases the strength of the London forces among molecules. With stronger London forces, higher temperatures are needed to vaporize the liquid, even though the strength of the dipole-dipole interactions decreases within this group. In addition, as the molecular mass of a molecule increases, the faster it has to move to escape from the liquid.

Problem 12.6   (a) Predict the type of intermolecular forces in the following liquids: Xe(l), $H_2Te(l)$, $CH_3CH_2CH_2OH(l)$, $CH_3CH_2CH_2SH(l)$. (b) Arrange the liquids in part a from lowest to highest boiling point.

Solution 12.6

(a)   1. Xe(l) Xenon is a member of the noble gases. Xe atoms are neutral and do not have a charge separation. Hence, liquid Xe has London forces among the atoms because they are the principal forces for atoms and nonpolar chemical species.

       2. $H_2Te(l)$ Because Te is in group 16 (VIA) it has six valence electrons. Therefore, it forms two single covalent bonds with the H atoms. In addition, the Te has two lone pairs.

Atoms with two bonds and two lone pairs have angular geometry. The electronegativity of Te is low (2.1) due to its large size. Hence, the molecule is only slightly polar and essentially nonpolar because it has about the same electronegativity as the H atoms (2.2). Nonpolar molecules exhibit London forces and the slightly polar nature of the molecule would allow it to form weak dipole-dipole forces.

3. $CH_3CH_2CH_2OH(l)$ 1-Propanol, $CH_3CH_2CH_2OH(l)$, has a H atom bonded to an O atom; therefore, it exhibits H bonding. The remaining part of the molecule, the propyl group $(CH_3CH_2CH_2-)$, is essentially nonpolar.

4. $CH_3CH_2CH_2SH(l)$ 1-Propanethiol, $CH_3CH_2CH_2SH$, has a H atom bonded to a S atom; hence, it does not exhibit H bonding. The angular geometry and difference in electronegativity between the H—S and H—C bonds makes 1-propanethiol a polar molecule; thus, it exhibits dipole-dipole interactions.

(b) For the four liquids in part (a), only 1-propanol has H-bonds; thus, it should have the highest boiling point (bp = $97.4°C$). Xe(l) and H_2Te both are essentially nonpolar and mainly exhibit London forces. However, H_2Te has a small amount of polar character; thus, it would be expected to have some dipole-dipole interactions. Considering these facts, Xe(l) should have the lowest boiling point (bp = $-108°C$) and H_2Te would be predicted to have the second lowest boiling point (bp = $-2.2°C$). $CH_3CH_2CH_2SH(l)$, with its dipole-dipole interactions should have a lower boiling point than $CH_3CH_2CH_2OH(l)$ (bp = $67.7°C$) but higher than the others. Hence, the following shows the boiling points from lowest to highest.

$$Xe(l) < H_2Te(l) < CH_3CH_2CH_2SH(l) < CH_3CH_2CH_2OH(l)$$

12.2   PROPERTIES OF LIQUIDS

Evaporation

Evaporation occurs when a liquid is placed in an open container. As time passes, the level of the liquid drops and the total volume of the liquid in the container decreases.

EVAPORATION AND THE KINETIC MOLECULAR THEORY

What happens at the molecular level when a liquid evaporates? Surface liquid particles overcome the intermolecular forces that bind them to other liquid particles and enter the vapor phase. At a constant temperature, the particles in the liquid phase have a range of kinetic energies just as those in the gas phase. Surface particles with enough kinetic energy to overcome the attractive forces that bind them escape from the liquid.

TEMPERATURE AND EVAPORATION

If the temperature of the liquid increases, the number of surface particles with enough energy to overcome the intermolecular forces increases and the rate of evaporation increases accordingly. Likewise, if the temperature decreases, the rate of evaporation decreases because fewer surface particles have sufficient energy to overcome the intermolecular forces that bind them.

Molar Enthalpy of Vaporization

The energy required to evaporate one mole of a liquid at a constant temperature is termed the molar enthalpy of vaporization, $\triangle H_{vap}$. $\triangle H_{vap}$ is the difference between the enthalpy of the vapor, H_{vapor}, and the enthalpy of the liquid, H_{liquid}.

$$\triangle H_{vap} = H_{vapor} - H_{liquid}$$

Neither H_{vapor} nor H_{liquid} can be measured, but the difference between the two, $\triangle H_{vap}$, can be measured.

INTERMOLECULAR FORCES AND ENTHALPIES OF VAPORIZATION

The magnitude of the molar enthalpy of vaporization is a good measure of the strength of the intermolecular forces in liquids. Water has one of the highest $\triangle H_{vap}$ (40.7 kJ/mol) of common liquids. This means that water has strong intermolecular forces. Recall that the strongest intermolecular forces in water are hydrogen bonds. Other hydrogen-bonded liquids such as methanol (34.5 kJ/mol) and ethanol (38.7 kJ/mol) also have high molar enthalpies of vaporization. Liquids, such as HCl(l) (15.1 kJ/mol) and HBr(l) (16.3 kJ/mol), with only dipole-dipole and London forces, have lower molar enthalpies of vaporization. Liquids with low values, such as He(l) (0.081 kJ/mol) and H_2(l) (4.40 kJ/mol), only have weak London forces.

Problem 12.7   The molar enthalpy of vaporization of water is 40.7 kJ/mol. (a) Calculate the enthalpy of vaporization of water in kJ/g. (b) How much heat, in MJ, is required to evaporate 1.00 kg H_2O?

Solution 12.7

(a)   40.7 kJ/mol $\times$ 1 mol H_2O/18.0 g = 2.26 kJ/g.
(b)   1.00 kg H_2O $\times$ 1000 g H_2O/1 kg $\times$ 2.26 kJ/g $\times$ 1 MJ/1000 kJ = 2.26 MJ

Vapor Pressure

Initially the level of a liquid in a closed container drops, with a corresponding decrease in total volume, but at some point in time the liquid level remains constant. What accounts for this behavior? If the pressure above the liquid is monitored, an increase in pressure is observed that ultimately levels off and becomes constant. The decrease in the liquid level is the result of the evaporation of the highest-energy surface molecules. In a closed container the vapor molecules cannot escape. Therefore, as molecules evaporate, the number of molecules in the vapor phase increases and causes an increase in pressure. Some of these vapor molecules lose energy and return to the liquid. The process by which vapor molecules enter the liquid state is called condensation. Initially, the rate at which the surface molecules evaporate is higher than the rate of condensation of vapor molecules because of the low concentration of the vapor molecules. As the concentration of vapor molecules increases, the rate of condensation increases. When the rate of evaporation equals the rate of condensation, the number of molecules that leave the surface equals the number that return to the liquid in a fixed time interval. Thus, the volume of the liquid and the vapor pressure remain constant.

EVAPORATION-CONDENSATION EQUILIBRIUM

A dynamic equilibrium results whenever opposing processes such as evaporation and condensation have equal rates. To represent a dynamic equilibrium, we use two arrows that point in opposite directions.

$$\text{Liquid} \underset{\text{condensation}}{\overset{\text{evaporation}}{\rightleftharpoons}} \text{vapor}$$

A system in dynamic equilibrium is a stable system that tends to remain in equilibrium until some property of the system changes. Systems not in equilibrium tend to be less stable and move spontaneously in the direction that approaches equilibrium.

EQUILIBRIUM VAPOR PRESSURE

The pressure exerted by the vapor in equilibrium with its liquid is termed equilibrium vapor pressure or just vapor pressure. At a constant temperature, liquids with strong intermolecular forces tend to have lower vapor pressures than liquids with weaker forces. Fewer molecules have enough energy to overcome the intermolecular forces at a particular temperature in hydrogen-bonded liquids when compared with liquids consisting of small nonpolar molecules with only weak London dispersion forces.

Problem 12.8 At 25°C, should water, H_2O, or diethylether, $(C_2H_6)_2O$, have a higher vapor pressure? Explain.

Solution 12.8 Water is a hydrogen-bonded liquid, which means it should have a significantly lower vapor pressure than diethylether, $(C_2H_6)_2O$, which is essentially a nonpolar molecule with London forces. At 25°C, the vapor pressures of water and diethylether are 24 and 545 torr, respectively.

TEMPERATURE AND VAPOR PRESSURE

As the temperature of a liquid increases, the vapor pressure increases because the average kinetic energy of the particles increases and the number of molecules with sufficient energy to overcome the intermolecular forces increases. Vapor pressure curves, plots of temperature versus vapor pressure, show this effect.

CRITICAL TEMPERATURE AND PRESSURE

Each vapor pressure curve extends to the critical temperature, the temperature *above which* a gas cannot be condensed to a liquid by an increase in pressure. The pressure required to condense a vapor at the critical temperature is the critical pressure. Above the critical temperature the kinetic energy of the gas phase molecules exceeds the energy of attraction of the intermolecular forces. Hence, the vapor molecules cannot condense to a liquid no matter what pressure is exerted.

Clausius-Clapeyron Equation

The quantitative relationship between the vapor pressure, Kelvin temperature, and molar enthalpy of vaporization, $\triangle H_{vap}$ of a liquid is known as the Clausius-Clapeyron equation. It is expressed as follows

$$\ln\left(\frac{P_2}{P_1}\right) = \frac{\triangle H_{vap}}{R}\left(\frac{T_2 - T_1}{T_1 T_2}\right) \qquad (12.2)$$

in which P_2 is the vapor pressure of the liquid at T_2 and P_1 is the vapor pressure at T_1. The Clausius-Clapeyron equation may be used to calculate the $\triangle H_{vap}$ if the vapor pressures of a liquid are known at two different temperatures. It can also be used to calculate the vapor pressure of a liquid at a specific temperature, if $\triangle H_{vap}$ and vapor pressure at some other temperature are known.

Problem 12.9 At 233.0 K liquid ammonia, $NH_3(l)$, has a vapor pressure of 0.7083 atm and at 221.0 K its vapor pressure is 0.3578 atm. Calculate the molar enthalpy of vaporization, $\triangle H_{vap}$, of liquid ammonia in kJ/mol.

Solution 12.9 Use Eq. 12.2 to calculate the $\triangle H_{vap}$ of liquid ammonia. P_1 is 0.7083 atm, P_2 is 0.3578 atm, T_1 is 221.0 K, and T_2 is 233.0 K. To calculate the $\triangle H_{vap}$ in kJ/mol, convert the ideal gas constant to kJ/(mol·K).

$$8.314 \text{ J/(mol·K)} \times 1 \text{ kJ/1000 J} = 0.008314 \text{ kJ/(mol·K)}$$

The following is obtained after substituting the values into Eq. 12.2.

$$\ln(0.7083 \text{ atm}/0.3578 \text{ atm}) = (\triangle H_{vap}/0.008314 \text{ kJ/mol·K}) \times ((233.0 \text{ K} - 221.0 \text{ K})/221.0 \text{ K·}233.0 \text{ K})$$

After the expressions inside the parentheses are evaluated the following equation results.

$$\ln 1.980 = (\triangle H_{vap}/0.008314 \text{ kJ/mol·K}) \times (2.33 \times 10^{-4} \text{K}^{-1})$$

Use a calculator or a natural logarithm table to calculate ln 1.980, which is 0.6831, and then complete the solution of the equation.

$$0.6831 = (\triangle H_{vap}/0.008314 \text{ kJ/mol·K}) \times (2.33 \times 10^{-4} \text{K}^{-1})$$
$$\triangle H_{vap} = 24.4 \text{ kJ/mol}$$

Boiling Point

The temperature at which the vapor pressure of a liquid equals the external pressure is called its boiling point. When the boiling point is reached, vapor produced throughout the liquid causes bubbles to form that then rise to the surface and enter the gas phase. Bubbles of vapor cannot form in a liquid below the boiling point because the higher external pressure would cause them to collapse.

NORMAL BOILING POINT

The maximum vapor pressure of a liquid in a container open to the atmosphere is atmospheric pressure. Nevertheless, if the external pressure is changed, the boiling point also changes. Because the boiling point varies with external pressure, the normal boiling point is most often used. The normal boiling point is the temperature at which the vapor pressure of the liquid equals one atmosphere.

Problem 12.10 Estimate the boiling point of water when the pressure is 100 torr. The molar enthalpy of vaporization of water is 40.7 kJ/mol.

Solution 12.10 The boiling point of water, T_{bp}, at 100 torr can be calculated using Eq. 12.2, knowing that the vapor pressure is 760 torr at the normal boiling point of water of 100°C.

$$\ln\left(\frac{P_2}{P_1}\right) = \frac{\triangle H_{vap}}{R}\left(\frac{T_2 - T_1}{T_1 T_2}\right)$$
$$\ln(760 \text{ torr}/100 \text{ torr}) = (40.7 \text{ kJ}/0.008314 \text{ kJ/mol K}) \times ((373 \text{ K} - T_{bp})/373 \text{ K } T_{bp})$$
$$2.028 = 4895 \, ((373 \text{ K} - T_{bp})/373 \text{ K } T_{bp})$$
$$T_{bp} = 323 \text{ K} = 50.1°C$$

BOILING POINTS AND INTERMOLECULAR FORCES

Hydrogen-bonded liquids with similar molecular masses boil at higher temperatures than those with dipole-dipole or London forces, which have weaker intermolecular forces. More energy in needed to break hydrogen bonds than most dipole-dipole and London forces.

Problem 12.11 The normal boiling points of the group 16 (VIA) hydrides, H_2O, H_2S, H_2Se, and H_2Te, are 100°C, −86°C, −66°C, and −49°C, respectively. Account for the trend in the boiling points of these compounds.

Solution 12.11 Water has a significantly higher boiling point than the next member of the series, H_2S. Hydrogen bonds are found among the water molecules and weaker dipole-dipole interactions among H_2S molecules. Continuing to H_2Se and H_2Te, an increasing trend in boiling points is found because of the increase in London dispersion forces that result from having more polarizable electrons.

12.3 SOLIDS

General Properties of Solids

Solids have both a constant volume and shape, and have very high viscosities; thus, they exhibit no observable fluid properties. Solids have the highest average densities, melting points, and boiling points of the three physical states. Particles within solids are bound by strong intermolecular forces that inhibit the particles from moving from place to place. Solid particles are arranged in orderly geometric patterns.

Kinetic Molecular Theory of Solids

While virtually no movement from place to place (translocational motion) is possible in solids, the molecules and atoms in solids are in constant motion in a fixed position. Their motions are mainly vibrational in nature. Solid particles move rapidly back and forth, oscillating about a fixed position in space.

Classes of Solids– Crystalline and Amorphous Solids

Crystalline solids are the true solids; the particles are in a regular, recurring three-dimensional pattern called a crystal lattice. Amorphous solids lack the regular microscopic structure of crystalline solids. Actually, their structures more closely resemble those of liquids than solids (many are actually liquids with high viscosities). Examples of amorphous solids include glass, tars, and high-molecular-mass polymers, such as Plexiglas.

Ionic Solids

Ionic solids have alternating cations and anions at their lattice points. Ionic bonds (electrostatic attractions) are the forces that bind these ions. Because the ions hold their electrons tightly, ionic solids do not conduct an electric current when a voltage is applied. However, in the liquid state or when dissolved in solution they conduct electric currents because the ions are free to move. Due to the strength of the ionic bonds, many ionic solids are hard and tend to have high melting points.

Problem 12.12 Explain why some ionic compounds crumble when struck.

Solution 12.12 The mechanical forces displace ions in the lattice. This causes some ions with the same charge to contact each other. When this occurs, they repel each other, destroying the highly organized structure.

Network Covalent (Macro-molecular) Solids

Network covalent solids, also called macromolecular solids, have covalently bonded atoms in their lattice points. For example, diamond is a macromolecular solid because it has a network of C atoms each bonded tetrahedrally (four sp^3 hybrid orbitals) with the sp^3 hybrid orbitals from four other C atoms. Hence, each diamond crystal is as an extremely large C_n molecule, a macromolecule. Other examples of network covalent solids include quartz, SiO_2, and silicon carbide, SiC. Because of their strong covalent bonds and network of interconnected atoms, macromolecular solids are unusually hard substances with extremely high melting points. The electrons in network covalent solids are held tightly in the bonds and cannot be displaced, so network covalent solids do not conduct an electric current. Most macromolecular solids are also poor conductors of heat, except diamond which is an excellent thermal conductor.

Molecular Solids

Molecular solids have molecules in their crystal lattice points. These molecules are bound by the same intermolecular forces found in liquids: London dispersion forces, dipole-dipole interactions, and hydrogen bonds. Examples of molecular solids include $HCl(s)$, $H_2O(s)$, and $I_2(s)$. These three solids have HCl, H_2O, and I_2 molecules in their respective lattice points. The intermolecular forces for HCl, H_2O, and I_2 are dipole-dipole interactions, hydrogen bonds, and London forces, respectively. Besides the intermolecular forces, the properties of molecular solids depend on how well the molecules fit into the lattice points. Because their intermolecular forces are weak compared to ionic and covalent bonds, molecular solids tend to be soft and have low to moderate melting points. Some molecular solids sublime under normal atmosphere pressure. With the electrons tightly held in the covalent bonds within the molecules, molecular solids are poor conductors of heat and electricity.

Metallic Solids

Metallic solids differ significantly from the other classes of solids. They have positive nuclei at the crystal lattice points surrounded by delocalized electrons. Metal nuclei attract their own electrons as well as electrons from 8 to 12 adjacent atoms. An old chemistry cliché states that the structure of metals is "metal nuclei in a sea of electrons." Thus, the intermolecular forces in metals are the electrostatic attractions of nuclei for the delocalized electrons. This type of bond is called a metallic bond. As a result of having delocalized electrons and metallic bonds, metals are good conductors of heat and electricity, and have a wide range of melting points. The electrical conductivity of metals is from 10 to 10^5 times better than other types of solids. Some metals are hard while others can be cut easily with a knife.

BAND THEORY OF METALS

The Molecular Orbital (MO) theory may be used to explain the electrical conductivity of metals. Recall that in the Molecular Orbital theory, atomic orbitals combine to produce molecular orbitals. For example, when the 1s and 2s orbitals from two Li atoms interact, they produce four molecular orbitals–two bonding and two antibonding orbitals. In metals, however, many metal atoms interact. Consequently, many atomic orbitals combine to form an equal number of molecular orbitals. Figure 12.1 shows that the resulting molecular orbitals are widely separated when only two Li atoms interact, but as the number of interacting orbitals increases the energy between them decreases, producing a band of closely spaced orbitals. The resulting molecular orbitals should be viewed as a continuous energy band. This is termed the Band Theory of metallic bonding.

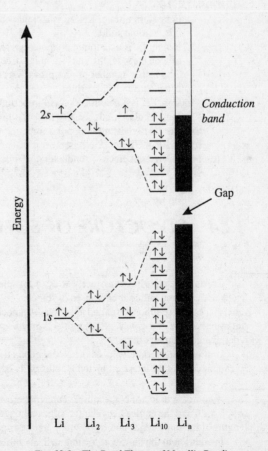

Fig. 12.1   The Band Theory of Metallic Bonding

CONDUCTION BANDS IN METALS

In Li ($1s^2\,2s^1$) atoms, the lower-energy band is full because the $1s$ is full. However, the higher-energy band is only half full because the higher energy $2s$ is half full. It is the higher-energy half-full orbitals that are called the "sea of electrons." The electrons in the higher-energy band are easily excited to the empty molecular orbitals where they can flow depending on the electric potential applied to the metal. The energy band in which electrons are free to flow is termed the conduction band. The electrons in the conduction band are loosely held by the nuclei and are free to flow, but those in the lower band are held tightly and cannot reach the conduction band.

Problem 12.13 Use the Band Theory of metals to explain why metals are good thermal conductors.

Solution 12.13 When heat is applied to one end of a metal, the mobile electrons in the conduction band transfer thermal energy to each other and cause the metal to conduct heat.

Problem 12.14 (a) Predict the class of solid to which each of the following belongs. 1. $KNO_3(s)$, 2. $I_2(s)$, 3. $SiC(s)$, 4. $Fe(s)$. (b) Which has the highest melting point? (c) Which is the best electric conductor?

Solution 12.14
  (a) 1. Potassium nitrate, KNO_3, is an ionic compound composed of K^+ and NO_3^- ions; thus, it is an ionic solid.
      2. Iodine, I_2, is a diatomic nonpolar covalent molecule; hence, it is a molecular solid.
      3. Silicon carbide, SiC, has a similar structure to diamond. This is not a surprise because Si is also a member of group 14 (IVA) and has four valence electrons. Therefore, SiC is a macromolecular solid.
      4. Iron, Fe, is a metallic element in period 4; hence, it is a metallic solid.
  (b) Macromolecular solids usually have the highest melting points. Therefore in this group, SiC has the highest melting point (mp > 2500°C). It is significantly higher than that of Cu (mp = 1084°C)
  (c) Metals are best electric conductors. Hence, Cu is the best conductor of electricity in this group of solids.

12.4 STRUCTURE OF SOLIDS

Unit Cells in Crystal Lattices

Crystalline solids have an orderly array of particles in a crystal lattice (also called a space lattice). Think of the crystal lattice as composed of "blocks" or "bricks" stacked upon each other. The repeating units that compose solids are called unit cells. A unit cell is the smallest repeating unit that determines the overall shape of a crystal. Each unit cell may be made up of atoms, ions, molecules, or nuclei in a definite geometric pattern.

Unit cells are parallelepipeds; i.e., solid geometric figures in which each face is a parallelogram. Each unit cell is characterized by the lengths of its edges and the angles between them.

Types of Unit Cells

A common unit cell is the simple cubic pattern. A simple cubic pattern has equal edge lengths ($a = b = c$), and the angles between the edges all equal 90° ($\alpha = \beta = \gamma = 90°$), where a, b, and c are lengths of the three edges and α, β, and γ are the angles between the edges.

In addition to the simple cubic unit cell, six other simple, sometimes called primitive, unit cells are found in crystalline solid.

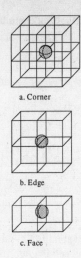

a. Corner

b. Edge

c. Face

Fig. 12.2   Lattice Points

BODY-CENTERED AND FACE CENTERED UNIT CELLS

In addition to the primitive crystal lattice systems that have lattice points only at the corners of the unit cell, it is possible to have lattice points on or within the faces of unit cells. For example, a body-centered cube is a cubic structure with a lattice point in the center. A face-centered cube has a lattice point in the center of each of the six faces. In an end-centered unit cell, such as end-centered orthorhombic, two lattice points are in opposite faces of an orthorhombic unit cell. A total of 14 crystal lattices exist in nature.

Lattice Points and Unit Cell Calculations

The distances between lattice points and density can be calculated from the characteristics of the unit cell. Some lattice points are located in the corners, others in the faces, and still others within the unit cell. If a crystal lattice point is in the corner, it is a member of eight different unit cells (see Figure 12.2A). Therefore, only 1/8 of the lattice point belongs to any one unit cell at the intersection. A lattice point on the edge is in four unit cells and 1/4 lies within one cell (see Figure 12.2B). A lattice point in a face belongs to two units, which means that 1/2 is in each (see Figure 12.2C). The lattice point in the center of a body-centered structure lies totally within the unit cell. Therefore, it contributes one lattice point to the unit cell.

To calculate the number of lattice points within a particular unit cell, determine the number of each type of lattice point, multiply each by its contribution to the cell, and calculate the sum.

Problem 12.15   Compare the lattice points in each of the following: (a) simple cubic unit cell, (b) body-centered cubic unit cell, (c) face-centered cubic unit cell.

Solution 12.15

(a) A simple cubic structure has eight positions, one in each corner. Because each only contributes 1/8 of a lattice point, $8 \times 1/8$, or 1, lattice point is in a simple cubic structure.

(b) In addition to the eight corner points, a lattice point is entirely inside of body-centered cube; thus, it has 2 lattice points.

(c) A face-centered cube has eight corner points and six points within the faces. The eight corner points contribute 1 lattice point and the six face points contribute $1/2 \times 6$ or 3, lattice points, which gives a total of 4 lattice points per face-centered cube unit cell.

Problem 12.16 Copper atoms have a face-centered cubic structure and each face is as follows.

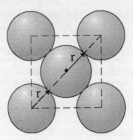

Fig. 12.3 Face of a Copper Unit Cell

The radius of a Cu atom is 128 pm. (a) Calculate the volume of the unit cell in cm3. (b) Calculate the mass of the unit cell in grams. (c) Calculate the density of Cu in g/cm3.

Solution 12.16

(a) To calculate the volume of the unit cell, first calculate the edge length, a, and cube it ($V_{cube} = a^3$). Figure 12.3 shows that the Cu atom in the center of the face is tangent to the corner Cu atoms. Thus, the diagonal distance across the face equals four times the atomic radius; i.e., the radius of each corner atom and the diameter (double the radius) of the central atom.

$$4 \times 128 \text{ pm} = 512 \text{ pm}$$

The diagonal distance across the unit cell, 512 pm, is the hypotenuse of an isosceles right triangle in which the other two sides equal a, the edge length. Application of the Pythagorean Theorem, $a^2 + b^2 = c^2$, allows us to calculate the edge length. In the equation, a^2 equals b^2, thus

$$a^2 + a^2 = c^2$$

and c equals 512 pm, therefore

$$2a^2 = (512 \text{ pm})^2$$

Solving for a gives 362 pm for the edge length. After a is cubed, the volume in pm^3 is obtained. This is then converted to cm^3.

$$
\begin{aligned}
V_{cube} &= a^3 \\
&= (362 \text{ pm})^3 = 4.74 \times 10^7 \text{ pm}^3 \\
&= 4.74 \times 10^7 \text{ pm}^3 \times 1 \text{ m}^3/1 \times 10^{36} \text{ pm}^3 \times 1 \times 10^6 \text{ cm}^3/1 \text{ m}^3 \\
&= 4.74 \times 10^{-23} \text{ cm}^3
\end{aligned}
$$

(b) Each face-centered cube has four crystal lattice points. Therefore, four Cu atoms are in each unit cell. To calculate the mass in grams of one Cu atom divide the mass of one mole of Cu by Avogadro's number.

$$\text{Mass of Cu atom} = 63.5 \text{ g Cu}/1 \text{ mol Cu} \times 1 \text{ mol Cu}/6.02 \times 10^{23} \text{ atoms Cu}$$
$$= 1.05 \times 10^{-22} \text{ g Cu}/1 \text{ atom Cu}$$
$$\text{Mass of 4 Cu atoms} = 4 \text{ atoms} \times 1.05 \times 10^{-22} \text{ g Cu}/1 \text{ atom Cu}$$
$$= 4.22 \times 10^{-22} \text{ g Cu}$$

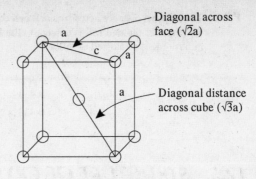

Diagonal across face ($\sqrt{2}a$)

Diagonal distance across cube ($\sqrt{3}a$)

Fig. 12.4

(c) Density is the mass per unit volume

$$\text{Density} = \text{mass/volume}$$
$$= 4.22 \times 10^{-22} \text{ g Cu/4.74} \times 10^{-23} \text{ cm}^3 = 8.89 \text{ g/cm}^3$$

Problem 12.17 Potassium crystals have a body-centered cubic lattice. The edge length of the unit cell is 520 pm. (a) What is the diagonal distance across the face? (b) What is the diagonal distance across the cube? (c) What is the atomic radius of K?

Solution 12.17

(a) Figure 12.4 shows that diagonal distance across the face is the hypotenuse, *c*, of the right triangle in which each length is equal to *a*. Hence, this distance is calculated as follows using the Pythagorean Theorem ($a^2 + b^2 = c^2$). Because $a = b$, then

$$a^2 + a^2 = c^2$$
$$2a^2 = c^2$$

and

$$c = \sqrt{2}a$$
$$c = 1.414 \times 520 \text{ pm} = 735 \text{ pm}$$

(b) Figure 12.4 also shows that the diagonal distance across the cube has one edge equal to *a* and the other edge equal to $\sqrt{2}a$. Thus, using the Pythagorean Theorem shows that this distance equals $\sqrt{3}a$.

$$a^2 + b^2 = c^2$$
$$a^2 + (\sqrt{2}a)^2 =$$
$$3a^2 =$$
$$c = \sqrt{3}a$$
$$= 1.732 \times 520 \text{ pm}$$
$$= 901 \text{ pm}$$

(c) The diagonal distance across the unit cell equals four radii, r, assuming that the K atom in the center of the unit cell is tangent to the K atoms in the corners. Therefore, the atomic radius of K is calculated as follows.

$$4r = \sqrt{3}a$$
$$r = 0.433\,a$$
$$= 0.433 \times 520 \text{ pm} = 225 \text{ pm}$$

12.5   STRUCTURE OF CRYSTALLINE SOLIDS

Closest Packing

Generally, particles in crystalline solids tend to occupy as little volume as possible. The closer particles pack into the crystal structure, the greater the attractive forces among them. Many of the particles discussed are spherical, and for those that are not reasonable predictions can be made if they are assumed to be spheres. Thus, let us consider how spheres pack most efficiently. The most efficiently packed arrangements of particles are called the closest-packed structures.

Hexagonal and Cubic Closest Packing

The particles in a lattice can be in one of two closest-packed structures. For convenience the arrangement of the first layer of particles is called A and the arrangement of the second layer in the gaps between particles in the first layer is termed B. If the third layer of particles lie directly over the first layer, then the layers are represented as $ABABAB$. This arrangement is called hexagonal closest packing, hcp. Figure 12.5a shows the arrangement in hexagonal-closest pattern, which produces a hexagonal unit cell. When the third layer does not lie directly over either of the first two layers, it is known as the C layer. Thus, the second closest-packing pattern is $ABCABCABC$, in which every fourth layer lies directly over top of each other. Such a packing pattern is cubic closest packing, ccp. Figure 12.5b shows the cubic-closest packing structure, which has a face-centered cubic unit cell. In both closest-packed structures, 12 equidistant particles surround each particle, of which three are above, three are below, and six are in the same plane. The number of equidistant particles that surround another particle in a crystal lattice is its coordination number.

EXAMPLES OF CLOSEST-PACKING STRUCTURES

The noble gases in the solid state have closest-packing structures. For example, solid helium, He(s), has a hexagonal closest-packed structure (hcp), while the remaining solid noble gases have cubic closest-packed structures (ccp). Many metals have closest-packed structures. For example, metals such as Cu, Ag, Au, and Ni have cubic closest-packed structures; i.e., face-centered cubic unit cells. Zn, Cd, Be, and Mg have hexagonal closest-packed structures; i.e., hexagonal unit cells.

Structures of Ionic Solids

The structures of ionic compounds are slightly more complicated because the positions of the anions and cations must be distinguished. Many ionic compounds that have ions of different sizes tend to have closest-packed structures in which the smaller ions fill the gaps between the larger ions.

STRUCTURE OF NaCl—OCTAHEDRAL HOLES

Figure 12.4 shows the cubic-closest packing of the larger Cl^- ions in which the smaller Na^+ ions fill the octahedral holes in the NaCl structure. An octahedral hole is one surrounded by six particles (six Cl^- ions in NaCl) that form the shape of an octahedron. Other ionic compounds with the same structure are AgCl, AgBr, MgO, CaO, and NiO.

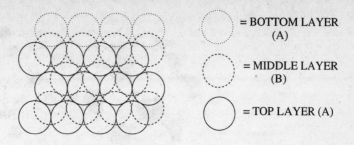

a. Hexagonal closest packing

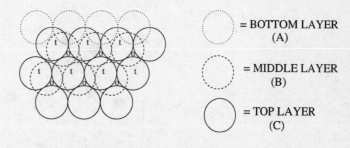

b. Cubic closest packing

Fig. 12.5   Two Closest-Packed Structures of Particles in a Lattice

STRUCTURE OF ZnS—TETRAHEDRAL HOLES

Figure 12.7 shows that the S^{2-} ions are at the lattice points in a face-centered cubic unit cell. Four S^{2-} ions in tetrahedral holes surround alternate Zn^{2+} ions. A tetrahedral hole is surrounded by four particles that take the shape of a tetrahedron. Looking carefully at Fig. 12.7, notice that a tetrahedral hole is between four S^{2-} ions on alternate corners of each of the smaller cubes. Each unit cell has four Zn^{2+} and four S^{2-} ions, which gives a formula unit of ZnS. Other compounds with the same structure are ZnO, CuCl, CuBr, and BeO.

Structure Determination by X-Ray Diffraction

In the laboratory, the size of unit cells and the structures of crystals are identified by x-ray diffraction analysis. In 1912, Max von Laue showed that solids diffract (scatter) x-rays, a type of electromagnetic radiation, with wavelengths about the same length as the distance between particles in solids (about 100 pm). Later other scientists showed that the atoms in crystals exposed to x-rays re-emit energy in the form of new waves called secondary waves. Some of the emitted waves are in phase and reinforce each other, constructive interference, and others are out of phase and cancel each other, destructive interference. Therefore different crystals produce different patterns of emitted x-rays.

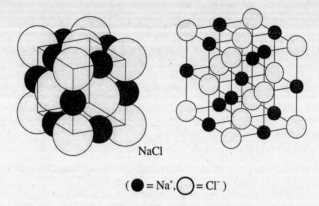

NaCl

$(\bullet = Na^+, \bigcirc = Cl^-)$

Fig. 12.6   Cubic-Closest Packing of Larger Cl^- Ions in NaCl Structure

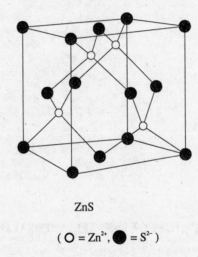

ZnS

$(\bigcirc = Zn^{2+}, \bullet = S^{2-})$

Fig. 12.7 S^{2-} Ions at the Lattice Points in a Face-Centered Cubic Unit Cell

BRAGG EQUATION

Figure 12.8 shows that the distance traveled by the x-rays reflected by the first layer is shorter than the distance traveled by those reflected by the second layer. In order for the reflected radiation to be detected, the x-rays must be in phase or they cancel. This means that the additional distance traveled by the x-rays must be an integral multiple of the wavelength of the x-rays. The Braggs derived the mathematical relationship between the distance between layers in the crystal and the wavelength of the x-rays. It is as follows

$$n\lambda = 2d \sin \theta \qquad (12.3)$$

in which n is a positive integer, λ is the wavelength of the x-rays, d is the distance between layers of atoms, and θ is the angle that the x-rays enter and leave the crystal when reflected. Other angles produce destructive interference of the x-rays and cannot be observed.

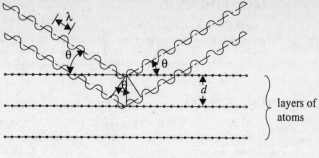

Fig. 12.8

Problem 12.18 An unknown crystal is analyzed using x-rays with a wavelength 165 pm. The first-order ($n = 1$) reflection angle is 11.3°. What distance separates the layers of atoms in the unknown crystal?

Solution 12.18 Use the Bragg equation, Eq. 12.3, to calculate the distance, d, between layers. First, rearrange the equation and solve for d. Then, substitute the known values into the equation.

$$n\lambda = 2d \sin \theta$$
$$d = n\lambda/(2 \sin \theta)$$
$$= 1 \times 165 \text{ pm}/[2 \sin(11.3°)] = 421 \text{ pm}$$

12.6   CHANGES OF STATE

Heating Curves   A heating curve shows the relationship between the regular addition of heat to a substance and temperature. Figure 12.9 presents the heating curve for one mole of a typical substance.

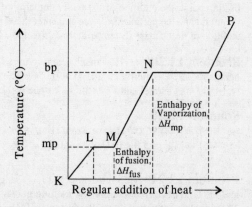

Fig. 12.9   Heating Curve for One Mole of a Typical Structure

HEATING THE SOLID

Initially at K, the substance is in the solid state. As heat is added, the average kinetic energy of the solid particles increases which means the temperature of the solid rises. An increase in the average kinetic energy is the result of the increased vibrations of the particles in their crystal lattice positions.

MELTING POINT

At L, the added heat starts to break particles free from their crystal lattice points. Hence, the substance begins to melt. The temperature that corresponds to L is the melting point. As heat is added at the melting point, many but not all of the attractive forces among the solid particles break, and the orderly pattern of particles within the solid is lost and the more disorganized liquid pattern results. At the melting point, both the solid and liquid phases coexist at equilibrium.

MOLAR ENTHALPY OF FUSION

The amount of heat required to change one mole of solid to liquid at the melting point is called the molar enthalpy of fusion, ΔH_{fus}.

Problem 12.19 Calculate the amount of heat needed to melt an ice cube at $0.0°C$ that has a mass of 45 g. The molar heat enthalpy of fusion of water is 5.98 kJ/mol.

Solution 12.19

$$q = 45 \text{ g H}_2\text{O} \times 1 \text{ mol H}_2\text{O}/18 \text{ g} \times 5.98 \text{ kJ/mol} = 15 \text{ kJ}$$

HEATING THE LIQUID

At M on the heating curve, all of the substance is in the liquid state. Hence, the addition of heat causes an increase in temperature until N is reached. An increase in temperature occurs because the average kinetic energy of the particles in the liquid increases.

BOILING POINT

At N, the boiling point of the liquid is reached and the curve levels out because the added heat increases the average potential energy and not the average kinetic energy of the particles. At the boiling point, the addition of the molar enthalpy of vaporization overcomes the attractive forces in the liquid and the particles separate and enter the vapor phase. At O, the substance is a vapor and the addition of heat causes its temperature to rise according to the heat capacity of the vapor, C_{vapor}.

Problem 12.20 (a) How much heat is required to vaporize 95.0 g H_2O at $100°C$? (b) How much heat is required to melt 95.0 g H_2O at $0.0°C$? The molar enthalpies of vaporization and fusion for water are 40.7 kJ/mol and 5.98 kJ/mol, respectively.

Solution 12.20

(a) $q_{vapor} = 95.0 \text{ g H}_2\text{O} \times 1 \text{ mol H}_2\text{O}/18 \text{ g} \times 40.7 \text{ kJ/mol} = 215 \text{ kJ}$

(b) $q_{fusion} = 95.0 \text{ g H}_2\text{O} \times 1 \text{ mol H}_2\text{O}/18 \text{ g} \times 5.98 \text{ kJ/mol} = 31.6 \text{ kJ}$

Problem 12.21 How much heat, in kJ, is needed to convert 1.50 g $CCl_4(s)$ at $-23.0°C$ to a vapor at $76.8°C$? The normal boiling and melting points of CCl_4 are $76.8°C$ and $-23.0°C$, respectively. The enthalpies of vaporization and fusion are 0.194 kJ/g and 16.3 J/g, respectively. The specific heat of $CCl_4(l)$ is 0.837 J/(g °C).

Solution 12.21 First, calculate the amount of heat, in kJ, to melt 1.50 g CCl_4 at the melting point, using the enthalpy of fusion.

$$q = 1.50 \times 16.3 \text{ J/g} \times 1 \text{ kJ/1000 J} = 0.0244 \text{ kJ}$$

Next, calculate the amount of heat, in kJ, to raise 1.50 g $CCl_4(l)$ at $-23.0°C$ to $76.8°C$.

$$q = 1.50 \text{ g} \times (76.8°C - 23.0°C) \times 0.837 \text{ J/(g °C)} \times 1 \text{ kJ/1000 J}$$
$$= 0.125 \text{ kJ}$$

Then, calculate the amount of heat, in kJ, to vaporize 1.50 g $CCl_4(l)$.

$$q = 1.50 \text{ g} \times 0.194 \text{ kJ/g} = 0.291 \text{ kJ}$$

Finally, add the three values to obtain the total heat needed.

$$q_{total} = 0.0244 \text{ kJ} + 0.125 \text{ kJ} + 0.291 \text{ kJ} = 0.440 \text{ kJ}$$

Problem 12.22 A cube of ice at $0.0°C$ with an edge length of 3.20 cm is placed in 200 g $H_2O(l)$ at $25.0°C$. To what temperature is the water cooled when the ice is totally melted and temperature equilibrium is obtained? The specific heat of water is 4.184 J/(g·C), the molar enthalpy of fusion of water is 5.98 kJ/mol, and the density of ice is 0.980 kJ/cm^3.

Solution 12.22 First, calculate the mass of ice.

$$(3.20 \text{ cm})^3 \times 0.980 \text{ g ice/cm}^3 = 32.1 \text{ g ice}$$

Then, calculate the amount of heat needed to melt the ice.

$$32.1 \text{ g} \times 1 \text{ mol } H_2O/18.0 \text{ g} \times 5.98 \text{ kJ/mol} = 10.7 \text{ kJ}$$

Next, calculate the decrease in temperature of the water when 10.7 kJ of heat is removed.

$$10.7 \text{ kJ} \times 1000 \text{ J/kJ} \times 1 \text{ g·°C/4.184 J} \times 1/200 \text{ g } H_2O = 12.8°C$$

This lowers the liquid water temperature from $25.0°C$ to $12.2°C$ ($25.0°C - 12.8°C$). The liquid water from the ice is at $0.0°C$. Because the heat lost by the warmer water equals the heat gained by the colder water, the equilibrium temperature can be calculated as follows.

$$q(\text{warm}) = -q(\text{cold})$$
$$m(\text{warm})\triangle T(\text{warm})c = -m(\text{cold})\triangle T(\text{cold}) \, c$$
$$m(\text{warm})\triangle T(\text{warm}) = -m(\text{cold})\triangle T(\text{cold})$$
$$200 \text{ g } (T - 12.2°C) = -32.1 \text{ g } (T - 0.0°C)$$
$$T = 10.5°C$$

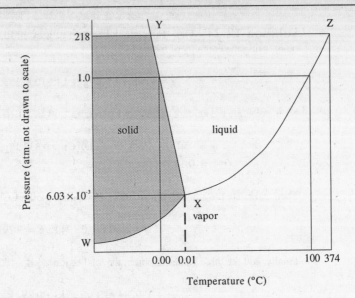

Fig. 12.10   Phase Diagram for Water

Phase Diagrams

ORGANIZATION OF A PHASE DIAGRAM

A phase diagram is a P-T graph for a substance. Phase diagrams may be used to identify what physical state or states a substance is in at a particular temperature and pressure. Figure 12.10 shows a phase diagram for water. Three curves separate the phase diagram into three regions: solid, liquid, and vapor. At higher pressures and lower temperatures, water is in the solid state. The region that represents the solid state is to the left of line *XY* and above line *WX*. At low pressures and high temperatures, water is a vapor. The vapor region is found to the right and below lines *WX* and *WZ*. Between the solid and vapor phases, bound by lines *XY* and *XZ*, are the limits of the liquid state.

MELTING LINE

Line *XY* separates the solid and liquid regions and is thus the melting-point line. Points on this line represent the temperature and pressure when solid water is in equilibrium with liquid water. Projecting a line to the temperature axis from line *XY* at 1 atm gives the normal melting point (freezing point) of water ($0.0°C$). Note that line *XY* is nearly vertical because pressure changes have little effect on the melting point. However, a very slight decrease in the melting point occurs when the pressure increases. Such is the case for water and a few other substances in which the solid state is less dense than the liquid. Increasing the pressure favors the most dense phase of matter. For most other substances, the melting-point line leans very slightly to the right because their solid states are more dense than their liquid states.

VAPOR PRESSURE LINE

Line *XZ* on the phase diagram of water is the vapor-pressure line that separates the liquid and vapor regions. Line *XZ* gives the conditions when the liquid and vapor phases are in equilibrium. At 1.00 atm, the boiling point of water is $100°C$. As the pressure decreases, the boiling point of water decreases, and as the pressure increases, the boiling point of water increases. Line *XZ* terminates at its critical temperature of $374°C$ and 218 atm.

SUBLIMATION LINE

Line *WX* is the vapor-pressure line that separates the solid and vapor regions. A solid sublimes when it changes directly to a vapor. Line *WX* gives the pressures and temperatures at which the solid and vapor phases are in equilibrium.

TRIPLE POINT

Line *WX* intersects the other two lines at point *X*, the triple point. At the triple-point pressure and temperature all three physical states exist in equilibrium. The triple point conditions for water are 6.03×10^{-3} atm (4.58 torr) and $0.0098°C$. Note that the liquid phase cannot exist below the triple point pressure.

Problem 12.23 Use the phase diagram in Figure 12.10 to answer the following questions. (a) In what physical state does water exist at 0.5 atm and 110°C? (b) In what physical state does water exist at 100 atm and −20°C? (c) Describe what happens to water at 100°C and 0.01 atm when the pressure is increased to 200 atm.

Solution 12.23

(a) To read the phase diagram in Figure 12.10, start by moving up the pressure axis to 0.5 atm. Then move across the temperature axis to 110°C. This point lies in the vapor region; thus, at these conditions, water exists in the vapor state.

(b) Once again move up the pressure axis to 100 atm and across the temperature axis to −20°C. This point lies in the solid region. Hence, under these conditions water exists as ice.

(c) First move across the temperature axis to 100°C. At a low pressure such as 0.01 atm, water is in the vapor phase. As the pressure increases, water remains in the vapor phase until it reaches line *XZ*. At line *XZ*, 1 atm, the vapor condenses to a liquid. As the pressure increases to 200 atm, the water remains in the liquid phase.

SUMMARY

Dipole-dipole interactions are short-range forces found among molecules that have a permanent dipole. Hydrogen bonds are dipole-dipole forces among molecules that have a H atom bonded to one of the three most electronegative atoms–F, O, or N. A much larger charge separation is found among such molecules than those with only dipole-dipole interactions. Hence, H bonds are significantly stronger than dipole-dipole interactions. London dispersion forces are found among all liquid molecules but they are most important in nonpolar liquids. When the distance between nonpolar molecules is small, one molecule generates an instantaneous dipole in the other, resulting in very weak attractive forces among the molecules.

Evaporation of liquids occurs when higher-energy surface molecules break free and enter the vapor phase. In a closed system, a liquid reaches a point when the rate of evaporation equals the rate of condensation. At this point a dynamic equilibrium is established. The pressure exerted by a vapor in equilibrium with a liquid is termed equilibrium vapor pressure. As the temperature increases, the vapor pressure of a liquid increases because more molecules have sufficient energy to overcome the forces that bind them to the liquid. The temperature at which the vapor pressure equals the external pressure is called the boiling point. The molar enthalpy of vaporization, ΔH_{vap}, must be added to evaporate one mole of a liquid at a constant temperature.

Liquids behave as if they have a membrane stretched across their surface. This behavior results from the unbalanced forces on the surface molecules. A measure of this effect is termed surface tension, which is the energy required to increase the surface area of a liquid by a unit amount. A measure of the resistance of a liquid to flow is its viscosity.

Solids have constant volumes and shapes, do not exhibit fluid properties, and are incompressible. Crystalline solids have a regular pattern of particles. A few solids, called amorphous solids, have a more random arrangement of particles that more closely resembles the structures of liquids. Solids are classified according to the particles in their crystal lattices and the type of force among the particles. The four principal classes of solids are ionic, macromolecular, molecular, and metallic.

Crystalline solids have an orderly array of particles called a crystal lattice. The smallest repeating pattern of particles in the structure is the unit cell. X-ray diffraction analysis is used to determine the structure of solids, because x-rays with wavelengths approximately the same length as the spacing between layers of atoms are reflected at fixed angles.

A heating curved is used to show the temperature of a substance as heat is added. A phase diagram shows what physical state a substance is in at a particular temperature and pressure. In addition, phase diagrams are used to determine the conditions when state changes occur.

CHAPTER 12 REVIEW EXERCISE

1. (a) Predict the type of intermolecular forces in the following liquids: $CH_3OH(l)$, $CH_3CH_2OH(l)$, $CH_4(l)$, $CH_3CH_3(l)$. (b) Arrange the liquids in part a from lowest to highest boiling point.

2. Which of the following are hydrogen-bonded liquids? (a) $HCl(l)$, (b) $H_2S(l)$, (c) $CH_3OH(l)$, (d) $NH_3(l)$, (e) $CH_4(l)$, (f) $CH_3NH_2(l)$, (g) $HF(l)$

3. Which of the following liquids have London forces as their only intermolecular force? (a) $OCl_2(l)$, (b) $SiCl_4(l)$, (c) $NCl_3(l)$, (d) $SCl_6(l)$, (e) $C_3H_8(l)$, (f) $BF_3(l)$

4. If the vapor pressure of ethyl acetate is 0.395 atm at 51°C and 1.00 atm at 77°C, what is its molar enthalpy of vaporization?

5. The vapor pressure of $N_2(l)$ is 109.7 torr at −209°C and the molar enthalpy of vaporization of N_2 is 5.58 kJ/mol. (a) Calculate the vapor pressure of N_2 at −201°C. (b) Calculate the normal boiling point of N_2.

6. Rank the following compounds in order of increasing boiling points: (a) CH_4, (b) CH_3OH, (c) CH_3CH_2OH, (d) CH_3OCH_3

7. Benzene, C_6H_6, has a molar enthalpy of vaporization of 30.8 kJ/mol at its boiling point, 80.1°C. (a) Calculate the quantity of heat released when 625 g $C_6H_6(g)$ at 80.1°C condenses to liquid at the same temperature. (b) If the heat released from the benzene could be totally transferred to 625 g $H_2O(l)$ at 0.0°C, what is the final temperature of the water?

8. (a) Predict the class of solid to which each of the following belong: 1. $Li(s)$, 2. $CO_2(s)$, 3. $SiO_2(s)$, 4. $NH_4Cl(s)$. (b) Which has the highest melting point? (c) Which is the best electric conductor? (d) Which is a soft solid that sublimes?

9. (a) Classify each of the following in one of the four classes of solids: 1. silicon carbide, $SiC(s)$, 2. calcium, $Ca(s)$, 3. iron(III) oxide, $Fe2O_3(s)$, 4. tetraphosphorus decoxide, $P_4O_{10}(s)$. (b) Describe the intermolecular forces in each substance listed in part (a).

10. Which substance of each of the following pairs would be expected to have the highest melting point? (a) KCl or CaO, (b) Xe or Kr, (c) H_2S or HF, (d) H_2O or Na_2O, (e) $C_{10}H_{22}$ or C_5H_{12}

11. Potassium metal has a body-centered cubic structure with an edge length of 520 pm. Calculate the density of K.

12. Iron atoms form body-centered cubic unit cells. (a) How many Fe atoms are in each unit cell? (b) What is the coordination number for the Fe atoms?

13. Vanadium has an atomic radius of 134 pm and has a body-centered cubic structure. (a) What is the volume of the unit cell of V in cm^3? (b) What is the mass of the unit cell of V in grams? (c) What is the density of V in g/cm^3?

14. Palladium, Pd, atoms are in a face-centered crystal lattice. If the density of Pd is 12.0 g/cm^3 and the atomic mass is 106, calculate the edge length in pm of the unit cell of Pd.

15. X-rays with a wavelength of 154 pm are used to analyze a Ni crystal. A first-order reflection angle of 25.9° is found. What is the distance associated with this angle? Compare it to 352 pm, the length of nickel's unit cell.

16. When gold undergoes x-ray analysis using radiation with a wavelength of 154.0 pm, the first-order ($n = 1$) angle of diffraction is 19.14°. Calculate the spacing between planes of gold atoms.

17. (a) In what physical state does water exist at 50 atm and 50°C? (b) Describe what happens to water at 0.0°C and 0.01 atm when the pressure is increased to 200 atm.

18. The specific heat capacity of ice is 2 J/g°C and its molar enthalpy of fusion at 0.0°C is 5.98 kJ/mol. Calculate the amount of heat required to totally melt a block of ice that has a mass of 215 g at −14.2°C.

19. The surface tension of water and mercury are 7.3×10^{-2} J/m^2 and 4.6×10^{-1} J/m^2, respectively. Compare the amount of energy required to change spherical drops of water and mercury each with a diameter of 3.0 mm to two spherical drops with a diameter of 10.0 mm. The surface area of a sphere equals $4\pi r^2$.

20. A metal with density of 10.2 g/cm^3 has a body-centered cubic lattice and edge length of 315 pm. Calculate the atomic mass of this metal.

ANSWERS TO REVIEW EXERCISE

1. (a) $CH_3OH(l)$, H-bonds; $CH_3CH_2OH(l)$, H-bonds; CH_4, London forces; $CH_3CH_3(l)$, London forces, (b) $CH_4 < CH_3CH_3 < CH_3OH < CH_3CH_2OH$

2. CH_3OH, NH_3, CH_3NH_2, HF

3. $SiCl_4$, SCl_6, C_3H_8, BF_3

4. 37.7 kJ/mol

5. (a) 352 torr, (b) −195°C

6. $CH_4 < CH_3OCH_3 < CH_3OH < CH_3CH_2OH$

7. (a) 247 kJ, (b) 94.4°C

8. (a) Li(s), metallic; CO_2, molecular; SiO_2, macromolecular; NH_4Cl, ionic, (b) $SiO_2(s)$, (c) Li(s), (d) $CO_2(s)$

9. (a) 1. macromolecular, 2. metal, 3. ionic; (b) 1. covalent bonds, 2. metallic bonds, ionic bonds

10. (a) CaO, (b) Xe, (c) HF, (d) Na_2O, (e) $C_{10}H_{22}$

11. 0.925 g/cm^3

12. (a) 2, (b) 8

13. (a) 2.95×10^{-23} cm^3, (b) 1.69×10^{-22} g, (c) 5.73 g/cm^3

14. 389 pm

15. 176 pm, one-half the distance across the unit cell

16. 235 pm

17. (a) liquid, (b) Water changes from vapor to solid and then to a liquid.
18. 77.6 kJ
19. $H_2O = 2.1 \times 10^{-5}$ J, Hg $= 1.3 \times 10^{-4}$ J
20. 96.0 g/mol

13

Solutions and Colloids

S*olutions are homogeneous mixtures of substances. The term homogeneous implies that a solution has a uniform composition throughout its volume. Unlike pure substances with fixed compositions, the composition of a solution may vary. A solution contains one or more solutes and a solvent. A solute dissolves and becomes incorporated into the structure of the solvent.*

13.1 UNITS OF SOLUTION CONCENTRATION

Molarity and Mole Fraction Revisited

In Section 4.5, the concentration unit called molarity was introduced. Recall that molarity, M, is the number of moles of solute per liter of solution.

$$Molarity\ (M) = \frac{moles\ of\ solute}{liter\ of\ solution} \tag{13.1}$$

If necessary go back and review Section 4.5. Another solution concentration unit previously discussed in Section 6.4 is mole fraction. The *mole fraction*, X, for a component of a solution is the number of moles of that component divided by the total number of moles of all components.

$$Mole\ fraction\ (X) = \frac{moles\ of\ a\ competent}{total\ number\ of\ moles\ of\ all\ competents} \tag{13.2}$$

Problem 13.1 (a) What is the molarity of a solution that has 256 mg ethanol, C_2H_6O, dissolved in 85.0 mL of solution? (b) What is the molarity of this ethanol solution after it is diluted to 100 mL?

Solution 13.1

(a) Molarity is the number of moles of solute, C_2H_6O, per liter of solution. Thus, calculate the number of moles of C_2H_6O and divide by the number of liters of solution.

$$mol\ C_2H_6O = 256\ mg \times 1\ g/1000\ mg \times 1\ mol\ C_2H_6O/46.0\ g$$
$$= 5.57 \times 10^{-3}\ mol\ C_2H_6O$$
$$L = 85.0\ mL \times 1\ L/1000\ mL = 0.0850\ L$$

$$M_{C_2H_6O} = 5.57 \times 10^{-3} \text{ mol } C_2H_6O/0.0850 \text{ L} = 0.0655 \text{ } M$$

(b) The same number of moles of C_2H_6O are present, but the total volume changes to 100 mL or 0.100 L. Thus, the new concentration is calculated as follows.

$$M_{C_2H_6O} = 5.57 \times 10^{-3} \text{ mol } C_2H_6O/0.100 \text{ L} = 0.0557 \text{ } M$$

Problem 13.2 A solution is prepared by dissolving 3.42 g sucrose, $C_{12}H_{22}O_{11}$, in 15.0 g H_2O. Calculate the mole fractions of sucrose and water in this solution.

Solution 13.2 Calculate the moles of sucrose and water, and the total number of moles.

$$\text{mol } C_{12}H_{22}O_{11} = 3.42 \text{ g } C_{12}H_{22}O_{11} \times 1 \text{ mol } C_{12}H_{22}O_{11}/342 \text{ g}$$
$$= 0.0100 \text{ mol } C_{12}H_{22}O_{11}$$
$$\text{mol } H_2O = 15.0 \text{ g } H_2O \times 1 \text{ mol } H_2O/18.0 \text{ g} = 0.833 \text{ mol } H_2O$$
$$\text{mol}_{total} = 0.833 \text{ mol} + 0.0100 \text{ mol} = 0.843 \text{ mol}$$

Then, calculate the mole fraction of each component.

$$X_{C_{12}H_{22}O_{11}} = 0.0100 \text{ mol}/0.0843 \text{ mol} = 0.0119$$
$$X_{H_2O} = 0.833 \text{ mol}/0.843 \text{ mol} = 0.988$$

Problem 13.3 What is the mole fraction of methanol, $CH_3OH(l)$, and water, $H_2O(l)$, when 100.0 cm^3 of each liquid is mixed? The densities of methanol and water at 20°C are 0.7913 g/cm^3 and 0.9982 g/cm^3, respectively.

Solution 13.3 First, calculate the number of moles of methanol and water, and the total number of moles.

$$\text{mol } CH_3OH = 100.0 \text{ cm}^3 \times 0.7913 \text{ g/cm}^3 \times 1 \text{ mol } CH_3OH/32.04 \text{ g}$$
$$= 2.470 \text{ mol}$$
$$\text{mol } H_2O = 100.0 \text{ cm}^3 \times 0.9982 \text{ g/cm}^3 \times 1 \text{ mol } H_2O/18.02 \text{ g}$$
$$= 5.539 \text{ mol}$$
$$\text{mol}_{total} = 2.470 \text{ mol} + 5.539 \text{ mol} = 8.009 \text{ mol}$$

Then, calculate the mole fraction of each component.

$$X_{CH_3OH} = 2.470 \text{ mol}/8.009 \text{ mol} = 0.3084$$
$$X_{H_2O} = 5.539 \text{ mol}/8.009 \text{ mol} = 0.6916$$

Percent by Mass (% m/m)

Percent by mass, % m/m, expresses the mass of solute dissolved in 100 grams of *solution*.

$$Percent \text{ } by \text{ } mass \text{ } \% \text{ } (m/m) = \frac{mass \text{ } of \text{ } solute}{100 \text{ } grams \text{ } of \text{ } solution} \qquad (13.3)$$

To calculate the percent by mass, multiply the ratio of the mass of solute to the mass of the solution by 100.

$$Percent\ by\ mass = \frac{mass\ of\ solute}{mass\ of\ solution} \times 100 \tag{13.4}$$

Problem 13.4   Calculate the mole fraction of KNO_3 and H_2O in a 10.0% (m/m) KNO_3 solution.

Solution 13.4   First, calculate the masses of KNO_3 and H_2O for a given mass of solution. A 10.0% (m/m) KNO_3 is composed of 10.0 g KNO_3 dissolved in 100 g solution. If the total mass of the solution is 100 g, then the mass of water is 90.0 g.

$$g\ H_2O = 100.0\ g\ soln - 10.0\ g\ KNO_3 = 90.0\ g$$

Then convert to moles

$$mol\ KNO_3 = 10.0\ g\ KNO_3 \times 1\ mol\ KNO_3/101\ g\ KNO_3 = 0.0990\ mol\ KNO_3$$
$$mol\ H_2O = 90.0\ g\ H_2O \times 1\ mol\ H_2O/18.0\ g\ H_2O = 5.00\ mol\ H_2O$$

The total number of moles is 5.10 mol (0.0990 mol KNO_3 + 5.00 mol H_2O).

$$X_{KNO_3} = 0.0990\ mol\ KNO_3/5.10\ mol = 0.0194$$
$$X_{H_2O} = mol\ H_2O/mol\ total = 5.00\ mol\ H_2O/5.10\ mol = 0.980$$

Problem 13.5   Calculate (a) the percent by mass and (b) the mole fraction of a 15.9 M HNO_3 solution, concentrated nitric acid, which has a density of 1.42 g/cm^3.

Solution 13.5
(a) First, obtain the mass of HNO_3 and the total mass of the solution. To get the percent by mass, % m/m, of the solution, divide the mass of pure HNO_3 by the total mass of the solution before multiplying by 100. To calculate the mass of HNO_3 assume that 1.00 L of solution is present. Because the molarity of the solution is 15.9 M, then the solution contains 15.9 moles of HNO_3. Then, multiply the molar mass of HNO_3, 63.0 g/mol, times the number of moles to get the mass of HNO_3.

$$mass\ of\ HNO_3 = 15.9\ mol \times 63.0\ g\ HNO_3/mol\ HNO_3$$
$$= 1001.7\ g\ HNO_3 = 1.00 \times 10^3\ g\ HNO_3$$

Next, compute the total mass of the solution by using the density of the solution.

$$mass\ of\ solution = 1\ L \times 1000\ cm^3/L \times 1.42\ g\ HNO_3/cm^3$$
$$= 1420\ g\ solution = 1.42 \times 10^3\ g\ solution$$

To calculate the percent by mass, divide the mass of HNO_3 by the total mass and then multiply by 100.

$$\%(m/m)\ HNO_3 = (1.00 \times 10^3\ g\ HNO_3/1.42 \times 10^3\ g\ solution) \times 100$$
$$= 70.4\ \%\ HNO_3\ solution$$

(b) To obtain the mole fraction of HNO_3, X_{HNO_3}, (mol_{HNO_3}/mol_{total}), calculate the number of moles of water from the mass of water in the solution. In part (a) the total mass of the solution and the mass of HNO_3 was calculated. Thus, subtract the mass of HNO_3 from the total mass to obtain the mass of water.

$$\text{mass of water} = 1.42 \times 10^3 \text{ g soln} - 1.00 \times 10^3 \text{ g } HNO_3$$
$$= 4.2 \times 10^2 \text{ g } H_2O$$
$$\text{moles of water} = 4.2 \times 10^2 \text{ g } H_2O \times 1 \text{ mol } H_2O/18.0 \text{ g } H_2O$$
$$= 23 \text{ mol } H_2O$$

To calculate the mole fraction of HNO_3, X_{HNO_3}, divide the number of moles of HNO_3 by the total number of moles.

$$X_{HNO_3} = 15.9 \text{ mol } HNO_3/(15.9 \text{ mol } HNO_3 + 23 \text{ mol } H_2O) = 0.41$$

Parts per Million and Parts per Billion

Parts per million, ppm, and parts per billion, ppb, are units closely related to percent by mass. While percent by mass is grams of solute per 100 g of solution, ppm is the grams of solute per million grams of solution, and ppb is the grams of solute per billion grams of solution.

$$\text{ppm} = \frac{\text{mass of solute}}{\text{mass of solution}} \times 10^6$$
$$\text{ppb} = \frac{\text{mass of solute}}{\text{mass of solution}} \times 10^9$$

These two units are often used when the mass of the solute is small compared with the total mass of the solution. Usually the units ppm and ppb are by *mass* when they refer to solid and liquid solutions, but refer to *atoms* or *molecules* in gaseous solutions.

Problem 13.6 An acetone solution contains 4.30 mg of acetone in enough water to have a total volume of 10.7 L. What is the concentration of acetone in (a) ppm and (b) ppb? The density of water is 0.997 g/cm^3.

Solution 13.6

(a) With aqueous solutions, the concentration unit ppm means the number of grams of solute per 10^6 grams of water. Because the mass of acetone is so small, assume that the volume of the solution equals the volume of water. Therefore, calculate the ppm of acetone as follows.

$$\text{ppm acetone} = \frac{\text{mass of acetone}}{\text{mass of } H_2O} \times 10^6$$

It is most convenient to express the masses in grams.

$$\text{mass of acetone} = 4.30 \text{ mg acetone} \times 1 \text{ g acetone}/1000 \text{ mg acetone}$$
$$= 0.00430 \text{ g acetone} = 4.30 \times 10^3 \text{ g acetone}$$
$$\text{mass of water} = 10.7 \text{ L } H_2O \times 1000 \text{ mL/L} \times 0.997 \text{ g } H_2O/\text{mL } H_2O$$
$$= 1.07 \times 10^4 \text{ g } H_2O$$
$$\text{ppm acetone} = (4.30 \times \times 10^{-3} \text{ g acetone}/1.07 \times 10^4 \text{ g } H_2O) \times 10^6$$
$$= 0.402 \text{ ppm acetone}$$

(b) The concentration of this solution in ppb is as follows.

$$\text{ppb acetone} = \frac{\text{mass of acetone}}{\text{mass of } H_2O} \times 10^9$$

In ppm calculations, multiply the mass ratio by 10^6, and in ppb calculations, multiply the mass ratio by 10^9. Subsequently, the magnitude of ppb is 10^3 times larger than the ppm, or the concentration of the acetone solution is 10^3 times 0.402 ppm which equals 402 ppb.

Problem 13.7 Calculate the concentration of Hg^{2+} in ppm in a 5.00×10^{-4} M Hg^{2+} solution. Assume that the density of this solution is 1.00 g/cm³.

Solution 13.7 The ppm of Hg^{2+} is calculated as follows.

$$\text{ppm } Hg^{2+} = \frac{g \, Hg^{2+}}{g \, total} \times 10^6$$

To begin, assume that the volume is 1.00 L and calculate the masses of Hg^{2+} and the total solution.

$$\text{mass } Hg^{2+} = 1.00 \text{ L} \times 5.00 \times 10^{-4} \text{ mol } Hg^{2+}/\text{L} \times 201 \text{ g } Hg^{2+}/\text{mol}$$
$$= 0.100 \text{ g } Hg^{2+}$$
$$\text{mass total} = 1.00 \text{ L solution} \times 1000 \text{ cm}^3/1 \text{ L} \times 1.00 \text{ g/cm}^3$$
$$= 1000 \text{ g solution}$$

Finally, calculate ppm as follows.

$$\text{ppm } Hg^{2+} = (0.100 \text{ g } Hg^{2+}/1000 \text{ g solution}) \times 10^6 = 100 \text{ ppm}$$

Molality

Molality, m, is the number of moles of solute per kilogram of solvent.

$$\text{Molality } (m) = \frac{\text{moles of solute}}{\text{kilogram of solvent}} \tag{13.5}$$

The way that molality is calculated is altogether different from that of molarity. For molarity, the denominator of the ratio is the total volume of the solution in liters, but for molality, the denominator is the mass of the solvent in kilograms.

Problem 13.8 A solution is prepared by dissolving 8.95 g KBr in 78.3 cm³ of water. If the density of water is 0.997 g/cm³, calculate the molality of the solution.

Solution 13.8 First, calculate the number of moles of KBr from the molar mass of KBr, 119 g KBr/mol, and the mass of water in kg from the density of water, 0.997 g/cm³. Then divide the moles of KBr by the mass of water in kg to get the molality.

$$\text{mol KBr} = 8.95 \text{ g KBr} \times 1 \text{ mol KBr}/119 \text{ g KBr} = 0.0752 \text{ mol KBr}$$
$$\text{mass } H_2O = 78.3 \text{ cm}^3 \, H_2O \times 0.997 \text{ g } H_2O/1 \text{ cm}^3 \text{ g } H_2O \times \text{kg } H_2O/1000 \text{ g } H_2O$$
$$= 0.0781 \text{ kg } H_2O$$
$$\text{molality} = \text{mol of KBr/kg } H_2O$$
$$= 0.0752 \text{ mol KBr}/0.0781 \text{ kg } H_2O = 0.963 \text{ } m$$

Problem 13.9 What is the (a) molality, (b) mole fraction, and (c) molarity of an ethanol solution prepared by mixing 25.0 cm³ of ethanol, C_2H_6O, with 25.0 cm³ of H_2O. The densities of ethanol and water are 0.789 g/cm³ and 0.997 g/cm³, respectively. Assume that the volumes of the liquids are additive even though this is not a good assumption in this case.

Solution 13.9

(a) mol C_2H_6O = 25.0 cm^3 C_2H_6O × 0.789 g C_2H_6O/1 cm^3 C_2H_6O

$$\times 1 \text{ mol } C_2H_6O/46.0 \text{ g } C_2H_6O$$

$$= 0.429 \text{ mol } C_2H_6O$$

kg H_2O = 25.0 cm^3 H_2O × 0.997 g H_2O/1 cm^3 H_2O × 1 kg H_2O/1000 g H_2O

$$= 0.0249 \text{ kg } H_2O$$

To calculate the molality of ethanol divide the moles of C_2H_6O by the kilograms of H_2O.

molality = 0.429 mol C_2H_6O/0.0249 kg H_2O = 17.2 m C_2H_6O

(b) In part (a) the number of moles of ethanol, 0.429 mol, was calculated. Hence, the moles of water must be calculated before the mole fraction of ethanol may be obtained.

mol of H_2O = 0.0249 kg H_2O × 1000 g H_2O/kg H_2O × 1 mol H_2O/18.0 g H_2O

$$= 1.38 \text{ mol } H_2O$$

To find the mole fraction, X, of C_2H_6O, divide the moles of C_2H_6O by the total number of moles.

$X_{C_2H_6O}$ = 0.429 mol C_2H_6O/(0.429 mol C_2H_6O + 1.38 mol H_2O)

$$= 0.237$$

(c) The molarity of the ethanol solution is the moles of ethanol per liter of solution. If 25.0 cm^3 of C_2H_6O are mixed with 25.0 cm^3 of H_2O, 50.0 cm^3 (50.0 mL) or 0.0500 L result, assuming the volumes are additive. Accordingly, the molarity is

$M_{C_2H_6O}$ = 0.429 mol C_2H_6O/0.0500 L = 8.58 M C_2H_6O

13.2 DISSOLUTION OF SOLUTES— THE SOLUTION PROCESS

Dissolution

Dissolution describes the process of dissolving a solute in a solvent. When dissolution occurs, the attractive forces among the solute particles break and the solvent molecules surround and attract the solute particles. The process by which solvent molecules surround and associate with solute molecules is termed solvation. If the solvent is water, this process is specifically called hydration.

THE SOLUTION PROCESS

The solution process occurs in three steps. First, the bonds among the solute particles break, separating the solute particles. Next, some of the intermolecular forces in the solvent break. Finally, the solvent molecules surround and bond to the solute particles.

The Enthalpy of Solution– Energy Considerations

Overcoming the forces of attraction in the solute and solvent requires the addition of energy–an endothermic process. Formation of attractive forces between the solute and the solvent liberates energy–an exothermic process. If the energy required to overcome the attractive forces in the solute and solvent exceeds the energy liberated during solvation, then the overall enthalpy change is endothermic. If the energy liberated by solvation exceeds the energy required to overcome the attractive forces in the solute and solvent, then the overall enthalpy change is exothermic. The energy transferred when a solute dissolves is the enthalpy of solution, ΔH_{soln}.

LATTICE AND SOLVATION ENERGIES

The energy required to effect a total separation of the particles in a solid is the lattice energy, $\Delta H_{lattice}$. The energy liberated when these particles associate with the solvent is the solvation energy, $\Delta H_{solvation}$.

Problem 13.10   The lattice and hydration energies for $NaCl(s)$ are 776 kJ/mol and −771 kJ/mol, respectively. (a) Write an equation that shows the change when the lattice energy is added to $NaCl(s)$. (b) Write an equation that shows what happens during hydration. (c) Calculate the enthalpy of solution of $NaCl(s)$ from the lattice and hydration energies. Explain the result.

Solution 13.10

(a) $NaCl(s) \rightarrow Na^+(g) + Cl^-(g)$ $\Delta H_{lattice} = 776$ kJ
    The addition of the lattice energy changes the solid NaCl to gaseous ions.
(b) $Na^+(g) + Cl^-(g) \rightarrow Na^+(aq) + Cl^-(aq)$ $\Delta H_{solvation} = -771$ kJ
(c) Apply Hess' law and calculate the sum of the lattice and solvation energies. Using this method predicts that the enthalpy of solution of $NaCl(s)$ is 5 kJ.

$$\Delta H_{soln} = 776 + (-771 \text{ kJ}) = 5 \text{ kJ}$$

A positive value for the enthalpy of solution tells us that NaCl dissolves endothermically. While this method gives us an *estimate* of the enthalpy of solution, telling us if the solute dissolves exothermically or endothermically, it generally does not yield accurate values. The experimental value for the enthalpy of solution of NaCl as 3.9 kJ/mol.

Problem 13.11   Consider the dissolution of sodium bromide, $NaBr(s)$.

$$NaBr(s) \xrightarrow{H_2O} Na^+(aq) + Br^-(aq)$$

The lattice energy of NaBr is 728 kJ/mol and its solvation energy is −741 kJ/mol. Estimate the molar enthalpy of solution for $NaBr(s)$ and compare it to the experimentally determined value of −0.6 kJ/mol

Solution 13.11   Applying Hess' law allows us to estimate the molar enthalpy of solution of NaBr. Adding the lattice energy, $\Delta H_{lattice}$, and the solvation energy, $\Delta H_{solvation}$, gives the enthalpy of solution, ΔH_{soln}.

$$
\begin{array}{rcll}
NaBr(s) & \rightarrow & Na^+(g) + Br^-(g) & \Delta H_{lattice} = 728 \text{ kJ} \\
\underline{Na^+(g) + Br^-(g)} & \rightarrow & \underline{Na^+(aq) + Br^-(aq)} & \underline{\Delta H_{solvation} = -741 \text{ kJ}} \\
NaBr(s) & \rightarrow & Na^+(aq) + Br^-(aq) & \Delta H_{soln} = -13 \text{ kJ}
\end{array}
$$

The resulting value, −13 kJ, tells us that NaBr dissolves exothermically. The calculated value is not in good agreement with the experimentally obtained value of −0.6 kJ.

13.3   FACTORS THAT AFFECT SOLUBILITY

Saturated and Unsaturated Solutions

As a solute mixes with a solvent, a point is reached when no additional solute dissolves. A solution that has the maximum amount of dissolved solute at a given temperature is called a saturated solution. Until the saturation point is reached, it is classified as an unsaturated solution.

Solubility

The mass of a given solute required to just saturate a fixed quantity of solvent at a constant temperature is termed solubility. Most solubility tables list the mass of solute required to saturate 100 grams of solvent.

Solubility Equilibrium

The initial rate at which the solute particles enter solution is faster than the rate at which the molecules return to the undissolved portion of the solute. When the solution becomes saturated these rates become equal–the rate at which the solute molecules dissolve equals the rate at which the molecules crystallize out of solution; i.e., leave solution and bond to the undissolved solute. When the rates of two opposing processes are equal a dynamic equilibrium establishes–specifically in this case a solubility equilibrium. A solubility equilibrium is represented in an equation by drawing arrows that point in opposite directions ($\rightleftharpoons$).

Problem 13.12

(a) Write an equation that shows the solubility equilibrium in a saturated solution of glucose, $C_6H_{12}O_6$. (b) What does this equation mean?

Solution 13.12

(a) $C_6H_{12}O_6(s) \overset{H_2O}{\rightleftharpoons} C_6H_{12}O_6(aq)$

(b) The rate at which solid glucose enter solution equals the rate at which dissolved glucose crystallizes out of solution.

Nature of the Solute and Solvent Molecules

For a solute to be soluble in a solvent, it must have similar intermolecular forces, or the solvent will not have the capacity to overcome the attractive forces in the solute and then surround and associate with it. Chemists often summarize this by saying that "likes dissolve likes." In other words, usually the more similar the molecular structures of the solute and solvent, the more likely they will be soluble. Polar liquids tend to dissolve polar and ionic solutes. Nonpolar liquids tend to dissolve nonpolar liquids and solids.

Problem 13.13

(a) Predict the solubility of methanol, $CH_3OH(l)$, in water.

(b) Predict the solubility of pentanol, $CH_3CH_2CH_2CH_2CH_2OH(l)$, in water.

Solution 13.13

(a) Methanol, CH_3OH, has a H atom bonded to an O atom; thus, it exhibits hydrogen bonding. Water is also a hydrogen-bonded liquid. Because both have similar intermolecular and both are rather small molecules, methanol and water are miscible liquids (mutually soluble).

(b) Pentanol, $CH_3CH_2CH_2CH_2CH_2OH$, also form hydrogen bonds with water molecules because it has a H atom bonded to an O atom. However, the nonpolar chain of five C atoms gives the molecule significant nonpolar character. Therefore, pentanol and water are immiscible liquids (form two layers).

Problem 13.14   Predict the miscibility of pure acetic acid, CH_3COOH ($HC_2H_3O_2$), in each of the following liquids: (a) H_2O, (b) CH_3CH_2OH (ethanol), (c) $CHCl_3$ (chloroform).

Solution 13.14 The Lewis structure for acetic acid shows that the two O atoms bonded to the C atom make acetic acid a relatively polar molecule.

$$
\begin{array}{ccc}
\text{H} & \text{O} & \\
| & || & \\
\text{H} - \text{C} - \text{C} & - \text{OH} \\
| & & \\
\text{H} & &
\end{array}
$$

Acetic Acid

Polar molecules tend to be miscible with other polar liquids.
(a) Water, H_2O, is a highly polar liquid; thus, acetic acid should be miscible with water.
(b) Ethanol, CH_3CH_2OH, is a polar molecule that is similar in structure to acetic acid; thus, ethanol and acetic acid should be miscible liquids.
(c) Chloroform, $CHCl_3$, is essentially a nonpolar molecule; hence, chloroform and acetic acids should be immiscible liquids.

Each of these predictions is consistent with the observed solubilities.

Effect of Temperature on Solubility

For most ionic solutes an increase in temperature is accompanied by an increase in solubility. For example, a steady increase in the solubility of $AgNO_3$, KI, and KBr occurs from 0°C to 100°C. But some solutes (e.g., NaCl) have a fairly constant solubility, while others decrease in solubility (e.g., $Ce_2(SO_4)_3 \cdot 9H_2O$) with increasing temperature.

Problem 13.15 The solubility of sodium nitrate, $NaNO_3$, is 73 g/100 g H_2O at 0.0°C and is 148 g/100 g H_2O at 80°C. (a) What mass of $NaNO_3$ is needed to just saturate 75 g H_2O at 80°C? (b) If 75 g of a saturated $NaNO_3$ solution at 80°C is cooled to 0.0°C, what mass of $NaNO_3$ remains in solution? (c) What mass of $NaNO_3$ precipitates from solution after cooling to 0.0°C?

Solution 13.15 Use the solubilities as conversion factors to answer these questions.
(a) 75 g H_2O × 148 g $NaNO_3$/100 g H_2O = 111 g $NaNO_3(aq)$ at 80°C
(b) 75 g H_2O × 73 g $NaNO_3$/100 g H_2O = 55 g $NaNO_3(aq)$ at 0.0°C
(c) The difference between the mass dissolved at 80°C and 0.0°C is the mass that precipitates. 111 g − 55 g = 56 g $NaNO_3(s)$

Effect of Pressure on Solubility

Liquid solutions that contain dissolved gases are the only solutions in which pressure changes have a significant effect. An equilibrium is established when a gas dissolves in a liquid. At a constant temperature and pressure, the rates at which gas molecules leave and enter the solution are equal. Thus, this equilibrium is represented as follows.

$$\text{Gas + liquid} \rightleftharpoons \text{dissolved gas}$$

Hence, the pressure of the gas above the solution is constant. If gas is added to the container or the volume of the container is decreased, the pressure of the gas increases over the solution. To absorb the pressure increase, the equilibrium shifts to the right in favor of the dissolved gas–the direction that decreases the pressure by decreasing the number of gas molecules.

HENRY'S LAW

William Henry (1774–1836) first proposed the relationship between the pressure and solubility of a gas in a liquid, so today this relationship is called Henry's Law. A mathematical statement of Henry's Law is

$$C_g = kP_g \tag{13.6}$$

in which C_g is the concentration of the dissolved gas most often in the units molality, mole fraction, and molarity, P_g is the partial pressure of the gas over the solution, and k is the Henry's Law constant, which is a proportionality constant between the concentration and pressure units.

Problem 13.16 At sea level the partial pressure of O_2 is 159 torr. (a) Calculate the molar concentration of dissolved O_2 in water at sea level. (b) What is the concentration of dissolved O_2 in mg O_2/100 mL? The Henry's Law constant for O_2 is 1.3×10^{-3} M/atm at 25°C (298 K).

Solution 13.16
(a) Substitute into Eq. 13.6 as follows to calculate the molar concentration of O_2 at sea level.

$$C_{O_2} = kP_{O_2}$$
$$= 1.3 \times 10^{-3} M/\text{atm} \times 159 \text{ torr} \times 1 \text{ atm}/760 \text{ torr}$$
$$= 2.7 \times 10^{-4} M \text{ O}_2$$

(b) 2.7×10^{-4} mol O_2/L $\times$ 32 g O_2/mol $\times$ 1000 mg O_2/g $\times$ 0.100 L = 0.86 mg O_2/100 mL

Problem 13.17 The Henry's Law constant for CO_2 at 0.0°C is 1.37×10^{-3} atm^{-1}. For this Henry's Law constant the concentration unit is the unitless mole fraction. What mass of CO_2 dissolves in 1000 g of water at 0.0°C, if the partial pressure of CO_2 is 7.00 atm?

Solution 13.17 First, use Eq. 13.6 to find the mole fraction of CO_2 at the stated conditions.

$$X_{CO_2} = 1.37 \times 10^{-4} \text{ atm}^{-1} \times 7.00 \text{ atm} = 9.6 \times 10^{-4}$$

Then, calculate the number of moles of water.

$$\text{mol H}_2\text{O} = 1000 \text{ g} \times 1 \text{ mol H}_2\text{O}/18.0 \text{ g} = 55.6 \text{ mol H}_2\text{O}$$

The mole fraction gives the ratio of the number of moles of CO_2 to the total number of moles. Therefore, calculate the number of moles of CO_2 as follows.

$$X_{CO_2} = \text{mol CO}_2/(\text{mol CO}_2 + \text{mol H}_2\text{O})$$
$$9.6 \times 10^{-4} = \text{mol CO}_2/(\text{mol CO}_2 + 55.6 \text{ mol})$$
$$\text{mol CO}_2 = 0.053 \text{ mol}$$

Finally to complete the problem, change the moles of CO_2 to grams.

$$0.053 \text{ mol CO}_2 \times 44 \text{ g CO}_2/1 \text{ mol} = 2.3 \text{ g CO}_2$$

13.4 VAPOR PRESSURE OF SOLUTIONS

Colligative Properties

Colligative properties are interrelated properties of solutions that depend only on the concentration of the dissolved solute particles in a specific solvent. These properties vary as the number of dissolved solute particles changes and do not usually change when different solutes with the same number of particles are used. The four colligative properties are vapor-pressure lowering, boiling-point elevation, freezing-point depression, and osmotic pressure.

IDEAL SOLUTION

An ideal solution is composed of a solute and solvent with similar structures and intermolecular forces. Ideal solutions are those whose behavior is exactly described by the colligative property relationships that will be discussed. Initially, to avoid complications this discussion of colligative properties of solutions is restricted to nonvolatile solutes that do not dissociate. A nonvolatile solute is one that has a small enough vapor pressure so that its vapor pressure can be disregarded. For each one mole of a nonelectrolyte solute that dissolves, only one mole of solute particles enters the solution.

Raoult's Law

When a nonvolatile, nonelectrolyte solution is added to a solvent, it lowers the vapor pressure of the solution. In other words, the vapor pressure of a solution with a nonvolatile solute is always less than the vapor pressure of the pure solvent. This statement is called Raoult's Law after Francois-Marie Raoult (1830-1901), the scientist who first proposed this relationship.

MATHEMATICAL EXPRESSION OF RAOULT'S LAW

Raoult's Law is expressed as follows

$$P_A = X_A P_A^{\circ} \tag{13.7}$$

in which P_A is the vapor pressure of the solution, X_A is the mole fraction of the solvent, and P_A° is the vapor pressure of the pure solvent. The vapor pressure lowering can be directly calculated from Eq. 13.9.

$$\triangle P_A = X_B P_A^{\circ} \tag{13.8}$$

Problem 13.18 A solution has 35.5 g of glucose, $C_6H_{12}O_6$, dissolved in 95.5 g of water. If the vapor pressure of pure water is 23.8 torr at 25°C, what is the vapor pressure of the solution?

Solution 13.18 First, find the mole fraction of water, X_{H_2O}, by calculating the moles of water and glucose. Then, divide the moles of water by the total number of moles.

$$\text{mol } H_2O = 95.5 \text{ g } H_2O \times 1 \text{ mol } H_2O/18.0 \text{ g } H_2O = 5.31 \text{ mol } H_2O$$

$$\text{mol } C_6H_{12}O_6 = 35.5 \text{ g } C_6H_{12}O_6 \times 1 \text{ mol } C_6H_{12}O_6/1.80 \times 10^2 \text{ g } C_6H_{12}O_6$$

$$= 0.197 \text{ mol } C_6H_{12}O_6$$

$$X_{H_2O} = 5.31 \text{ mol } H_2O/(5.31 \text{ mol } H_2O + 0.197 \text{ mol } C_6H_{12}O_6)$$

$$= 0.964$$

Finally, substitute the known values into the Raoult's Law equation and solve for P.

$$P = X_{H_2O} P_{H_2O} = 0.964 \times 23.8 \text{ torr} = 22.9 \text{ torr}$$

Problem 13.19 Urea is a water-soluble nonvolatile-nonelectrolyte solute. Calculate the mass of urea, CH_4N_2O, that must be dissolved in 275 g H_2O at 25°C to lower its vapor pressure by 2.00 torr. The vapor pressure of pure water is 23.8 torr at 25°C (298 K).

Solution 13.19 First, calculate the mole fraction, X, of urea, CH_4N_2O. To find the mole fraction of CH_4N_2O, $X_{CH_4N_2O}$, use Eq. 13.9 because the vapor pressure must be lowered by 2.00 torr ($\triangle P = 2.00$ torr).

$$\triangle P = X_{CH_4N_2O} P_{H_2O}^{\circ}$$

$$2.00 \text{ torr} = X_{CH_4N_2O} \times 23.8 \text{ torr}$$

$$X_{CH_4N_2O} = 2.00 \text{ torr}/23.8 \text{ torr} = 0.0840$$

Before moles of CH_4N_2O can be calculated, calculate the number of moles of H_2O.

$$\text{mol } H_2O = 275 \text{ g } H_2O \times 1 \text{ mol } H_2O/18.0 \text{ g } H_2O = 15.3 \text{ mol } H_2O$$

The mole fraction of CH_4N_2O is obtained as follows.

$$X_{CH_4N_2O} = \text{mol } CH_4N_2O/(\text{mol } CH_4N_2O + \text{mol } H_2O)$$

Because the moles of H_2O and the mole fraction of CH_4N_2O are known, solve for the moles of CH_4N_2O and then convert to grams.

$$0.0840 = \text{mol } CH_4N_2O/(\text{mol } CH_4N_2O + 15.3 \text{ mol } H_2O)$$

To solve this equation let x equal the number of moles of CH_4N_2O. Therefore, the equation becomes as follows.

$$0.0840 = x/(x + 15.3)$$
$$0.0840x + 1.29 = x$$
$$0.9160\,x = 1.29$$
$$x = 1.41 \text{ mol } CH_4N_2O$$
$$\text{mass } CH_4N_2O = 1.41 \text{ mol } CH_4N_2O \times 60.1 \text{ g } CH_4N_2O/1 \text{ mol } CH_4N_2O$$
$$= 84.7 \text{ g } CH_4N_2O$$

VAPOR PRESSURE OF SOLUTIONS WITH TWO VOLATILE COMPONENTS

If an ideal solution is composed of two volatile components, the total vapor pressure of the solution equals the sum of the vapor pressures of each component.

Problem 13.20 A solution is prepared by mixing 75.0 g benzene, C_6H_6, and 25.0 g toluene, C_7H_8. Calculate the vapor pressure of this solution at 25°C. The vapor pressures for benzene and toluene at 25°C are 95.3 torr and 28.4 torr, respectively.

Solution 13.20 First, calculate the mole fractions of benzene and toluene.

$$\text{mol } C_6H_6 = 75.0 \text{ g } C_6H_6 \times 1 \text{ mol } C_6H_6/78.0 \text{ g} = 0.962 \text{ mol } C_6H_6$$
$$\text{mol } C_7H_8 = 25.0 \text{ g } C_7H_8 \times 1 \text{ mol } C_7H_8/92.0 \text{ g} = 0.272 \text{ mol } C_7H_8$$
$$X_{C_6H_6} = 0.962 \text{ mol } C_6H_6/(0.962 \text{ mol} + 0.272 \text{ mol}) = 0.780$$
$$X_{C_7H_8} = 1 - 0.780 = 0.220$$

Then, calculate the vapor pressures of benzene and toluene and add them to get the total vapor pressure.

$$P_{\text{total}} = P_{C_6H_6} + P_{C_7H_8}$$
$$P_{C_6H_6} = X_{C_6H_6}P^{\circ}_{C_6H_6} = 0.780 \times 95.2 \text{ torr} = 74.3 \text{ torr}$$
$$P_{C_7H_8} = X_{C_7H_8}P^{\circ}_{C_7H_8} = 0.220 \times 28.4 \text{ torr} = 6.25 \text{ torr}$$
$$P_{\text{total}} = 74.3 \text{ torr} + 6.25 \text{ torr} = 80.6 \text{ torr}$$

13.5   BOILING AND FREEZING POINTS OF SOLUTIONS

Boiling-Point Elevation

The addition of a nonvolatile solute lowers the vapor pressure of the solution. Thus, at all temperatures, the vapor pressure of the solution is less than the vapor pressure of pure water. At 100°C, the vapor pressure of pure water is 760 torr, but the vapor pressure of the solution is less than 760 torr. This means that the solution will not boil at 100°C. The temperature of the solution must increase above 100°C to reach a vapor pressure of 760 torr. The increase in the boiling point of the solution over the boiling point of the pure solvent is symbolized as $\triangle T_b$. In other words, $\triangle T_b$ is the boiling-point elevation.

MOLALITY AND BOILING POINT ELEVATION

An increase in the molal concentration of the solute in the solution causes an increase in $\triangle T_b$. Stated differently, the increase in the boiling point is directly proportional to the molality of the solution. Mathematically, this approximate relationship is expressed as follows

$$\triangle T_b = K_b m \tag{13.9}$$

in which $\triangle T_b$ is the increase in boiling point, m is the molality of the solution, and K_b is the molal boiling-point-elevation constant.

Problem 13.21   What is the boiling point of a solution that has 43.1 g of ethylene glycol, $C_2H_6O_2$, (a nonvolatile-nonelectrolyte) dissolved in 123 g H_2O? The K_b value and normal boiling point for water are 0.51°C/m and 100.0°C, respectively.

Solution 13.21   First, calculate the molality of the solution.

$$\text{molality} = \frac{43.1 \text{ g } C_2H_6O_2 \times 1 \text{ mol } C_2H_6O_2/62.0 \text{ g } C_2H_6O_2}{123 \text{ g } H_2O \times 1 \text{ kg } H_2O/1000 \text{ g}} = 5.65 \text{ } m \text{ } C_2H_6O_2$$

Then, substitute the known values into Eq. 13.9.

$$\triangle T_b = K_b m = 0.51°C/m \times 5.65m = 2.9°C$$

The boiling-point elevation is 2.9°C. Therefore, it must be added to the normal boiling point of water which is 100.0°C.

$$\text{bp} = 100.0°C + 2.9°C = 102.9°C$$

Freezing-Point Depression

The freezing point of a liquid is the temperature at which the solid and liquid phases coexist. At this temperature the vapor pressure of the liquid equals that of the solid. We just learned that vapor pressure of the liquid in a solution is less than that of the pure solvent. Such is not the case for the solid phase of the solvent because the solute usually does not dissolve in the solid phase of the solvent and thus does not lower its vapor pressure. Hence, the temperature at which the vapor pressure of the solution equals the vapor pressure of the solid is lower than that for the pure solvent. The difference between these freezing points is symbolized as $\triangle T_f$, the freezing-point depression.

MOLALITY AND FREEZING POINT DEPRESSION

An approximate quantitative relationship for the freezing-point depression is

$$\triangle T_f = K_f m \tag{13.10}$$

in which $\triangle T_f$ is the freezing-point depression, m is the molality of the solution, and K_f is the molal-freezing-point-depression constant.

Problem 13.22 The K_f value for water is $1.86°C/m$. At what temperature does a $1.00\,m$ solution that contains a nonvolatile, nonelectrolyte solute freeze?

Solution 13.22 This means that the freezing point of a $1.00\,m$ aqueous solution of a nonelectrolyte is depressed by $1.86°C$ from $0.0°C$ to $-1.86°C$.

Problem 13.23 A nonvolatile-nonelectrolyte solute depresses the freezing point of benzene to $4.90°C$. Calculate the molality of the benzene solution. The freezing point and molal freezing point depression constant for benzene are $5.53°C$ and $5.12\,°C/m$, respectively.

Solution 13.23 First, determine the depression of the freezing point, $\triangle T_f$, which is the difference between the freezing points of the solvent and solution ($\triangle T_f = 5.53°C - 4.90°C = 0.63°C$). Then, rearrange Eq. 13.10 and solve the equation for molality, and substitute the known values.

$$\triangle T_f = K_f m$$
$$m = \triangle T_f / K_f = 0.63°C/5.12\,°C/m = 0.12\text{ mol/kg}$$

Problem 13.24 When a 1.25-g sample of an unknown organic compound dissolves in 53.7 g of cyclohexane, C_6H_{12}, the solution freezes at $1.32°C$. Calculate the molar mass of the unknown compound. The freezing point of cyclohexane is $6.54°C$, and its molal-freezing-point-depression constant is $20.0°C/m$.

Solution 13.24 First, calculate the molality of the solution. To obtain the molality, calculate the $\triangle T_f$ ($\triangle T_f = 6.54°C - 1.32°C = 5.22°C$). Rearrangement of Eq. 13.11 and substitution of the known values gives the molality of the solution.

$$\triangle T_f = K_f m$$
$$m = \triangle T_f / K_f = 5.22°C/20.0\,°C/m = 0.261\text{ mol/kg }C_6H_{12}$$

This solution contains 0.261 mol solute per kg of cyclohexane. To calculate the moles of solute multiply the molality of the solution by the number of kilograms of C_6H_{12}.

$$\text{mol of solute} = 0.261\text{ mol solute/kg }C_6H_{12} \times 53.7\text{ g }C_6H_{12} \times 1\text{ kg }C_6H_{12}/1000\text{ g }C_6H_{12}$$
$$= 0.0140\text{ mol solute}$$

Molar mass is the ratio of the grams of solute per one mole.

$$\text{Molar mass} = 1.25\text{ g solute}/0.0140\text{ mol solute} = 89.2\text{ g solute/mol solute}$$

13.6 OSMOTIC PRESSURE

Osmosis

Osmosis is the net movement of solvent molecules across a semipermeable membrane from a dilute to a more concentrated solution. Stated differently, osmosis is the net movement of solvent across a semipermeable membrane from a higher to a lower region of solvent concentration. A semipermeable membrane, more specifically an osmotic membrane, allows only solvent molecules to pass and blocks the movement of the solute particles. During osmosis a net movement of water occurs from a more dilute solution to the more concentrated solution until the concentrations of the solutions equalize.

Osmotic Pressure

Osmotic pressure, π, is the pressure required to just stop the movement of solvent across a semipermeable membrane that separates a pure solvent and a solution. It is convenient to think that osmotic pressure results from solvent particles hitting either side of the semipermeable membrane in a manner similar to gas particles hitting the walls of their container. The rate of collisions on the solvent side is greater than the rate on the solution side because of the higher concentration of solvent molecules. Hence, the net flow is from the solvent to the solution. When the solvent concentrations equalize, the rates of collisions become equal and the net flow of solvent ceases.

Osmotic Pressure and Molarity

The osmotic pressure of a solution, π, is directly proportional to the molar concentration, M, of the dissolved solute particles. Hence, osmotic pressure is a colligative property. Quantitatively, Eq. 13.11 shows how osmotic pressure, π, is calculated.

$$\pi = MRT \qquad (13.11)$$

In this equation, π is the osmotic pressure, M is the molar concentration of solute particles, R is the ideal gas constant in 0.0821 (L·atm)/(mol·K), and T is the Kelvin temperature.

Problem 13.25   What is the osmotic pressure of a solution with 50.0 g glucose, $C_6H_{12}O_6$ dissolved in 350 mL of solution at 298 K?

Solution 13.25   Use Eq. 13.11 to find the osmotic pressure, π, of this solution. Thus, begin by calculating the molarity of the solution.

$$n_{C_6H_{12}O_6} = 50.0 \text{ g } C_6H_{12}O_6 \times 1 \text{ mol } C_6H_{12}O_6/180 \text{ g} = 0.278 \text{ mol } C_6H_{12}O_6$$
$$M_{C_6H_{12}O_6} = 0.278 \text{ mol}/0.350 \text{ L} = 0.794 \text{ M}$$
$$\pi = MRT$$
$$= 0.794 \text{ M} \times 0.0821 \text{ L·atm}/(\text{mol·K}) \times 298 \text{ K} = 19.4 \text{ atm}$$

Problem 13.26   The osmotic pressure of a solution that has 6.74 g of an unknown cytochrome (a biologically-important compound) in 1.00 L of solution is 3.58 torr at 298 K. Calculate the molar mass of the unknown cytochrome.

Solution 13.26   Before applying Eq. 13.11, convert the osmotic pressure to atmospheres, atm, because the value of R in the equation is 0.0821 L·atm/(mol·K).

$$\pi = 3.58 \text{ torr} \times 1 \text{ atm}/760 \text{ torr} = 4.71 \times 10^{-3} \text{ atm}$$

Rearrange Eq. 13.11 and solve for M.

$$M = \pi/RT = 4.71 \times 10^{-3} \text{ atm}/(0.0821 \text{ L·atm}/(\text{mol·K}) \times 298 \text{ K})$$
$$= 1.93 \times 10^{-4} \text{ mol cytochrome/L}$$

The molar mass of the cytochrome equals the grams per one mole.

$$\text{molar mass} = 6.74 \text{ g}/(1.93 \times 10^{-4} \text{ mol/L} \times 1.00 \text{ L}) = 3.50 \times 10^4 \text{ g/mol}$$

13.7 COLLIGATIVE PROPERTIES OF ELECTROLYTE SOLUTIONS

Freezing Point Depression of Electrolyte Solutions

You might expect that the freezing point depression of a strong electrolyte such as sodium chloride, NaCl(s), should be twice that of a nonelectrolyte because for each mole of NaCl(s) that dissolves two moles of particles enter solution.

$$NaCl(s) \rightarrow Na^+(aq) + Cl^-(aq)$$
$$\text{1 mol} \qquad \text{2 mol}$$

Nonetheless, this is not exactly what is found experimentally. For example, if the freezing point of a 0.100 m NaCl solution is measured, the observed freezing-point depression is 0.348°C instead of 0.372°C. The value 0.372°C is obtained by doubling the depression obtained if the solution had an ideal nonelectrolyte (0.372°C = 2 × 0.100 m × 1.86°C/m).

ION PAIRS AND INTERIONIC ATTRACTIONS

When the freezing-point depression of NaCl is predicted to be twice that of a nonelectrolyte the assumption is made that the Na^+ and Cl^- ions do not interact after they enter solution. Such is not the case for ions in real solutions (nonideal solutions). In most electrolyte solutions some of the ions associate with other ions and produce ion pairs. This effectively decreases the total number of dissolved ions. An ion pair is composed of a cation, anion, and sometimes water molecules that are held by attractive forces, called interionic attractions. Therefore, a smaller number of dissolved particles are effectively in solution than if all solute particles were 100% separated. Subsequently, a smaller freezing-point depression is observed.

Problem 13.27 Explain why the freezing point depression of 0.100 m $MgSO_4$ ($\triangle T_f = 0.225°C$) is significantly less than that of 0.100 m NaCl ($\triangle T_f = 0.348°C$).

Solution 13.27 Ion pairs with higher charges (Mg^{2+}, SO_4^{2-}) tend to associate more readily than those with lower charges (Na^+, Cl^-). In other words, as the charges on the ions increase, the smaller the observed freezing point depression.

The van't Hoff Factor

How can accurate predictions be made for the colligative properties of electrolyte solutions? The actual freezing-point depression, $\triangle T_f$(actual) is divided by the expected value, $\triangle T_f$(nonelectrolyte), the value in which the assumption is made that the solute does not dissociate in solution. What results is a ratio that is designated by the letter i–the van't Hoff factor.

$$i = \frac{actual\ freezing\text{-}point\ depression}{predicted\ freezing\ point\ assuming\ no\ dissociation}$$

$$i = \frac{\triangle T_f(actual)}{\triangle T_f(nonelectrolyte)}$$

For electrolyte solutions, the van't Hoff factor, i, is included in the equations for the colligative properties: freezing-point depressions, boiling-point elevations, and osmotic pressures.

$$\triangle T_f = iK_f m \qquad (13.12)$$
$$\triangle T_b = iK_b m \qquad (13.13)$$
$$\pi = iMRT \qquad (13.14)$$

Problem 13.28 A 74.6-mg sample of KCl is dissolved in 100 g H_2O. A 0.0361°C depression of the freezing point is observed. (a) Calculate the value of the van't Hoff factor, i. (b) What is the osmotic pressure of this solution at 298 K?

Solution 13.28

(a) Use Eq. 13.12 to calculate the value of i for this KCl solution.

$$\triangle T_f = iK_f m$$
$$i = \triangle T_f / K_f m \qquad (13.15)$$

Thus, divide the observed freezing-point depression, $\triangle T_f$, by the product of molal freezing-point depression constant, $\triangle K_f$, and the molality, m. The first two values are given, and the molality must be calculated.

$$m = \frac{74.6 \text{ mg} \times 1 \text{ g}/1000 \text{ mg} \times 1 \text{ mol KCl}/74.6 \text{ g KCl}}{100 \text{ g } H_2O \times 1 \text{ kg } H_2O/1000 \text{ g } H_2O}$$
$$= 0.0100 \text{ } m \text{ KCl}$$

Substituting into Eq. 13.15 gives us the value of i.

$$i = \triangle T_f / K_f m$$
$$= 0.0361°C/(1.86°C/m \ 0.0100m) = 1.94$$

(b) Use Eq. 13.15 to calculate the osmotic pressure of the solution. To calculate the osmotic pressure of this solution, the molarity of the solution, M, is needed. In part (a) the molality (0.0100 m) was calculated. Because this is a rather dilute solution, the assumption can be made that the molarity very nearly equals the molality ($m = M = 0.0100$). Therefore, substitute the known values into Eq. 13.15 as follows.

$$\pi = 1.94 \times 0.0100 \text{ mol/L} \times 0.0821 \text{ L·atm/(mol·K)} \times 298 \text{ K}$$
$$= 0.475 \text{ atm}$$

SUMMARY

S*olutions are homogeneous mixtures of substances composed of one or more solutes and a solvent. The solute is usually the component present in smaller amount, and the solvent is the one present in larger amount.*

Molarity is the unit of solution concentration that gives the moles of solute per liter of solution. Mole fraction is the ratio of the moles of a component to the total number of moles of all of components in the solution. Percent by mass is the mass of solute per 100 g of solution. Molality is the moles of solute per kilogram of solvent.

Dissolution is the term used to describe the incorporation of a solute into a solvent. When a solute dissolves in a solvent, the attractive forces among the solute particles break and the solvent molecules surround and attract the solute particles in a process called solvation. Overcoming the forces of attraction in the solute and solvent is an endothermic process, and the solvation of the solute particles is an exothermic process. The overall energy transferred when a solute enters solution is the enthalpy of solution, $\triangle H_{soln}$.

A solution with the maximum amount of dissolved solute is a saturated solution. Before the point of saturation the solution is unsaturated. In a saturated solution, the dissolved solute is in equilibrium with the undissolved solute. The amount of a given solute required to just saturate a fixed amount of solvent at constant temperature is called solubility. Solubility depends on the nature of the solute and solvent molecules, temperature, and pressure. Generally, likes dissolve likes–solutes and solvents with similar structures and intermolecular forces tend to be soluble. For most solutes an increase in temperature increases the solubility. Pressure mainly effects gaseous solutions. As the partial pressure of the gas over the solution increases, its solubility increases (Henry's Law).

Colligative properties of solutions are interrelated properties that depend on the concentration of the dissolved particles. When a nonvolatile solute dissolves in a solvent, it lowers the vapor pressure (Raoult's Law). A decrease in the vapor pressure of a solution causes an elevation of the boiling point and a depression of the freezing point. Osmotic pressure, π, is also a colligative property. Osmotic pressure is the pressure that must be exerted to just stop the osmosis of a solvent to a solution. Osmosis is the net movement of solvent molecules across a semipermeable membrane (osmotic membrane).

CHAPTER 13 REVIEW EXERCISE

1. Calculate the mole fraction of NaOH and H_2O in a 25.0%(m/m) NaOH solution.
2. Calculate the molarity and mole fraction of a 57.4%(m/m) HI solution. The density of the solution is 1.70 g/cm^3.
3. Commercial perchloric acid, $HClO_4$ is often sold as a 11.7 M solution. If the density of this solution is 1.67 g/cm^3, calculate the percent by mass and mole fraction of perchloric acid.
4. A 50.0%(m/m) aqueous ethanol, CH_3CH_2OH, solution has a density of 0.9139 g/cm^3. (a) What is the molarity of this ethanol solution? (b) What is the molality of this ethanol solution? (c) What is the mole fraction of ethanol?
5. A solution contains 0.100 g of table sugar, $C_{12}H_{22}O_{11}$, in 12.50 L of solution. If the density of water is 0.9970 g/cm^3, calculate the concentration of sugar in ppm and ppb.
6. A solution has 12.1 g $NaNO_3$ dissolved in 145.9 g of solution. What is the molality of $NaNO_3$?
7. What is the molality, mole fraction, and molarity of a methanol (wood alcohol) solution prepared by mixing 1.00 cm^3 of methanol, CH_3OH, with 99.00 cm^3 of H_2O. The densities of methanol and water are 0.791 g/cm^3 and 0.997 g/cm^3, respectively. Assume that the volumes of the liquids are additive.
8. The lattice energy of AgCl is 916 kJ/mol and its solvation energy is −851 kJ/mol. Estimate the molar enthalpy of solution for AgCl(s), and determine if it dissolves exothermically or endothermically.
9. (a) In which of the following solvents would you predict that $I_2(s)$ is most soluble: $CCl_4(l)$, $CH_3CH_2OH(l)$, or $H_2O(l)$? (b) In which of these solvents is I_2 least soluble?
10. Predict the miscibility of benzene in each of the following: (a) H_2O, (b) C_6H_{14}, (c) CH_3COOH, (d) $CHCl_3$
11. Calculate the volume of CO_2 released from a 500-mL cola drink that was bottled at a pressure of 4.3 atm of CO_2 after it is opened at 21°C and 753 torr. The Henry's Law constant for CO_2 is 3.4×10^{-2} M/atm.
12. A student prepares a solution by mixing 50.0 g $C_{12}H_{22}O_{11}$ with 150 g H_2O. If the vapor pressure of water at 25°C is 23.8 torr, calculate the vapor pressure of this solution.
13. Heptane, C_7H_{16}, and octane, C_8H_{18}, form an ideal solution. (a) What is the vapor pressure of the solution in which equal number of moles of heptane and octane are mixed at 40°C? (b) What is the vapor pressure of the solution when equal masses are mixed at 40°C? The vapor pressures of heptane and octane at 40°C are 92.0 torr and 31.2 torr, respectively.

14. What mass of glucose, $C_6H_{12}O_6$, should be mixed with 82.0 g H_2O to lower its vapor pressure by 0.50 torr? The vapor pressure of pure water at 25°C is 23.8 torr.

15. A student finds that 155 g of an aqueous solution of $C_{12}H_{22}O_{11}$ boils at 100.54°C. What mass of $C_{12}H_{22}O_{11}$ is in this solution?

16. A solution contains 4.44 g $HOCH_2CH_2OH$ dissolved in 55.5 g of pure ethanol, CH_3CH_2OH. The K_f value for ethanol is 1.99°C/*m* and its freezing point is −114°C. What is the freezing point of this solution?

17. A student finds that a solution with 2.54 g of an unknown nonvolatile nonelectrolyte dissolved in 35.5 g H_2O freezes at −1.44°C. Calculate the molar mass of the unknown solute.

18. What mass of naphthalene, $C_{10}H_8$, should be added to camphor to lower its freezing point in °C by 10.0%? The freezing point of camphor is 178.8°C and the K_f value is 37.7°C/*m*.

19. The osmotic pressure of blood is 7.65 atm at 37°C. What mass of glucose, $C_6H_{12}O_6$, should be dissolved in 100 cm³ H_2O to produce a solution with the same osmotic pressure as blood?

20. Calculate the osmotic pressure of a solution that has 4.09 g urea, CH_4N_2O, in 68.9 mL of an aqueous solution at 21°C.

21. A student finds that a solution with 1.60 g NaOH in 40.0 g H_2O freezes at −3.40°C. (a) What is the van't Hoff factor for this solution? (b) What is the boiling point of this solution? (c) What is the predicted boiling point if the ions did not associate in solution?

22. Arrange the following from lowest to highest freezing point: (a) 0.01 *m* KI, (b) 0.01 *m* CaI_2, (c) 0.01 *m* CH_3OH, (d) 0.01 *m* $Al(NO_3)_3$.

23. Polymers are high-molecular mass molecules composed of a large number of repeating units. If the formula of a polymer is $[H_2C–C(CH_3)_2]_x$, in which x is the number of repeating units, and the osmotic pressure, π, is 8.854 torr for a solution at 298 K that has 20.00 g of this polymer per liter, what is its molecular mass and what is the value of x?

ANSWERS TO REVIEW EXERCISE

1. $X_{NaOH} = 0.130, X_{H_2O} = 0.0870$
2. 7.63 *M* HI, $X_{HI} = 0.159, X_{H_2O} = 0.841$
3. $M = 70.4$ %(m/m), $X_{HClO_4} = 0.298$
4. (a) 9.93 *M*, (b) 21.8 *m*, (c) 0.282
5. 8.02 ppm, 8.02×10^3 ppb
6. 1.06 *m* $NaNO_3$
7. molality = 0.250 *m* CH_3OH, $X_{CH_3OH} = 0.00448$, molarity = 0.247 *M* CH_3OH
8. $\triangle H_{soln} = 65$ kJ/mol, an endothermic process
9. (a) CCl_4, (b) H_2O
10. (a) immiscible, (b) miscible, (c) immiscible, (d) miscible
11. 1.8 L CO_2
12. 23.4 torr
13. (a) $P_{total} = 61.6$ torr, (b) $P_{total} = 63.6$ torr
14. 18 g $C_6H_{12}O_6$
15. 55 g $C_{12}H_{22}O_{11}$
16. −117°C
17. 90.4 g/mol
18. 60.7 g $C_{10}H_8$/kg camphor
19. 5.41 g $C_6H_{12}O_6$
20. 23.9 atm
21. (a) 1.83, (b) 100.933°C, (c) 101.02°C
22. 0.01 *m* CH_3OH < 0.01 *m* KI < 0.01 *m* CaI_2 < 0.01 *m* $Al(NO_3)_3$
23. 4.20×10^4 g/mol, $x = 750$

14

Rates of Chemical Reactions

*C*hemical kinetics, also called reaction kinetics, is the study of the rates of chemical reactions and the underlying mechanisms by which reactants change to products.

An important outcome for studying the rates of chemical reactions is to develop an understanding of how chemical reactions take place. Chemists attempt to identify the molecular events that occur when reactants change to products. The series of steps that take place in a reaction is termed the reaction mechanism.

14.1 RATES OF CHEMICAL REACTIONS

Reaction Rates

A rate refers to a change that occurs over a time interval. An average rate is a change that occurs over a relatively long time interval. An instantaneous rate is one that occurs over a short interval.

Chemical reaction rates may be monitored by measuring the change in concentration or pressure of a reactant or product over a time interval. Recall that the Greek letter delta, Δ, is used to represent a change. Therefore, this expression can be represented as follows.

$$\text{Reaction rate} = \frac{\Delta \text{ concentration}}{\Delta \text{ time}} \tag{14.1}$$

Problem 14.1 Consider the rate of the gas-phase reaction when nitrosyl fluoride, ONF, forms from F_2 and NO.

$$F_2(g) + 2NO(g) \longrightarrow 2ONF(g)$$

(a) Write an expression that shows the rate of formation of ONF. (b) What are the units of reaction rate? (c) Write an expression that shows the rate of disappearance of NO. (d) Write an expression that shows the relationship between the rate of formation of ONF and rate of disappearance of NO. (e) Write an expression that shows the relationship between the rates of disappearance of F_2 and NO. Explain these answers.

Solution 14.1

(a) The rate of formation of ONF is expressed as

$$\text{Reaction rate} = \frac{\Delta[ONF]}{\Delta t}$$

(b) The units most commonly encountered for reaction rates are M/s ($M\ s^{-1}$) and M/min ($M\ \text{min}^{-1}$).

(c) The rate of disappearance of NO is expressed as follows.

$$\text{Reaction rate} = -\frac{\Delta[NO]}{\Delta t}$$

(d) A comparison of the rate at which ONF forms to the rate at which NO disappears shows that they are equal.

$$-\frac{\Delta[NO]}{\Delta t} = \frac{\Delta[ONF]}{\Delta t}$$

This is true because for each one mole of NO consumed, one mole of ONF forms.

(e) The rate of disappearance of F_2 differs from the others because only one mole of F_2 is consumed for each two moles of NO. Hence, within a specific time interval half the number of moles of F_2 disappear, which means that its rate of disappearance is one-half that of the rate of disappearance of NO and rate of appearance of ONF.

$$-\text{Rate}_{F_2} = -1/2 \times \text{Rate}_{NO} = 1/2 \times \text{Rate}_{ONF}$$
$$-(\Delta[F_2]/\Delta t) = -1/2(\Delta[NO]/\Delta t) = 1/2(\Delta[ONF]/\Delta t)$$

Multiplying these rates by 2 clears the fractions, giving the following relationships.

$$-2(\Delta[F_2]/\Delta t) = -(\Delta[NO]/\Delta t) = (\Delta[ONF]/\Delta t)$$

Rate Relationships in Chemical Reactions

For the general equation

$$wA + xB \longrightarrow yC + zD$$

the rates of consumption of reactants and the rates of formation for the products are

$$-\frac{1}{w}\frac{\Delta[A]}{\Delta t} = -\frac{1}{x}\frac{\Delta[B]}{\Delta t} = \frac{1}{y}\frac{\Delta[C]}{\Delta t} = \frac{1}{z}\frac{\Delta[D]}{\Delta t} \qquad (14.2)$$

Problem 14.2 Consider the following gas-phase reaction.

$$N_2(g) + 3H_2(g) \longrightarrow 2NH_3(g)$$

(a) Use Eq. 14.2 to show the relationships between the rates of disappearance of N_2 and H_2 and the rate of appearance of NH_3. (b) Remove the fractions in the equation found in part (a), and express in terms of whole numbers.

Solution 14.2

(a) Equation 14.2 shows that to find the relationships between the rates of disappearance and rate of appearance, the reciprocal of the coefficients in the balanced equation are multiplied by their respective rate expressions.

$$-\frac{\Delta[N_2]}{\Delta t} = -\frac{1}{3}\frac{\Delta[H_2]}{\Delta t} = \frac{1}{2}\frac{\Delta[NH_3]}{\Delta t}$$

(b) To clear the fractions in the above equation, first determine the lowest common multiple and multiply the equation by this number. The lowest common multiple of 1, 1/3, and 1/2 is 6. Thus, multiplying the equation by six gives the following equation.

$$-6\frac{\Delta[N_2]}{\Delta t} = -2\frac{\Delta[H_2]}{\Delta t} = 3\frac{\Delta[NH_3]}{\Delta t}$$

Rates of Gas-Phase Reactions

The rates of gas-phase reactions may be expressed in terms of partial pressure changes, ΔP, per time interval, Δt, because the partial pressure of a gas is directly proportional to its concentration. Recall that the ideal gas equation is expressed as follows.

$$PV = nRT \tag{14.3}$$

Dividing both sides of the equation by volume, V, results in Eqn 14.3.

$$P = \frac{n}{V}RT \tag{14.4}$$

The term n/V expresses the number of moles per liter or the molarity, M. Therefore, the ideal gas equation may be expressed as follows.

$$P = MRT \tag{14.5}$$

If T is constant, then the partial pressure of a gas is directly proportional to its molarity, M.

Problem 14.3 Consider the gas-phase decomposition of dinitrogen pentoxide, N_2O_5.

$$2N_2O_5(g) \longrightarrow 4NO(g) + O_2(g)$$

Write an equation that shows the relationship between the rate of disappearance of N_2O_5 and rate of appearance of NO and O_2.

Solution 14.3 The following relationship is obtained between the rate at which N_2O_5 decomposes and the rates at which NO and O_2 form.

$$-1/2(\Delta P_{N_2O_5}/\Delta t) = 1/4(\Delta P_{NO}/\Delta t) = \Delta P_{O_2}/\Delta t$$

Problem 14.4 At a specific set of reaction conditions the rate of decomposition of $BrF_5(g)$ is -6.4×10^3 atm/s.

$$2BrF_5(g) \longrightarrow Br_2(g) + 5F_2(g)$$

Calculate the rates at which Br_2 and F_2 form.

Solution 14.4 This equation shows that the rate of appearance of Br_2 is one-half the rate of disappearance of BrF_5 because the coefficient of Br_2 is one-half that of BrF_5. Hence, to find the rate that Br_2 appears, multiply the rate of disappearance of BrF_5, -6.4×10^{-3} atm/s, by one-half.

$$\Delta P_{Br_2}/\Delta t = -1/2(\Delta P_{BrF_5}/\Delta t) = -1/2 \times (-6.4 \times 10^{-3} \text{atm/s})$$

$$= 3.2 \times 10^{-3} \text{ atm/s}$$

Considering the coefficients of F_2 and BrF_5, the relationship between the rates of F_2 and BrF_5 is expressed as follows.

$$1/5(\Delta P_{F_2}/\Delta t) = -1/2(\Delta P_{BrF_5}/\Delta t)$$

Multiplying each side of this equation by 5 gives us

$$(\Delta P_{F_2}/\Delta t) = \Delta 5/2(\Delta P_{BrF_5}/\Delta t)$$

which states that rate of formation of F_2 is $-5/2$ the rate that BrF_5 decomposes.

$$\Delta P_{F_2}/\Delta t = -5/2 \times (-6.4 \times 10^{-3} atm/s)$$
$$= 1.6 \times 10^{-3} atm/s$$

Calculating Average Reaction Rates

The average rate of a reaction is obtained over a relatively long time interval. The rate of disappearance of reactant A is expressed as follows.

Problem 14.5   (a) For the decomposition of N_2O_5 at 45°C, the initial concentration of N_2O_5 is 0.0176 M and after 600 s elapse the concentration decreases to 0.0124 M. Calculate the average rate of disappearance over this interval. (b) At 1800 s the concentration is 0.0071 M and at 2400 s it decreases to 0.0053 M. Calculate the average rate of disappearance over this interval.

Solution 14.5

(a) To calculate the average rate of disappearance over the first 600 s, divide the change in concentration, $\Delta[N_2O_5]$, by the change in time, Δt.

$$\text{Reaction rate} = \frac{-\Delta[N_2O_5]}{\Delta t} = -([N_2O_5]_{600} - [N_2O_5]_0)/(600\text{ s} - 0\text{ s})$$
$$= -(0.0124\ M - 0.0176\ M)/600\text{ s} = 8.67 \times 10^{-6}\ M/s$$

(b) $\text{Reaction rate} = -([N_2O_5]_{2400} - [N_2O_5]_{1800})/(2400\text{ s} - 1800\text{ s})$
$$= -(0.0053\ M - 0.0071\ M)/600\text{ s} = 3.0 \times 10^{-6}\ M/s$$

Problem 14.6   The following concentration-time data were collected for the decomposition of ammonia to N_2 and H_2.

$$2NH_3(g) \longrightarrow N_2(g) + 3H_2(g)$$

Time, s	[NH_3], M
0.0	1.00
1.0	0.991
2.0	0.983
3.0	0.976
4.0	0.970

(a) Calculate the average rate that NH_3 disappears over the entire 4.0-s time interval. (b) What is the average rates that N_2 and H_2 form over the first two seconds?

Solution 14.6

(a) $\text{Rate} = -\Delta[NH_3]/\Delta t$
$$= -(0.970\text{ M} - 1.00\text{ M})/(4.0\text{ s} - 0.0\text{ s}) = 7.5 \times 10^{-3}\ M/s$$

(b) The rate of formation of N_2 is one-half the rate that NH_3 disappears. The rate of formation of H_2 is 3/2 the rate of disappearance of NH_3. Thus, first calculate the rate of disappearance of NH_3 and multiply by 1/2 and 3/2 to get the rates of N_2 and H_2, respectively.

$$\text{Rate} = -\triangle[NH_3]/\triangle t$$

$$= -(0.983\ M - 1.00\ M)/(2.0\ s - 0.0\ s) = 8.5 \times 10^{-3}\ M/s$$

$$\triangle[N_2]/\triangle t = 1/2 \times 8.5 \times 10^{-3}\ M/s = 4.2 \times 10^{-3}\ M/s$$

$$\triangle[H_2]/\triangle t = 3/2 \times 8.5 \times 10^{-3}\ M/s = 1.3 \times 10^{-2}\ M/s$$

Instantaneous Rates

To find an instantaneous rate of reaction, the time interval over which the concentration change is measured must be decreased. When the time interval approaches 0 s, the instantaneous rate can be calculated. The instantaneous rate for the decomposition of reactant A is expressed in the following equation.

$$\text{Instantaneous rate} = \lim_{\triangle t \to 0} \frac{-\triangle[A]}{\triangle t} \tag{14.6}$$

Equation 14.6 states that the instantaneous rate is the limit, lim, of the average rate of disappearance of A as the time interval approaches zero. In calculus, the instantaneous rate is expressed as $d[A]/dt$, the first derivative. This instantaneous rate corresponds to the slope of the line tangent to the curve representing concentration versus time at the point of interest.

14.2   EFFECT OF CONCENTRATION CHANGES ON REACTION RATES

Rate Expressions

To obtain the dependence of concentration on reaction rate the initial *instantaneous rate* is measured for different starting concentrations. From these data, the rate expression is derived. For example, if compound A decomposes to products,

$$A \longrightarrow \text{products}$$

a rate expression with the following form can be derived.

$$\text{Instantaneous rate} = k[A]^x$$

In this rate expression, k is the rate constant, $[A]$ is the molar concentration of A, and x is the reaction order.

Reaction Orders

The exponents of the concentration terms in the rate law are termed the reaction orders. When the molar concentration of A is raised to the first power, the reaction is said to be first order with respect to A. If the molar concentration of A is raised to the second power, the reaction is said to be second order with respect to A. If a reactant is first order, when its molar concentration doubles, the initial instantaneous rate doubles. If the concentration triples, the reaction rate triples.

$$\text{Instantaneous rate} \propto [A]$$

However, if the reaction order with respect to the reactant is second order, then the reaction rate increases four times, 2^2, when the concentration doubles and increases eight times, 2^3, when the concentration triples.

$$\text{Instantaneous rate} \propto [A]^2$$

OVERALL REACTION ORDERS

For reactions that have more than one reactant, the sum of the reaction orders in the rate law equals the overall reaction order. For example, consider the following rate expression.

$$\text{Instantaneous rate} = k[A]^x[B]^y$$

The overall reaction order equals $x + y$. Thus, if $x = 1$ and $y = 2$, then the overall reaction order equals 3—third order. This means if the molar concentrations of both reactants doubles, the rate of the reaction increases eight times, 2^3.

Problem 14.7 Consider the following reaction and its rate expression.

$$H_2 + I_2 \longrightarrow 2HI \qquad \text{Initial rate} = k[H_2][I_2]$$

(a) What is the order of the reaction with respect to H_2? (b) What is the order of the reaction with respect to I_2? (c) What is the overall order for the reaction? (d) What is the effect of doubling the concentration of H_2? (e) What is the effect of doubling the concentration of I_2? (f) What is the effect of doubling both the concentrations of H_2 and I_2?

Solution 14.7
(a) It is first order with respect to H_2.
(b) It is first order with respect to I_2.
(c) It is second order overall.
(d) The initial rate doubles because the rate is proportional to $[H_2]$.
(e) The initial rate doubles because the rate is proportional to $[I_2]$.
(f) The initial rate quadruples because the overall order is second.

Problem 14.8 The rate constant for the first-order decomposition of substance A to products is 9.22×10^3 s^1. (a) Write the rate law for this reaction. (b) What is the initial rate of decomposition starting with 0.100 M A? (c) At what concentration of A is the initial rate of the reaction 5.12×10^4 M/s?

Solution 14.8
(a) Rate $= k[A]$
(b) Rate $= 9.22 \times 10^{-3}\text{s}^{-1} \times 0.100\ M$
$= 9.22 \times 10^{-4}\ M\text{s}^{-1}$
(c) $5.12 \times 10^4\ M/s = 9.22 \times 10^3\text{s}^{-1} \times [A]$
$[A] = 5.55 \times 10^{-2}\ M$

Zero and Fractional Reaction Orders

Reaction orders are often integers but may be zero or fractional. The rate of a zero-order reaction is independent of the reactant concentration, which means that the rate remains unchanged as the reactant concentration decreases.

Problem 14.9 Consider the decomposition of acetaldehyde, CH_3CHO:

$$CH_3CHO \longrightarrow CH_4 + CO$$

The rate expression for this reaction is as follows.

$$\text{Initial rate} = k[CH_3CHO]^{1.5}$$

(a) What effect does doubling the concentration of acetaldehyde have on the initial rate?
(b) What effect does halving the concentration have on the reaction rate?

Solution 14.9

(a) If the order with respect to a reactant such as acetaldehyde is 1.5, this means that if the reactant concentration doubles, then the rate increases by $2^{1.5}$ or 2.83 times.
(b) The initial rate becomes 0.35 $(0.5^{1.5})$ times as fast.

Calculating Reaction Orders

Reaction orders can only be calculated from experimental data in which the initial instantaneous rate is measured at different initial concentrations.

Problem 14.10   At 50°C, the gas-phase reaction of $NO(g)$ and $Cl_2(g)$ produces nitrosyl chloride, $NOCl(g)$.

$$Cl_2(g) + 2NO(g) \longrightarrow 2NOCl(g)$$

The following rate-concentration data were collected.

Experiment	$[NO]_{initial}$	$[Cl_2]_{initial}$	Initial Rate, M/s
1	0.175	0.245	6.87×10^{-7}
2	0.175	0.490	1.37×10^{-6}
3	0.175	0.980	2.75×10^{-6}
4	0.264	0.115	7.33×10^{-7}
5	0.520	0.115	2.93×10^{-6}
6	1.06	0.115	1.18×10^{-5}

(a) Compare the data from Experiments 1 and 2, and Experiments 1 and 3 to determine the reaction order with respect to Cl_2. (b) Compare the data from Experiments 4 and 5, and Experiments 4 and 6 to determine the reaction order with respect to NO. (c) Write the rate expression for this reaction. (d) Calculate the value for the rate constant, k.

Solution 14.10

(a) Experiments 1 and 2 show that if the concentration of Cl_2 doubles from 0.245 M to 0.490 M and the concentration of the NO remains constant (0.175 M), the initial instantaneous rate of reaction doubles. Experiments 1 and 3, also show that the concentration of NO is constant but the concentration of Cl_2 quadruples (from 0.245 M to 0.980 M). This time the reaction rate quadruples. Accordingly, the initial rate of the reaction is related directly to the molar concentration of Cl_2, $[Cl_2]$, raised to the first power.
(b) Comparison of experiments 4 and 5 shows that when the Cl_2 concentration remains constant and the NO concentration doubles the rate of the reaction quadruples, increasing from 7.33 $\times 10^{-7}$ M/s to 2.93 $\times 10^{-6}$ M/s. A fourfold increase in the reaction rate means that it must have increased 22 or 4 times. If the concentration of NO quadruples as in experiments 4 and 6, the reaction rate increases 16 times (4^2), and if the concentration of NO halves as in experiments 4 and 7, the reaction rate decreases by $1/4$ $(1/2^2)$. Thus, the initial instantaneous rate is directly related to the molar concentration of NO raised to the second power, $[NO]^2$.
(c) Initial rate = $k[Cl_2][NO]^2$

(d) Data from experiment 1 show that the rate constant, k, equals $9.16 \times 10^{-5} \ M^{-2}s^{-1}$ $(1/(M^{-2}s)$ at 50°C.

$$\text{Initial rate} = k[Cl_2][NO]^2$$
$$k = \text{Initial rate}/([Cl_2][NO]^2)$$
$$= 6.87 \times 10^{-7} M/s/(0.245M \times 0.175^2 M^2) = 9.16 \times 10^{-5} M^{-2}s^{-1}$$

Problem 14.11   For the reaction

$$2NO(g) + 2H_2(g) \longrightarrow N_2(g) + 2H_2O(g)$$

the following rate data were collected at 900°C.

Experiment	[NO]	[H₂]	Initial rate, M/s
1	0.388	0.214	0.204
2	0.388	0.428	0.407
3	0.259	0.115	0.0488
4	0.777	0.115	0.439

(a) Determine the rate law for the reaction. (b) Calculate the rate constant, k. (c) Calculate the rate of the reaction when the initial concentrations are 0.199 M NO and 0.266 M H₂.

Solution 14.11

(a) The rate law is calculated directly by finding the ratio of the rates from two different experiments in which one of the reactant concentration terms cancels. To begin, let's take the ratio of experiment 2 to experiment 1.

$$\frac{Rate(Exp2)}{Rate(Exp1)} = \frac{k[NO]_2^x[H_2]_2^y}{k[NO]_1^x[H_2]_1^y}$$

The rate constants and concentrations of NO are equal. Hence, the

$$\frac{Rate(Exp2)}{Rate(Exp1)} = \frac{[H_2]_2^y}{[H_2]_1^y} = \left(\frac{[H_2]_2}{[H_2]_1}\right)^y$$

Substituting the known values into the equation gives the following.

$$\frac{0.407 \ M/s}{0.204 \ M/s} = \left(\frac{0.428 \ M}{0.214 \ M}\right)^y$$
$$2.00 = 2.00^y$$
$$y = 1$$

The value of y, the reaction order for H₂, is 1. In other words it is first order with respect to H₂. To calculate the reaction order for NO, data from experiments 3 and 4 are used similarly.

$$\frac{0.439 \ M/s}{0.0488 \ M/s} = \left(\frac{0.777M}{0.259 \ M}\right)^x$$
$$9.00 = 3.00^x$$
$$x = 2$$

The reaction order for NO is 2—a second-order reaction. Accordingly, the rate law for the reaction is

$$\text{Rate} = k[NO]^2[H_2]$$

(b) Rearrange the equation to solve for k and then substitute values from one of the experiments (experiment 1 in this case).

$$\text{Rate} = k[NO]^2[H_2]$$
$$k = \text{Rate}/([NO]^2[H_2])$$
$$= 0.204 \ M/s/((0.388 \ M)^2 \times 0.214 \ M) = 6.33 \ M^2 s^1$$

(c) Substitute the given values, 0.199 M NO and 0.266 M H_2, into the equation.

$$\text{Rate} = k[NO]^2[H_2]$$
$$= 6.33 \ M^2 s^1 \times (0.199 \ M)^2 \times 0.266 \ M = 0.0667 \ M/s$$

14.3   CONCENTRATION AND TIME RELATIONSHIPS

Zero-Order Reactions

Consider the zero-order reaction when A decomposes to products. The rate equation of a zero order reaction has the following general form.

$$\text{rate} = k[A]^0$$

Because $[A]^0$ equals one, the rate equation becomes rate = k. Thus, in zero-order reactions the rate of reaction is independent of the concentration of the reactant. The instantaneous rate of a zero-order reaction can be expressed as follows.

$$-d[A]/dt = k$$

This equation can be converted to the following more useful equation by using calculus

$$[A] = -kt + [A]_0 \tag{14.7}$$

Equation 14.7 shows that a linear relationship exists between time and the concentration of A. The slope of this line is $-k$ and the y intercept is $[A]_0$

First-Order Reactions— Concentration- Time Relationship

If reactant A undergoes a first-order decomposition to products ($A \longrightarrow$ products), then the instantaneous rate is expressed as follows

$$\text{Rate} = -d[A]/dt$$

and the rate law as

$$\text{Rate} = k[A]$$

thus

$$\text{Rate} = -d[A]/dt = k[A]$$

The following relationship is obtained for first-order reactions by using calculus

$$\ln \frac{[A]_0}{[A]_t} = kt \tag{14.8}$$

In Eq. 14.8 ln is the natural logarithm ($\log_e$), $[A]_0$ is the initial concentration of A, $[A]_t$ is the concentration of A at time t, and k is the rate constant with a reciprocal time unit such as s^{-1}. Alternatively, this equation may be expressed in terms of a common logarithm instead of a natural logarithm.

$$\log \frac{[A]_0}{[A]_t} = \frac{kt}{2.303} \tag{14.9}$$

Problem 14.12   The decomposition of acetone, CH_3COCH_3, at 600°C to CO and several C—H compounds follow first-order kinetics. A rate study reveals that it takes 12.3 s for the concentration of acetone to decrease from 0.100 M to 0.0900 M. (a) Calculate the rate constant for the reaction. (b) How long does it take for the initial concentration of 0.100 M acetone to decrease to 10.0% of this value? (c) What concentration of acetone remains if initially 0.230 M decomposes for 175 s?

Solution 14.12   Calculate the first-order rate constant, by using the following rate equation.

$$\ln([CH_3COCH_3]_0/[CH_3COCH_3]_t) = kt$$

Substitute the known values into the equation and solve for k

$$\ln(0.100\ M/0.0900\ M) = k \times 12.3\ s$$
$$\ln 1.11 = 12.3k$$
$$k = 8.57 \times 10^{-3}\ s^{-1}$$

(a) Because the initial concentration is 0.100 M, 10.0% of this value is 0.0100 M. Thus, substitute 0.100 M for the initial concentration and 0.0100 M for the final concentration into the first-order rate equation.

$$\ln([CH_3COCH_3]_0/[CH_3COCH_3]_t) = kt$$
$$\ln(0.100\ M/0.0100M) = 8.57 \times 10^{-3}s^{-1}t$$
$$t = 269\ s$$

(b) Once again substitute the known values into the first-order rate equation and solve for the acetone concentration at 175 s.

$$\ln([CH_3COCH_3]_0/[CH_3COCH_3]_t) = kt$$
$$\ln(0.230M/[CH_3COCH_3]_{175}) = 8.57 \times 10^{-3}s^{-1} \times 175\ s$$
$$= 1.50$$

To solve the equation from this point, take the natural antilogarithm of both sides of the equation; this gives

$$0.230\ M/[CH_3COCH_3]_{175} = e^{1.50} = 4.48$$
$$[CH_3COCH_3]_{175} = 5.13 \times 10^{-2}\ M$$

FIRST-ORDER—GRAPHICAL DISPLAY OF CONCENTRATION-TIME DATA

Figure 14.1a shows a plot of concentration versus time for the first-order decomposition of sulfuryl chloride, SO_2Cl_2, to SO_2 and Cl_2.

$$SO_2Cl_2 \longrightarrow SO_2 + Cl_2$$

The graph shows a nonlinear relationship between $[SO_2Cl_2]$ and time. As the reaction proceeds the rate of disappearance of SO_2Cl_2 decreases and begins to level off. Another way to display the data is to plot $\ln[SO_2Cl_2]$ versus time. Figure 14.1b reveals that such a plot is a straight line (a linear relationship). To understand why a linear relationship exists between the $\ln[SO_2Cl_2]$ and time, let's consider the following equation:

$$\ln([SO_2Cl_2]_0/[SO_2Cl_2]_t) = kt$$

Because the natural logarithm, ln, of a ratio such as $\ln(x/y)$ equals $\ln x - \ln y$, the equation may be rewritten as follows.

$$\ln[SO_2Cl_2]_0 - \ln[SO_2Cl_2]_t = kt$$

Rearrangement of the equation allows us to express it in the general form of a linear equation.

$$\ln[SO_2Cl_2]_t = -kt + \ln[SO_2Cl_2]_0$$

Recall that a linear equation has the general form of $y = mx + b$ in which x is the independent variable, y is the dependent variable, m is the slope, and b is the y intercept. In our equation t is the independent variable, $\ln[SO_2Cl_2]_t$ is the dependent variable, $-k$ is the slope, and $\ln[SO_2Cl_2]_0$ is the y intercept. This relationship is used to determine if a reaction follows first- order kinetics. After concentration-time data for the reaction of interest are collected, a plot is made of the natural logarithm of the reactant concentration versus time. If a linear relationship is found, then the reaction follows first-order kinetics. By measuring the slope of the line, the rate constant (2.2×10^{-5} s^{-1}) can be determined.

Problem 14.13   Consider the following data collected when the decomposition of trichloroacetic acid, CCl_3COOH, to CO_2 and $CHCl_3$ was studied.

$$CCl_3COOH \longrightarrow CO_2 + CHCl_3$$

Time, hr	$[CCl_3COOH]$
0.0	0.100 M
5.0	0.0735 M
10.0	0.0540 M
15.0	0.0397 M

Determine if this reaction follows zero or first-order kinetics.

Solution 14.13   To determine if this reaction follows zero or first-order kinetics, plot two graphs. One should be the concentration of trichloroacetic acid versus time, and the other should be the natural log of the concentration versus time. The one that gives a linear plot is the correct order. Begin by calculating the natural logarithms of the concentrations.

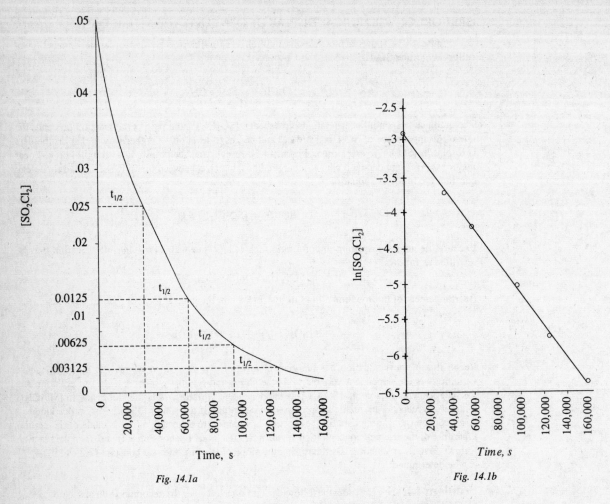

Fig. 14.1a   Fig. 14.1b

Time, hr	[CCl₃COOH]	ln[CCl₃COOH]
0	0.100	−2.303
5.0	0.0735	−2.610
10.0	0.0540	−2.919
15.0	0.0397	−3.226

Figure 14.2 shows both plots. Because the plot of ln[CCl₃COOH] is linear, this reaction is first order.

First-Order Half-Life

The half-life of a reaction is the time that elapses when one-half of the reactant molecules change to products. For example, if a reaction has a half-life of 10 min, it means that after 10 min, the initial concentration decreases by one-half. After 20 min, two-half lives, the concentration decreases to one-fourth. The equation for the first-order kinetics can be modified so the half-life, $t_{1/2}$, of a reaction can be found.

$$t_{1/2} = \frac{0.693}{k}$$

(14.10)

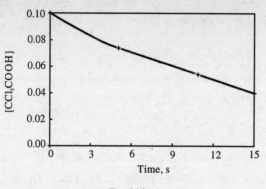

Fig. 14.2a

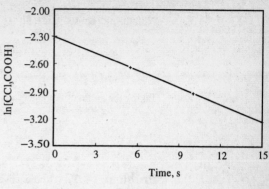

Fig. 14.2b

Problem 14.14 The rate constant for a reaction is 0.0111 s^{-1}. What is the half- life, $t_{1/2}$, for this reaction?

Solution 14.14 Use Eq. 14.10 to calculate the half-life, $t_{1/2}$.

$$t_{1/2} = 0.693/k = 0.693/0.0111 \text{ s}^{-1} = 62.4 \text{ s}$$

Problem 14.15 A reaction takes 4.84 min to be 10.0% complete. Calculate the half-life of the reaction.

Solution 14.15 Starting with 100 concentration units, the reaction decreases to 90.0 units when it is 10.0% complete.

$$\ln([A]_0/[A]) = kt$$
$$\ln(100/90.0) = k \times 4.84 \text{ min}$$
$$k = 0.0218 \text{ min}^{-1}$$
$$t_{1/2} = 0.693/k = 31.8 \text{ min}$$

Problem 14.16 Dichlorine heptoxide, Cl_2O_7, undergoes a gas-phase first-order decomposition to Cl_2 and O_2 at 127°C. If the half-life of this reaction is 112 s, calculate the pressure of Cl_2O_7 after 285 s when the initial pressure of Cl_2O_7 is 0.0553 atm.

Solution 14.16 The unit of concentration in this problem is the atm. The partial pressure of a gas in a reaction is directly related to its concentration. Knowing the half-life for the reaction, use Eq. 14.9 to calculate the rate constant.

$$t_{1/2} = 0.693/k$$
$$k = 0.693/t_{1/2} = 0.693/112 \text{ s} = 6.19 \times 10^{-3} \text{s}^{-1}$$

With the rate constant, use Eq. 14.8 to calculate the pressure at 285 s.

$$\ln(P_0/P_{285}) = kt$$
$$\ln(0.0553 \text{ atm}/P_{285}) = 6.19 \times 10^{-3} \text{ s}^{-1} \times 285 \text{ s} = 1.76$$

Taking the antiln of both sides gives the following.

$$0.0553 \text{ atm}/P_{285} = e^{1.76} = 5.8$$
$$P_{285} = 9.5 \times 10^{-3} \text{ atm}$$

Problem 14.17   Radioactive substances follow first-order kinetics as they decay. The rate of decay is related to the mass or number of atoms present. ^{18}F has a half-life of 109.7 s. (a) How long would it take for the mass of ^{18}F to decay from 10.0 g to 0.100 g? (b) How long would it take for 99.9% of the ^{18}F atoms in the sample to decay?

Solution 14.17
(a) First calculate the rate constant.

$$t_{1/2} = k/0.6931$$
$$k = 0.6931/t_{1/2} = 0.6931/109.7 \text{ s} = 0.006319 \text{ s}^{-1}$$

Then, use the first-order equation, Eq. 14.8, to calculate the amount of time.

$$\ln([^{18}F]_0/[^{18}F]) = kt$$
$$\ln(10.0g/0.100g) = 0.006319 \text{ s}^{-1} \times t$$
$$t = 729 \text{ s}$$

(b) For each 1000 ^{18}F atoms that decay, only 1 ^{18}F remains after 99.9% decay; thus, the amount of time can be calculated as follows.

$$\ln([^{18}F]_0/[^{18}F]) = kt$$
$$\ln(1000/1) = 0.006319 \text{ s}^{-1} \times t$$
$$t = 1093 \text{ s}$$

Second-Order Reactions

Only second-order reactions in which a single reactant decomposes to products will be considered because those that involve two reactants are more complex. The rate law for the equation is

$$\text{Rate} = -\Delta[A]/\Delta t = k[A]^2 \qquad (14.11)$$

Once again using calculus, the relationship between concentration and time is obtained.

$$\frac{1}{[A]_t} = kt + \frac{1}{[A]_0} \qquad (14.12)$$

The form of this equation is that of a linear relationship between $1/[A]_t$ and t, in which k is the second-order rate constant with the units of $M^{-1}s^{-1}$ (L/(mol· s)), and $1/[A]_0$ is the y-intercept

$$1/[A]_t = kt + 1/[A]_0$$
$$y = mx + b$$

Problem 14.18 (a) From Eq. 14.12, derive the half-life equation for a second-order reaction. (b) Compare the second-order half-life equation to that of the first order half-life equation.

Solution 14.18

(a)
$$1/[A]_t = kt + 1/[A]_0$$
$$[A]_t = 1/2[A]_0 \text{ when } t = t_{1/2}$$
$$1/(1/2[A]_0) = kt_{1/2} + 1/[A]_0$$
$$2/[A]_0 - 1/[A]_0 = kt_{1/2}$$
$$1/[A]_0 = kt_{1/2}$$
$$t_{1/2} = 1/(k[A]_0)$$

(b) In this equation, unlike first-order reactions, the half-life of a second-order reaction depends on the initial concentration of the reactant, $[A]_0$. Therefore, the half-lives of second-order reactions are less useful than those of first-order reactions. The second-order rate constant can be calculated only if the initial concentration of the reactant is known.

Problem 14.19 The decomposition of $NO(g)$ to $N_2(g)$ and $O_2(g)$ follows second-order kinetics. Over a 1500 s time interval, the concentration of $NO(g)$ decreases from 0.0050 M to 0.0044 M. What is the second-order rate constant for this reaction?

Solution 14.19 The rate constant can be calculated from Eq. 14.12.

$$\frac{1}{[NO]_t} = kt + \frac{1}{[NO]_0}$$

Therefore, the known values for the concentrations and time should be substituted into the Eq. 14.12 and solved for k. The initial concentration of NO, $[NO]_0$ is 0.0050 M, the final concentration is 0.0044 M, and the time is 1500 s.

$$1/0.0044 \, M = 1/0.0050 \, M + k \times 1500s$$
$$1500 \, k = 1/0.0044 - 1/0.0050$$
$$= 27.3$$
$$k = 0.018 M^{-1}s^{-1}$$

Problem 14.20 Consider the following data for the decomposition of dimethylether, $(CH_3)_2O$, to CH_4, CO, and H_2.

Time, s	$P_{(CH_3)_2O}$, atm
0	0.411
390	0.347
777	0.295
1195	0.246

(a) Use these data to determine if the reaction proceeds by first-order or second-order kinetics. (b) What is the rate constant for the reaction?

Solution 14.20 Construct a table that contains $\ln P$ and $1/P$ and plot both versus time to determine which gives a linear plot.

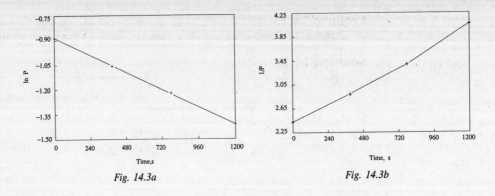

Fig. 14.3a   Fig. 14.3b

Time, s	$P_{(CH_3)_2O}$, atm	$\ln P_{(CH_3)_2O}$	$1/P_{(CH_3)_2O}$
0	0.411	−0.889	2.43
390	0.347	−1.058	2.88
777	0.295	−1.221	3.39
1195	0.246	−1.402	4.07

Figure 14.3a shows that the plot of $\ln P_{(CH_3)_2O}$ is linear; thus, the reaction is first order with respect to dimethylether.
(b) The slope of the $\ln P_{(CH_3)_2O}$ versus time plot shows that the rate constant for the reaction is $4.30 \times 10^{-4}\ s^{-1}$.

14.4   COLLISION AND TRANSITION STATE THEORIES

Collision Theory and Effective Collisions

The Collision Theory explains the rates of reactions in terms of collisions that occur among the reacting molecules. According to Collision Theory, a reaction rate is proportional to the number of collisions per second between the reacting molecules and the fraction of effective collisions—the ones in which products result.

Effective Collisions and Activation Energy, E_a

Most reactions occur at much slower rates than the diffusion-controlled reactions because other factors influence the collision of reactant particles. In these reactions, the mere collision of the reactant particles does not necessarily result in the formation of the products. An effective collision, one that yields the products, requires that the colliding particles have the proper orientation and a collision energy equal to or greater than the activation energy, E_a. The activation energy is the minimum energy that reactant particles must have in order to produce the products. The value of the E_a for a reaction depends on the characteristics of the reacting molecules.

ACTIVATED COMPLEX

The activated complex is a high-energy transient species composed of colliding molecules in which their reactant bonds are partially broken and the product bonds are partially formed. The activated complex can break apart as either the products or the reactants. Activated complexes are always written in brackets to show that they cannot be isolated.

Problem 14.21 Consider the gas-phase reaction of $NO_2(g)$ and $CO(g)$ to produce $NO(g)$ and $CO_2(g)$ at 250°C:

$$NO_2(g) + CO(g) \longrightarrow NO(g) + CO_2(g)$$

(a) What type of effective collision must occur for this reaction to take place? (b) Discuss the nature and structure of the activated complex in this reaction.

Solution 14.21

(a) In this reaction the NO_2 molecule must collide with the CO molecule so that a N–O bond breaks and a C–O bond forms. Effective collisions may occur when an O atom from NO_2 comes close to the C atom in CO–all other collisions are ineffective.

(b) The colliding reactant molecules must have sufficient energy to overcome the electrostatic repulsive forces between the molecules to initiate the reaction. When this occurs, the N–O bond partially breaks and the C–O bond partially forms before the products form. The resulting unstable combination of the reacting molecules is the activated complex.

$$O = N\text{—}O + C \equiv O \longrightarrow [O = N \cdots O \cdot \cdot C \stackrel{=}{\equiv} O]$$
$$\text{activated complex}$$

Transition State Theory

Transition state theory explains the rates of reactions in terms of the factors that influence the formation and stability of activated complexes. Factors that tend to lower the energy of activated complexes (those that stabilize them) tend to increase the reaction rate, and factors that raise the energy of activated complexes (those that destabilize them) tend to decrease the reaction rate.

Energy Diagrams and Activation Energy

Activation energy, E_a, is the minimum energy required to produce the activated complex. In other words, the energy needed to reach the transition state. To show activation energies and the energy pathways followed by a reaction, consider the energy diagrams such as those in Figure 14.4. Figure 14.4 shows the reaction pathway for an exothermic reaction, one that releases energy to the surroundings. At the beginning of the reaction the reactants A and B have a fixed total energy (potential and kinetic). As they approach each other, the potential energy increases because the repulsive forces among the molecules increase due to the interactions of the outer electrons. This means that the kinetic energy of the molecules must decrease because energy is conserved (the law of conservation of energy). Only molecules with sufficient kinetic energy have enough total energy to reach the peak of the curve, the transition state.

14.5   REACTION RATES AND TEMPERATURE CHANGES

The Arrhenius Equation gives the relationship between the activation energy, E_a, temperature, T, and the rate constant, k. One way to express the Arrhenius Equation is as follows

$$\ln k = \frac{-E_a}{RT} + \ln A \qquad (14.13)$$

in which ln is the natural logarithm, k is the rate constant, E_a is the activation energy, R is the ideal gas constant 8.314 J/(mol· K), T is the Kelvin temperature, and A is the frequency factor. The value of the frequency factor corresponds to the number of collisions that have the correct orientation to

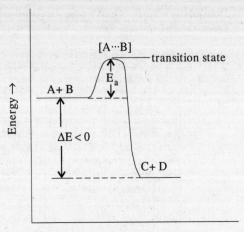

Reaction Coordinate

(a) Forward reaction A + B → C + D

Fig. 14.4

yield the products. This form of the Arrhenius Equation shows the linear relationship between $\ln k$ and $1/T$ in which $-E_a/R$ is the slope and $\ln A$ is the y intercept.

$$\ln k = -\frac{E_a}{R} \times \frac{1}{T} + \ln A$$
$$y = \quad mx \quad + \quad b$$

Thus, if $\ln k$ versus $1/T$ is plotted, a straight line is obtained with a negative slope.

A more useful form of the Arrhenius Equation can be derived in terms of the rate constants at two different temperatures. If the reaction has rate constants of k_1 at T_1 and k_2 at T_2, then the following equation is obtained.

$$\ln\left(\frac{k_2}{k_1}\right) = \frac{E_a}{R}\left(\frac{T_2 - T_1}{T_1 T_2}\right) \tag{14.14}$$

Problem 14.22   Consider the following gas-phase reaction.

$$NO(g) + Cl_2(g) \longrightarrow NOCl(g) + Cl(g)$$

The rate constant for this reaction is $32.5\ M^{-1}s^{-1}$ at 550.0 K and is $45.2\ M^{-1}s^{-1}$ at 560.0 K. Calculate the activation energy, E_a, in kJ/mol for the reaction.

Solution 14.22   Substitute the known values into Eqn 14.14 to find the E_a.

$$\ln\left(\frac{k_2}{k_1}\right) = \frac{E_a}{R}\left(\frac{T_2 - T_1}{T_1 T_2}\right)$$

$$\ln(45.2\ M^{-1}\ s^{-1}/32.5\ M^{-1}\ s^{-1}) = E_a/8.314\,J/(mol \cdot K) \times ((560.0\ K - 550.0\ K)/550.0\ K \cdot 560.0\ K)$$

$$0.330 = E_a \times 3.91 \times 10^{-6}\ mol/J$$

$$E_a = 8.45 \times 10^4\ J/mol \times s\ 1\ kJ/1000\ J$$

$$= 84.5\ kJ/mol$$

Problem 14.23 What is the activation energy in kJ for a reaction in which the rate of the reaction doubles when the temperature is increased from 25°C to 35°C?

Solution 14.23 When the rate of the reaction doubles, k_2 equals $2k_1$. Thus, substitute these values into Eq. 14.4 along with the Kelvin temperatures.

$$\ln\left(\frac{k_2}{k_1}\right) = \frac{E_a}{R}\left(\frac{T_2 - T_1}{T_1 T_2}\right)$$

$$\ln(2k_1/k_1) = E_a/8.314\text{J}/(\text{mol} \cdot \text{K}) \times ((308 \text{ K} - 298 \text{ K})/308 \text{ K} \cdot 298 \text{ K})$$

$$\ln 2 = E_a \times 1.31 \times 10^{-5}$$

$$E_a = 5.29 \times 10^4 \text{ J} \times 1 \text{ kJ}/1000 \text{ J} = 52.9 \text{ kJ}$$

14.6   REACTION MECHANISMS

What Are Reaction Mechanisms?

A reaction mechanism is a description of the series of steps that occur as the reactants change to products. Reaction mechanisms describe how reactions occur—they account for the bonds that break and form, and describe the characteristics of the activated complexes. The individual steps in a reaction mechanism are called elementary reactions. They always occur as written and are the simplest steps in the reaction. The addition of the elementary reactions gives the overall reaction and eliminates the reaction intermediates, those chemical species produced and consumed in the reaction mechanism.

Problem 14.24 The proposed mechanism for the conversion of ozone, $O_3(g)$ to $O_2(g)$ is as follows.

$$O_3(g) \rightleftharpoons O_2(g) + O(g)$$

$$O(g) + O_3(g) \rightarrow 2O_2(g)$$

(a) What is the overall reaction? (b) What are the reaction intermediates? (c) Explain what happens in this mechanism.

Solution 14.24

(a) The addition of the two elementary reactions gives the overall equation.

$$O_3 \rightleftharpoons O_2 + O$$
$$\underline{+ O + O_3 \rightarrow 2O_2}$$
$$2O_3 \rightarrow 3O_2$$

(b) Adding the elementary reactions eliminates the reaction intermediate, the reactive O atom, in this reaction.

(c) In the first step of this mechanism, an O–O bond in O_3 breaks to yield O_2 and an O atom. In the second step, the reactive O atom forms a bond with an O atom in O_3 at the same time an O–O bond breaks; thus producing two molecules of O_2.

Molecularity

The number of reactant particles that produce the activated complex in an elementary reaction is called its molecularity. If a single molecule or ion produces one or more molecules in the elementary reaction, which means the activated complex consists of only one particle, then the molecularity is unimolecular. A bimolecular step occurs when two particles combine to produce the activated complex.

Reaction Mechanisms and Rate Expressions

Consider the proposed reaction mechanism of NO_2 and CO to produce CO_2 and NO.

$$NO_2(g) + CO(g) \xrightarrow{k} CO_2(g) + NO(g)$$

Experimentally, the overall rate law for the reaction above 225°C is

$$\text{Rate} = k[NO_2][CO]$$

It is first-order with respect to both reactants and second-order overall. The accepted mechanism for this reaction is a single one-step bimolecular elementary reaction. Note that the overall reaction order for one-step mechanisms equals its molecularity.

If the same reaction occurs below 225°C, the experimentally determined rate expression is second order with respect to NO_2.

$$\text{Rate} = k_1[NO_2]_2 = k_1[NO_2][NO_2]$$

Because the reaction has a different rate expression below 225°C, it goes through a different mechanism. The accepted mechanism has two elementary reactions and proceeds as follows.

$$NO_2 + NO_2 \xrightarrow{k_1} NO_3 + NO \quad \text{(slow)}$$
$$NO_3 + CO \xrightarrow{k_2} NO_2 + CO_2 \quad \text{(fast)}$$

Note that adding these elementary reactions gives the overall equation. The first step proceeds at a significantly slower rate than the second one. The slowest step of a reaction mechanism is termed the rate-determining or rate-limiting step because the overall formation of the products depends on this step. The experimentally determined rate law for this reaction (Rate = $k_1[NO_2]_2$) is the rate law for the rate-determining step. Usually, if the rate-determining step is the first one in the mechanism, then it determines the rate for the entire mechanism. The faster steps generally have no effect on the overall rate.

Problem 14.25 Consider the reaction mechanism of the aqueous acidic oxidation of I^- to I_3^- by hydrogen peroxide, H_2O_2.

$$2H^+(aq) + 3I^-(aq) + H_2O_2(aq) \longrightarrow I_3^-(aq) + 2H_2O(l)$$

Experimentally, the rate law for the reaction is Rate = $k[H_2O_2][I^-]$. The generally accepted mechanism shows that the rate-determining step occurs first.

$$H_2O_2 + I^- \rightarrow H_2O + IO^- \quad \text{(slow)}$$
$$IO^- + H^+ \rightleftharpoons HOI \quad \text{(fast)}$$
$$HOI + H^+ + I^- \rightleftharpoons H_2O + I_2 \quad \text{(fast)}$$
$$I^- + I_2 \rightleftharpoons I_3^- \quad \text{(fast)}$$

(a) What is the rate-limiting step? (b) What are the reaction intermediates and what effect do they have on the rate of this reaction? Explain.

Solution 14.25

(a) The rate-limiting step is a bimolecular elementary reaction between H_2O_2 and I^-.

(b) The concentrations of H^+ and the reaction intermediates such as HOI and I_2 have no effect on the overall reaction rate. The steps that come after the rate-limiting step generally do not affect the overall rate of the reaction. In this mechanism the last three steps are reversible and each equilibrium establishes rapidly.

Problem 14.26   Consider the combination of $H_2(g)$ and $Br_2(g)$ to produce $HBr(g)$.

$$H_2(g) + Br_2(g) \longrightarrow 2HBr(g)$$

The rate law for this complex reaction is Rate $= k[Br_2]^{0.5}[H_2]$. The proposed mechanism for this gas-phase reaction is as follows.

$$Br_2 \underset{k_1}{\overset{k_1}{\rightleftharpoons}} 2Br \quad \text{(fast)}$$

$$Br + H_2 \rightarrow HBr + H \quad \text{(slow)}$$

$$H + Br_2 \rightarrow HBr + Br \quad \text{(fast)}$$

(a) What is the rate-limiting step? (b) What is the rate law for the rate-limiting step? (c) Derive the rate expression for this reaction in terms of the reactants.

Solution 14.26

(a) The second step is the rate limiting because it is slowest.

(b) The rate law for rate-limiting step is as follows.

$$\text{Rate} = k_2[Br][H_2]$$

(c) This rate law has the molar concentration of Br, [Br], a reaction intermediate. Intermediates are usually in very low concentration, and their concentrations are often difficult to measure. Consequently, [Br] must be eliminated from the rate law. This is accomplished by expressing the rate law in terms of the reactants. The first elementary step in the mechanism is an equilibrium that is established rapidly. The rate of the forward reaction (Rate_f) of a chemical equilibrium equals the rate of the reverse reaction (Rate_r). Thus, their rate expressions may be equated as follows.

$$\text{Rate}_f = k_1[Br_2]$$

$$\text{Rate}_r = k_1[Br]^2$$

$$k_1[Br_2] = k_1[Br]^2$$

Solving this equation for the concentration of Br, [Br], gives the following equation.

$$[Br] = (k_1/k_1[Br_2])^{0.5}$$

Substituting this equation into the rate law for step 2 yields the following.

$$\text{Rate} = (k_1/k_1[Br_2])^{0.5}k_2[H_2]$$

Next, the three constants are combined to obtain the constant k which equals $(k_1k_1)^{0.5}k_2$.

The rate law then becomes that which is obtained experimentally.

$$\text{Rate} = k[Br_2]^{0.5}[H_2]$$

Problem 14.27   The following is the proposed mechanism for the reaction of NO and Br_2 to produce NOBr.

$$NO(g) + Br_2(g) \underset{k_{-1}}{\overset{k_1}{\rightleftharpoons}} NOBr_2(g) \quad \text{(fast)}$$

$$NOBr_2(g) + NO(g) \overset{k_2}{\rightarrow} 2NOBr(g) \quad \text{(slow)}$$

(a) What is the overall reaction? (b) Show that this mechanism is consistent with the experimentally determined rate law, Rate = $k[NO]^2[Br_2]$.

Solution 14.27

(a) The overall reaction is the sum of the elementary reactions.

$$NO(g) + Br_2(g) \rightleftharpoons NOBr_2(g)$$
$$+ NOBr_2(g) + NO(g) \rightarrow 2NOBr(g)$$

$$\overline{2NO(g) + Br_2(g) \rightarrow 2NOBr(g)}$$

The only reaction intermediate, $NOBr_2$, cancels leaving the overall equation.

(b) The second step is the rate-limiting step; consequently, its rate law is

$$\text{Rate} = k_2[NOBr_2][NO]$$

This expression contains the molar concentration of the intermediate $NOBr_2$. Therefore, it should be removed so that the rate law can be expressed in terms of the reacting molecules. Because the first step goes rapidly to equilibrium, the rates of the forward and reverse reactions may be equated as follows.

$$k_1[NO][Br_2] = k_{-1}[NOBr_2]$$

Then the equation is solved for the concentration of $NOBr_2$, $[NOBr_2]$.

$$[NOBr_2] = k_1/k_{-1}[NO][Br_2]$$

Substituting this expression into the rate equation for step 2 yields the following equation.

$$\text{Rate} = k_2(k_1/k_{-1}[NO][Br_2])[NO]$$

If k equals $k_1 k_2/k_{-1}$, then the equation becomes

$$\text{Rate} = k[NO]_2[Br_2]$$

which is the experimentally-observed equation.

SUMMARY

C*hemical kinetics is the study of the rates of chemical reactions and the underlying mechanisms by which reactants change to products.*

The rates of reactions are determined by measuring the change in concentration of reactants or products over a time interval. If the concentration change is measured over a relatively long time interval, the average reaction rate is obtained. If the concentration is measured over a very short interval, the instantaneous reaction rate is obtained.

To study the effect of reactant concentration on reaction rates, the initial instantaneous rates at different concentrations are measured. From such data the rate law for a reaction is determined. The rate law is an equation that gives the initial instantaneous reaction rate in terms of the concentrations of the reactants raised to a power. In addition, a rate law has the rate constant which is characteristic of a reaction at a constant temperature. The general form for the rate law is

$$Rate = k[A]^x[B]^y$$

The relationship of time versus concentration for a first-order reaction is

$$\ln[A]_0/[A]_t = kt$$

This equation may be rearranged and expressed as a linear relationship between the $\ln[A]_t$ and time in which k is the slope and $\ln[A]_0$ is the y intercept. It is convenient to measure the half-lives for reactions. The half-life is the time for one-half of the reactant molecules to change to products. For first-order reactions, the half-life is calculated from the following equation. $t_{1/2} = 0.693/k$.

Collision Theory attempts to explain the rates of reactions in terms of collisions among the reacting molecules. The rate of a reaction is proportional to the number of collisions per second between the reacting molecules and the fraction of effective collisions. An effective collision is one that yields the products. Such collisions require that the reactant particles have the proper orientation and an energy of collision equal to or greater than the activation energy, E_a. The activation energy is the minimum energy needed to produce the products. When the activation energy is added to reacting particles with the correct orientation the activated complex results. An activated complex is a high-energy transient species formed from colliding molecules in which reactant bonds are partially broken and product bonds are partially formed.

A temperature rise increases the average kinetic energy of the reactant particles and allows more of them to reach the activated complex. Thus, when the temperature increases, the reaction rate increases. The Arrhenius Equation is used to calculate the rate constants at different temperatures. One way to express the Arrhenius Equation is as follows. $\ln k = -E_a/RT + \ln A$.

A reaction mechanism is a description of the series of steps that occur as the reactants change to products. Reaction mechanisms describe how reactions occur. They can be found experimentally by collecting rate data. The elementary reactions are the individual steps in a reaction mechanism. The number of reactants that produce the transition state in an elementary reaction is the molecularity. In a reaction mechanism, the slowest step usually determines the overall rate of the reaction and is known as the rate-limiting step.

CHAPTER 14 REVIEW EXERCISE

1. Consider the following gas-phase reaction ($2O_3(g) \longrightarrow 3O_2(g)$). (a) Show the relationships between the rates of disappearance of O_3 and the rate of appearance of O_2. (b) Remove the

fractions in the equation found in part (a), and express in terms of whole numbers.

2. Consider the following reaction ($N_2(g) + 3H_2(g) \longrightarrow 2NH_3(g)$). If the rate of disappearance of N_2 is -1.0×10^{-3} M/s, calculate the rate of disappearance of H_2 and rate of appearance of NH_3.

3. Consider the following reaction:

$$2H_2(g) + 2NO(g) \longrightarrow N_2(g) + 2H_2O(g)$$

In an experiment the initial rate of formation of N_2 is 1.35×10^2 M/s. (a) At what rate does H_2O form? (b) At what rates do NO and H_2 disappear?

4. Consider the following rate data collected for the gas phase decomposition of N_2O to N_2 and O_2.

Time, s	P_t, atm
0	0.830
450	0.845

P_t is the total pressure of the reaction mixture. (a) What is the rate of disappearance of N_2O and the rate of appearance of O_2 over the 450 s time interval? (b) What is the rate of appearance of O_2 over this time interval?

5. Consider the following hypothetical reaction and rate data

$$2A(g) + B_2(g) \longrightarrow 2AB(g)$$

Experiment	[A]	[B_2]	Reaction rate, M/s
1	0.125	0.293	0.548
2	0.125	0.0977	0.183
3	0.377	0.185	0.346
4	0.250	0.586	1.10
5	0.198	0.185	0.346

(a) Determine the rate law for this reaction. (b) Calculate the rate constant. (c) Calculate the initial rate of the reaction when the concentration of A is 0.471 M and B_2 is 0.313 M.

6. Consider the following reaction ($2NO(g) + Br_2(g) \longrightarrow 2NOBr(g)$). The following concentration-rate data were collected at 546K.

Experiment	[NO], M	[Br_2], M	Initial Rate, M/s
1	0.25	0.25	1.80×10^2
2	0.25	0.50	3.60×10^2
3	0.45	0.75	1.75×10^3
4	0.55	1.00	3.48×10^3

(a) Calculate the rate expression for this reaction. (b) What is the rate constant, k? (c) Calculate the initial reaction rate when the concentrations of both NO and Br_2 are 0.10 M.

7. A student studies the rate that sucrose, $C_{12}H_{22}O_{11}$, decomposes to glucose and fructose, both with the formula $C_6H_{12}O_6$. The concentration of sucrose drops from 0.200 M to 0.175 M in 2310 s. (a) If the reaction is first order, calculate the rate constant. (b) Calculate the time it takes for the initial concentration, 0.200 M, to drop 40.0%.

8. The first-order rate constant for the fermentation of sucrose, $C_{12}H_{22}O_{11}$, to ethanol, CH_3CH_2OH,

and CO_2 is 1.9×10^{-5} s^{-1}. (a) Calculate the half-life for this reaction. (b) How long would it take for 95.0% of a 0.300 M sucrose solution to ferment?

9. The first-order rate constant for the conversion of cyclopropane, C_3H_6, to propene, C_3H_6, is 9.2 s^{-1} at 1000°C. (a) What is the half-life for this reaction? (b) How long does it take for 99% of the cyclopropane to react?

10. ^{14}C is a radioactive isotope of C. It undergoes first-order radioactive decay with a rate constant of 1.21×10^{-4} yr^{-1}. (a) What is the half-life for the decay of ^{14}C? (b) How long does it take for 90.0% of the atoms in a sample of ^{14}C to decay? (c) How many ^{14}C atoms remain after 2000 yr from a pure sample that has a mass of 1.00 mg?

11. The second-order reaction of A to products ($A \longrightarrow$ products) has a rate constant of 9.11×10^{-2} M^{-1} s^{-1}. (a) What is the half-life of the reaction when the initial concentration of A is 0.0100 M? (b) What concentration of A remains after 55.3 s when the initial concentration is 0.0100 M? (c) How long does it take for 95.0% of A to react when the initial concentration is 0.0100 M?

12. Reactant X undergoes a second-order decomposition to products. The initial concentration of X is 0.077 M. It takes 1.2 min for the concentration to decrease to 0.069 M. (a) What is the second-order rate constant? (b) What is the concentration of X after 5.0 min?

13. The first-order rate constant for the reaction of methyl chloride, CH_3Cl, and water is 2.78×10^{-11} s^{-1} at 283 K and is 1.24×10^{-8} s^{-1} at 323 K. (a) Calculate the energy of activation, E_a, for this reaction. (b) Calculate the rate constant at 273 K.

14. Methyl iodide, CH_3I, combines with sodium ethoxide, C_2H_5ONa, to produce dimethylether, CH_3OCH_3, and sodium iodide, NaI. The rate constant for the reaction is 5.60×10^{-5} $M^{-1}s^{-1}$ at 273 K, and the rate constant is 1.00×10^{-3} $M^{-1}s^{-1}$ at 297 K. (a) Calculate the activation energy for the reaction in kJ. (b) At what temperature is the rate constant for this reaction 2.55×10^{-4} $M^{-1}s^{-1}$?

15. (a) Show mathematically what happens to the ratio of the rate constants, k_2/k_1, and thus the reaction rates, when the Kelvin temperature increases from 300 K to 310 K for a reaction with an activation energy of 75 kJ/mol. (b) What is the ratio of k_2/k_1 when the temperature increases from 300 K to 310 K for a reaction with an activation energy of 250 kJ/mol?

16. The activation energy for the gas-phase decomposition of NOCl to NO and Cl_2 is 103 kJ. The rate constant for the reaction at 475 K is 4.71×10^{-2} s^{-1}. (a) Calculate the frequency factor for the reaction. (b) At what temperature will the reaction rate quadruple from that at 475 K?

17. The generally accepted mechanism for the reaction of $ICl(g)$ and $H_2(g)$ is as follows:

$$ICl(g) + H_2(g) \longrightarrow HI(g) + HCl(g) \quad \text{(slow)}$$
$$HI(g) + ICl(g) \longrightarrow I_2(g) + HCl(g) \quad \text{(fast)}$$

(a) What is the overall reaction? (b) What rate law is consistent with this mechanism? (c) What reaction intermediate forms?

18. Aqueous hypochlorite, ClO^-, converts I^-(aq) to IO^-(aq) in a basic solution (aqueous OH^-) as follows:

$$ClO^-(aq) + I^-(aq) \longrightarrow IO^-(aq) + Cl^-(aq)$$

The proposed mechanism for this reaction is

$$ClO^-(aq) + H_2O(l) \rightleftharpoons HClO(aq) + OH^-(aq) \quad \text{(fast)}$$
$$I^-(aq) + HClO(aq) \longrightarrow HIO(aq) + Cl^-(aq) \quad \text{(slow)}$$
$$OH^-(aq) + HIO(aq) \rightleftharpoons H_2O(l) + IO^-(aq) \quad \text{(fast)}$$

What is the rate equation for this reaction?

19. The fraction of molecules, f, that have an energy equal to or greater than the activation energy is given by the equation $f = e^{-Ea/(RT)}$. Consider a reaction that has an activation energy of 45 kJ. (a) Calculate the value of f at 25°C. (b) What is the value for f at 125°C? (c) At what temperature will 50% of the molecules have energies that equal or exceed E_a?

ANSWERS TO REVIEW EXERCISE

1. (a) $-1/2(\Delta[O_3]/\Delta t) = 1/3(\Delta[O_2]/\Delta t)$, (b) $-3(\Delta[O_3]/\Delta t) = 2(\Delta[O_2]/\Delta t)$
2. $-3.0 \times 10^{-3} M\ H_2/s, 2.0 \times 10^{-3} M\ NH_3/s$
3. (a) 2.70×10^{-2} M/s, (b) -2.70×10^{-2} M/s
4. (a) -6.67×10^{-5} atm/s, (b) 3.33×10^{-5} atm/s
5. (a) Rate $= k[A]^0[B] = k[B]$, (b) $1.87\ s^{-1}$, (c) 0.585 M/s
6. (a) Rate $= k[NO]^2[Br_2]$, (b) $1.2 \times 10^4\ M^{-2}s^{-1}$, (c) 12 M/s
7. (a) $k = 5.78 \times 10^{-5}\ s^{-1}$, (b) 8.84×10^3 s
8. (a) $t_{1/2} = 3.65 \times 10^4$ s (10.1 hours), (b) 1.58×10^5 s (43.8 hr)
9. (a) 0.075 s, (b) 0.50 s
10. (a) 5.73×10^3 yr, (b) 1.90×10^4 yr, (c) 3.95×10^{19} atoms
11. (a) 1.10×10^3 s, (b) $0.00952\ M$, (c) 2.09×10^4 s
12. (a) $k = 1.3\ M^{-1}\ min^{-1}$, (b) $[X]_{5.0} = 0.052\ M$
13. (a) 116 kJ/mol, (b) $4.56 \times 10^{-12}\ s^{-1}$
14. (a) 81.0 kJ/mol, (b) 285 K
15. (a) $k_2/k_1 = 2.64$, (b) $k_2/k_1 = 25.4$
16. (a) 1.00×10^{10}, (b) 501.7 K
17. (a) $2ICl + H_2 \longrightarrow I_2(g) + 2HCl(g)$, (b) Rate $= k[ICl][H_2]$, (c) HI
18. Rate $= k([I^-][ClO^-])/[OH^-]$
19. (a) 1.29×10^{-8}, (b) 1.24×10^{-6}, (c) 7.81×10^3 K

15

Introduction to Chemical Equilibria

*C*hemical reactions proceed spontaneously until they reach a state of dynamic equilibrium. At equilibrium the rate of the forward reaction equals the rate of the reverse reaction. At this point, the reactant and product concentrations remain constant. Chemical equilibrium systems are more resistant to change than those that are not in equilibrium. When an equilibrium system is disturbed, it attempts spontaneously to reestablish a state of equilibrium.

15.1 THE EQUILIBRIUM STATE

Establishing Equilibrium

Consider the following model reaction as it establishes equilibrium.

$$H_2(g) + CO_2(g) \rightarrow CO(g) + H_2O(g)$$

When H_2 and CO_2 mix at constant temperature in a reaction vessel, they combine and begin to form the products, CO and H_2O. Hence, the concentrations of H_2 and CO_2 decrease and the concentrations of CO and H_2O increase. As the reactant concentrations decrease, the rate of the forward reaction decreases and the rate of the reverse reaction increases. At some point, the rate of the forward reaction equals the rate of the reverse reaction and a chemical equilibrium establishes. After this time, the concentrations of the reactants and products do not change.

Forward and Reverse Reactions

Arrows that point in opposite directions, $\rightleftharpoons$, show that an equilibrium has established. For example, the following equation is written for the equilibrium of H_2 and CO_2 with CO and H_2O.

$$\overset{\text{forward}}{\underset{\text{reverse}}{H_2(g) + CO_2(g) \rightleftharpoons CO(g) + H_2O(g)}}$$

The reaction that goes from left to right is the forward reaction, and the reaction that goes from right to left is the reverse reaction.

The Equilibrium Constant Expression

An important quantitative relationship exists between the concentrations of the reactants and products. This relationship was identified by Guldberg and Waage in 1864 when they proposed the Law of Mass Action that expresses the equilibrium concentrations of the reactants and products in terms of an equilibrium constant, K. For the equilibrium of H_2 and CO_2 with CO and H_2O, the equilibrium constant expression (equilibrium expression, for short) is

$$K_c = \frac{[CO][H_2O]}{[CO_2][H_2]}$$

in which K_c is the equilibrium constant expressed in terms of molar concentrations, [CO] and [H_2O] are the molar concentrations of the products, and [CO_2] and [H_2] are the molar concentrations of the reactants.

For the general reaction

$$wA + xB \rightleftharpoons yC + zD$$

the equilibrium constant expression becomes

$$K_c = \frac{[C]^y[D]^z}{[A]^w[B]^x} \tag{15.1}$$

Problem 15.1 Write the equilibrium expressions for the following.
(a) $N_2(g) + 3F_2(g) \rightleftharpoons 2NF_3(g)$

(b) $IF(g) \rightleftharpoons \frac{1}{2}I_2(g) + \frac{1}{2}F_2(g)$

Solution 15.1

(a) $K_c = \dfrac{\left[NF_3\right]^2}{\left[N_2\right]\left[F_2\right]^3}$

(b) $K_c = \dfrac{\left[I_2\right]^{0.5}\left[F_2\right]^{0.5}}{\left[IF\right]}$

Problem 15.2 Consider two sets of data obtained for the following equilibrium.

$$H_2(g) + CO_2(g) \rightleftharpoons CO(g) + H_2O(g)$$

(a) In experiment 1, a mixture of 0.100 M H_2 and 0.100 M CO_2 at 873 K is allowed to attain equilibrium, the concentrations of H_2 and CO_2 decrease to 0.0609 M and the concentrations of CO and H_2O increase to 0.0390 M. Calculate the value of K_c. (b) In experiment 2, a mixture of 0.100 M H_2 and 0.200 M CO_2 at 873 K is allowed to reach equilibrium. The equilibrium concentrations of H_2O and CO are both 0.0531 M and the concentrations of H_2 and CO_2 are 0.0469 M and 0.147 M, respectively. Calculate the value of K_c.

Solution 15.2 Substituting the equilibrium concentrations from both experiments into the equilibrium expression gives the same results for the equilibrium constant.

(a) $K_c(\text{exp.1}) = (0.0390M)(0.0390M)/((0.0609M)(0.0609M))$

$= 0.410$

(b) $K_c(\text{exp.2}) = ((0.0531M)(0.0531M))/(0.147M)(0.0468M)$

$= 0.410$

Problem 15.3   Consider the following hypothetical equilibrium.

$$A + B \rightleftharpoons C + D$$

The mechanism for this reaction proceeds by the following two steps

$$A + A \underset{K_{-1}}{\overset{k_1}{\rightleftharpoons}} C + X$$

$$X + B \underset{K_{-2}}{\overset{k_2}{\rightleftharpoons}} D + A$$

in which X is a reaction intermediate and both elementary reactions are reversible.   Derive the equilibrium expression

Solution 15.3   Because an equilibrium establishes in each elementary reaction, the rates of the forward and reverse reactions are equal.

$$k_1[A][A] = k_{-1}[C][X]$$
$$k_2[X][B] = k_{-2}[D][A]$$

If both equations are solved for the concentration of the reaction intermediate X, and then are equated, Eq. 15.2 is obtained. setcounterequation1

$$[X] = k_1[A][A]/k_{-1}[C]$$
$$[X] = k_{-2}[D][A]/k_2[B]$$
$$k_1[A][A]/k_{-1}[C] = k_{-2}[D][A]/k_2[B] \tag{15.1}$$

Grouping the concentration terms on the right side and the rate constants on the left side yields the equilibrium expression.

$$K_c = \frac{k_1 k_2}{k_{-1}k_{-2}} = \frac{[C][D]}{[A][B]} \tag{15.3}$$

Heterogeneous Equilibria

An equilibrium in which all of the reactants and products are in one phase is a homogeneous equilibrium. All of the equilibria discussed to this point are homogeneous equilibria. An equilibrium with reactants and products in more than one phase is a heterogeneous equilibrium. For example, the following chemical equilibrium occurs in a blast furnace and is used to recover iron from its ore.

$$CO_2(g) + C(graphite) \rightleftharpoons 2CO(g)$$

CO_2 and CO are gases and graphite is a solid. Because graphite is a pure solid, and thus has a constant concentration, it is not included in the equilibrium expression. In general, the concentrations of any pure solids and liquids are constant because they have a fixed ratio of moles of substance to volume. Varying the mass of graphite in this equilibrium system produces no changes while graphite is present. Consequently, the concentration of pure substances are not included as terms in the equilibrium expressions of heterogeneous equilibria. Thus, the equilibrium expression is as follows.

$$K_c = \frac{[CO]^2}{[CO_2]}$$

Problem 15.4   Write the equilibrium expression for the following equilibrium: $3CuO(s) + 2NH_3(g) \rightleftharpoons 3Cu(s) + N_2(g) + 3H_2O(g)$

Solution 15.4 This is a heterogeneous equilibrium because CuO and Cu are solids and the remaining substances are gases. Thus, terms for the concentration of CuO and Cu are not included in the equilibrium expression.

$$K_c = \frac{[N_2]\,[H_2O]^3}{[NH_3]^2}$$

15.2 EQUILIBRIUM CONSTANTS

Magnitude of the Equilibrium Constant

If the value of the equilibrium constant is greater than one ($K_c > 1$), then the magnitude of the numerator of the equilibrium expression is larger than that of the denominator. Hence, the equilibrium concentrations of the products are usually higher than those of the reactants. If the value of K_c is less than one, the equilibrium concentrations of the reactants are usually greater than those of the products.

Problem 15.5 Consider the following equilibria.
- (a) $2H_2O(g) \rightleftharpoons H_2(g) + O_2(g)$ $K_c = 1.4 \times 10^{-11}$ (1700 K)
- (b) $H_2(g) + Cl_2(g) \rightleftharpoons 2HCl(g)$ $K_c = 4.4 \times 10^{32}$ (298 K)

In which direction do these equilibria lie?

Solution 15.5
- (a) A very small K_c, 1.4×10^{-11}, shows that very few H_2 and O_2 molecules are present in the equilibrium mixture. In the decomposition of H_2O, the reaction quickly reaches equilibrium before proceeding too far to the right.
- (b) Such a large equilibrium constant, 4.4×10^{32}, shows that the principal component of the equilibrium mixture is HCl molecules with very few H_2 and Cl_2 molecules. In other words, this reaction almost goes to completion before the equilibrium establishes.

EQUILIBRIUM CONSTANT WHEN THE EQUATION IS REVERSED

If the equation for an equilibrium is reversed, the equilibrium constant becomes the reciprocal of the original constant. If K is the value for the forward direction, $1/K$ is the value for the reverse direction.

Problem 15.6 Consider the following equilibrium.

$$N_2(g) + 3H_2(g) \rightleftharpoons 2NH_3(g) \quad K_c = 0.51 \ (673 \text{ K})$$

(a) Write the equilibrium expression for the forward reaction. (b) Write the equilibrium expression for the reverse reaction. (c) What is the equilibrium constant for the reverse reaction?

Solution 15.6
- (a) The equilibrium expression is for the reaction is as follows.

$$K_c = [NH_3]^2/([N_2][H_2]^3) = 0.51$$

- (b) Reversing the equation gives

$$2NH_3(g) \rightleftharpoons N_2(g) + 3H_2(g)$$

and its equilibrium expression becomes

$$1/K_c = ([N_2][H_2]^3)/[NH_3]^2$$

(c) Because K_c equals 0.51 then $1/K_c$ equals $1/0.51$ or 2.0.

Problem 15.7   Consider the following equilibrium

$$SO_2(g) + 1/2O_2(g) \rightleftharpoons SO_3(g) \quad K_c' = 20.4 \ (973K)$$

Determine the equilibrium constants, K_c for each of the following.
  (a) $SO_3(g) \rightleftharpoons SO_2(g) + 1/2O_2$
  (b) $2SO_2(g) + O_2(g) \rightleftharpoons 2SO_3(g)$

Solution 15.7   The equilibrium expression for the given reaction is as follows.

$$K_c = \frac{[SO_3]}{[SO_2][O_2]^{0.5}}$$

(a) This equilibrium is the reverse of the given equilibrium. Therefore, take the reciprocal of K_c'.

$$K_c = 1/K_c' = 1/20.4 = 0.0490$$

(b) This equation is double the given equation; hence, its equilibrium expression is as follows.

$$K_c = \frac{[SO_3]^2}{[SO_2]^2[O_2]}$$

Note that each term in the equilibrium expression has been squared. Therefore, K_c equals the square of K_c'

$$K_c = (K_c')^2 = 20.4^2 = 416$$

Gas-Phase Equilibrium Constants, K_p

For gas-phase reactions, the equilibrium constants are often expressed in terms of the partial pressures of the components of the equilibrium mixture. For example, the equilibrium between N_2O_4 and NO_2.

$$N_2O_4(g) \rightleftharpoons 2NO_2(g)$$

may be expressed as follows

$$K_p = \frac{P_{NO_2}^2}{P_{N_2O_4}} \tag{15.4}$$

in which K_p is the equilibrium constant expressed in terms of the partial pressures of the components of the equilibrium. Values for K_p often differ from K_c, so you must be careful to identify the type of equilibrium constant given.

Problem 15.8   Consider the following gas-phase equilibria.
  (a) $2CO_2(g) \rightleftharpoons 2CO(g) + O_2(g)$
  (b) $CaCO_3(s) \rightleftharpoons CaO(s) + CO_2(g)$
Write the K_p expressions for these equilibria.

Solution 15.8

(a) This is a homogeneous gas-phase equilibrium; thus, all components are included in the K_p expression.

$$K_p = \frac{P_{CO}^2 P_{O_2}}{P_{CO_2}^2}$$

(b) This is a heterogeneous equilibrium and the only gas is CO_2; thus, the equilibrium expression only has one term ($K_p = P_{CO_2}$).

RELATIONSHIP OF K_p AND K_c

The relationship between K_p and K_c is expressed in Eq. 15.5

$$K_p = K_c(RT)^{\triangle n} \tag{15.5}$$

in which $\triangle n$ is the difference between the moles of gaseous products and moles of gaseous reactants in the balanced equation ($\triangle n = n_{products} - n_{reactants}$).

Problem 15.9 Consider the following equilibrium

$$CO(g) + Cl_2(g) \rightleftharpoons COCl_2(g) \quad K_c = 4.6 \times 10^9 \ (373 \ K)$$

Calculate the K_p for the equilibrium.

Solution 15.9 To calculate the value of K_p, substitute the known values in Eq. 15.5. This equilibrium has one mole of gaseous products and two moles of gaseous reactants; therefore the $\triangle n$ is -1. Therefore, the equation becomes

$$K_p = 4.6 \times 10^9 (RT)^{-1}$$

in which R equals 0.0821 (L $\cdot$ atm)/(mol $\cdot$ K) and T is 373 K.

$$K_p = 4.6 \times 10^9 (0.0821(L \cdot atm)/(mol \cdot K) \times 373 \ K)^{-1}$$
$$= 4.6 \times 10^9 \times 1/(0.0821(L \cdot atm)/(mol \cdot K) \times 373 \ K)$$
$$= 1.5 \times 10^8$$

Calculating Equilibrium Constants

To determine equilibrium constants, the equilibrium concentrations or partial pressures of all components of an equilibrium mixture are measured experimentally and then they are substituted into the equilibrium expression.

Problem 15.10 Consider the following equilibrium at 2773 K.

$$H_2(g) + Cl_2(g) \rightleftharpoons 2HCl(g)$$

Initially, 0.250 M H_2 and 0.250 M Cl_2 are introduced into a reaction vessel and the system is allowed to equilibrate. At equilibrium the concentrations of H_2 and Cl_2 become 0.0314 M. (a) Calculate K_c. (b) Calculate K_p.

Solution 15.10

(a) To calculate the value of K_c, first determine the equilibrium concentrations of all species and substitute them into the equilibrium expression. From the given concentrations of H_2 and Cl_2, calculate the equilibrium concentration of HCl. Initially the concentrations of both reactants are 0.250 M and at equilibrium the concentrations decrease to 0.0314 M. Hence, the difference between the initial and final values is the concentration that reacts to produce HCl.

$$[H_2]_{reacted} = [H_2]_{initial} - [H_2]_{final} = 0.250\ M - 0.0314\ M = 0.219\ M$$

Because H_2 and Cl_2 combine in a 1-to-1 mole ratio, the molarity of Cl_2 is the same as that of H_2. For each one mole of H_2 and Cl_2 that combine, two moles of HCl form. Therefore, twice the concentration lost in the reactants equals the equilibrium concentration of HCl ($2 \times 0.219\ M = 0.438\ M$). To calculate K_c, substitute each of the equilibrium concentrations into the equilibrium expression.

$$K_c = (0.438\ M)^2/(0.0314\ M \times 0.0314\ M) = 195$$

(b) To calculate K_p, substitute the known values into Eq. 15.5. Because the number of moles of gaseous products (2HCl) equals that of gaseous reactants ($H_2 + Cl_2$), the $\triangle n$ for the equilibrium is 0. When the RT term is raised to the zero power, 1 is obtained, which means that K_p equals K_c. The K_p for the equilibrium is 195.

Problem 15.11   Consider the following gas-phase equilibrium.

$$SO_2Cl_2(g) \rightleftharpoons SO_2(g) + Cl_2(g)$$

A 3.35-g sample of SO_2Cl_2 at 300 K is added to a 1.00-L reaction vessel and is allowed to reach equilibrium. At equilibrium, 0.120 atm SO_2 results in the vessel. (a) What is the K_p for the equilibrium? (b) What is K_c?

Solution 15.11

(a) To calculate K_p, determine the equilibrium partial pressures for the gases. Begin by calculating the initial partial pressure of SO_2Cl_2 from the ideal gas equation, $PV = nRT$. Before using the equation, convert the mass of SO_2Cl_2 to moles.

$$n = 3.35g\ SO_2Cl_2 \times 1\ mol\ SO_2\ Cl_2/135\ g\ SO_2Cl_2 = 0.0248\ mol\ SO_2Cl_2$$

Then solve the ideal gas equation for P and substitute the known values into the equation.

$$PV = nRT$$
$$P_{SO_2Cl_2} = (nRT)/V = (0.0248\ mol \times 0.0821\ L \cdot atm/mol \cdot K \times 300\ K)/1.00\ L$$
$$= 0.611\ atm$$

The initial pressure of SO_2Cl_2 in the reaction vessel is 0.611 atm. The balanced equation shows that for each mole of SO_2Cl_2 that decomposes, one mole of SO_2 and one mole of Cl_2 result. Because the partial pressures are directly proportional to the number of moles, calculate the equilibrium pressures of SO_2Cl_2 and Cl_2 from the equilibrium partial pressure of SO_2. The equilibrium partial pressure of SO_2 is 0.120 atm. Hence, the same partial pressure of Cl_2 is found at equilibrium because they form in the same mole ratio.

$$P_{Cl_2} = P_{SO_2} = 0.120\ atm$$

To calculate the equilibrium partial pressure of SO_2Cl_2, subtract 0.120 atm from the initial pressure (0.611 atm) because the mole ratio is 1-to-1 between SO_2Cl_2 and SO_2.

$$P_{SO_2Cl_2} = 0.611 \text{ atm} - 0.120 \text{ atm} = 0.491 \text{ atm}$$

The value of K_p is obtained by substituting the equilibrium partial pressures into the equilibrium expression.

$$K_p = P_{SO_2}P_{Cl_2}/P_{SO_2Cl_2} = (0.120 \text{ atm} \times 0.120 \text{ atm})/0.491 \text{ atm} = 0.0293$$

(b) The value of K_c is calculated by using Eq. 15.5. The $\triangle n$ for the reaction is 1 (2 mol − 1 mol), R is 0.0821 (L · atm)/(mol · K), T is 300 K, and K_p is 0.293. Rearrange the equation first, solve for K_c, and then substitute the known values into the equation.

$$K_c = K_p/(RT)^{\triangle n}$$
$$= 0.0293/(0.0821(\text{L} \cdot \text{atm})/(\text{mol} \cdot \text{K}) \times 300\text{K}) = 1.19 \times 10^{-3}$$

Problem 15.12   Consider the following gas-phase equilibrium.

$$PCl_5(g) \rightleftharpoons PCl_3(g) + Cl_2(g)$$

At a fixed temperature, 0.75 atm PCl_5 is introduced into a reaction vessel and is allowed to reach equilibrium. The total pressure, P_t, at equilibrium is 0.90 atm. Calculate the value of K_p.

Solution 15.12   If the partial pressure of PCl_5 decreases by x to reach equilibrium, the partial pressure of PCl_3 and Cl_2 are each x.

$$PCl_5(g) \rightleftharpoons PCl_3(g) + Cl_2(g)$$
$$-x \qquad\qquad +x \qquad +x$$

Thus, the equilibrium partial pressure of PCl_5, PCl_3, and Cl_2 are $0.75 -x, x$, and x. The total pressure, P_t (0.90 atm), in the flask equals the sum of the partial pressures.

$$P_t = P_{PCl_5} + P_{PCl_3} + P_{Cl_2}$$
$$= (0.75 - x) + x + x$$
$$0.90 \text{ atm} = 0.75 + x$$
$$x = 0.15 \text{ atm}$$

Hence, the equilibrium partial pressure of PCl_5 is 0.60 atm (0.75 atm − 0.15 atm), and the equilibrium partial pressure of PCl_3 and Cl_2 are 0.15 atm. Substitute these values into the K_p expression.

$$K_p = (P_{PCl_3}P_{Cl_2})/P_{PCl_5}$$
$$= (0.15 \text{ atm})^2/0.60 \text{ atm} = 0.038$$

Rule of Multiple Equilibria

The Rule of Multiple Equilibria states that if a reaction is the sum of two or more reactions, the equilibrium constant for that reaction is the product of the equilibrium constants of the added reactions. In other words, if $K_c(1)$ and $K_c(2)$ are the equilibrium constants for reactions 1 and 2, respectively, and their sum yields reaction 3, then the equilibrium constant for reaction 3 equals the product of $K_c(1)$ and $K_c(2)$.

$$\text{Reaction 1 } (K_c(1)) + \text{Reaction 2 } (K_c(2)) = \text{Reaction 3 } (K_c(1) \times K_c(2))$$

Problem 15.13   Apply the rule of multiple equilibrium to calculate the equilibrium constant for the following equilibrium system at 1120 K:

$$C(s) + CO_2(g) + 2Cl_2(g) \rightleftharpoons 2COCl_2(g)$$

given the following equations and equilibrium constants.

$$
\begin{array}{ll}
CO(g) + Cl_2(g) \rightleftharpoons COCl_2(g) & K_p(1) = 6.0 \times 10^{-3} \\
C(s) + CO_2(g) \rightleftharpoons 2CO(g) & K_p(2) = 1.3 \times 10^{14}
\end{array}
$$

Solution 15.13   These equations cannot be added as written to give the overall equation. First, multiply the first equation by 2 so that the CO cancel when added.

$$
\begin{array}{l}
\quad 2CO(g) + 2Cl_2(g) \rightleftharpoons 2COCl_2(g) \\
+ \qquad\quad C(s) + CO_2(g) \rightleftharpoons 2CO(g) \\
\hline
\quad C(s) + CO_2(g) + 2Cl_2(g) \rightleftharpoons 2COCl_2(g)
\end{array}
$$

When the first equation is doubled, the equilibrium constant is changed to $(6.0 \times 10^{-3})^2$ or 3.6×10^{-5}; because each term in the equation now has a coefficient of 2, the equilibrium constant must be squared. Therefore, the equilibrium constant, K_p, for the overall equilibrium is 4.7×10^9, the product of 3.6×10^{-5} and 1.3×10^{14}.

Problem 15.14   Consider the following equilibrium.

$$BrF_3(g) \rightleftharpoons BrF(g) + F_2(g)$$

Calculate K_p for this equilibrium using the following equations.

$$
\begin{array}{ll}
\tfrac{1}{2}Br_2(g) + \tfrac{1}{2}F_2(g) \rightleftharpoons BrF(g) & K_p = 148 \\
\tfrac{1}{2}Br_2(g) + 3/2F_2(g) \rightleftharpoons BrF_3(g) & K_p = 2.3
\end{array}
$$

Solution 15.14

$$
\begin{array}{ll}
\quad \tfrac{1}{2}Br_2(g) + \tfrac{1}{2}F_2(g) \rightleftharpoons BrF(g) & K_p = 148 \\
+ \quad BrF_3(g) \rightleftharpoons \tfrac{1}{2}Br_2(g) + 3/2F_2(g) & K_p = 1/2.3 = 0.43 \\
\hline
\quad BrF_3(g) \rightleftharpoons BrF(g) + F_2(g) & K_p = 64
\end{array}
$$

15.3 THE REACTION QUOTIENT AND DIRECTION OF REACTION

Reaction Quotient, Q

When a chemical system is in equilibrium, the concentrations or partial pressures of the reactants and products are expressed in terms of either K_c or K_p. However, before the system reaches equilibrium, the concentrations or partial pressures are expressed in terms of the reaction quotient, Q. Let us consider the following general nonequilibrium system.

$$wA + xB \longrightarrow yC + zD$$

The reaction quotient for this reaction is as follows.

$$Q = \frac{[C]^y[D]^z}{[A]^w[B]^x}$$

Note the expression for Q has the same algebraic form as the expression for K_c. While a reaction goes to equilibrium, the value of Q changes continually until it reaches equilibrium and the value of Q equals K_c.

Predicting the Direction from Which Equilibrium Establishes

The value of the reaction quotient, Q, is used to determine from what direction an equilibrium establishes–either from left to right or from right to left. If the reaction goes to equilibrium from left to right, the concentrations of the reactants decrease and those of the products increase. Therefore, the value of Q is less than K_c ($Q < K_c$) until equilibrium establishes. If the reaction goes to equilibrium from right to left, the concentrations of the products decrease and those of the reactants increase. Hence, the value of Q is greater than K_c ($Q > K_c$) until equilibrium establishes.

Problem 15.15 Consider the equilibrium in which methanol vapor, $CH_3OH(g)$, results from carbon monoxide, CO, and hydrogen, H_2.

$$CO(g) + 2H_2(g) \rightleftharpoons CH_3OH(g) \quad K_c = 290 \text{ (700K)}$$

(a) From what direction does the equilibrium establish, if the initial concentrations are 1.0 M CO, 1.0 M H_2, and 2.0 M CH_3OH? (b) From what direction does the equilibrium establish, if the initial concentrations are 0.10 M CO, 0.10 M H_2, and 2.0 M CH_3OH?

Solution 15.15

(a)
$$Q = [CH_3OH]/([CO][H_2]^2)$$
$$= 2.0 \, M/(1.0 \, M \times 1.0^2 \, M^2) = 2.0$$

Because the value of Q (2.0) is less than that of K (290), the reaction proceeds from left to right to reach equilibrium.

(b)
$$Q = [CH_3OH]/([CO][H_2]^2)$$
$$= 2.0 \, M/(0.10 \, M \times 0.10^2 \, M^2) = 2.0 \times 10^3$$

Because the value of $Q(2.0 \times 10^3)$ is greater than that of K (290), the reaction proceeds from right to left to reach equilibrium.

Problem 15.16 The equilibrium constant K_p for the Haber reaction is 4.5×10^{-5} at 723 K.

$$N_2(g) + 3H_2(g) \rightleftharpoons 2NH_3(g)$$

Determine the direction equilibrium establishes when initially 20 atm of N_2, 15 atm of H_2, and 5.0 atm of NH_3 are present in the reaction vessel.

Solution 15.16

$$Q = P_{NH_3}^2 / P_{N_2} P_{H_2}^3$$
$$= (5.0 \text{ atm})^2 / (20 \text{ atm} \times (15 \text{ atm})^3) = 3.70 \times 10^{-4}$$

Because the value of Q, 3.70×10^{-4}, is larger than the value of K_p, 4.5×10^{-5}, the system approaches equilibrium from right to left.

15.4 EQUILIBRIUM CONCENTRATION CALCULATIONS

The equilibrium concentrations of the reactants and products can be calculated from the equilibrium expression and the initial reactant and product concentrations or partial pressures. To be most successful in solving this type of equilibrium problem, consider each of the following steps:

1. Construct a summary table that shows the initial concentrations, concentration changes, and equilibrium concentrations of all components of the equilibrium. If necessary, calculate the value for Q before starting the table to decide from which direction the equilibrium establishes.
2. Substitute the equilibrium concentrations from the table into the equilibrium expression and solve for the change in concentration or pressure.
3. Calculate the equilibrium concentrations by substituting the value from Step 2 into the equilibrium terms in the table.
4. Check the answers by substituting the concentrations or partial pressures in the equilibrium expression to see if it gives the equilibrium constant.

Problem 15.17 Consider the following equilibrium.

$$H_2(g) + I_2(g) \rightleftharpoons 2HI(g) \quad K_c = 45.9 \text{ (763 K)}$$

Initially, 0.100 M H_2 and 0.100 M I_2 are introduced into a reaction vessel and are then allowed to reach equilibrium. What are the equilibrium concentrations of all components of the equilibrium?

Solution 15.17 As the reaction goes to equilibrium the concentrations of H_2 and I_2 decrease and the concentration of HI increases. Because the decrease in the concentration of the reactants is unknown, algebra must be used. Use the variable x to equal the decrease in reactants concentrations. For each x mol/L of H_2 and I_2 that disappear, $2x$ mol/L of HI form. The changes in concentration in the attainment of equilibrium always follow the stoichiometry of the reaction. Next, construct a table of the initial concentration, concentration change, and equilibrium concentration of the components of the equilibrium.

Compound	Initial Concentration, M	Concentration Change, M	Equilibrium Concentration, M
$[H_2]$	0.100	$-x$	$0.100 - x$
$[I_2]$	0.100	$-x$	$0.100 - x$
$[HI]$	0	$+2x$	$2x$

From the table, substitute the terms from the equilibrium concentrations into the K_c expression and solve for x.

$$K_c = [HI]^2/[H_2][I_2]$$
$$45.9 = (2x)^2/(0.100 - x)^2$$

Note that the right side of this equation is a perfect square. Thus, to solve for x, the square root of both side is taken as follows.

$$\pm 6.77 = 2x/(0.100 - x)$$
$$x = 0.0772 \ M \text{ or } 0.142 \ M$$

Because the square root of 45.9 could be either $+6.77$ or -6.77, two values of x are obtained. These values of x are then substituted into the equilibrium terms in the table. Using the first value, both $[H_2]$ and $[I_2]$ equal $0.100 - x$; thus they are $0.100 \ M - 0.0772 \ M$ or $0.023 \ M$. Using the second value leads to $[H_2]$ and $[I_2]$ of $-0.042 \ M(0.100 - 0.142)$. Since a negative concentration is not physically possible, it can be concluded that the first root of this quadratic equation gives a physically meaningful result. Having determined that the first value is the proper value for x, at equilibrium $[HI]$ equals $2x$ or $2 \times 0.0772 \ M$, which is $0.154 \ M$.

Problem 15.18   Consider the following equilibrium system.

$$PCl_3(g) + Cl_2(g) \rightleftharpoons PCl_5(g) \quad K_c = 13.7 \ (546 \ K)$$

What are the equilibrium concentrations of all components of the equilibrium if $0.350 \ M$ PCl_3, 0.350 M Cl_2, and $0.100 \ M$ PCl_5 are present initially in the reaction vessel?

Solution 15.18   First, calculate the value of Q to determine from which direction the equilibrium develops ($Q = 0.100 \ M/0.350^2 = 0.82$). Because Q (0.82) is less than K_c (13.7), this reaction goes from left to right as it establishes equilibrium. The initial molar concentrations of PCl_3 and Cl_2 are both $0.350 \ M$ and as equilibrium establishes their concentrations decrease by x mol/L. Initially the $[PCl_5]$ equals $0.100 \ M$, and at equilibrium the concentration of PCl_5 increases by x mol/L.

Compound	Initial Concentration, M	Concentration Change, M	Equilibrium Concentration, M
$[PCl_3]$	0.350	$-x$	$0.350 - x$
$[Cl_2]$	0.350	$-x$	$0.350 - x$
$[PCl_5]$	0.100	$+x$	$0.100 + x$

Substitute the equilibrium concentrations into the K_c expression and solve for x. This time, the quadratic formula is required to solve for x. Subsequently, simplify the equation and convert it to the general form of a quadratic equation ($ax^2 + bx + c = 0$) so that the quadratic formula can be applied ($x = \frac{-b \pm \sqrt{b^2 - 4ac}}{2a}$). Begin by substituting the values into the equilibrium expression and then rearranging the equation so that it is in the general form of a quadratic, $ax^2 + bx + c = 0$.

$$K_c = [PCl_5]/([PCl_3][Cl_2])$$
$$13.7 = (0.100 + x)/(0.350 - x)^2$$
$$13.7 = (0.100 + x)/(0.123 - 0.700x + x^2)$$
$$13.7x^2 - 9.59x + 1.68 = 0.100 + x$$
$$13.7x^2 - 10.59x + 1.58 = 0$$

For this equation $a = 13.7$, $b = -10.59$, and $c = 1.58$. Substitution into the quadratic formula gives the following.

$$x = \frac{-10.59 \pm \sqrt{-10.59^2 - (4 \times 13.7 \times 1.58)}}{2 \times 13.7}$$
$$= 0.202 \, M \text{ and } 0.571 \, M$$

Two possible values for x are obtained. Hence, it is necessary to determine which is physically meaningful. Because our initial concentrations of PCl_3 and Cl_2 are both $0.350 \, M$, only the $0.202 \, M$ value of x is meaningful in this problem. The other has no physical significance. Accordingly, use $0.202 \, M$ to calculate the equilibrium concentrations.

$$[PCl_3] = 0.350 - x = 0.350 \, M - 0.202 \, M = 0.148 \, M$$
$$[Cl_2] = 0.350 - x = 0.350 \, M - 0.202 \, M = 0.148 \, M$$
$$[PCl_5] = 0.100 + x = 0.100 \, M + 0.202 \, M = 0.302 \, M$$

Solving Equilibrium Problems Using the Method of Successive Approximation

Problem 15.19 The K_p value for

$$2PH_3(g) \rightleftharpoons P_2(g) + 3H_2(g)$$

is 1.04×10^{-6} at 500 K. Initially 2.75 atm PH_3 is introduced into a reaction vessel and the system is allowed to reach equilibrium. What are the equilibrium partial pressures of all components of the system?

Solution 15.19 The initial Q value for this reaction is zero because only the reactant PH_3 is present initially. Accordingly, this equilibrium develops from left to right. For each 2 atm of PH_3 that disappear, 1 atm of P_2 and 3 atm of H_2 appear. Because of the small value of K_p, the reaction will proceed to only a small extent before equilibrium is established. Therefore, the final pressure should not be much different from the initial value.

Compound	Initial Pressure, atm	Pressure Change, atm	Equilibrium pressure, atm
P_{PH_3}	2.75	$-2x$	$2.75 - 2x$
P_{P_2}	0	$+x$	x
P_{H_2}	0	$+3x$	$3x$

Substitute the values of the partial pressures at equilibrium into the equilibrium expression and solve for x.

$$K_p = P_{P_2}P_{H_2}^3/P_{PH_3}^2$$
$$1.04 \times 10^{-6} = x(3x)^3/(2.75 - 2x)^2$$
$$= 27x^4/(2.75 - 2x)^2$$

In order to solve such an equation, assume that the decrease in the partial pressure of PH_3 is very small and does not significantly change the initial pressure because of the small value for K_p, 1.04×10^{-6}. If this is true, drop the very small $2x$ term in the denominator. Thus, a simpler equation may be solved.

$$1.04 \times 10^{-6} \approx x(3x)^3/(2.75)^2$$
$$\approx 27x^4/7.56$$
$$x^4 \approx 2.91 \times 10^{-7}$$

The fourth root of each side of the equation gives us the value of x. To get the fourth root of 2.91×10^{-7}, use the y^x or x^y key on your calculator and find $(2.91 \times 10^7)^{0.25}$.

$$x = 0.0232 \text{ atm}$$

To obtain an even better value for x sometimes it is necessary to use the method of successive approximation. After obtaining the first value or approximation of x use it to calculate the equilibrium partial pressure of PH_3.

$$P_{PH_3} = 2.75 - 2x = 2.75 - 2(0.0232) = 2.70 \text{ atm}$$

Then, solve the equilibrium equation using the better estimate, 2.70 atm, of the final partial pressure of PH_3.

$$1.04 \times 10^{-6} = x(3x)^3/(2.70)^2 = 27x^4/7.29$$
$$x^4 = 2.81 \times 10^{-7}$$
$$x = 0.0230 \text{ atm}$$

The second approximation was not necessary for this problem because the difference was only 2 parts out of 230 parts (<1%), but in some other problems a second or third approximation may be required. Finally, calculate the equilibrium partial pressures.

$$P_{PH_3} = 2.75 - 2x = 2.75 - 2(0.0230) = 2.70 \text{ atm}$$
$$P_{P_2} = x = 0.0230 \text{ atm}$$
$$P_{H_2} = 3x = 3(0.0230) = 0.0690 \text{ atm}$$

15.5 FACTORS THAT AFFECT CHEMICAL EQUILIBRIA

Le Chatelier's Principle

Le Chatelier's Principle states that equilibrium systems tend to shift in such a way as to reduce changes in temperature, pressure, and concentration. If possible, disrupted equilibrium systems return to a state of equilibrium.

Concentration Changes

Le Chatelier's Principle states that an increase in the concentration of a component of an equilibrium shifts the equilibrium in the direction that consumes some of the added substance. The opposite effect is observed when a substance is removed from a chemical equilibrium. Le Chatelier's Principle states that an equilibrium system shifts in the direction that replaces the substance removed.

Pressure and Volume Changes

The effect of pressure and volume changes on chemical equilibria only changes the volume of gases. Both liquids and solids have constant volumes that do not change appreciably when the pressure changes. Hence, this discussion only pertains to gas-phase equilibria or heterogeneous equilibria with a gas phase. Le Chatelier's Principle predicts that the equilibrium shifts in the direction that occupies the smaller volume, i.e., the side of the equilibrium with the smaller number of moles of gaseous molecules. If the pressure is constant, the total number of moles of particles determines the volume of a gaseous system.

Problem 15.20   What effect will a decrease in volume have on the Haber equilibrium?

$$N_2(g) + 3H_2(g) \rightleftharpoons 2NH_3(g)$$

Solution 15.20   Four moles of molecules (1 mol N_2 and 3 mol H_2) are on the right side and two moles of molecules (2 mol NH_3) are on the left side. A decrease in volume of the system favors the forward reaction because it is the one that decreases the total number of moles in the system. Therefore, as the volume decreases the number of ammonia molecules increases and the number of N_2 and H_2 molecules decreases. A decrease in the pressure, which results in an increase in the volume of the system, causes the equilibrium to shift to the left, the direction that increases the total number of moles in the system.

Problem 15.21   Consider the following equilibrium.

$$H_2(g) + Cl_2(g) \rightleftharpoons 2HCl(g)$$

(a) Explain what effect an increase in pressure has on this equilibrium. (b) Use Q to explain the effect of a pressure increase.

Solution 15.21   (a) If the pressure is increased or decreased, it cannot shift to absorb the change because equal number of moles of molecules are on either side of the reaction. Therefore systems with equal numbers of moles of gaseous reactants and products do not shift when the pressure or volume changes. (b) Writing the Q expression shows that all the volume terms cancel in the HCl equilibrium; thus, a change in volume does not affect the value of Q.

$$Q = (n_{HCl}/V)^2/(n_{H_2}/V \times n_{Cl_2}/V) = (n_{HCl})^2/(n_{H_2}n_{Cl_2})$$

Temperature Changes

A temperature change results in a change in the value of K. When an equilibrium system is heated at constant pressure, the system shifts in the direction that favors the endothermic reaction. Conversely, when heat is removed, the equilibrium system shifts in the direction that favors the exothermic reaction. This relationship can be shown mathematically as follows.

$$\ln\frac{K_2}{K_1} = \frac{\Delta H}{R}\left(\frac{T_2 - T_1}{T_1 T_2}\right) \tag{15.6}$$

In Eq. 15.6, K_2 is the equilibrium constant at temperature T_2, K_1 is the equilibrium constant at T_1, ΔH is the enthalpy change of the reaction, and R is the ideal gas constant (0.008314 kJ/(mol·K). This is the van't Hoff equation.

Problem 15.22 Consider the following equilibrium.

$$2Hg(l) + O_2(g) \rightleftharpoons 2HgO(s) \qquad \Delta H° = -181kJ$$

(a) If the value for K_p is 3.2×10^{20} at 298 K, what is the K_p at 450 K? (b) Explain the answer to part (a).

Solution 15.22 (a) Substitute the given values into Eq. 15.6.

$$\ln(K_2/3.2 \times 10^{20}) = -181 \text{ kJ}/0.008314 \, kJ/K((450K - 298K)/(298K \cdot 450K))$$
$$= -24.7$$
$$K_2/3.2 \times 10^{20} = e^{-24.7} = 1.919 \times 10^{-11}$$
$$K_2 = 6.1 \times 10^9$$

(b) The forward reaction is exothermic and the reverse reaction is endothermic. An increase in temperature favors the reverse endothermic reaction. The equilibrium lies farther to the left at 450 K; hence, the value of K_p decreases, significantly.

Addition of Catalysts

A catalyst is a substance that lowers the activation energy, E_a, of a reaction. Because a catalyst lowers the activation energy in both directions, the rates of the forward and reverse reactions increase equally, which means that the equilibrium concentrations remain unchanged. However, a catalyst increases the rate at which the equilibrium establishes.

Problem 15.23 Consider the following equilibrium

$$2NO(g) + O_2(g) \rightleftharpoons 2NO_2(g) \qquad \Delta H = -117kJ$$

For each of the following changes predict the effect on the concentration of NO_2. (a) an increase in [NO], (b) a pressure decrease as a result of increased volume, (c) a volume decrease, (d) a temperature decrease.

Solution 15.23 (a) When a reactant concentration, such as NO, is increased, the equilibrium shifts to the right to absorb the increased number of NO molecules; therefore, the [NO_2] increases. (b) A pressure decrease that results in an increase in volume favors the reaction that yields the larger number of molecules. Because the reverse reaction produces three moles and the forward reaction produces two moles, the reverse reaction is favored; accordingly, the [NO_2] decreases. (c) The volume decreases when the pressure increases. At smaller volumes and higher pressures the reaction favors the side of the reaction that produces a smaller number of moles of particles. The forward reaction, which produces two moles of molecules, decreases the total number of moles in the system; therefore, the [NO_2] increases. (d) The enthalpy change for the reaction is -117 kJ, which means the forward reaction is exothermic and the reverse reaction is endothermic. A temperature decrease favors the exothermic reaction because it replaces the heat removed; subsequently, the [NO_2] increases.

SUMMARY

A chemical equilibrium establishes when the rate of the forward reaction equals the rate of the reverse reaction. At that time the concentrations of the reactants and products remain constant. The Law of Mass Action expresses the concentration of the reactants and products in terms of an equilibrium constant, K_c. The equilibrium constant equals the product of the molar concentrations of the products each raised to the power that corresponds to their coefficients in the balanced equation divided by the product of the molar concentrations of the reactants each raised to the power corresponding to their coefficients. Equilibria that have reactants and products in more than one phase are heterogeneous equilibria and those in which all substances in one phase are homogeneous equilibria.

If the value of the equilibrium constant is greater than one ($K_c > 1$), then the magnitude of the numerator of the equilibrium expression is larger than that of the denominator. Hence, the equilibrium concentrations of the products are usually higher than those of the reactants. If the value of K_c is less than one, the equilibrium concentrations of the reactants are usually greater than those of the products.

Equilibrium constants for gas-phase equilibria are often expressed in terms of their partial pressures. This is known as the K_p equilibrium constant. The following equation shows the relationship of K_p to K_c.

$$K_p = K_c(RT)^{\Delta n}$$

Equilibrium constants are obtained by measuring the equilibrium concentrations or partial pressures of each component of an equilibrium mixture and substituting these values into the equilibrium expression.

Before a system reaches equilibrium, the concentrations or partial pressures are expressed in terms of the reaction quotient, Q. The expression for Q is in the same form as that of K. The value of Q is used to determine the direction from which an equilibrium develops.

Concentration, pressure, volume, and temperature changes affect the concentrations of the components of a chemical equilibrium. Their effects may be predicted by the application of Le Chatelier's Principle which states that equilibrium systems tend to absorb any changes that may occur in such a way to reduce the change and return to a state of equilibrium.

CHAPTER 15 REVIEW EXERCISE

1. Write the equilibrium expression for the following:

$$CaCO_3(s) + 2HF(g) \rightleftharpoons CaF_2(s) + H_2O(g) + CO_2(g)$$

2. Write the equilibrium expressions, K_c, for each of the following:

   (a) $ZnSO_4(s) \rightleftharpoons ZnO(s) + SO_3(g)$
   (b) $Fe_2O_3(s) + 3CO(g) \rightleftharpoons 2Fe(s) + 3CO_2(g)$

3. Consider the following equilibrium:

$$N_2(g) + 3H_2(g) \rightleftharpoons 2NH_3(g) \quad K_c = 0.0060 \text{ (298K)}$$

   Determine the equilibrium constants, K_c for each of the following.
   (a) $2NH_3(g) \rightleftharpoons N_2(g) + 3H_2(g)$, (b) $NH_3(g) \rightleftharpoons \frac{1}{2}N_2(g) + 3/2H_2(g)$

4. The following gas-phase equilibrium has a K_p value of 1.78 at 523 K:

$$PCl_5(g) \rightleftharpoons PCl_3(g) + Cl_2(g)$$

(a) Calculate the value of K_c. (b) Calculate the value of K_p for the reverse of this reaction.

5. Consider the following equilibrium:

$$2HBr(g) \rightleftharpoons H_2(g) + Br_2(g)$$

Initially, 0.0145 atm HBr is added to a reaction vessel at 1400 K and is allowed to equilibrate. At equilibrium, 0.0136 atm HBr remains in the vessel. Calculate the value of K_p.

6. Consider the following equilibrium:

$$2NO_2(g) \rightleftharpoons N_2O_4(g)$$

Initially, 0.75 atm NO_2 is introduced in a reaction vessel and 0.10 atm N_2O_4 results at equilibrium. Calculate the value of K_p for this equilibrium.

7. Consider the following equilibrium:

$$COCl_2(g) \rightleftharpoons CO(g) + Cl_2(g)$$

Initially 9.90 g $COCl_2$ is introduced into a 1.00-L reaction vessel at 600 K. At equilibrium, 4.79 atm $COCl_2$ are found. What is the K_p for this equilibrium?

8. Consider the following equilibrium:

$$CO(g) + 1/2O_2(g) \rightleftharpoons CO_2(g)$$

Calculate K_p for this equilibrium using the following equations.

$$C(s) + 1/2O_2(g) \rightleftharpoons CO(g) \quad K_p \doteq 2.9 \times 10^{10}$$
$$C(s) + O_2 \rightleftharpoons CO_2(g) \quad K_p = 4.8 \times 10^{20}$$

9. Calculate the equilibrium constant for the following equilibrium at 2000 K:

$$BrF_3(g) \rightleftharpoons BrF(g) + F_2(g)$$

given the following equations and equilibrium constants.

$$Br_2(g) + F_2(g) \rightleftharpoons 2BrF(g) \quad K_p = 2.2 \times 10^4$$
$$\frac{1}{2}Br_2(g) + 3/2F_2(g) \rightleftharpoons BrF_3(g) \quad K_p = 2.3$$

10. The equilibrium constant K_p for the Haber reaction is 4.5×10^{-5} at 723 K.

$$N_2(g) + 3H_2(g) \rightleftharpoons 2NH_3(g)$$

Determine the direction the Haber equilibrium establishes with the following initial partial pressures: $P_{N_2} = 2.09$ atm, $P_{H_2} = 1.33$ atm, and $P_{NH_3} = 0.0144$ atm.

11. At 500 K the equilibrium constant K_p for:

$$2PH_3(g) \rightleftharpoons P_2(g) + 3H_2(g)$$

is 1.04×10^{-6}. A reaction vessel contains 0.00788 atm P_2, 0.236 atm H_2, and 0.299 atm PH_3. Determine if this system is in equilibrium, and if not, from what direction will it approach equilibrium?

12. Consider the following equilibrium system.

$$PCl_3(g) + Cl_2(g) \rightleftharpoons PCl_5(g) \quad Kc = 13.7 \ (546K)$$

Calculate the equilibrium concentrations when the initial concentrations of PCl_3, Cl_2, and PCl_5 are all 0.500 M.

13. The K_p value for $2PH_3(g) \rightleftharpoons P_2(g) + 3H_2(g)$ is 1.04×10^{-6} at 500 K. Calculate the equilibrium concentrations of all components when the initial concentrations are 1.00 atm P_2 and 1.00 atm H_2.

14. The equilibrium constant K_c for $N_2O_4(g) \rightleftharpoons 2\ NO_2(g)$ is 0.125 at 298 K. What is the percent dissociation of N_2O_4 when initially 138 g N_2O_4 is placed into a 1.00-L reaction vessel?

15. Consider the following equilibrium:

$$4HCl(g) + O_2(g) \rightleftharpoons 2H_2O(g) + 2Cl_2(g) \quad \triangle H = -116 \ kJ$$

What effect do each of the following have on the concentration of Cl_2? (a) addition of H_2O, (b) removal of HCl, (c) adding a catalyst, (d) decreasing the volume, (e) decreasing the temperature

16. Consider the following equilibrium:

$$2BrF_3(g) \rightleftharpoons Br_2(g) + 5F_2(g) \quad \triangle H^\circ = 858 \ kJ$$

At 1000 K, the K_p for this reaction is 7.4×10^{-16}. What is the K_p value at 1250 K?

17. The equilibrium constant K_c for $2NO(g) \rightleftharpoons N_2(g) + O_2(g)$ is 8.36×10^3 at 1800 K. What are the equilibrium concentrations of N_2, O_2, and NO, if 0.100 mol NO is initially present in a 2.70-L reaction vessel?

18. The equilibrium constant K_p for $2IF(g) \rightleftharpoons I_2(g) + F_2(g)$ is 2.9×10^{-14} at 2675 K. (a) If 1.0 atm IF and 1.0 atm F_2 is placed into a reaction vessel, what is the final partial pressure of I_2 at equilibrium? (b) What is the final partial pressure of I_2 if only 1.0 atm IF is initially introduced into the reaction vessel?

19. At elevated temperatures solid ammonium chloride, NH_4Cl, dissociates to $NH_3(g)$ and $HCl(g)$.

$$NH_4Cl(s) \rightleftharpoons NH_3(g) + HCl(g)$$

When a sample of ammonium chloride is allowed to equilibrate in an evacuated container at 613 K, the total pressure becomes 1.00 atm. (a) What is the K_p for this equilibrium? (b) What change occurs in the equilibrium partial pressures of the gases when 5.00 g solid ammonium chloride is added to the container? (c) Additional NH_3 is introduced into the container without a temperature change until the partial pressure of NH_3 is 0.75 atm. What is the partial pressure of HCl and the total pressure?

ANSWERS TO REVIEW EXERCISE

1. $K_c = ([H_2O][CO_2])/[HF]^2$
2. (a) $K_c = [SO_3]$, (b) $K_c = [CO_2]^3/[CO]^3$
3. (a) 17, (b) 4.1
4. (a) 0.0415, (b) 0.562
5. 1×10^{-3}
6. $K_p = 0.33$
7. $K_p = 4.09 \times 10^{-3}$
8. $K_p = 1.7 \times 10^{10}$
9. 64
10. $Q(4.22 \times 10^{-5}) < K(4.5 \times 10^{-5})$ thus the equilibrium establishes from left to right
11. $Q(1.16 \times 10^{-3})$ is greater than K_p which means that equilibrium is established from right to left
12. $[PCl_3] = [Cl_2] = 0.236\ M$, $[PCl_5] = 0.764\ M$
13. $P_{P_2} = 0.67$ atm, $P_{H_2} = 0.01$ atm, $P_{PH_3} = 0.66$ atm
14. 13.4%
15. (a) decreases, (b) decreases, (c) remains constant, (d) increases, (e) increases
16. 6.8×10^{-7}
17. $[N_2] = [O_2] = 0.0184\ M$, $[NO] = 2 \times 10^{-4}M$
18. (a) $2.9 \times 10^{-14}M$, (b) $1.7 \times 10^{-7}M$
19. (a) 0.25, (b) no change, (c) $P_{HCl} = 0.39$ atm, $P_t = 1.03$ atm

16

Aqueous Equilibria: Acids, Bases, and Salts

---

*A*cids taste sour while bases taste bitter. Acids change the color of acid-base indicators exactly the opposite to that of bases. Acids and bases neutralize each other and produce salts. Many acids dissolve metals and release hydrogen gas. Bases have a slippery feeling when they come in contact with the skin.

16.1 ARRHENIUS ACID AND BASE DEFINITIONS

Arrhenius Definitions

Arrhenius defined an acid as a substance that increases the hydrogen ion, H^+, concentration when it dissolves in water. He defined a base as a substance that increases the hydroxide ion, OH^-, concentration when it dissolves in water.

Hydronium Ions, H_3O^+

A hydrogen ion is a proton–a very small body with a high positive charge density. When a H^+ ion combines with a H_2O molecule it produces a hydronium ion, H_3O^+. After the hydronium ion forms, it hydrogen bonds to other water molecules producing a polyatomic ion with the formula of $H_9O_4^+$, which interacts with other water molecules. Therefore, a good representation for the hydrogen ion in water is $H^+(aq)$, which shows that many water molecules surround a hydrogen ion.

16.2 BRØNSTED-LOWRY ACID AND BASE DEFINITIONS

Brønsted-Lowry Definitions

Johannes Brønsted and Thomas Lowry extended the Arrhenius definitions of acids and bases. They defined an acid as a proton donor and a base as a proton acceptor. The Brønsted-Lowry definition of an acid is similar to the Arrhenius definition because a proton and a H^+ are the same chemical species ($p^+ = H^+$).

Monoprotic, Diprotic, and Triprotic Acids

A monoprotic acid is one that donates only one proton. Examples of monoprotic acids include HCl and $HC_2H_3O_2$. Diprotic acids are those that donate two protons. A good example of a diprotic acid is sulfuric acid, H_2SO_4. Triprotic acids can donate a maximum of three protons. Phosphoric acid, H_3PO_4, is a good example of a triprotic acid.

Problem 16.1   Write two equations that show the diprotic nature of sulfuric acid, $H_2SO_4(aq)$.

Solution 16.1
$$H_2SO_4(aq) \longrightarrow H^+(aq) + HSO_4^-(aq)$$
$$HSO_4^-(aq) \longrightarrow H^+(aq) + SO_4^{2-}(aq)$$

Problem 16.2   Explain why phosphorous acid, H_3PO_3, is a diprotic and not a triprotic acid.

Solution 16.2   Phosphorous acid is a diprotic acid because one of the H atoms forms a strong covalent bond with the P atom and thus does not dissociate.

$$
\begin{array}{c}
H \\
| \\
H-O-P-O-H \\
\| \\
O
\end{array}
$$

Conjugate Acid-Base Pairs

When HF donates a H^+ ion, the fluoride ion, F^-, remains. If the F^- ion accepts a proton, it produces HF; thus, F^- is a Brønsted-Lowry base. The base the results after an acid releases a proton is termed the conjugate base of the acid because it can accept a proton and re- form the acid. In a similar manner, after a base accepts a proton it produces its conjugate acid. A conjugate acid yields the base after it donates the proton. Another example of a conjugate acid-base pair is ammonia, NH_3, and the ammonium ion, NH_4^+. Ammonia accepts a proton and produces the ammonium ion, which donates a proton to return to ammonia.

Problem 16.3   (a) What are the conjugate bases of HNO_3, NH_3, and OH^-? (b) What are the conjugate acids of HNO_3, NH_3, OH^-?

Solution 16.3

(a)

Acid	Conjugate Base
HNO_3	NO_3^-
NH_3	NH_2^-
OH^-	O^{2-}

(b)

Base	Conjugate Acid
HNO_3	$H_2NO_3^+$
NH_3	NH_4^+
OH^-	H_2O

Amphiprotic Species

Some molecules and ions exhibit both acidic and basic behavior depending on the reaction conditions. Chemical species that can either donate or accept protons are called amphiprotic. For example, water is an amphiprotic molecule. If water combines with a stronger acid, such as HCl, it accepts a proton and becomes a hydronium ion. However, if water combines with a stronger base such as NH_3, it donates a proton and a hydroxide ion results.

Amphoteric Species

Amphoteric is a closely related term to amphiprotic, but these terms have slightly different meanings. An amphoteric species is one that can act as either an acid or a base. For example, aluminum oxide, Al_2O_3, is classified as an amphoteric oxide. This means that it behaves as a base in the presence of a stronger acid and behaves as an acid in the presence of a stronger base. When $Al_2O_3(s)$ is mixed with hydrochloric acid, $HCl(aq)$, water and aluminum chloride, $AlCl_3$, result.

$$Al_2O_3(s) + 6HCl(aq) \longrightarrow 2AlCl_3(aq) + 3H_2O(l)$$
$$\text{base}$$

Nevertheless, when $Al_2O_3(s)$ mixes with sodium hydroxide, $NaOH(aq)$, sodium aluminum hydroxide, $NaAl(OH)_4(aq)$, results.

$$Al_2O_3(s) + 2NaOH(aq) + 3H_2O(l) \longrightarrow 2NaAl(OH)_4(aq)$$
$$\text{acid}$$

Problem 16.4 Explain why $Be(OH)_2$ is amphoteric but not amphiprotic, but water is both amphoteric and amphiprotic.

Solution 16.4 $Be(OH)_2$ reacts with acids to produce $Be^{2+}(aq)$ and reacts with strong hydroxide bases to produce $Be(OH)_4^-(aq)$.

$$Be(OH)_2(s) + 3H^+(aq) \longrightarrow Be^{2+}(aq) + 2H_2O(l)$$
$$Be(OH)_2(s) + 2OH^-(aq) \longrightarrow Be(OH)_4^-(aq)$$

16.3 THE RELATIVE STRENGTHS OF ACIDS AND BASES

Proton-Donating Tendency

A stronger acid has a greater tendency to donate a proton than a weaker acid. If hydrobromic acid, a strong acid, combines with water, HBr donates a proton to the water producing hydronium and bromide ions.

$$HBr(g) + H_2O(l) \longrightarrow H_3O^+(aq) + Br^-(aq)$$

Measurements reveal that 100% of the HBr molecules produce ions in dilute solutions. Thus, HBr is classified as a strong acid because it has a large capacity to donate protons to water. By contrast, when hydrofluoric acid, combines with water only a small percent of the HF molecules ionize.

$$HF(aq) + H_2O(l) \rightleftharpoons H_3O^+(aq) + F^-(aq)$$

In this equation the unequal arrows, $\rightleftharpoons$, show that the equilibrium lies far to the left. Therefore, HF is classified as a weak acid because it has a limited capacity to transfer protons to water.

Conjugate Acids and Bases and Proton-Donating Tendency

Stronger acids have weaker conjugate bases than weaker acids. The stronger the conjugate base the greater the tendency to accept protons and shift the equilibrium to the left towards the un-ionized acid. Thus, the equilibria of acids with weak conjugate bases are shifted to the right in favor of the free ions.

Conjugate Acids and Bases and Proton-Accepting Tendency

In terms of the Brønsted-Lowry definitions, the strength of bases is measured in terms of their proton-accepting tendency. A stronger base has a greater tendency to accept a proton than a weaker base. Bases that are stronger than the conjugate base of water, the hydroxide ion (OH^-), are leveled to the strength of the hydroxide ion. For example, aqueous NH_2^- readily removes protons from water and produces NH_3 and OH^-.

$$NH_2^-(aq) + H_2O(l) \longrightarrow NH_3(aq) + OH^-(aq)$$

Bases listed between the hydroxide ion and water have decreasing basic strength. Accordingly, the equilibrium for these bases lies to the left in favor of the undissociated base.

16.4   LEWIS ACID AND BASE DEFINITIONS

Lewis Definitions

A Lewis acid is an electron-pair acceptor. A Lewis base is an electron pair donor. Using the Lewis definitions, any atom or molecule that accepts a pair of electrons is an acid, and any atom or molecule that donates a pair of electrons in the formation of a bond is a base.

Problem 16.5   Consider the following reaction in which boron trifluoride combines with ammonia ($BF_3 + :NH_3 \longrightarrow F_3B-NH_3$). (a) Describe what happens in this reaction. (b) Identify the Lewis acid and base.

Solution 16.5

(a) In the reaction of boron trifluoride, BF_3, and ammonia, NH_3, the B atom in BF_3 accepts the lone-pair electrons from the N atom in NH_3 and produces the B—N bond in F_3B—NH_3.

(b) NH_3 is a Lewis base because it donates the electron pair and BF_3 is a Lewis acid because it accepts the pair of electrons. The product of a Lewis acid-base reaction is called an acid-base adduct because it is a combination of the Lewis acid and Lewis base.

Problem 16.6   Consider the following reactions.

(a) $AlF_3 + :\ddot{F}:^- \longrightarrow AlF_4^-$
(b) $Ag^+ + 2 :\ddot{N}H_3 \longrightarrow [Ag(NH_3)_2]^+$
(c) $Fe^{3+} + 3 :\ddot{B}r:^- \longrightarrow FeBr_3$

(a) Identify the Lewis bases in these reactions. (b) Identify the Lewis acids.

Solution 16.6

(a) F^-, NH_3, and Br^- are the three Lewis bases in these reactions. Each Lewis base donates a pair of electrons to the Lewis acid and forms a bond.

(b) AlF_3, Ag^+, and Fe^{3+} are the three Lewis acids in these reactions because they accept the electron pair from the Lewis base.

Nature of Lewis Acids

Lewis acids are electron-deficient species–those that require a pair of electrons to become more stable. The three general groups of Lewis acids are most positive ions (including H^+), compounds that have an electron-deficient atom, and compounds with atoms that can expand the number of valence electrons.

Problem 16.7   Which of the following are Lewis acids? (a) Na^+, (b) $AlCl_3$, (c) Fe^{3+}, (d) $SbCl_3$

Solution 16.7

(a) Na^+ is not a Lewis acid because it has a noble gas configuration and does not readily accept electron pairs.
(b) $AlCl_3$ is a Lewis acid because the central Al atom can accept an electron pair and obtain a noble gas configuration.
(c) Fe^{3+} and other cations are Lewis acids because they can readily accept electron pairs.
(d) $SbCl_3$ is a Lewis acid because the Sb atom can expand its octet.

Nature of Lewis Bases

Lewis bases are electron-rich species–those that donate electron density. The two principal classes of Lewis bases are negative ions and neutral molecules with at least one lone pair. Any anion can be a Lewis base because it is an electron-rich species. Molecules that have one or more lone pairs that can be donated are also Lewis bases. NH_3, PH_3, H_2O, and amines such as CH_3NH_2 and $(CH_3)_2NH$ are examples of Lewis bases.

Problem 16.8   Which of the following acids are Lewis acids but are not Brønsted-Lowry acids: $HBrO_3$, SbF_3, HSO_4^-, AlF_3?

Solution 16.8   A Lewis acid is an electron-pair acceptor. A Brønsted-Lowry acid is a proton donor. In this group, both $HBrO_3$ and HSO_4^- are Brønsted-Lowry acids because they can donate protons. SbF_3 and AlF_3 are not Brønsted-Lowry acids because they cannot donate protons, but are Lewis acids because the central atoms can accept electron pairs.

16.5   NEUTRALIZATION REACTIONS AND THE FORMATION OF SALTS

Neutralization Reactions

A neutralization reaction occurs when an acid and base react. One general way to express this reaction is as follows:

$$HA + MOH \longrightarrow MA + H_2O$$

in which HA is a monoprotic acid, MOH is a base, and MA is a salt. Though these reactions are termed neutralization reactions, the resulting solutions may be may be acidic, basic, or neutral after the addition of equivalent amounts of acid and base.

REACTIONS OF STRONG ACIDS WITH STRONG BASES

Hydrochloric acid, HCl(*aq*), reacts with a solution of sodium hydroxide, NaOH(*aq*), to produce sodium chloride and water. Because hydrochloric acid is a strong acid and sodium hydroxide is a strong base, they are written as individual ions and not as un-ionized molecules or formula units.

$$H^+(aq) + Cl^-(aq) + Na^+(aq) + OH^-(aq) \longrightarrow Na^+(aq) + Cl^-(aq) + H_2O(l)$$

The net ionic equation for this reaction and all reactions in which a strong acid reacts with a strong base is $H^+(aq) + OH^-(aq) \longrightarrow H_2O(l)$. This reaction goes to completion and the resulting solution is neutral because neither Na^+ nor Cl^- undergo hydrolysis.

REACTIONS OF WEAK ACIDS WITH STRONG BASES

Consider the reaction of acetic acid, $HC_2H_3O_2(aq)$, a weak acid, and sodium hydroxide, NaOH(*aq*), a strong base. Because acetic acid is a weak acid, it is written as an un-ionized molecule, $HC_2H_3O_2(aq)$.

$$HC_2H_3O_2(aq) + Na^+(aq) + OH^-(aq) \longrightarrow Na^+(aq) + C_2H_3O_2^-(aq) + H_2O(l)$$

The products are water and an aqueous solution of sodium acetate, $NaC_2H_3O_2(aq)$. After the spectator ion, Na^+, is canceled, the net ionic equation is

$$HC_2H_3O_2(aq) + OH^-(aq) \longrightarrow C_2H_3O_2^-(aq) + H_2O(l)$$

Because the acetate ion is the conjugate base of a weak acid, it has basic properties and can accept protons from water. In general, the resulting solutions are basic when equivalent amounts of a weak acid and a strong base undergo a neutralization reaction.

REACTIONS OF STRONG ACIDS WITH WEAK BASES

Consider the reaction of hydrochloric acid, HCl(*aq*), a strong acid, and ammonia, $NH_3(aq)$, a weak base, to produce an aqueous solution of ammonium chloride, $NH_4Cl(aq)$.

$$H^+(aq) + Cl^-(aq) + NH_3(aq) \longrightarrow NH_4^+(aq) + Cl^-(aq)$$

Hydrochloric acid is written as ions because it is a strong acid, and ammonia as an un-ionized molecule because it is a weak base. The net ionic reaction that occurs is

$$H^+(aq) + NH_3(aq) \longrightarrow NH_4^+(aq)$$

Because the ammonium ion is an acidic cation (the conjugate acid of a weak base) it releases H^+ ions and produces an acidic solution. Equivalent amounts of strong acids and weak bases yield acidic solutions.

REACTIONS OF WEAK ACIDS WITH WEAK BASES

Consider the neutralization of acetic acid and ammonia. To begin, write both acetic acid and ammonia as un-ionized molecules because both are weak electrolytes.

$$HC_2H_3O_2(aq) + NH_3(aq) \rightleftharpoons NH_4^+(aq) + C_2H_3O_2^-(aq)$$

The product of this reaction is an aqueous solution of ammonium acetate, $NH_4C_2H_3O_2(aq)$. Because the strength of acetic acid almost equals the strength of ammonia, the resulting solution is nearly neutral. However, if one of the reactants is a stronger acid or base than the other, the resulting solution becomes acidic or basic, depending upon the strengths of each reactant.

Problem 16.9 (a) Write the overall ionic and net ionic equation for the reaction of aqueous potassium hydroxide and nitrous acid. (b) When equivalent amounts are mixed, is the solution acidic, basic, or neutral? Explain.

Solution 16.9

(a)
$$HNO_2(aq) + K^+(aq) + OH^-(aq) \longrightarrow K^+(aq) + NO_2^-(aq) + H_2O(l)$$

K^+ is the only spectator ion in this reaction; therefore, the net ionic reaction is as follows.

$$HNO_2(aq) + OH^-(aq) \longrightarrow NO_2^-(aq) + H_2O(l)$$

(b) When equivalent amounts of $HNO_2(aq)$ and $KOH(aq)$ are mixed, the nitrite ion, NO_2^-, and water results. The nitrite ion is the conjugate base of a weak acid. Therefore, it can accept protons from water and produce a basic solution.

Salts

Salts are ionic compounds that result when acids combine with bases. Salts consist of a cation other than H^+ and an anion other than O_2^- or OH^-. In dilute aqueous solutions, salts usually dissociate totally into ions. Salts may be acidic, neutral, or basic. The acid-base properties of salts are predicted from the type of neutralization reaction that occurs to produce these salts.

NEUTRAL SALTS

When a strong acid reacts with a strong base, a neutral salt results. If a neutral salt is dissolved in water, it produces a neutral solution–one that is neither acidic nor basic. Examples of neutral salts include KCl, NaBr, and NaI. Each of these salts results from the reaction of strong acids such as HCl, HBr, or HI and strong base such as KOH, NaOH, or NaOH.

BASIC SALTS

Basic salts result when a strong base reacts with a weak acid. An example of a basic salt is sodium fluoride, NaF(s), which results when NaOH, a strong base, reacts with HF, a weak acid. The Na^+ ion has little tendency to react with water, but the F^- ion is the conjugate base of a weak acid; i.e., a base stronger than water. Thus, F^- accepts a H^+ from water and produces HF and OH^-. The F^- ion is said to hydrolyze water because it splits the water molecule and produces OH^- ions. All conjugate bases of very weak acids can hydrolyze water and produce basic solutions.

ACIDIC SALTS

Acidic salts result when strong acids react with weak bases. An example of an acidic salt is ammonium chloride, NH_4Cl. It results when the weak base ammonia combines with the strong acid hydrochloric acid. The conjugate acids of weak bases are relatively strong acids. Accordingly, the ammonia ion is a stronger acid than water, which means it can donate H^+ ions to water and increase the hydronium ion concentration. In addition, most metallic cations except those of the alkali metals and the heavier alkaline earths (Ca^{2+}, Sr^{2+}, and Ba^{2+}) are to some degree acidic. Metal ions are electron deficient (Lewis acids) which allows them to accept electrons from water molecules. The higher the charge on the metal ion, the greater the force of attraction and greater the acidic properties.

Problem 16.10 For each of the following salts predict if they are acidic, basic, or neutral: (a) NH_4NO_3, (b) KCN, (c) $CsClO_4$.

Solution 16.10

(a) Ammonium ions are the conjugate acids of the weak base ammonia, NH_3; therefore, they are acidic. Nitrate ions are the conjugate bases of the very strong acid nitric acid, HNO_3; hence, nitrate ions are neutral. The combination of an acidic cation and a neutral anion gives an acidic salt.

(b) Potassium ions are the result of the dissociation of the strong base KOH. Thus, they have little tendency to combine with water to produce an acidic solution–they are neutral cations. A cyanide ion is the conjugate base of the weak acid HCN. Thus, they are relatively strong bases. A neutral cation and basic anion give a basic salt.

(c) Cesium ions, like all alkali metal ions, are neutral cations. Perchlorate ions are the conjugate base of the very strong perchloric acid, $HClO_4$; as a result, they are neutral anions. Two neutral ions in a salt produces a neutral salt.

16.6   SELF-IONIZATION (AUTOIONIZATION) OF WATER

Water Ionizes to a Small Degree

Water is essentially a nonelectrolyte, but it ionizes to a very small degree. This may be attributed to the self-ionization, also called autoionization, of water. Self-ionization occurs when two like molecules react and produce ions. For water, Eq. 16.1 shows its self-ionization.

$$H_2O(l) + H_2O(l) \rightleftharpoons H_3O^+(aq) + OH^-(aq) \tag{16.1}$$

In pure water a hydronium ion and hydroxide ion are in equilibrium with two water molecules. Note that the moles of H_3O^+ and OH^- ions are equal in pure water.

Ion-Product Equilibrium Constant of Water, K_w

The degree to which water undergoes self-ionization is expressed by writing the ion-product equilibrium expression for water.

$$K_w = [H_3O^+][OH^-] \tag{16.2}$$

The equilibrium constant K_w is called the ion-product equilibrium constant. Because it is most common to write $H^+(aq)$ instead of $H_3O^+(aq)$ the form of this equation is as follows.

$$K_w = [H^+][OH^-] \tag{16.3}$$

Equation 16.3 shows that product of the molar concentrations of H^+ and OH^- is constant. At 25°C, the value for K_w is 1.0×10^{-14}.

Problem 16.11   (a) Use Eq. 16.3 to calculate the molar concentrations of H^+ and OH^- in pure water. (b) What percent of the water molecules are ionized in pure water? The molarity of pure water is 55.6 M.

Solution 16.11

(a) If x equals the molar concentration of H^+, then x is also the molar concentration of OH^- because one mole of H^+ and one mole of OH^- results from the self-ionization of water. Substituting x into the equation for the ion-product equilibrium constant for water gives the following.

$$x^2 = 1.0 \times 10^{-14}$$
$$x = 1.0 \times 10^{-7} \ M$$

(b) To find the percent, %, of water molecules ionized, divide the molarity of pure water by the molarity of the ionized molecules and multiply by 100.

$$\% \text{ ionized} = (1.0 \times 10^{-7} M / 55.6 M) \times 100 = 1.8 \times 10^{-7} \%$$

16.7 H^+ AND OH^- ION CONCENTRATIONS IN STRONG ACIDIC AND BASIC SOLUTIONS

Adding Strong Acids and Bases to Water

If either an acid or base is added to water, the H^+ and OH^- ion concentrations change. For example, if a strong acid such as $HCl(g)$ is added, the H^+ ion concentration increases because HCl ionizes completely and produces H^+ and Cl^- ions. If a strong base such as $NaOH(s)$ is added to water, the OH^- ion concentration in water increases because it completely dissociates and produces Na^+ and OH^-.

Strong Acids and Bases and the Water Ionization Equilibrium

The addition of either H^+ or OH^- shifts the water ionization equilibrium to the left towards the un-ionized water molecule, H_2O. In pure water, both the H^+ and OH^- ion concentrations equal $1.0 \times 10^{-7} M$. In aqueous solutions of strong acids such as HCl, the H^+ ion concentration is greater than $1.0 \times 10^{-7} M$ and the OH^- ion concentration is less than $1.0 \times 10^{-7} M$. In aqueous solutions of strong bases such as NaOH, the H^+ ion concentration is less than $1.0 \times 10^{-7} M$ and the OH^- ion concentration is greater than $1.0 \times 10^{-7} M$.

Problem 16.12 What is the $[H^+]$ and $[OH^-]$ in a solution that has 0.010 mol HCl dissolved in enough water to produce 100 mL of solution?

Solution 16.12 First, calculate the molar concentration of HCl that equals the molar concentrations of H^+ and Cl^- because HCl ionizes 100%.

$$[HCl] = 0.010 \text{ mol HCl} / (100 \text{ mL} \times 1 \text{ L} / 1000 \text{ mL}) = 0.10 \ M$$
$$[H^+] = [Cl^-] = 0.10 \ M$$

The molar concentration of H^+ from the HCl is vastly greater than those contributed by water. Therefore, the H^+ ion concentration in this solution is $0.100 \ M$. The OH^- ion concentration is calculated from the ion-product equilibrium expression (Eq. 16.3) which is as follows.

$$1.0 \times 10^{-14} = [H^+][OH^-] = (0.10 \ M \ H^+) [OH^-]$$
$$[OH^-] = 1.0 \times 10^{-14} / 0.10 \ M = 1.0 \times 10^{-14} \ M \ OH^-$$

Problem 16.13 A 0.053-g sample of $Ca(OH)_2$ is dissolved in enough water to have a total volume of 115 mL. Calculate the $[H^+]$ and $[OH^-]$ for this solution.

Solution 16.13 First, write the equation for the dissociation of $Ca(OH)_2$ in water.

$$Ca(OH)_2(s) \xrightarrow{H_2O} Ca^{2+}(aq) + 2OH^-(aq)$$

Then, calculate the number of moles of OH^- present.

$$0.053 \text{ g Ca(OH)}_2 \times 1 \text{ mol Ca(OH)}_2/74.1 \text{ g Ca(OH)}_2$$

$$\times 2 \text{ mol OH}^-/1 \text{ mol Ca(OH)}_2 = 0.0014 \text{ mol OH}^-$$

To obtain the hydroxide ion concentration, divide the number of moles by the total volume in liters.

$$[OH^-] = 0.0014 \text{ mol OH}^-/(115 \text{ mL} \times 1 \text{ L}/1000 \text{ mL}) = 0.012 \text{ } M$$

Note that the OH^- ion concentration contributed by the self- ionization of water is insignificant (1×10^{-7} M versus 0.012 M) and does not play a role in this calculation. To complete this problem, calculate the molarity of the H^+ ion by substituting the OH^- ion concentration into the ion-product equilibrium expression.

$$1.0 \times 10^{-14} = [H^+](0.012 \text{ } M \text{ } OH^-)$$
$$[H^-] = 1.0 \times 10^{-14}/0.012 \text{ } M = 8.3 \times 10^{-13} \text{ } M \text{ } H^+$$

16.8   PH AND POH OF SOLUTIONS

pH

The unit pH is defined as the negative common logarithm of the molar concentration of the H^+ ion.

$$pH = -\log [H^+] \tag{16.4}$$

In pure water the H^+ ion concentration in pure water is 1×10^{-7} M; thus, its pH equals 7.0.

$$pH = -\log [H^+] = -\log (1 \times 10^{-7} \text{ } M) = 7.0$$

This shows that the center of the pH scale is 7.0. Acidic solutions have H^+ ion concentrations greater than 1.0×10^{-7} M. Thus, all acidic solutions have pH values less than 7. Basic solutions have H^+ ion concentrations less that 1.0×10^{-7} M; therefore, they have pH values greater than 7.

Problem 16.14   (a) What is the pH of a 0.1 M H^+ solution? (b) What is the pH of a 0.1 M OH^- solution?

Solution 16.14

(a)
$$pH = -\log [H^+] = -\log(0.1 \text{ } M) = 1.0$$

(b)
$$1.0 \times 10^{-14} = [H^+][0.1 \text{ } M \text{ } OH^-]$$
$$[H^+] = 1.0 \times 10^{-14}/0.1 \text{ } M = 1 \times 10^{-13} \text{ } M \text{ } OH^-$$

Then, take the negative logarithm of $1 \times 10^{-13} M$.

$$pH = -\log [H^+] = -\log (1 \times 10^{-13} \text{ } M) = 13.0$$

Problem 16.15   A solution is prepared by dissolving 150 mg perchloric acid, $HClO_4$, in 3.55 L of solution. What is the pH of solution?

Solution 16.15 Begin by writing the equation for the ionization of $HClO_4$:

$$HClO_4 \xrightarrow{H_2O} H^+(aq) + ClO_4^-(aq)$$

Then, calculate the molar concentration of the H^+ ions.

150 mg $HClO_4$ × 1 g $HClO_4$/1000 mg $HClO_4$ × 1 mol $HClO_4$/100.5 g $HClO_4$

$$\times \ 1 \ \text{mol} \ H^+/1 \ \text{mol} \ HClO_4 = 1.5 \times 10^{-3} \ \text{mol} \ H^+$$

To calculate the molarity, divide the moles of $HClO_4$ by the total volume, 3.55 L.

$$[H^+] = 1.5 \times 10^{-3} \ \text{mol} \ H^+/3.55 \ L = 4.2 \times 10^{-4} \ M \ H^+$$

Because the H^+ ion concentration is significantly greater than those contributed by the autoionization of water, this value can be used for the H^+ ion concentration. To obtain the pH take the negative logarithm of $[H^+]$.

$$pH = -\log[H^+] = -\log(4.2 \times 10^{-4} \ M) = 3.38$$

Problem 16.16 The pH of the blood is usually very close to 7.35. What are the H^+ and OH^- ion concentrations in blood?

Solution 16.16 In this problem the pH is known and the H^+ ion concentration must be calculated. Thus, begin by substituting the pH value into Eq. 16.4.

$$7.35 = -\log[H^+]$$

To solve this equation, first multiply both sides of the equation by -1 and then take the antilogarithm (10^x) of both sides.

$$-7.35 = \log[H^+]$$
$$\text{antilog}(-7.35) = \text{antilog}(\log[H^+])$$
$$4.5 \times 10^{-8} M = [H^+]$$
$$[H^+] = 4.5 \times 10^{-8} M \ H^+$$

To calculate the OH^- ion concentration, substitute the H^+ ion concentration into the ion-product equilibrium expression of water.

$$K_w = [H^+][OH^-]$$
$$[OH^-] = K_w/[H^+]$$
$$= 1.0 \times 10^{-14}/4.5 \times 10^{-8} \ M = 2.2 \times 10^{-7} \ M \ OH^-$$

pOH

The measurement pOH is the negative common logarithm of the OH^- ion concentration.

$$pOH = -\log[OH^-] \tag{16.5}$$

Problem 16.17 Derive the mathematical relationship between pH and pOH.

Solution 16.17 This relationship is determined by taking the negative logarithm of both sides of the ion-product equilibrium expression for water.

$$K_w = [H^+][OH^-]$$
$$-\log(K_w) = -\log([H^+][OH^-])$$
$$= -\log[H^+] - \log[OH^-]$$

The negative logarithm of K_w is given the symbol pK_w, and from our previous definitions, $-\log[H^+] = pH$ and $-\log[OH^-] = pOH$. Hence, the expression becomes

$$pK_w = pH + pOH \qquad (16.6)$$

Because K_w equals 1.0×10^{-14} at $25°C$, pK_w equals 14.00, and the equation becomes

$$14.00 = pH + pOH \qquad (16.7)$$

Problem 16.18 What is the pH, pOH, $[H^+]$, and $[OH^-]$ of a NaOH solution that has 0.055 g NaOH dissolved in 35 L of solution?

Solution 16.18 Begin by writing the equation for the dissociation of NaOH in water.

$$NaOH(s) \xrightarrow{H_2O} Na^+(aq) + OH^-(aq)$$

Then, calculate the molar concentration of OH^-, $[OH^-]$. The moles of hydroxide is calculated as follows.

$$0.055 \text{ g NaOH} \times 1 \text{ mol NaOH/40.0 g NaOH} \times 1 \text{ mol } OH^-/1 \text{ mol NaOH} = 1.4 \times 10^{-3} \text{ mol } OH^-$$

Next, calculate the molar concentration of the OH^- ion by dividing 1.4×10^{-3} mol OH^- by the total volume, 35 L.
$$[OH^-] = 1.4 \times 10^{-3} \text{ mol } OH^-/35 \text{ L} = 3.9 \times 10^{-5} M \text{ } OH^-$$

Because this value is much larger (over 100 times) than the OH^- ions contributed by the water, those produced from the self-ionization of water are disregarded. Next, calculate the pOH of this solution by taking the negative logarithm of $3.9 \times 10^{-5} M$.

$$pOH = -\log[OH^-] = -\log(3.9 \times 10^{-5} M \text{ } OH^-) = 4.41$$

To complete the calculation, subtract the pOH from 14.00, pK_w, to obtain the pH.

$$14.00 = pH + pOH$$
$$pH = 14.00 - pOH$$
$$= 14.00 - 4.41 = 9.59$$

The pH of this NaOH solution is 9.59. To calculate the H^+ ion concentration, take the antilog of -9.59, which gives $2.57 \times 10^{-10} M \text{ } H^+$. Multiplying this value by the OH^- ion concentration, $3.9 \times 10^{-5} M$, gives K_w.

16.9   WEAK ACID SOLUTIONS

Weak Acids

Weak acids only partially ionize in solution. Some common examples of weak molecular acids are acetic acid, $HC_2H_3O_2(aq)$; hydrofluoric acid, $HF(aq)$; and nitrous acid, $HNO_2(aq)$. In addition, some polyatomic ions such as hydrogencarbonate, $HCO_3^-(aq)$; hydrogensulfate, $HSO_4^-(aq)$; and dihydrogenphosphate, $H2PO_4^-(aq)$ are also weak acids.

WEAK ACID EQUILIBRIA AND K_a

Consider the model weak acid, acetic acid, $HC_2H_3O_2(aq)$. Acetic acid establishes the following equilibrium in water.

$$HC_2H_3O_2(aq) \rightleftharpoons H^+(aq) + C_2H_3O_2^-(aq)$$

Less than 2% of the acetic acid molecules ionize in a 0.1 M solution. Therefore, acetic acid contributes far fewer H^+ ions to water than a strong acid of equal concentration which ionizes totally. The degree to which acetic acid ionizes is expressed by writing the acid-ionization equilibrium expression, which is as follows:

$$K_a = \frac{[H^+][C_2H_3O_2^-]}{[HC_2H_3O_2]}$$

in which K_a is the acid-ionization equilibrium constant. The value of K_a for acetic acid is 1.8×10^{-5}. What does this mean? Because 1.8×10^{-5} is a relatively small value, it tells us that this equilibrium lies far to the left.

Acid-Ionization Equilibrium Expressions

If the following is the general equation for any weak acid, HA,

$$HA(aq) \rightleftharpoons H^+(aq) + A^-(aq)$$

then, the acid-ionization equilibrium expression is as follows.

$$K_a = \frac{[H^+][A^-]}{[HA]}$$

Problem 16.19

A 0.010 M butanoic acid solution, $HC_4H_7O_2(aq)$, is 3.9% ionized at 298 K. Calculate the K_a value for butanoic acid.

Solution 16.19

The equilibrium that butanoic acid establishes in water is

$$HC_4H_7O_2(aq) \rightleftharpoons H^+(aq) + C_4H_7O_2^-(aq)$$

and its acid-ionization equilibrium expression is

$$K_a = \frac{[H^+][C_4H_7O_2^-]}{[HC_4H_7O_2]}$$

Then, construct an equilibrium summary table and determine the equilibrium concentrations. The problem states that the 0.010 M butanoic acid is 3.9% ionized. This means that 3.9 butanoic acid molecules ionize per each 100 molecules. The initial concentration of the butanoic acid is 0.010 M, and before ionization the concentrations of H^+ and $C_4H_7O_2^-$ are 0.0 M. As the equilibrium develops the butanoic acid concentration decreases by x and the concentrations of H^+ and $C_4H_7O_2^-$ increase by x. The following table summarizes this information.

	Initial Concentration, M	Concentration Change, M	Equilibrium Concentration, M
$[HC_4H_7O_2]$	0.010	$-x$	$0.010 - x$
$[H^+]$	0.0	$+x$	x
$[C_4H_7O_2^-]$	0.0	$+x$	x

The value of x can easily be calculated because the percent ionization of butanoic acid is known. Thus, take 3.9% of the initial concentration 0.010 M to calculate x.

$$x = 0.010 \ M \ HC_4H_7O_2 \times 3.9 \text{ molecules ionize}/100 \text{ molecules } = 3.9 \times 10^{-4} M$$

Substituting this value into the table allows us to determine the equilibrium concentrations for H^+ and $C_4H_7O_2^-$ are $3.9 \times 10^{-4} M$ and the equilibrium concentration of butanoic acid remains the same as the initial concentration because of the small degree of ionization.

$$[HC_4H_7O_2] = 0.010 \ M - 0.00039 \ M = 0.010 \ M$$

Finally, substitute these values into the acid-ionization equilibrium expression.

$$K_a = \frac{[H^+][C_4H_7O_2^-]}{[HC_4H_7O_2]}$$
$$K_a = (3.9 \times 10^{-4} \ M)(3.9 \times 10^{-4} \ M)/0.010 \ M = 1.5 \times 10^{-5}$$

Problem 16.20 A pH meter is used to measure the pH of a 0.25 M hypochlorous acid solution, $HOCl(aq)$. The pH of this solution is 4.03. Calculate the K_a value for hypochlorous acid.

Solution 16.20 First, write the equation for the equilibrium and the acid-ionization equilibrium expression.

$$HOCl(aq) \rightleftharpoons H^+(aq) + OCl^-(aq)$$
$$K_a = \frac{[H^+][OCl^-]}{[HOCl]}$$

Then, construct a table that shows the development of the equilibrium.

	Initial Concentration, M	Concentration Change, M	Equilibrium Concentration, M
$[HOCl]$	0.25	$-x$	$0.25 - x$
$[H^+]$	0.0	$+x$	x
$[OCl^-]$	0.0	$+x$	x

In this problem the pH of the solution is known, which allows us to calculate the H^+ ion concentration at equilibrium, which equals the value of x. Because HOCl produces one OCl^- for each H^+, then the OCl^- concentration equals that of H^+.

$$x = [H^+] = [OCl^-]$$

These values are calculated as follows

$$pH = -\log [H^+]$$
$$4.03 = -\log [H^+]$$
$$\text{antilog}(-4.03) = [H^+]$$
$$[H^+] = 9.3 \times 10^{-5}\ M$$

and

$$x = [H^+] = [OCl^-] = 9.3 \times 10^{-5}$$

Because the value for x is small, the calculated equilibrium concentration of HOCl is effectively the same as the initial concentration. Finally, calculate the K_a value for HOCl

$$K_a = \frac{[H^+][OCl^-]}{[HOCl]}$$
$$K_a = (9.3 \times 10^{-5}\ M)(9.3 \times 10^{-5}\ M)/0.25\ M = 3.5 \times 10^{-8}$$

Calculating pH and Equilibrium Concentrations

Given the K_a value for a weak acid, the molar concentrations of all species in equilibrium can be calculated. One of these values is the H^+ ion concentration, $[H^+]$. Therefore, the pH of the solution can also be calculated. These problems will be solved in the same way that other equilibrium problems have been solved. First write the acid-ionization equilibrium and its equilibrium expression. Because it is a weak acid, the equilibrium lies to the left.

SOURCES OF H^+

Additionally, remember that the equilibrium concentration of the H^+ ions (that which is calculated) arises from two sources. One is the ionization of the weak acid and the other is the self-ionization of water. Because the H^+ ions produced by the ionization of the weak acid affect the position of the self-ionization equilibrium of water, the assumption can no longer be made that the contribution to the H^+ ion concentration from the self-ionization of water is $1.0 \times 10^{-7} M$. However, if the weak acid in question is a significantly stronger acid than is water, it will produce many more H^+ ions than water. As a result, the self-ionization of water equilibrium is displaced to the left (Le Chatelier's Principle) and the contribution of H^+ ions from the water is less than $1.0 \times 10^{-7} M$. In many instances, the H^+ ions produced by the water will be so small by comparison with those produced by the weak acid, they can be considered negligible by comparison. As a rough rule of thumb, if the concentration of the weak acid is C molar, then provided $K_a \cdot C > 10^{-12}$ the H^+ ions produced by the acid will be sufficiently large by comparison with those produced by water that the latter can be neglected. Under these conditions, the weak acid can be thought of as the sole source of H^+ ions in the equilibrium system. Note that if $K_a \cdot C$ is less than 10^{-12}, then the weak acid cannot produce enough H^+ ions to make its contribution large by caparison with that from water and a more elaborate treatment is required. Fortunately, the latter situation is not commonly encountered.

Problem 16.21   Consider a 1.0 M acetic acid, $HC_2H_3O_2$, solution. (a) Is it a good assumption that the H^+ ions from water are small relative to those from the acetic acid? (b) What is the molar concentration of H^+ and pH of this solution?

Solution 16.21
(a) The equation for the equilibrium and the equilibrium expression are as follows.

$$HC_2H_3O_2(aq) \rightleftharpoons H^+(aq) + C_2H_3O_2^-(aq)$$
$$K_a = \frac{[H]^+[C_2H_3O_2^-]}{[HC_2H_3O_2]} = 1.8 \times 10^{-5}$$

The initial concentration of acetic acid is $1.0\ M$ and the concentrations of the hydrogen and acetate ions are $0.0\ M$. Since $C = 1.0$,

$$K_a \cdot C = 1.0\ M \times 1.8 \times 10^{-5} = 1.8 \times 10^{-5} \gg 10^{-12}$$

allows us to neglect water as a source of H^+ ions. Therefore, it is a good assumption that essentially all of the H^+ ions in solution come from the acetic acid.

(b) For each H^+ ion in solution, one $C_2H_3O_2^-$ ion is produced and one $HC_2H_3O_2$ molecule disappears. Hence, the equilibrium concentration of acetic acid is $1.0 - x$ and the concentration of the H^+ and $C_2H_3O_2^-$ ions are x. Substituting these values into the acid-ionization equilibrium expression gives the following.

$$K_a = \frac{x^2}{1.0 - x} = 1.8 \times 10^{-5}$$

To solve this equation either rearrange it and use the quadratic formula or make the assumption that the equilibrium concentration of acetic acid is $1.0\ M$. In other words, x is so small, within the limits of significant figures, that it will not change the initial concentration of $1.0\ M$. Let's see if this is a good assumption.

$$K_a = \frac{x^2}{1.0\ M} = 1.8 \times 10^{-5}$$
$$x^2 = 1.8 \times 10^{-5}$$
$$x = 0.0042\ M$$

Our assumption that x is small enough not to change the value of the initial concentration of acetic acid is a good one. When $0.0042\ M$ is subtracted from $1.0\ M$, the difference is still $1.0\ M$ (remember significant figures). It is a common practice to assume that if x is less than 3 to 4% of the initial concentration, then it is small enough to drop. For this calculation, x is only 0.42% of the initial concentration.

$$\% = (0.0042\ M/1.0\ M) \times 100 = 0.42\%$$

Because x equals $0.0042\ M$, the H^+ and $C_2H_3O_2^-$ concentrations are also $0.0042\ M$.

$$[H^+] = [C_2H_3O_2^-] = 0.0042\ M$$

The pH of this solution equals the negative logarithm of $0.0042\ M$ H^+ or 2.38.

Problem 16.22 (a) What are the equilibrium molar concentrations of lactic acid ($HC_3H_5O_3$), lactate ($C_3H_5O_3^-$), and H^+ of a $0.0010\ M$ $HC_3H_5O_3$ solution? (b) What is the pH of this solution? The K_a value for lactic acid is 1.4×10^{-4}.

Solution 16.22

(a) This problem has two equilibria: the ionization of lactic acid to the H^+ and $C_3H_5O_3^-$ ions and the self-ionization of water.

$$HC_3H_5O_3(aq) \rightleftharpoons H^+(aq) + C_3H_5O_3^-(aq) \quad K_a = 1.4 \times 10^{-4}$$
$$H_2O(l) \rightleftharpoons H^+(aq) + OH^-(aq) \quad K_a = 1.0 \times 10^{-14}$$

Using the $K_a \cdot C > 10^{-12}$ rule of thumb, $1.4 \times 10^{-4} \cdot 0.0010\ M = 1.4 \times 10^{-7} > 10^{-12}$ indicates that lactic acid is a significantly stronger acid than water. Thus, assume that only the contribution of lactic acid to the H^+ ion concentration is important. Then, write the acid-ionization equilibrium expression for lactic acid.

$$K_a = \frac{[H^+][C_3H_5O_3^-]}{[HC_3H_5O_3]}$$

Next, construct a table with the initial concentrations, change in concentrations, and equilibrium concentrations.

	Initial Concentration, M	Concentration Change, M	Equilibrium Concentration, M
$[HC_3H_5O_3]$	0.0010	$-x$	$0.0010 - x$
$[H^+]$	0.0	$+x$	x
$[C_3H_5O_3^-]$	0.0	$+x$	x

Substitute the equilibrium concentrations into the equilibrium expression and solve for x.

$$K_a = \frac{x^2}{0.0010 - x} = 1.4 \times 10^{-4}$$

We are not justified in assuming that x is small with respect to the initial lactic acid concentration. If x is dropped and the equation solved, $3.7 \times 10^{-4}\ M$ is obtained, which is 37% of the initial concentration (prove this to yourself). This value is significantly larger than the acceptable 3 to 4% mentioned previously. Therefore, the quadratic formula is used to solve this equation. Recall that the general form of a quadratic equation is $ax^2 + bx + c = 0$ and the quadratic formula is

$$x = -b \pm \sqrt{\frac{b^2 - 4ac}{2a}}$$

Thus, rearrange the equation to get it into the general form and then substitute the values of a, b, and c into the quadratic formula.

$$x^2 = 1.4 \times 10^{-4}(0.0010 - x)$$
$$= 1.4 \times 10^{-7} - 1.4 \times 10^{-4}x$$
$$x^2 + (1.4 \times 10^{-4})x - (1.4 \times 10^{-7}) = 0$$

The values to be substituted into the quadratic equation are: $a = 1$, $b = 1.4 \times 10^{-4}$, and $c = -1.4 \times 10^{-7}$.

$$x = \frac{-1.4 \times 10^{-4} \pm \sqrt{(1.4 \times 10^{-4})^2 - (4 \times 1 \times -1.4 \times 10^{-7})}}{2 \times 1}$$
$$= 3.1 \times 10^{-4}\ M$$

A second negative value is disregarded because it does not have any physical significance in this problem. Calculate the equilibrium concentrations by substituting x, $3.1 \times 10^{-4}M$, into the equilibrium expression in the table.

$$x = [H^+] = [C_3H_5O_3^-] = 3.1 \times 10^{-4}M$$
$$[HC_3H_5O_3] = 0.0010\ M - 0.00031\ M = 7 \times 10^{-4}M\ HC_3H_5O_3$$

(b) Calculate the pH of the solution as follows.

$$pH = -\log [H^+] = -\log (3.1 \times 10^{-4}M) = 3.51$$

Mixtures of Weak and Strong Acids– Common Ion Effect

Sometimes solutions are encountered that have both a weak and a strong acid in solution. A strong acid ionizes 100% and a weak acid ionizes to a much smaller extent. How will the H^+ ions contributed by a strong acid affect the acid-ionization equilibrium of a weak acid? Le Chatelier's Principle is used to answer this question. An increase in the concentration of the H^+ shifts the equilibrium to the left. In other words, the H^+ ions from the strong acid suppress the ionization of the weak acid. This is known as the Common Ion Effect, which states that an ionic equilibrium shifts in response to the addition of a substance that gives an ion common with one in equilibrium. In our example, the common ion is the H^+ ion from the strong acid.

Problem 16.23 (a) Calculate the molar concentration of HF in 0.100 M HF. (b) Calculate the molar concentration of HF in a mixture of 0.100 M HF and 0.010 M HCl. (c) Compare the answers from the first two parts. The K_a value of HF is 7.4×10^{-4}.

Solution 16.23

(a) Begin by writing the acid-ionization equilibrium for HF and its equilibrium expression.

$$HF(aq) \rightleftharpoons H^+(aq) + F^-(aq)$$

$$K_a = \frac{[H^+][F^-]}{[HF]} = 7.2 \times 10^{-4}$$

Next, decide if the autoionization of water contributes to the $[H^+]$. Using the $K_a \cdot C > 10^{-12}$ rule of thumb, $7.2 \times 10^{-4} \cdot 0.010\,M = 7.2 \times 10^{-6} > 10^{-12}$, shows us that HF($aq$) is a significantly stronger acid than water. Thus, assume that only the contribution of HF(aq) to the H^+ ion concentration is important. Then, construct a table with the initial and final concentrations.

	Initial Concentration, M	Concentration Change, M	Equilibrium Concentration, M
[HF]	0.100	$-x$	$0.100 - x$
[H$^+$]	0.0	$+x$	x
[F$^-$]	0.0	$+x$	x

Substitute into the equilibrium expression

$$K_a = \frac{x^2}{0.100 - x} = 7.2 \times 10^{-4}$$

Solving this equation results in a value of 0.0081 M for x. Thus, the equilibrium molar concentration of HF in the solution is $0.100\,M - 0.0081\,M$ or 0.092 M.

(b) The same equilibrium and equilibrium expression are used as in part (a). Initially 0.100 M HF and 0.010 M HCl are present. After the HF ionizes, $0.100 - x\,M$ HF, $0.010 + x\,M$ H$^+$, and $x\,M$ F$^-$ result.

	Initial Concentration, M	Concentration Change, M	Equilibrium Concentration, M
[HF]	0.100	$-x$	$0.100 - x$
[H$^+$]	0.010	$+x$	$0.010 + x$
[F$^-$]	0.0	$+x$	x

Then, substitute into the equilibrium expression:

$$K_a = \frac{(0.010 + x)x}{0.100 - x} = 7.2 \times 10^{-4}$$

Solving for x gives a value of 0.0047 M. Thus, the molar concentration of HF in this solution is 0.100 M − 0.0047 or 0.095 M HF.

(c) Comparing the value from part (b) to the result from part (a) shows that the common ion, H^+, shifts the equilibrium to the left. Thus, the concentration of HF is greater in the presence of 0.010 M H^+.

Polyprotic Acids

Polyprotic acids are those that donate more than one proton. For example, sulfuric acid, $H_2SO_4(aq)$, can donate two protons; thus, it is a diprotic acid. First it releases a proton and produces the hydrogensulfate ion, HSO_4^-, which can also donate a proton. The equations for the ionization of sulfuric acid and the hydrogensulfate ion are as follows.

$$H_2SO_4(aq) \rightleftharpoons H^+(aq) + HSO_4^-(aq) \quad K_{a1} = \text{large}$$
$$HSO_4^-(aq) \rightleftharpoons H^+(aq) + SO_4^{2-}(aq) \quad K_{a2} = 1.2 \times 10^{-2}$$

In most polyprotic acids the second acid-ionization constant, K_{a2}, is significantly smaller than the first one. It is always easier for a proton to leave a neutral species such as H_2SO_4 than it is to leave a negatively charged species such as HSO_4^-.

Problem 16.24 Calculate the pH and the molar concentrations of all dissolved species in a 1.5 M H_3PO_4 solution. The K_{a1}, K_{a2}, and K_{a3} values are 7.5×10^{-3}, 6.2×10^{-8}, and 4.8×10^{-13}, respectively.

Solution 16.24 First, write the equations for the three ionizations of phosphoric acid.

$$H_3PO_4(aq) \rightleftharpoons H^+(aq) + H_2PO_4^-(aq) \qquad K_{a1} = 7.5 \times 10^{-3}$$
$$H_2PO_4^-(aq) \rightleftharpoons H^+(aq) + H_2PO_4^{2-}(aq) \qquad K_{a2} = 6.2 \times 10^{-8}$$
$$HPO_4^{2-}(aq) \rightleftharpoons H^+(aq) + PO_4^{3-}(aq) \qquad K_{a2} = 4.8 \times 10^{-13}$$

Then, write the three acid-ionization equilibrium expressions.

$$K_{a1} = \frac{[H^+][H_2PO_4^-]}{[H_3PO_4]} = 7.5 \times 10^{-3}$$

$$K_{a2} = \frac{[H^+][HPO_4^{2-}]}{[H_2PO_4^-]} = 6.2 \times 10^{-8}$$

$$K_{a3} = \frac{[H^+][PO_4^{3-}]}{[HPO_4^{2-}]} = 4.8 \times 10^{-13}$$

Next, construct the table of initial and equilibrium concentrations for the first ionization.

	Initial Concentration, M	Concentration Change, M	Equilibrium Concentration, M
$[H_3PO_4]$	1.5	$-x$	$1.5 - x$
$[H^+]$	0.0	$+x$	x
$[H_2PO_4^-]$	0.0	$+x$	x

Then, substitute the equilibrium concentrations into K_{a1} equilibrium expression.

$$K_{a1} = \frac{x^2}{1.5 - x} = 7.5 \times 10^{-3}$$

After solving for x, the value 0.10 M is obtained. This value equals the molar concentrations of the H^+ and $H_2PO_4^-$ ions.

$$x = [H^+] = [H_2PO_4^-] = 0.10M$$

Because the contribution from the second and third ionization make an insignificant contribution to the H^+ ion concentration, the pH of the solution is calculated from this value.

$$pH = -\log [H^+] = -\log(0.10\ M) = 1.00$$

In addition, the equilibrium concentration of phosphoric acid may also be calculated.

$$[H_3PO_4] = 1.5 - x = 1.5 - 0.10\ M = 1.4\ M\ H_3PO_4$$

To calculate the hydrogenphosphate concentration, substitute the H^+ and $H_2PO_4^-$ concentrations obtained from the first ionization expression into the K_{a2} equilibrium expression.

$$K_{a2} = \frac{[H^+][HPO_4^{2-}]}{[H_2PO_4^-]} = 6.2 \times 10^{-8} = \frac{(0.10+x)[HPO_4^{2-}]}{(0.10-x)}$$

It is a good assumption that x is small because of the very small value for K_{a2}. After removing x from the equation, the 0.10 M in the numerator and denominator cancel. Hence, the HPO_4^{2-} ion concentration equals K_{a2}, 6.2×10^{-8}. Note that along with the HPO_4^{2-} ion that results, 6.2×10^{-8} $M\ H^+$ is produced. Adding these H^+ ions to those from the first ionization does not change the overall H^+ ion concentration. Hence, our assumption that the second and third ionizations of phosphoric acid are insignificant was a good one.

Finally, substitute the values for the hydrogen and hydrogenphosphate ions into the K_{a3} expression to obtain the phosphate ion concentration.

$$K_{a3} = \frac{[H^+][PO_4^{3-}]}{[HPO_4^{2-}]} = 4.8 \times 10^{-13}$$

$$= \frac{(0.10\ M)[PO_4^{3-}]}{6.2 \times 10^{-8}\ M} = 4.8 \times 10^{-13}$$

$$[PO_4^{3-}] = 3.0 \times 10^{-19}\ M$$

16.10 WEAK BASE SOLUTIONS

Nature of Weak Bases

To understand weak bases, the Brønsted-Lowry definition of bases is used. A Brønsted-Lowry base is a proton acceptor. The general equation for any weak molecular Brønsted-Lowry base, B, is as follows.

$$B(aq) + H_2O(l) \rightleftharpoons HB^+(aq) + OH^-(aq)$$

B accepts a proton from water and produces its conjugate acid HB^+. After water donates a proton to the base, its conjugate base, OH^-, remains.

Base-Ionization Equilibrium Constant, K_b

An equilibrium expression for the base ionization is written with its associated equilibrium constant, the base-ionization equilibrium constant, K_b. In general the base-ionization equilibrium expression for any weak molecular base, B, is as follows.

$$K_b = \frac{[B^+][OH^-]}{[B]}$$

K_b problems are solved in a manner similar to K_a problems. After writing the equation and equilibrium expression, determine if the OH^- ions contributed from the self-ionization of water makes a significant contribution, using the following rule of thumb $K_b \cdot C > 10^{-12}$. Then, construct a summary table and substitute the equilibrium concentrations into the K_b expression.

Problem 16.25 Calculate the pH, pOH, and OH^- ion concentration in a 0.12 M hydroxylamine, H_2NOH, solution. The K_b for hydroxylamine is 1.1×10^{-8}.

Solution 16.25 Write the equation for the equilibrium and base-ionization equilibrium expression.

$$H_2NOH(aq) + H_2O(l) \rightleftharpoons H_3NOH^+(aq) + OH^-(aq)$$

$$K_b = \frac{[H_3NOH^+][OH^-]}{[H_2NOH]} = 1.1 \times 10^{-8}$$

Using the $K_b \cdot C > 10^{-12}$ rule of thumb, $1.1 \times 10^{-8} \cdot 0.12\ M = 1.3 \times 10^{-9} > 10^{-12}$ shows us that $H_2NOH(aq)$ is a significantly stronger base than water. Thus, assume that only the contribution of $H_2NOH(aq)$ to the OH^- ion concentration is important. Next, construct a table of the initial and equilibrium concentrations.

	Initial Concentration, M	Concentration Change, M	Equilibrium Concentration, M
$[H_2NOH]$	0.12	$-x$	$0.12 - x$
$[OH^-]$	0.0	$+x$	x
$[H_3NOH^+]$	0.0	$+x$	x

Substitute the equilibrium concentrations into the K_b expression and solve for x.

$$K_b = \frac{[H_3NOH^+][OH^-]}{[H_2NOH]} = 1.1 \times 10^{-8}$$

$$= x^2/(0.12\ M - x)$$

$$x = [OH^-] = 3.6 \times 10^{-5} M$$

Finally, calculate the pH and pOH

$$pOH = -\log[OH^-] = -\log(3.6 \times 10^{-5}\ M) = 4.44$$

$$pH = 14 - pOH = 14 - 4.44 = 9.56$$

16.11   RELATIONSHIP BETWEEN K_a AND K_b

What is the relationship between the K_a of a weak acid and K_b of its conjugate base? Let us consider acetic acid which establishes the following equilibrium with the H^+ and $C_2H_3O_2^-$ ions.

$$HC_2H_3O_2(aq) \rightleftharpoons H^+(aq) + C_2H_3O_2^- (aq) \qquad (16.8)$$

The equilibrium constant for this is K_a. The conjugate base of acetic acid is the acetate ion, which establishes the following equilibrium.

$$C_2H_3O_2^- (aq) + H_2O(l) \rightleftharpoons HC_2H_3O_2(aq) + OH^- (aq) \qquad (16.9)$$

The equilibrium constant for this is K_b. The rule of multiple equilibria states that when two or more equilibria are added to obtain an overall equilibrium, then the equilibrium constant for the overall equilibrium equals the product of the equilibrium constants of the equations added. Thus, add Eqns 16.8 and 16.9 to obtain the equation for the self-ionization of water, which has K_w for its equilibrium constant.

$$
\begin{array}{ll}
HC_2H_3O_2(aq) \rightleftharpoons H^+(aq) + C_2H_3O_2^- (aq) & K_a \\
C_2H_3O_2^- (aq) + H_2O(l) \rightleftharpoons HC_2H_3O_2(aq) + OH^- (aq) & K_b \\
\hline
H_2O(l) \rightleftharpoons H^+(aq) + OH^-(aq) & K_w
\end{array}
$$

The Rule of Multiple Equilibria shows that K_w equals the product of K_a times K_b.

$$K_w = K_a \cdot K_b \qquad (16.10)$$

Problem 16.26   The hypoiodite ion, IO^-, is the conjugate base of the acid hypoiodous acid, HIO. If the pH of a 0.030 M IO^- solution is 11.56, calculate the K_a of hypoiodous acid.

Solution 16.26   Because data is given for the conjugate base (IO^-) of hypoiodous acid (HIO), first calculate its K_b value and then determine the K_a of hypoiodous acid from Eq. 16.10. Next, write the equation for the base ionization of the hypoiodite ion and its K_b expression.

$$IO^- (aq) + H_2O(l) \rightleftharpoons HIO(aq) + OH^- (aq)$$

$$K_b = \frac{[HIO][OH^-]}{[IO^-]}$$

Then, construct a table of the initial and equilibrium concentrations.

	Initial Concentration, M	Concentration Change, M	Equilibrium Concentration, M
$[IO^-]$	0.030	$-x$	$0.030 - x$
$[OH^-]$	0.0	$+x$	x
$[HIO]$	0.0	$+x$	x

From the pH of the solution, 11.56, calculate its pOH and OH^- ion concentration.

$$pOH = 14 - pH = 14 - 11.56 = 2.44$$

$$pOH = -\log [OH^-]$$
$$2.44 = -\log [OH^-]$$
$$[OH^-] = 3.6 \times 10^{-3} \, M$$

The table shows that x equals the OH^- ion. Thus, the equilibrium concentrations are as follows.

$$x = [OH^-] = [IO^-] = 3.6 \times 10^{-3} \, M$$
$$[HOI] = 0.030 \, M - 3.6 \times 10^{-3} \, M = 0.026 \, M$$

Substitute these values into the K_b expression and solve for K_b.

$$K_b = \frac{[HIO][OH^-]}{[IO^-]}$$
$$= (3.6 \times 10^{-3})^2 / 0.026$$
$$= 5.0 \times 10^{-4}$$

To calculate the K_a of HIO, divide the K_b value of IO^- into the K_w value.

$$K_a = K_w / K_b = 1.0 \times 10^{-14} / 5.0 \times 10^{-4} = 2.0 \times 10^{-11}$$

pK_a and pK_b

Often the negative logarithms of the K_a and K_b values are calculated so that more convenient numbers can be used. Therefore, the negative logarithms of the K_a and K_b values are pK_a and pK_b, respectively.

$$pK_a = -\log K_a \tag{16.11}$$

$$pK_b = -\log K_b \tag{16.12}$$

What is the relationship between K_a and K_b? The product of K_a and K_b is K_w. Thus, taking the negative logarithm of both sides shows that the sum of pK_a and pK_b equals pK_w, 14.

$$K_w = K_a \times K_b$$
$$-\log K_w = -\log K_a + (-\log K_b)$$
$$pK_w = pK_a + pK_b$$
$$14 = pK_a + pK_b \tag{16.15}$$

Problem 16.27 (a) If the pK_a of hypobromous acid, $HBrO(aq)$ is 8.60, calculate the pK_b of its conjugate base, the hypobromite ion (BrO^-). (b) What is the K_a of HBrO? (c) What is the K_b of BrO^-?

Solution 16.27

(a)
$$pK_b = 14.00 - pK_a = 14.00 - 8.60 = 5.40$$

(b)
$$pK_a = -\log K_a$$
$$8.60 =$$
$$\log K_a = -8.60$$
$$\text{antilog}(\log K_a) = \text{antilog}(-8.60)$$
$$K_a = 2.5 \times 10^{-9}$$

(c)

$$pK_b = -\log K_b$$
$$5.40 =$$
$$\log K_b = -5.40$$
$$\text{antilog}(\log K_b) = \text{antilog}(-5.40)$$
$$K_b = 4.0 \times 10^{-6}$$

SUMMARY

*A*rrhenius defined acids as substances that increase the H^+ ion concentration in aqueous solution, and bases as substances that increase the OH^- ion concentration in aqueous solution. When a H^+ ion enters aqueous solution it combines with a water molecule and produces a hydronium ion, H_3O^+, which is hydrated by additional water molecules.

A Brønsted-Lowry acid is a proton donor, and a Brønsted-Lowry base is an proton acceptor. When an acid releases a proton it produces its conjugate base, and when a base accepts a proton it produces its conjugate acid. After a conjugate base accepts a proton it re-forms the acid, and after a conjugate acid releases a proton it re-forms the base.

Strong acids almost totally ionize in dilute solutions and weak acids only partially ionize, usually less than 10%. Proton-donating tendency is related to the strength of the conjugate base. Stronger acids have weaker conjugate bases than weaker acids. It is generally true that the strongest Brønsted-Lowry acid that exists in a solution is the conjugate acid of the solvent.

A Lewis acid is an electron-pair acceptor and a Lewis base is an electron pair donor. After a Lewis acid accepts an electron pair from a Lewis base it forms an acid-base adduct. Lewis acids are electron deficient species such as cations, molecules that have an atom with less than eight outer-level electrons, and molecules that can expand their octets. Lewis bases are electron-rich species such as anions and molecules with atoms with one or more lone pairs.

When equivalent amounts react, strong acids neutralize strong bases and produce neutral solutions. Equivalent amounts of strong bases and weak acids react, producing basic solutions. Equivalent amounts of weak bases neutralize strong acids to produce acidic solutions. Weak bases and weak acids combine to produce neutral, acidic, or basic solutions, depending on the strength of the reactants.

Salts are ionic compounds that result when acids combine with bases. Each salt is composed of a cation other than H^+ and an anion other than O^{2-} or OH^-. Neutral salts result from the reaction of strong acids and strong bases, basic salts result from the reaction of strong bases and weak acids, and acidic salts result from the reaction of strong acids and weak bases.

Water is a very weak electrolyte and undergoes self-ionization to produce H^+ and OH^- ions. The K_w value for water equals 1.0×10^{-14}. This means that the molar concentrations of both the H^+ and OH^- ions are 1.0×10^{-7} M in pure water. In all acidic solutions the H^+ ion concentration is greater than 10^{-7} M and the OH^- ion concentration is less than 10^{-7} M. In all basic solutions the H^+ ion concentration is less than 10^{-7} M and the OH^- ion concentration is greater than 10^{-7} M.

The pH of a solution is the negative common logarithm of the H^+ ion concentration. Neutral solutions and pure water have a pH of 7, acidic solutions have pH values less than 7, and basic solutions have pH values above 7. The pOH of a solution is the negative common logarithm of the OH^- ion concentration. Basic solutions have pOH values less than 7, and acidic solutions have values above 7. The sum of the pH and pOH for a given solution equals 14, the pK_w for water.

Weak acids only ionize to a small degree, producing far fewer H^+ ions. Thus weak acids have lower H^+ ion concentrations than strong acids of equal concentration. The degree to which weak acids ionize is expressed by writing the acid-ionization equilibrium expression. This expression gives us the acid-ionization equilibrium constant, K_a.

Strong bases are substances that completely dissociate in solution and release OH^- ions. Ex-

amples of strong bases include NaOH and KOH. Most common weak bases produce OH$^-$ ions by undergoing hydrolysis. The base-ionization equilibrium expression is used to show the degree to which a weak base undergoes this reaction. This expression gives the base-ionization equilibrium constant, K_b. The product of the K_a of a weak acid and the K_b of its conjugate base equals the K_w of water.

CHAPTER 16 REVIEW EXERCISE

1. (a) What are the conjugate bases of H_3PO_4 and HSO_3^-? (b) What are the conjugate acids of PO_4^{3-} and HSO_3^-?

2. (a) Which of the following has the strongest conjugate base: acetic acid, nitrous acid, or water? (b) Which of the following has the weakest conjugate base: HI, H_2S, $HClO_4$?

3. Predict in which direction the following equilibrium lies.

$$H_2S + Cl^- \rightleftharpoons HCl + HS^-$$

4. Consider the following reaction: $Cd^{2+}(aq) + 4I^-(aq) \rightleftharpoons CdI_4^{2-}$. In this reaction, which reactant is the Lewis acid and base. Explain.

5. (a) Write the overall ionic and net ionic equation for the reaction of aqueous potassium hydroxide and nitric acid. (b) When equivalent amounts are mixed, is the solution acidic, basic, or neutral? Explain.

6. Classify each of the following salts as being acidic, basic, or neutral: NaI, $Mg(HCO_3)_2$, NH_4NO_3, $Ca(CN)_2$, KF, Cs_2SO_4.

7. Calculate the H$^+$ and OH$^-$ ion concentrations in a solution that has 0.019 g HNO_3 dissolved in 2.6 L of solution.

8. Rank the following solutions in order of increasing H$^+$ ion concentration. (a) pH = 3.33, (b) $[H^+] = 7.5 \times 10^{-3} M$, (c) pOH = 10.88, (d) $[OH^-] = 1.4 \times 10^{-12} M$

9. A solution contains 150 mg perchloric acid, $HClO_4$, in 3.55 L of solution. If an additional 75 mg $HClO_4$ is added and the solution is diluted to 10.0 L, what is the pH of the resulting solution?

10. Calculate the H$^+$ and OH$^-$ ion concentrations in a solution with a pH of 5.55.

11. Calculate the pOH and pH of a solution that has 225 mg KOH dissolved in 975 mL of solution.

12. Solution I has a pH of 2.90. (a) What is the pH of solution II that has exactly five times the H$^+$ ion concentration of solution I? (b) What is the pH of solution III that has five times the OH$^-$ ion concentration of solution I?

13. Calculate the K_a value for a 0.10 M hypoiodous acid solution, $HIO(aq)$, which is 0.0015% ionized.

14. A 0.015 M HCN solution has a pH = 5.57. Calculate the K_a value for HCN.

15. Calculate the pH and equilibrium concentrations of all dissolved species in a 0.050 M chlorous acid solution, $HClO_2(aq)$, using the quadratic formula. The K_a value for chlorous acid is 0.012.

16. Calculate the pH value for each of the following solutions: (a) 0.30 M HCl, (b) 0.30 M HOCl, (c) Explain the difference in the values obtained in parts (a) and (b).

17. Calculate the pH of a 0.065 M HF solution using the method of successive approximation. The K_a for HF is 7.2×10^{-4}.

18. Calculate the concentration of acetic acid and acetate in a mixture of 0.100 M $HC_2H_3O_2$ and 0.100 M HCl. The K_a of acetic acid is 1.8×10^{-5}.

19. Calculate the pH and molar concentrations of all dissolved species in a 0.25 M carbonic acid, $H_2CO_3(aq)$, solution. The K_{a1} and K_{a2} for carbonic acid are 4.3×10^{-7} and 5.6×10^{-11}, respectively.

20. Calculate the pH, pOH, and hydroxide ion concentration of a 0.75 M pyridine, C_5H_5N, solution. The K_b value for pyridine is 1.4×10^{-9}.

21. A 0.15 M formate, CHO_2^-, solution has a pH of 8.46. Calculate the K_a of formic acid, the conjugate acid of the formate ion, CHO_2^-.

22. Calculate the pH of a 0.10 M $NaNO_2$ solution. The K_a for nitrous acid, HNO_2, is 4.0×10^{-4}.

23. What mass of HF should be dissolved in 1.2 L of solution to produce a pH of 2.00? The K_a of HF is 7.2×10^{-4}.

24. Calculate the pH of a 0.45 M $NaCN$ solution. The K_a of HCN is 6.2×10^{-10}.

ANSWERS TO REVIEW EXERCISE

1. (a) $H_2PO_4^-$ and SO_3^{2-}, (b) HPO_4^{2-} and H_2SO_3
2. (a) water, (b) $HClO_4$
3. The equilibrium lies towards the left.
4. Lewis acid = Cd^{2+}, Lewis base = I^- Cd^{2+} accepts a pair of electrons from I^- in the formation of CdI_4^{2-}.
5. (a) $H^+(aq) + NO_3^-(aq) + K^+(aq) + OH^-(aq) \longrightarrow K^+(aq) + NO_3^-(aq) + H_2O(l)$
6. Acidic = $Mg(HCO_3)_2$, NH_4NO_3; Basic = $Ca(CN)_2$, KF; Neutral = NaI, Cs_2SO_4
7. $[H^+] = 1.2 \times 10^{-4}M$, $[OH^-] = 8.6 \times 10^{-11}M$
8. (a) < (c) < (d) < (b)
9. 3.65
10. $[H^+] = 2.8 \times 10^{-6}M$, $[OH^-] = 3.6 \times 10^{-9}$ M
11. pOH = 2.386, pH = 11.614
12. (a) 2.20, (b) 3.60
13. 2.3×10^{-11}
14. 4.9×10^{-10}
15. pH = 1.72, $[H^+] = [ClO_2^-] = 0.0192$ M, $[HClO_2] = 0.031$ M
16. (a) 0.52, (b) 3.99, (c) HCl is a strong acid and thus has a significantly lower pH than the weak acid HOCl
17. 2.19
18. $[HC_2H_3O_2] = 0.100$ M, $[C_2H_3O_2^-] = 1.8 \times 10^{-5}$ M
19. pH = 3.47, $[H_2CO_3] = 0.25$ M, $[H^+] = 3.35 \times 10^{-4}$ M, $[HCO_3^-] = 3.35 \times 10^{-4}$ M, $[CO_3^{2-}] = 5.6 \times 10^{-11}$ M
20. pOH = 4.49, pH = 9.51, $[OH^-] = 3.2 \times 10^{-5}$ M
21. 1.8×10^{-4}
22. 8.20
23. 3.6 g HF
24. 11.43

17

Aqueous Equilibria: Buffers, Titrations, Solubility, and Complex Ion Equilibria

In this chapter, our discussion of acids and bases continues by considering buffer solutions, those that resist changes in pH, and titrations, volumetric procedures in which unknown acid or base solutions are neutralized with known base or acid solutions. Additionally, solubility and complex ion equilibria will be discussed. A solubility equilibrium establishes between undissolved solutes and their dissolved ions. Complex ion equilibria establish between coordination complexes and their ions.

17.1   BUFFER SOLUTIONS

The Nature of Buffer Solutions

Buffer solutions maintain a nearly constant pH with the addition of small amounts of either acids or bases. In other words, buffer solutions resist changes in pH.

Components of a Buffer Solution

If an acid is added to a buffer solution, it must have a basic component to neutralize the acid, and if a base is added to a buffer solution, it must have an acidic component to neutralize the base. Hence, buffer solutions are prepared by mixing either a weak acid and its conjugate base, or a weak base and its conjugate acid.

Buffering Action–Adding Acid to a Buffer Solution

To understand how buffer solutions maintain a constant pH, let us consider a buffer prepared by mixing equimolar amounts of the weak acid acetic acid, $HC_2H_3O_2$, and the sodium salt of its conjugate base, sodium acetate, $NaC_2H_3O_2$. The net ionic equation for the equilibrium that establishes in this buffer solution is as follows.

$$HC_2H_3O_2(aq) \rightleftharpoons H^+(aq) + C_2H_3O_2^-(aq)$$

The Na$^+$ ion from the sodium acetate is present as a spectator ion. If a small amount of a strong acid such as HCl is added to this buffer solution, the resulting H$^+$ ions shift the equilibrium to the left. The net result of adding the HCl(aq) is to decrease the acetate ion concentration and increase the acetic acid concentration.

Buffering Action–Adding Base to a Buffer Solution

Similarly, if a small quantity of a strong base such as sodium hydroxide, NaOH, is added to this buffer solution, the OH$^-$ ions neutralize some of the acetic acid and shift the equilibrium to the right. The net result of adding the NaOH is to decrease the acetic acid concentration and increase the acetate ion concentration. The added OH$^-$ ions did not raise the pH of the solution. The acetic acid molecules neutralized them, producing more acetate ions.

Buffer Calculations

Problem 17.1 (a) What is the pH of a buffer with 0.100 M HC$_2$H$_3$O$_2$ and 0.100 M C$_2$H$_3$O$_2^-$?
(b) Calculate the pH after adding 0.0010 mol of a strong solid acid to 100 mL this buffer solution.

Solution 17.1

(a) The equilibrium expression for the equilibrium in this buffer is as follows.

$$K_a = \frac{[H^+][C_2H_3O_2^-]}{[HC_2H_3O_2]} = 1.8 \times 10^{-5}$$

Because acetic acid is a weak acid and the acetate ions are a common ion, the degree of ionization is small compared to its initial concentration of 0.10 M. Therefore, the equilibrium concentrations of both HC$_2$H$_3$O$_2$ and C$_2$H$_3$O$_2^-$ ions equal 0.10 M. Substituting into the equilibrium expression gives the following.

$$K_a = \frac{[H^+](0.100\ M)}{0.100\ M} = 1.8 \times 10^{-5}$$
$$[H^+] = 1.8 \times 10^{-5}\ M$$

To calculate the pH of this buffer solution, take the negative logarithm of the H$^+$ ion concentration.

$$pH = -\log[H^+] = -\log(1.8 \times 10^{-5}\ M) = 4.74$$

(b) Assume that the addition of the solid acid does not change the total volume of the buffer solution. First, write the equation for the reaction that occurs when a strong acid mixes with a buffer solution. The acetate ions, C$_2$H$_3$O$_2^-$, neutralize the added acid, H$^+$, as follows.

$$H^+(aq) + C_2H_3O_2^-(aq) \longrightarrow HC_2H_3O_2(aq)$$

The assumption can be made that this reaction goes essentially to completion. Hence after the addition of the acid, the moles of acetate decrease by 0.0010 mol and the moles of acetic acid increase by 0.0010 mol. Thus, calculate the number of moles of acetic acid and acetate initially present as follows.

$$\text{mol HC}_2\text{H}_3\text{O}_2 = \text{mol C}_2\text{H}_3\text{O}_2^- = 0.100\ \text{L} \times 0.100\ \text{mol/L} = 0.0100\ \text{mol}$$

Then, subtract 0.0010 mol from the moles of acetate and add 0.0010 mol to the moles of acetic acid to determine the final number of moles.

$$\text{mol C}_2\text{H}_3\text{O}_2^- = 0.0100\ \text{mol} - 0.0010\ \text{mol} = 0.0090\ \text{mol C}_2\text{H}_3\text{O}_2^-$$
$$\text{mol HC}_2\text{H}_3\text{O}_2 = 0.0100\ \text{mol} + 0.0010\ \text{mol} = 0.0110\ \text{mol HC}_2\text{H}_3\text{O}_2$$

The final molar concentrations are found by dividing the moles by the total volume, 100 mL of 0.100 L.

$$[C_2H_3O_2^-] = 0.0090 \text{ mol } C_2H_3O_2^-/0.100 \text{ L} = 0.090 \ M \ C_2H_3O_2^-$$
$$[HC_2H_3O_2] = 0.0110 \text{ mol } HC_2H_3O_2/0.100 \text{ L} = 0.110 \ M \ HC_2H_3O_2$$

Because of the small degree of ionization of acetic acid due to the presence of a relatively high concentration of acetate ions, assume that the equilibrium concentration equals the initial concentration. Therefore, substitute these values into the equilibrium expression and solve for the H^+ ion concentration.

$$K_a = \frac{[H^+](0.090 \ M)}{0.0110 \ M} = 1.8 \times 10^{-5}$$
$$[H^+] = 2.2 \times 10^{-5} \ M$$
$$pH = -\log[H^+] = -\log(2.2 - 10^{-5} \ M) = 4.66$$

The addition of 0.0010 mol of strong solid acid to this buffer lowers the pH by only 0.08 pH units–a small pH change.

Problem 17.2 A student prepares 250 mL of a buffer solution that contains 0.500 M HOCl and 0.350 M NaOCl. The K_a for HOCl is 3.5×10^{-8}. (a) What is the pH of this buffer solution? (b) What is the pH of the solution after 1.0 mL 1.0 M NaOH is added?

Solution 17.2

(a) First, write the equation for the equilibrium and the equilibrium expression.

$$HOCl(aq) \rightleftharpoons H^+(aq) + OCl^-(aq)$$
$$K_a = \frac{[H^+][OCl^-]}{[HOCl]} = 3.5 \times 10^{-8}$$

Then, construct a table that gives the initial concentrations, concentration change, and equilibrium concentrations.

	Initial Concentration, M	Concentration Change, M	Equilibrium Concentration, M
[HOCl]	0.500	$-x$	$0.500-x$
[H^+]	0.0	$+x$	x
[OCl^-]	0.350	$+x$	$0.350 + x$

After substituting these values into the equilibrium expression, the following equation is obtained.

$$\frac{x(0.350M + x)}{(0.500 \ M - x)} = 3.5 \times 10^{-8}$$

Because HOCl is a weak acid, $K_a = 3.5 \times 10^{-8}$, assume the value of x is small and the equilibrium concentrations of the HOCl and OCl^- remain constant. Thus, the equation simplifies to the following.

$$\frac{x(0.350 \ M)}{(0.500 \ M)} = 3.5 \times 10^{-8}$$

After solving for x, $5.0 \times 10^{-8} \ M$ is obtained. Note that the assumption that x is small and that the HOCl and OCl$^-$ concentrations are constant is a good assumption because of this small value. To find the pH, take the negative logarithm of the H$^+$ ion concentration.

$$pH = -\log[H^+] = -\log(5.0 - 10^{-8}\ M) = 7.30$$

(b) Write the equation for the neutralization of the OH$^-$ ions from NaOH by HOCl.

$$OH^-(aq) + HOCl(aq) \longrightarrow H_2O(l) + OCl^-(aq)$$

This equation shows that the moles of HOCl decrease and the moles of OCl$^-$ increase with the addition of OH$^-$. Hence, calculate the number of moles of the OH$^-$ and subtract it from the moles of HOCl and add it to the moles of OCl$^-$. To calculate the moles of OH$^-$, multiply the volume in L, 0.0010 L, times the molar concentration, 1.0 mol OH$^-$/L.

$$\text{mol OH}^- = 1.0\ \text{mL OH}^- \times 1\ \text{L}/1000\ \text{mL} \times 1.0\ \text{mol OH}^-$$
$$= 1.0 \times 10^{-3}\ \text{mol OH}^- = 0.0010\ \text{mol OH}^-$$

Next, calculate the initial number of moles of HOCl and OCl$^-$.

$$\text{mol HOCl} = 0.250\ \text{L} \times 0.500\ \text{mol HOCl/L} = 0.125\ \text{mol HOCl}$$
$$\text{mol OCl}^- = 0.250\ \text{L} \times 0.350\ \text{mol OCl}^-/\text{L} = 0.0875\ \text{mol OCl}^-$$

Then, subtract 0.0010 mol from the moles of HOCl and add 0.001 mol to the moles of OCl$^-$.

$$\text{mol HOCl} = 0.125\ \text{mol} \times 0.0010\ \text{mol} = 0.124\ \text{mol HOCl}$$
$$\text{mol OCl}^- = 0.0875\ \text{mol} + 0.0010\ \text{mol} = 0.0885\ \text{mol OCl}^-$$

To obtain the molar concentrations of each, divide by the total volume. Assuming the volumes are additive, the total volume is 251 mL, 250 mL from the buffer and 1.0 mL from the added OH$^-$.

$$[\text{HOCl}] = 0.124\ \text{mol HOCl}/0.251\ \text{L} = 0.494\ M\ \text{HOCl}$$
$$[\text{OCl}^-] = 0.0885\ \text{mol OCl}^-/0.251\ \text{L} = 0.353\ M\ \text{OCl}^-$$

Because of the small degree of ionization of HOCl, which results from its small equilibrium constant, the assumption can be made that these concentrations approximate their values at equilibrium. Therefore, substitute these values into the equilibrium expression.

$$\frac{[\text{H}^+](0.353\ M)}{0.0494\ M} = 3.5 \times 10^8$$
$$[\text{H}^+] = 4.9 \times 10^{-8}\ M$$

Taking the negative logarithm of $4.9 \times 10^{-8}\ M$, gives 7.31.

$$pH = -\log[H^+] = -\log(4.9 \times 10^{-8}\ M) = 7.31$$

Problem 17.3 Given 0.50 M HC$_2$H$_3$O$_2$ and 0.50 M NaC$_2$H$_3$O$_2$ explain how 1.00 L of a buffer solution is prepared with a pH of 4.60. The K_a for acetic acid is 1.8×10^{-5}.

Solution 17.3   The volumes of acetic acid and acetate that must be mixed to produce 1.00 L of a buffer solution that has a pH of 4.60 must be determined. Begin by writing the equation for the equilibrium and the equilibrium expression.

$$HC_2H_3O_2(aq) \rightleftharpoons H^+(aq) + C_2H_3O_2^-(aq)$$

$$K_a = \frac{[H^+][C_2H_3O_2^-]}{[HC_2H_3O_2]} = 1.8 \times 10^{-5}$$

Then, calculate the $[H^+]$ concentration of the buffer solution.

$$pH = -\log[H^+]$$
$$4.60 = -\log[H^+]$$
$$[H^+] = 2.5 \times 10^{-5} \, M$$

Next, calculate the ratio of $[C_2H_3O_2^-]$ to $[HC_2H_3O_2]$ in which the $[H^+]$ equals $2.5 \times 10^{-5} \, M$. Rearrange the K_a expression to give $[C_2H_3O_2^-]/[HC_2H_3O_2]$.

$$K_a = \frac{[H^+][C_2H_3O_2^-]}{[HC_2H_3O_2]} = 1.8 \times 10^{-5}$$

$$[C_2H_3O_2^-]/[HC_2H_3O_2] = 1.8 \times 10^{-5}/[H^+]$$
$$= 1.8 \times 10^{-5}/2.5 \times 10^{-5} \, M = 0.72$$

Finally, calculate the volumes of $C_2H_3O_2^-$ and $HC_2H_3O_2$. Since 1.00 L of this buffer is to be prepared and the molar concentrations of the acetic acid and acetate are 0.50 M, the volume ratio for acetic acid and acetate must be 0.72. If x equals the volume of acetate, then $1.00 - x$ is the volume of acetic acid because the total volume is 1.00 L. Therefore, the volume ratio is expressed as follows.

$$x/1.00 - x = 0.72$$

Solving this equation for x yields 0.42 L. This means that 0.42 L of acetate are required and 1.00 L − 0.42 L or 0.58 L of acetic acid are required to prepare 1.00 L of a buffer solution with a pH of 4.60.

Henderson-Hasselbalch Equation

Buffer calculations may be simplified and the relationship between the concentration of the components can be more easily understood by using the logarithmic form of the acid-ionization equation expression. This equation is called the Henderson-Hasselbalch Equation, and is as follows.

$$pH = pK_a + \log\frac{[A^-]}{[HA]} \qquad (17.1)$$

In this equation, pH is that of a buffer solution, pK_a is the negative logarithm of the acid-ionization equilibrium constant of a weak acid $(-\log K_a)$, $[A^-]$ is the equilibrium molar concentration of the conjugate base, and $[HA]$ is the equilibrium molar concentration of the weak acid.

Problem 17.4   A buffer solution is prepared by dissolving 4.6 g sodium propanoate, $NaC_3H_5O_2(s)$, in 165 mL of 0.36 M propanoic acid, $HC_3H_5O_2$. The K_a for propanoic acid is 1.3×10^{-5}. Use the Henderson-Hasselbalch Equation to calculate the pH of this buffer. Note, the assumption must be made that the addition of the solid sodium propanoate does not change the total volume of the solution.

Solution 17.4   The equilibrium established in a propanoic acid-propanoate buffer is

$$HC_3H_5O_2(aq) \rightleftharpoons H^+(aq) + C_3H_5O_2^-(aq)$$

Thus, the Henderson-Hasselbalch Equation is

$$pH = pK_a + \log\frac{[C_3H_5O_2^-]}{[HC_3H_5O_2]}$$

First, calculate the value of pK_a.

$$pK_a = -\log K_a = -\log(1.3 \times 10^{-5}) = 4.89$$

Then calculate the concentration of the $C_3H_5O_2^-$ ion.

$$mol\ C_3H_5O_2^- = 4.6\ g\ NaC_3H_5O_2 \times 1\ mol\ NaC_3H_5O_2/96.0g\ NaC_3H_5O_2$$
$$\times 1\ mol\ C_3H_5O_2^-/1\ mol\ NaC_3H_5O_2$$

$$= 0.048\ mol\ C_3H_5O_2^-$$
$$[C_3H_5O_2^-] = 0.048\ mol\ C_3H_5O_2^-/0.165\ L = 0.29\ M\ C_3H_5O_2^-$$

Finally, substitute all values into the Henderson-Hasselbalch Equation.

$$pH = pK_a + \log([C_3H_5O_2^-]/[HC_3H_5O_2])$$
$$= 4.89 + \log(0.29\ M\ C_3H_5O_2^-/0.36\ M\ HC_3H_5O_2) = 4.79$$

Henderson-Hasselbalch Equation with Basic Buffers

The general equilibrium for such a buffer system is as follows:

$$B^-(aq) + H_2O(l) \rightleftharpoons HB(aq) + OH^-(aq)$$

in which B^- is a weak base and HB is its conjugate acid. The Henderson-Hasselbalch Equation for this equilibrium is as follows.

$$pOH = pK_b + \log\frac{[HB]}{[B^-]} \tag{17.2}$$

In this equation, pOH is the negative common logarithm of the OH^- ion concentration, $[HB]$ is the molar concentration of the conjugate acid, and $[B^-]$ is the molar concentration of the weak base.

Problem 17.5   A scientist prepares 100 mL of a buffer that contains 0.550 M NH_3 and 0.650 M NH_4Cl. (a) What is the pH of this buffer? (b) What is the pH of the buffer after the addition of 0.20 g $NaOH(s)$? Assume that the solid NaOH does not change the total volume of the buffer solution. The K_b for NH_3 is 1.8×10^{-5}.

Solution 17.5

(a) The equilibrium in the ammonia-ammonium ion buffer is as follows.

$$NH_3(aq) + H_2O(l) \rightleftharpoons NH_4^+(aq) + OH^-(aq)$$

Use Eq. 17.2 to solve this problem. First calculate the pK_b value.

$$pK_b = -\log K_b = -\log(1.8 \times 10^{-5}) = 4.74$$

Now, substitute all values into Eqn 17.2 and solve for pOH.

$$pOH = pK_b + \log([NH_4^+]/[NH_3])$$
$$= 4.74 + \log(0.650\ M\ NH_4^+/0.550M\ NH_3) = 4.81$$

To calculate the pH of this buffer, subtract the pOH from 14.

$$pH = 14 - pOH = 14 - 4.81 = 9.19$$

(b) The ammonium ion neutralizes the added strong base, NaOH, as follows.

$$OH^-(aq) + NH_4^+(aq) \rightleftharpoons H_2O(l) + NH_3(aq)$$

First calculate the moles of NaOH added, and the initial moles of NH_3 and NH_4^+.

$$mol\ OH^- = 0.20\ g\ NaOH \times 1\ mol\ NaOH/40.0g\ NaOH$$
$$\times 1\ mol\ OH^-/1\ mol\ NaOH$$
$$= 0.0050\ mol\ OH^-$$

$$mol\ NH_3 = 100\ mL \times 1\ L/1000mL \times 0.550\ mol\ NH_3/L$$
$$= 0.0550\ mol\ NH_3$$

$$mol\ NH_4^+ = 100\ mL \times 1\ L/1000mL \times 0.650\ mol\ NH_4Cl/L$$
$$\times 1\ mol\ NH_4^+/1\ mol\ NH_4Cl$$
$$= 0.0650\ mol\ NH_4^+$$

Subtract the mol OH^- from the mol NH_4^+ and add them to the mol NH_3.

$$mol\ NH_4^+ = 0.0650\ mol\ NH_4^+ - 0.0050\ mol = 0.0600\ mol\ NH_4^+$$
$$mol\ NH_3 = 0.0550\ mol\ NH_3 + 0.0050\ mol = 0.0600\ mol\ NH_3$$

The calculations show that the moles of NH_3 equal the moles of NH_4^+. Hence, their molar concentrations are equal (0.0600 mol/0.100 L = 0.60 M), which means that pOH equals pK_b.

$$pOH = pK_b + \log([NH_4^+]/[NH_3])$$
$$= 4.74 + \log(0.600\ M\ NH_4^+/0.600\ M\ NH_3) = 4.74$$

Subtract the pOH, 4.74, from 14 to obtain the pH, which is 9.26.

$$pH = 14 - 4.74 = 9.26$$

17.2   ACID-BASE TITRATION CURVES

Titrations and Titration Curves

    An acid-base titration is a volumetric laboratory procedure for determining the concentration or number of moles of an unknown acid or base, using either a standard base or acid. In an acid-base titration, the acid, which contains a few drops of an acid-base indicator such as phenolphthalein, is usually poured into an Erlenmeyer flask. Then, the base is carefully added until the equivalence point is reached. A titration curve is plotted to best understand what happens during a titration. These curves are plots of pH of the solution versus the volume of the titrant added.

Titration of a Strong Acid with a Strong Base

The net ionic equation for the reaction of a strong acid and strong base is as follows.

$$H^+(aq) + OH^-(aq) \longrightarrow H_2O(l)$$

The strong acid is the source of H^+ ions and the strong base is the source of the OH^- ions. At the equivalence point the moles of H^+ equals the moles of OH^-; thus the pH at the equivalence point is 7 because the reaction products are water and a neutral salt.

CHARACTERISTICS OF A TITRATION OF STRONG ACID AND BASE

The titration curve for a strong acid and strong base begins at a low pH value because a strong acid is present before base is added. The initial addition of base produces a small change in pH. A significant change in pH does not occur until the equivalence point, pH 7, is approached. An added drop of strong base near the equivalence point changes the pH by as much as five to six pH units, which means the H^+ ion concentration changes 10^5 to 10^6 times. Beyond the equivalence point, the pH initially rises rapidly and then levels off. Due to the steep segment of the curve near the equivalence point, acid-base indicators that change color between pH 4 and 10 may be used to detect the equivalence point. Figure 17.1 shows an example of such a curve.

Problem 17.6 Consider the titration of 25.00 mL 0.1000 M HCl with a standard 0.1000 M NaOH solution. (a) What is the initial pH of the solution before the addition of NaOH(aq)? (b) What is the pH after the addition of 15.00 mL NaOH? (c) What is the pH after the addition of 24.00 mL NaOH? d. What is the pH after the addition of 24.99 mL NaOH? (e) What is the pH after the addition of 25.00 mL NaOH? (f) What is the pH after the addition of 26.00 mL NaOH?

Solution 17.6

(a) Because HCl is a strong acid, it ionizes completely and gives 0.1000 M H$^+$ (1.000×10^{-1} M H$^+$), which has a pH of 1.0000. Figure 17.1 shows the titration curve for 0.1000 M HCl with 0.1000 M NaOH. Note the starting point is at a pH of 1.0000.

(b) A good way to calculate the pH is to find the volume of excess reactant and then calculate the molar concentration of the resulting solution. For example, 15.00 mL 0.1000 M NaOH neutralizes 15.00 mL 0.1000 M HCl, leaving 10.00 mL of excess HCl solution. To obtain the pH of the resulting solution, calculate the number of moles of H$^+$ in 10.00 mL 0.1000 M HCl and divide by the total volume, which is 40.00 mL or 0.04000 L (25.00 mL HCl + 15.00 mL NaOH).

$$\text{mol } H^+ = 10.00 \text{ mL} \times 1L/1000 \text{ mL} \times 0.1000 \text{ mol } H^+/L$$
$$= 1.000 \times 10^{-3} \text{ mol } H^+$$
$$[H^+] = 1.00010^{-3} \text{ mol } H^+/0.04000 \text{ L} = 2.500 \times 10^{-2} \text{ } M \text{ } H^+$$

To calculate the pH, take the negative logarithm of 2.500×10^{-2} M. This results in a pH of 1.6021.

(c) Only 1.00 mL of excess 0.1000 M HCl remains at this point. Once again, calculate the moles of excess acid and divide by the total volume, 49.00 mL or 0.04900 L.

$$\text{mol } H^+ = 1.00 \text{ mL} \times 1L/1000 \text{ mL} \times 0.1000 \text{ mol } H^+/L$$
$$= 1.00 \times 10^{-4} \text{ mol } H^+$$
$$[H^+] = 1.00 \times 10^{-4} \text{ mol } H^+/0.04900 \text{ L} = 2.04 \times 10^{-3} \text{ } M \text{ } H^+$$

Taking the negative logarithm of 2.04×10^{-3} M yields a pH of 2.690.

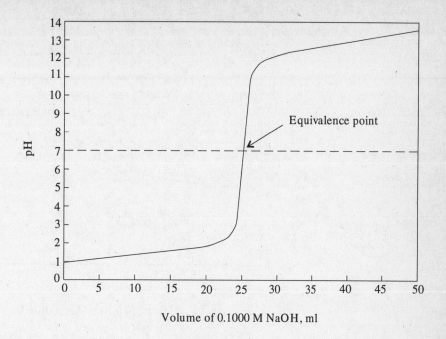

Volume of 0.1000 M NaOH, ml

Fig. 17.1

(d) Only 0.01 mL of excess 0.1000 M HCl remains at this point. Once again, calculate the moles of excess acid and divide by the total volume, 49.99 mL or 0.04999 L.

$$\text{mol } H^+ = 0.01 \text{ mL} \times 1 \text{ L}/1000 \text{ mL} \times 0.1000 \text{ mol } H^+/\text{L} = 1.00 \times 10^{-6} \text{ mol } H^+$$

$$[H^+] = 1.00 \times 10^{-6} \text{ mol } H^+/0.04999 L = 2 \times 10^{-5} M \ H^+$$

Taking the negative logarithm of $2 \times 10^{-5} M$, yields a pH of 4.7.

(e) At the equivalence point the number of moles of H^+ and moles of OH^- are equal. This means that the solution is neutral and the pH is 7.

(f) At this point there is 1.00 mL of excess NaOH. Thus, the $[OH^-]$ should be calculated and then the pH.

$$\text{mol } OH^- = 1.00 \text{ mL} \times 1 \text{ L}/1000 \text{ mL} \times 0.1000 \text{ mol } OH^-/\text{L}$$

$$= 1.00 \times 10^{-4} \text{ mol } OH^-$$

$$[OH^-] = 1.00 \times 10^{-4} \text{ mol } H^+/0.05100 \text{ L} = 1.96 \times 10^{-3} M \ OH^-$$

The pOH of 2.690 is found by taking the negative logarithm of $1.96 \times 10^{-3} M \ OH^-$. The pH of 11.290 is determined by subtracting the pOH from 14.

Titration of a Weak Acid with a Strong Base

The shape of the titration curve of a weak acid with a strong base differs significantly from that of a strong acid and strong base. The net equation for the reaction of a weak acid, HA, and a strong base is as follows.

$$HA(aq) + OH^-(aq) \longrightarrow A^-(aq) + H_2O(l)$$

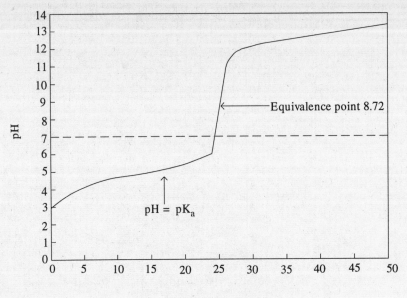

Volume of 0.1000 M NaOH, mL

Fig. 17.2

In this reaction, the conjugate base of a weak acid results, which is a stronger base than water. Hence, at the equivalence point the pH of solution is basic (pH > 7). Recognize that this reaction goes essentially to completion because it is the reverse of the base-ionization equilibrium (K_b expression).

$$A^-(aq) + H_2O(l) \rightleftharpoons HA(aq) + OH^-(aq)$$

Therefore, the equilibrium constant for the titration of a weak acid and a strong base equals the reciprocal of K_b, $1/K_b$. Because K_b values are usually quite small, the reciprocal of a small number is large. Figure 17.2 shows the titration of a weak acid, $HC_2H_3O_2$, and a strong base, NaOH.

COMPARISION OF STRONG ACID-STRONG BASE AND WEAK ACID-STRONG BASE TITRATIONS

The titration curve for a weak acid and strong base differs noticeably from that of a strong acid and strong base. First, the starting pH is higher than that of a strong acid-strong base titration because of the presence of a weaker acid. Second, the pH rises rapidly with the addition of the first few milliliters of base. Third, the curve levels off through the buffer region when the concentration of the weak acid approximately equals that of the conjugate base. Fourth, the increase in pH near the equivalence point is much less than with a strong acid and base, rising only 3 to 4 pH units instead of 5 to 6 pH units. Finally, the equivalence point occurs at a pH above 7.

Problem 17.7 Consider the titration of 25.00 mL of 0.1000 *M* $HC_2H_3O_2$ with 0.1000 *M* NaOH. The initial solution is just 0.1000 *M* $HC_2H_3O_2$, which has a pH of 2.87. The K_a of acetic acid is 1.8 $\times 10^{-5}$. (a) What is the pH after the addition of 10.00 mL 0.100 *M* NaOH? (b) What is the pH after the solution is half neutralized? (c) What is the pH at the equivalence point?

Solution 17.7   The net equation for the titration reaction is as follows.

$$HC_2H_3O_2(aq) + OH^-(aq) \longrightarrow C_2H_3O_2^-(aq) + H_2O(l)$$

(a)   The equation shows that the added NaOH decreases the number of moles of acetic acid, and for each mole of NaOH consumed one mole of acetate ions results. Because the volume of the solution containing OH^- is less than that of $HC_2H_3O_2$ and they both have the same molar concentration, OH^- is the limiting reactant. Thus, first calculate the initial number of moles of $HC_2H_3O_2$ and OH^-.

$$\text{mol } HC_2H_3O_2 = 25.00 \text{ mL} \times 1 \text{ L}/1000 \text{ mL} \times 0.1000 \text{ mol } HC_2H_3O_2/L$$
$$= 0.002500 \text{ mol } HC_2H_3O_2$$
$$\text{mol } OH^- = 10.00 \text{ mL} \times 1 \text{ L}/1000\text{mL} \times 0.1000 \text{ mol NaOH/L}$$
$$\times 1 \text{ mol } OH^-/1 \text{ mol NaOH}$$
$$= 0.001000 \text{ mol } OH^-$$

Then, subtract the moles of OH^-, which equals the moles of $HC_2H_3O_2$ consumed, from the initial number of moles of $HC_2H_3O_2$ to calculate the moles of $HC_2H_3O_2$ that remain.

$$\text{mol } HC_2H_3O_2 \text{ (remaining)} = \text{mol } HC_2H_3O_2 \text{ (initial)} - \text{mol } HC_2H_3O_2 \text{ (consumed)}$$
$$= 0.002500 \text{ mol } HC_2H_3O_2 \times (0.001000 \text{ mol } OH^-$$
$$\times 1 \text{ mol } HC_2H_3O_2 \text{ consumed}/1 \text{ mol } OH^-)$$
$$= 0.001500 \text{ mol } HC_2H_3O_2$$

For each one mole of OH^- neutralized, one mole of $C_2H_3O_2^-$ results. Therefore, 0.001000 mol of $C_2H_3O_2^-$ forms. The following table summarizes these calculations.

	Initial moles	Mole change	Equilibrium moles
$HC_2H_3O_2$	0.002500	−0.001000	0.001500
OH^-	0.001000	−0.001000	0
$C_2H_3O_2^-$	0.0	+0.001000	0.001000

Next, calculate the molar concentration of acetic acid and acetate by dividing the moles by the total volume in L, 0.03500 L (35.00 mL), the result of mixing 25.00 mL $HC_2H_3O_2$ and 10.00 mL NaOH.

$$[HC_2H_3O_2] = 0.001500 \text{ mol } HC_2H_3O_2/0.03500 \text{ L} = 0.04286 \text{ } M \text{ } HC_2H_3O_2$$
$$[C_2H_3O_2^-] = 0.001000 \text{ mol } C_2H_3O_2^-/0.03500 \text{ L} = 0.02857 \text{ } M \text{ } C_2H_3O_2^-$$

Substitute these values into the equilibrium expression and solve for the H^+ ion concentration. Because the value of the K_a for acetic acid is small, assume that ionization of acetic acid is insignificant.

$$\frac{[H^+][C_2H_3O_2^-]}{[HC_2H_3O_2]} = 1.8 \times 10^{-5}$$

$$\frac{[H^+](0.02857M)}{0.04286 \text{ } M} = 1.8 \times 10^{-5}$$

$$[H^+] = 2.7 \times 10^{-5} \text{ } M$$

Taking the negative common logarithm of $2.7 \times 10^{-5} \text{ } M \text{ } H^+$ gives a pH of 4.57.

(b) A solution that contains half the volume of base needed to reach the equivalence point is half neutralized. If 25 mL 0.1000 M NaOH neutralizes the 25.00 mL $HC_2H_3O_2$, then 12.50 mL are needed to half neutralize the solution. At this point the moles of $HC_2H_3O_2$ that remain equal the moles of $C_2H_3O_2^-$ produced. With equal number of moles of acetic acid and acetate ions, the $[H^+]$ of the solution equals K_a and the pH equals pK_a.

$$\frac{[H^+][C_2H_3O_2^-]}{[HC_2H_3O_2]} = 1.8 \times 10^{-5}$$

$$[H^+] = 1.8 \times 10^{-5}\ M$$

$$pH = -\log[H^+] = -\log K_a = pK_a = -\log(1.8 \times 10^{-5}\ M) = 4.74$$

(c) At the equivalence point the moles of OH^- added equal the moles of $HC_2H_3O_2$ originally present (mol OH^- = mol $HC_2H_3O_2$). Thus, all of the acetic acid is neutralized and converted to its conjugate base, $C_2H_3O_2^-$.

$$HC_2H_3O_2(aq) + OH^-(aq) \longrightarrow C_2H_3O_2^-(aq) + H_2O(l)$$

As soon as the $C_2H_3O_2^-$ forms, being a basic anion, it accepts protons from water and establishes the following equilibrium.

$$C_2H_3O_2^-(aq) + H_2O(l) \rightleftharpoons HC_2H_3O_2(aq) + OH^-(aq)$$

This is the equilibrium for the base ionization of acetate and is represented by the base-ionization equilibrium expression.

$$K_a = \frac{[HC_2H_3O_2][OH^-]}{[C_2H_3O_2^-]} = 5.6 \times 10^{-10}$$

Therefore, to calculate the pH at the equivalence point, first calculate the molar concentration of the acetate ion, $[C_2H_3O_2^-]$. For each mole of $HC_2H_3O_2$ neutralized, one mole of $C_2H_3O_2^-$ results. Hence, the moles of $C_2H_3O_2^-$ equal 0.002500 mol. After neutralizing the $HC_2H_3O_2$ with 25.00 mL 0.1000 M NaOH, the total volume is 50.00 mL or 0.05000 L. The molar concentration of $C_2H_3O_2^-$ is calculated as follows.

$$[C_2H_3O_2^-] = 0.002500\ \text{mol}\ C_2H_3O_2^-/0.05000\ L = 5.000 \times 10^{-2}\ M\ C_2H_3O_2^-$$

Substituting this value into the K_b expression, the OH^- ion concentration, x, is found to equal $5.3 \times 10^{-6}\ M$.

$$\frac{[H^+][C_2H_3O_2[OH^-]}{[C_2H_3O_2^-]} = 5.6 \times 10^{-10}$$

$$\frac{x^2}{5.000 \times 10^{-2} - x} = 5.6 \times 10^{-10}$$

$$x = [OH^-] = 5.3 \times 10^{-6}\ M$$

Taking the negative common logarithm of this value gives a pOH of 5.28. Subtracting 5.28 from 14 gives a pH of 8.72. Hence, the pH at the equivalence point for this titration is 8.72. Figure 17.2 shows the curve for this titration.

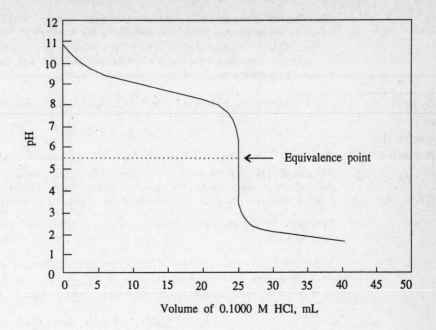

Fig. 17.3

Titration of a Weak Base with a Strong Acid

The general shape of the titration curve of a weak base with a strong acid resembles that of a weak acid and strong base, except that the addition of a strong acid decreases the pH. The net ionic equation for the reaction of a weak base, B, and a strong acid such as HCl is as follows.

$$B(aq) + H^+(aq) \longrightarrow HB^+(aq)$$

In this reaction, the conjugate acid of a weak base is produced, which is a stronger acid than water. Hence, at the equivalence point the pH of the solution is in the acidic range (pH < 7). Also, recognize that this reaction essentially goes to completion because it is the reverse of the acid-ionization equilibrium.

$$HB^+(aq) \rightleftharpoons H^+(aq) + B(aq)$$

Therefore, the equilibrium constant for the titration of a weak base and a strong acid equals the reciprocal of K_a, i.e., $1/K_a$. K_a values are usually quite small. Thus, the reciprocal of a small number is a large one. Figure 17.3 shows an example of a weak base-strong acid titration curve.

17.3 SOLUBILITY EQUILIBRIA

Solubility Equilibria of Partially Soluble Ionic Solids

To begin our discussion of solubility equilibria, let us consider the dissolution of barium sulfate, $BaSO_4(s)$. It has minimal solubility in water; therefore, few Ba^{2+} ions enter solution because Ba^{2+} ions are strongly bonded to the sulfate ions. The equilibrium established in a saturated solution of $BaSO_4$ is as follows.

$$BaSO_4(s) \overset{H_2O}{\rightleftharpoons} Ba^{2+}(aq) + SO_4^{2-}(aq)$$

When $BaSO_4$, or any relatively insoluble solid, enters solution, initially, the rate that $BaSO_4$ dissolves and enters solution exceeds the rate that the $Ba^{2+}(aq)$ and $SO_4^{2-}(aq)$ combine to produce the undissolved $BaSO_4$. At some point in time, the solubility equilibrium establishes when the rate of dissolution of $BaSO_4$ equals the rate at which the Ba^{2+} and SO_4^{2-} ions leave solution and attach to the undissolved $BaSO_4$.

Solubility-Product Equilibrium Expression

The equilibrium expression for the $BaSO_4$ solubility equilibrium is as follows

$$K_{sp} = [\,Ba^{2+}][SO_4^{2-}\,]$$

in which K_{sp} is the solubility-product equilibrium constant, $[Ba^{2+}]$ is the molar concentration of the Ba^{2+} ion, and $[SO_4^{2-}]$ is the molar concentration of the SO_4^{2-} ion. K_{sp} is called the solubility-product equilibrium constant because it only depends on the product of the molar concentration of the dissolved ions in equilibrium with undissolved solute, if the temperature remains constant.

Problem 17.8   The molar solubility of $BaSO_4$ at 298 K is 4×10^{-5} mol/L. Calculate the K_{sp} value for $BaSO_4$.

Solution 17.8   For each mole of $BaSO_4$ that dissolves, one mole of Ba^{2+} and one mole SO_4^{2-} result. Hence, the molar concentrations for both Ba^{2+} and SO_4^{2-} are 4×10^{-5} mol/L. Substituting these values into the K_{sp} expression gives the K_{sp} value for $BaSO_4$, 2×10^{-9}.

$$K_{sp} = [Ba^{2+}][SO_4^{2-}] = (4 \times 10^{-5} \text{ mol/L})^2 = 2 \times 10^{-9}$$

Problem 17.9   Consider the following solubility equilibria.

(a) $PbBr_2(s) \overset{H_2O}{\rightleftharpoons} Pb^{2+}(aq) + 2Br^-(aq)$

(b) $Ag_2CrO_4(aq) \overset{H_2O}{\rightleftharpoons} 2Ag^+(aq) + CrO_4^{2-}(aq)$

(c) $Ca_3(PO4)_2(aq) \overset{H_2O}{\rightleftharpoons} 3Ca^{2+}(aq) + 2PO_4^{3-}(aq)$

Write the K_{sp} expressions for each.

Solution 17.9

(a) $K_{sp} = [Pb^{2+}][Br^-]^2$

(b) $K_{sp} = [Ag^+]^2\,[CrO_4^{2-}]$

(c) $K_{sp} = [Ca^{2+}]^3\,[PO_4^{3-}]^2$

Problem 17.10   An experiment is performed to measure the aqueous solubility of lead(II) bromide, $PbBr_2$. In this experiment, a 0.384-g $PbBr_2$ sample was needed to just saturate 100 mL of water at 298 K. Calculate the K_{sp} value for $PbBr_2$.

Solution 17.10   First, write the equation and the equilibrium expression. When $PbBr_2(s)$ dissolves, it establishes the following equilibrium.

$$PbBr_2(s) \overset{H_2O}{\rightleftharpoons} Pb^{2+}(aq) + 2Br^-(aq)$$

Thus, its K_{sp} expression is

$$K_{sp} = [Pb^{2+}][Br^-]^2$$

Next, determine the equilibrium concentrations of Pb^{2+} and Br^-.

0.384 g $PbBr_2$/100 mL $\times$ 1 mol $PbBr_2$/367 g $PbBr_2$ $\times$ 1000 mL/1 L = 1.05×10^{-2} mol $PbBr_2$/L

The equation for the equilibrium shows that for each mole of $PbBr_2$ that dissolves, one mole of Pb^{2+} and two moles of Br^- enter solution. Hence, the molar concentrations of Pb^{2+} and Br^- are calculated as follows.

$$[Pb^{2+}] = 1.05 \times 10^{-2} \text{ mol } PbBr_2/L \times 1 \text{ mol } Pb^{2+}/1 \text{ mol } PbBr_2 = 1.05 \times 10^{-2} \text{ } M \text{ } Pb^{2+}$$

$$[Br^-] = 1.05 \times 10^{-2} \text{ mol } PbBr_2/L \times 2 \text{ mol } Br^-/1 \text{ mol } PbBr_2 = 2.10 \times 10^{-2} \text{ } M \text{ } Br^-$$

Finally, substitute the equilibrium concentrations into the K_{sp} expression and solve for K_{sp}.

$$K_{sp} = [Pb^{2+}][Br^-]^2 = (1.05 \times 10^{-2} \text{ } M)(2.10 \times 10^{-2} \text{ } M)^2 = 4.63 \times 10^{-6}$$

Problem 17.11 The K_{sp} for lead(II) chloride, $PbCl_2$, is 1.6×10^{-5} at 298 K. What is the aqueous molar solubility of a $PbCl_2$ solution at 298 K?

Solution 17.11

First, write the equation for the equilibrium and the K_{sp} expression.

$$PbCl_2(s) \overset{H_2O}{\rightleftharpoons} Pb^{2+}(aq) + 2 Cl^-(aq)$$
$$K_{sp} = [Pb^{2+}][Cl^-]^2 = 1.6 \times 10^{-5}$$

As in any other equilibrium problem, construct a table with the initial concentrations, concentration changes, and equilibrium concentrations.

	Initial Concentration, M	Concentration Change, M	Equilibrium Concentration, M
$[Pb^{2+}]$	0.0	$+x$	x
$[Cl^-]$	0.0	$+2x$	$2x$

Neither Pb^{2+} nor Cl^- are in solution initially (before $PbCl_2$ dissolves). Therefore, at equilibrium, the molar concentration of Pb^{2+} and Cl^- are x and $2x$, respectively. Next, substitute equilibrium values into the K_{sp} expression and solve for x.

$$[Pb^{2+}][Cl^-]^2 = 1.6 \times 10^{-5}$$
$$x(2x)^2 = 4x^3 = 1.6 \times 10^{-5}$$
$$x^3 = 4.0 \times 10^{-6}$$
$$x = 1.6 \times 10^{-2} \text{ } M$$

This calculation tells us that the molar concentration of Pb^{2+} is 1.6×10^{-2} M. Thus, the molar solubility is also 1.6×10^{-2} mol $PbCl_2$/L because one mole of Pb^{2+} dissolves for each mole of $PbCl_2$.

Solubility Equilibria and the Common Ion Effect

The presence of a common ion shifts the solubility equilibrium to the left, in the direction of the undissolved solid. Therefore, common ions decrease the solubility of solids.

Problem 17.12 (a) What is the solubility of $PbCl_2(s)$ in a 0.10 M Pb^{2+} solution? The K_{sp} of $PbCl_2$ is 1.6×10^{-5}. (b) Compare the results of part (a) to the molar solubility of $PbCl_2$ in pure water which is 1.6×10^{-2} mol/L.

Solution 17.12

(a) Write the equation for the equilibrium and the K_{sp} expression.

$$PbCl_2(s) \rightleftharpoons Pb^{2+}(aq) + 2Cl^-(aq)$$
$$K_{sp} = [Pb^{2+}][Cl^-]^2 = 1.6 \times 10^{-5}$$

To calculate the molar solubility of $PbCl_2$, let x equal the molar concentration of dissolved Pb^{2+} ions and $2x$ the molar concentration of the dissolved Cl^- ions. The Pb^{2+} ions contributed by the $PbCl_2(s)$, x, is very small compared to those already present in the 0.10 M Pb^{2+} solution because the equilibrium has been shifted to the left by the Pb^{2+} ions. Hence, assume that the equilibrium molar concentration of Pb^{2+} is 0.10 M. The summary table is as follows.

Compound	Initial Concentration, M	Concentration Change, M	Equilibrium Concentration, M
$[Pb^{2+}]$	0.10	$+x$	0.10
$[Cl^-]$	0.0	$+2x$	$2x$

Substituting into the K_{sp} expression gives the following.

$$[Pb^{2+}][Cl^-]^2 = 1.6 \times 10^{-5}$$
$$0.10\,M(2x)^2 = 1.6 \times 10^{-5}$$
$$x = 6.3 \times 10^{-3} \text{ mol/L}$$

(b) Application of Le Chatelier's Principle tells us that the presence of the Pb^{2+} ions shifts the equilibrium to the left, which means that less $PbCl_2(s)$ dissolves in a 0.10 M Pb^{2+} solution than in pure water. The results show that the molar solubility of $PbCl_2$ in 0.10 M Pb^{2+} solution is 6.3×10^{-3} mol/L compared to 1.6×10^{-2} mol/L in pure water.

Solubility and pH Changes

Changes in pH can significantly affect the solubility of some partially soluble ionic compounds. For example, most metallic hydroxides such as $Mg(OH)_2(s)$ are essentially insoluble in water and thus establish a solubility equilibrium.

$$Mg(OH)_2(s) \rightleftharpoons Mg^{2+}(aq) + 2OH^-(aq)$$

As a result of the common ion effect, the solubility of $Mg(OH)_2$ can either be increased or decreased. If a strong base is added, the additional OH^- ions shift the solubility equilibrium farther to the left, causing a decrease in solubility of $Mg(OH)_2$. However, if a strong acid is added, the additional H^+ ions neutralize the OH^- ions in equilibrium with the $Mg(OH)_2$ and shift the solubility equilibrium to the right, which causes the $Mg(OH)_2$ to dissolve.

Problem 17.13 What is the molar solubility of $Cu(OH)_2$ in 100 mL of a buffer solution that contains 0.10 M NH_3 and 0.10 M NH_4^+? The solubility product of $Cu(OH)_2$ is 1.6×10^{-19}, and the pK_b for NH_3 is 4.74.

Solution 17.13 First, write the equations for the equilibria of interest and their equilibrium expressions. The solubility equilibrium and K_{sp} expression is

$$Cu(OH)_2(s) \rightleftharpoons Cu^{2+}(aq) + 2OH^-(aq)$$
$$K_{sp} = [Cu^{2+}][OH^-]^2$$

The equation for the ammonia-ammonium ion buffer and the equilibrium expression are as follows

$$NH_3(aq) + H_2O(l) \rightleftharpoons NH_4^+(aq) + OH^-(aq)$$

$$pOH = pK_b + \log \frac{[NH_4^+]}{[NH_3]}$$

Since the buffer solution maintains a constant pOH, first calculate the OH^- ion concentration and then substitute it into the K_{sp} expression for $Cu(OH)_2$. Then, solve for the Cu^{2+} concentration, which equals the molar solubility of $Cu(OH)_2$.

Because the molar concentrations of NH_3 and NH_4^+ are equal, the ratio of $[NH_4^+]$ to $[NH_3]$ equals one. Thus, the pOH equals pK_b.

$$pOH = pK_b + \log([NH_4^+]/[NH_3])$$
$$= pK_b = 4.74$$

To calculate the $[OH^-]$, substitute into the equation for pOH.

$$pOH = -\log[OH^-]$$
$$4.74 =$$
$$[OH^-] = 1.8 \times 10^{-5} \, M$$

Then, calculate the molar solubility of $Cu(OH)_2$. The buffer solution maintains a OH^- ion concentration of $1.8 \times 10^{-5} \, M$. Hence, substitute this value into the K_{sp} expression and solve for the $[Cu^{2+}]$. Assume that the OH^- ions contributed by $Cu(OH)_2$ to the equilibrium OH^- concentration are insignificant because of the small value of K_{sp}, 1.6×10^{-19}, and the common ion effect.

$$1.6 \times 10^{-19} = [Cu^{2+}][OH^-]^2 = [Cu^{2+}](1.8 \times 10^{-5} \, M)^2$$
$$[Cu^{2+}] = 4.9 \times 10^{-10} \, M$$

Because one mole of Cu^{2+} forms for each mole of $Cu(OH)_2$, the molar solubility is 4.9×10^{-10} mol $Cu(OH)_2/L$.

17.4 PRECIPITATION REACTIONS

Does a Precipitate Form in a Precipitation Reaction?

To determine if a precipitate forms in a precipitation reaction, the reaction quotient, Q, is calculated. Recall that Q has the same form as the equilibrium expression and it is used for nonequilibrium systems. When Q equals K, then the system is at equilibrium. In solubility equilibria, the equilibrium expression is just the product of the molar concentrations of the dissolved ions raised to the appropriate powers. Hence, the Q value for solubility equilibria is called the ion product. For example, the ion product expression for AgCl is $Q = [Ag^+][Cl^-]$. If $Q < K_{sp}$, then the solution is unsaturated and a precipitate cannot form. As long as the ion product, Q, is less than K_{sp}, insufficient ions are present to establish a solubility equilibrium. However, as soon as $Q = K_{sp}$, the solution becomes saturated, and whenever $Q > K_{sp}$ then any excess solid comes out of solution so equilibrium may establish. Hence, to predict if a precipitate forms, calculate the value of Q and compare it to K_{sp}.

Problem 17.14 Will a precipitate form when 25 mL 0.0050 M Ag^+ and 25 mL 0.0050 M Cl^- mix? The K_{sp} for AgCl is 1.6×10^{-10}.

Solution 17.14   First, write the equation for the solubility equilibrium.

$$AgCl(s) \rightleftharpoons Ag^+(aq) + Cl^-(aq)$$

Because these solutions have equal volumes, each solution will become half the initial concentration on mixing. Therefore, the initial concentration on mixing is 0.0025 M for each ion. Then, substitute these values into the ion product expression as follows.

$$Q = [Ag^+][Cl^-] = 0.0025\ M\ Ag^+ \times 0.0025\ M\ Cl^- = 6.3 \times 10^{-6}$$

The K_{sp} value for AgCl is 1.6×10^{-10}, which means that Q is much larger than K_{sp}. Therefore, a precipitate should form when these solutions mix.

Problem 17.15   Will a precipitate form when 10 mL 0.030 M Pb(NO$_3$)$_2$ is mixed with 20 mL 0.0060 M NaCl? The K_{sp} value for PbCl$_2$, 1.6×10^{-5}.

Solution 17.15   First, write the equation for the reaction.

$$Pb(NO_3)_2(aq) + 2NaCl(aq) \rightleftharpoons PbCl_2(s) + 2NaNO_3(aq)$$

Write the K_{sp} and Q expression and find the value of K_{sp}.

$$K_{sp} = [Pb^{2+}][Cl^-]^2$$
$$Q = [Pb^{2+}][Cl^-]^2$$

Next, calculate the molar concentration of the ions after mixing. When 10 mL 0.030 M Pb(NO$_3$)$_2$ and 20 mL 0.0060 M NaCl mix, the total volume increases to 30 mL. Thus, the concentration of the Pb(NO$_3$)$_2$ is $\frac{1}{3}$ (10 mL/30 mL) its initial concentration and the NaCl concentration is $\frac{2}{3}$ (20 mL/30 mL) of its initial concentration.

$$[Pb^{2+}] = \frac{1}{3} \times 0.030\ M\ Pb(NO_3)_2 \times 1\ mol\ Pb^{2+}/1\ mol\ Pb(NO_3)_2$$
$$= 0.010\ M\ Pb^{2+}$$

$$[Cl^-] = \frac{2}{3} \times 0.0060\ M\ NaCl \times 1\ mol\ Cl^-/1\ mol\ NaCl$$
$$= 0.0040\ M\ Cl^-$$

Substitute these values into the ion-product expression and compare to K_{sp}.

$$Q = [Pb^{2+}][Cl^-]^2 = (0.010\ M)(0.0040\ M)^2 = 1.6 \times 10^{-7}$$

Because 1.6×10^{-7} is significantly less than the K_{sp} value, 1.6×10^{-5}, no precipitate forms.

Problem 17.16   If 75 mL 0.045 M AgNO$_3$ is mixed with 125 mL 1.00 M HCl, what percent of Ag$^+$ remains in solution?

Solution 17.16   First, write the equation for the precipitation reaction:

$$AgNO_3(aq) + HCl(aq) \longrightarrow AgCl(s) + HNO_3(aq)$$

Then, write the equation for the solubility equilibrium and the K_{sp} expression.

$$AgCl(s) \rightleftharpoons Ag^+(aq) + Cl^-(aq)$$

The K_{sp} expression for AgCl is $K_{sp} = 1.6 \times 10^{-10} = [Ag^+][Cl^-]$. To begin this problem, calculate the moles of each reactant, and subtract the moles of limiting reactant, Ag^+, from the excess reactant, Cl^-, because $AgNO_3$ and HCl combine in a one-to-one ratio.

$$\text{mol Ag}^+ = 75 \text{ mL} \times 1 \text{ L}/1000 \text{ mL} \times 0.045 \text{ mol AgNO}_3/\text{L} \times 1 \text{ mol Ag}^+/1 \text{ mol AgNO}_3$$
$$= 0.0034 \text{ mol Ag}^+$$
$$\text{mol Cl}^- = 125 \text{ mL} \times 1 \text{ L}/1000 \text{mL} \times 1.00 \text{ mol HCl/L} \times 1 \text{ mol H}^+/1 \text{ mol HCl}$$
$$= 0.125 \text{ mol Cl}^-$$
$$\text{mol excess Cl}^- = 0.125 \text{ mol} - (0.0034 \text{ mol Ag}^+ \times 1 \text{ mol Cl}^-/1 \text{ mol Ag}^+)$$
$$= 0.122 \text{ mol Cl}^-$$

The total volume of the solution becomes 0.200 L (200 mL) after mixing 75.0 mL 0.045 M $AgNO_3$ and 125 mL 1.00 M HCl. Thus, the molar concentration of the Cl^- ion that remains is calculated as follows.

$$[Cl^-] = 0.122 \text{ mol Cl}^-/0.200 \text{ L} = 0.610 \text{ } M \text{ Cl}^-$$

Next, construct an equilibrium summary table.

	Initial Concentration, M	Concentration Change, M	Equilibrium Concentration, M
$[Ag^+]$	0.0	$+x$	x
$[Cl^-]$	0.610	$+x$	$0.610 + x$

Because AgCl has a small K_{sp} value and the common Cl^- ion decreases the solubility of AgCl, assume that x is small and the equilibrium concentration of Cl^- equals 0.610 M. Substitute these values into the K_{sp} expression and solve for x which equals the $[Ag^+]$.

$$K_{sp} = 1.6 \times 10^{-10} = [Ag^+][Cl^-] = x \cdot 0.610 \text{ } M$$
$$x = 2.6 \times 10^{-10} \text{ } M$$

The $[Ag^+]$ after the addition of HCl decreases to 2.6×10^{-10} M.

To calculate the percent Ag^+ remaining, divide the $[Ag^+]_{final}$ by the initial $[Ag^+]_{initial}$ and multiply by 100.

$$\%Ag_{remaining} = (2.6 \times 10^{-10} \text{ } M/0.045 \text{ } M) \times 100$$
$$= 5.8 \times 10^{-7}\%$$

Selective Precipitation

Precipitation reactions can be used to separate ions. For example, if two compounds with different solubilities are to be separated, a precipitating reagent can be added in such a manner as to precipitate the less soluble compound, leaving the other in solution. Then, the precipitate is filtered from the solution, effectively separating the compounds with different solubilities. This procedure is called selective precipitation.

Problem 17.17 A solution contains 0.01M $AgNO_3$ and 0.01 M $Pb(NO_3)_2$. How can the Ag^+ and Pb^{2+} ions be separated using NaCl(*aq*)?

Solution 17.17 The metal cations from these solution, Ag^+ and Pb^{2+}, respectively, combine with the Cl^- and form precipitates. The net ionic equations for these reactions are

$$Ag^+(aq) + Cl^-(aq) \rightleftharpoons AgCl(s)$$
$$Pb^{2+}(aq) + 2Cl^-(aq) \rightleftharpoons PbCl_2(s)$$

The K_{sp} values for these two partially soluble solids can be used to show that the $PbCl_2$ (1.6×10^{-5}) is significantly more soluble than $AgCl$ (1.6×10^{-10}). Thus, as Cl^- is added to the solution, $AgCl$ precipitates initially from solution. Continual addition of Cl^- precipitates more $AgCl$ until the solution just becomes saturated with $PbCl_2$. Any additional Cl^- precipitates the $PbCl_2$ with $AgCl$. Thus, if the chloride ion concentration, $[Cl^-]$, is calculated to just saturate the $PbCl_2$ solution, the maximum Cl^- concentration to separate the Ag^+ from the Pb^{2+} is obtained. Therefore, substitute the molar concentration of the Pb^{2+} ($0.01\ M\ Pb^{2+}$) into its K_{sp} expression and solve for the Cl^- ion concentration.

$$1.6 \times 10^{-5} = [Pb^{2+}][Cl^-]^2 = (0.01\ M)[Cl^-]^2$$
$$[Cl^-] = 0.04\ M$$

This calculation shows that until the $[Cl^-]$ reaches $0.04\ M$, no $PbCl_2$ precipitates from solution. Substituting this value ($0.04\ M\ Cl^-$) into the K_{sp} expression for $AgCl$ gives the concentration of Ag^+ that remains in solution.

$$1.6 \times 10^{-10} = [Ag^+][Cl^-] = [Ag^+](0.04\ M)$$
$$[Ag^+] = 4 \times 10^{-9}\ M$$

HYDROGEN SULFIDE, $H_2S(g)$, AS PRECIPITATING AGENT

Frequently, inorganic cations are selectively precipitated as sulfides using $H_2S(g)$. H_2S is a rather weak diprotic acid that undergoes the following ionizations.

$$H_2S(aq) \rightleftharpoons H^+(aq) + HS^-(aq) \quad K_{a1} = 1.0 \times 10^{-7}$$
$$HS^-(aq) \rightleftharpoons H^+(aq) + S^{2-}(aq) \quad K_{a2} = 1.3 \times 10^{-13}$$

Adding these two equations gives the overall ionization of H_2S.

$$H_2S(aq) \rightleftharpoons 2H^+(aq) + S^{2-}(aq)$$

To find the overall acid-ionization equilibrium constant for H_2S, K_a, apply the rule of multiple equilibria and multiply K_{a1} by K_{a2}.

$$K_a = K_{a1} \times K_{a2} = 1.0 \times 10^{-7} \times 1.3 \times 10^{-13} = 1.3 \times 10^{-20}$$

Thus, the overall acid-ionization equilibrium expression for H_2S is

$$K_a = \frac{[H^+]^2[S^{2-}]}{[H_2S]} = 1.3 \times 10^{-20}$$

If the $[H^+]$ is increased, the equilibrium shifts to the left and decreases the $[S^{2-}]$. If the $[H^+]$ is decreased by adding OH^-, the equilibrium shifts to the right and increases the $[S^{2-}]$. Accordingly, the pH of saturated H_2S solutions can be adjusted to obtain the correct $[S^{2-}]$ to selectively precipitate ions.

Problem 17.18 What pH must a saturated solution of H_2S (0.10 M) be in order to effect the best separation of 0.01 M Co^{2+} and 0.01 M Mn^{2+}?

Solution 17.18 The K_{sp} values for CoS and MnS are 5×10^{-22} and 2×10^{-3}, respectively. The K_{sp} values show that the cobalt(II) sulfide, CoS, is less soluble and precipitates before manganese(II) sulfide, MnS. Therefore, the pH of a saturated H_2S solution (0.10 M) is adjusted so the more soluble MnS is just saturated ($Q = K_{sp}$), leaving it in solution. The $[S^{2-}]$ is calculated as follows.

$$2 \times 10^{-13} = [Mn^{2+}][S^{2-}] = (0.01 \ M) \ [S^{2-}]$$
$$[S^{2-}] = 2 \times 10^{-11} \ M$$

Because the concentration of H_2S in a saturated solution is 0.1 M and the $[S^{2-}]$ needed to precipitate the maximum amount of CoS is 2×10^{-11} M without precipitating MnS, substitute these values into the acid-ionization equilibrium expression for H_2S and calculate the H^+.

$$1.3 \times 10^{-20} = ([H^+]^2[S^{2-}])/[H_2S]$$
$$[H^+]^2 = 1.3 \times 10^{-20}[H_2S]/[S^{2-}]$$
$$= 1.3 \times 10^{-20}(0.1 \ M/2 \times 10^{-11} \ M)$$
$$[H^+] = 8 \times 10^{-6} \ M$$

Taking the negative common logarithm of 8×10^{-6} M, gives a pH of 5.1.

17.5 COMPLEX ION EQUILIBRIA AND SOLUBILITY

Complex Ions

Complex ions result when Lewis bases combine with metal ions. Recall that a Lewis base is an electron pair donor. Thus, in complex ion formation an electron donor molecule or ion donates a pair of electrons to a metal ion (a Lewis acid). The Lewis base that bonds to the metal ion is called a ligand. The following are three examples of complex ions.

$$[Co(NH_3)_6]^{3+} \qquad [Ag(CN)_2]^- \qquad [Zn(OH)_4]^{2-}$$
$$\text{I} \qquad\qquad \text{II} \qquad\qquad \text{III}$$

Complex Ion Equilibria and Solubility

In the qualitative analysis group I cations, AgCl(s) precipitates out with $Hg_2Cl_2(s)$ and $PbCl_2(s)$. One way to separate AgCl from this mixture is to add an NH_3 solution. The following reaction occurs.

$$AgCl(s) + 2NH_3(aq) \longrightarrow [Ag(NH_3)_2]^+(aq) + Cl^-(aq)$$

In this reaction, the insoluble AgCl dissolves and forms the soluble $[Ag(NH_3)_2]^+(aq)$ complex ion with ammonia. This reaction takes place in two steps as follows.

$$AgCl(s) \rightleftharpoons Ag^+(aq) + Cl^-(aq)$$
$$Ag^+(aq) + 2NH_3(aq) \rightleftharpoons [Ag(NH_3)_2]^+(aq)$$

Silver ions, Ag^+, in equilibrium with the insoluble AgCl combine with two ammonia molecules, NH_3, and produce $[Ag(NH_3)_2]^+(aq)$. The removal of the dissolved Ag^+ ions shifts the solubility equilibrium to the right and the AgCl dissolves. In other words, the addition of NH_3 reduces the Ag^+ concentration to a level that the ion product, Q, $(Q = [Ag^+][Cl^-])$ is less than the K_{sp} of AgCl.

COMPLEX ION EQUILIBRIUM EXPRESSION—K_f Expression

An equilibrium expression can be written that shows the formation of a complex ion from its metal ion and ligands. For example, the equilibrium expression for the formation of $[Ag(NH_3)_2]^+$ is

$$K_f = \frac{[Ag(NH_3)_2^+]^2}{[Ag^+][NH_3]^2}$$

in which K_f is the formation constant or stability constant. The value for the formation constant of $[Ag(NH_3)_2]^+(aq)$ is 1.6×10^{-7}. The large value shows that this complex ion is stable, and that the equilibrium lies far to the right, when NH_3 is added to a solution containing Ag^+.

Problem 17.19 Will a precipitate form if 0.0025 mol NaCl(s) is added to 1.0 L of a solution with 0.25 M $AgNO_3$ and 1.50 M NH_3?

Solution 17.19 The $[Cl^-]$ is 0.0025 M because 0.0025 mol NaCl dissolves in 1.0 L, and one mole of Cl^- ions result when one mole of NaCl dissolves. To calculate the $[Ag^+]$, consider the complex ion equilibrium of Ag^+ and NH_3 with $[Ag(NH_3)_2]^+$.

$$Ag^+(aq) + 2NH_3(aq) \rightleftharpoons [Ag(NH_3)_2]^+(aq)$$

Because of the large value of K_f, 1.6×10^7, assume that all of the Ag^+ combines initially with NH_3 to produce $[Ag(NH_3)_2]^+$. The initial 0.25 M Ag^+ combines with 2×0.25 M or 0.50 M NH_3 and produces 0.25 M $[Ag(NH_3)_2]^+$. This means that before equilibrium establishes, 0.0 M Ag^+, 1.0 M NH_3 (1.5 M − 0.50 M), and 0.25 M $[Ag(NH_3)_2]^+$ are present. Hence, the equilibrium establishes from right to left as $[Ag(NH_3)_2]^+$ dissociates and produces Ag^+ and NH_3. The equilibrium summary table of the concentrations is as follows.

	Initial Concentration, M	Concentration Change, M	Equilibrium Concentration, M
$[Ag^+]$	0.0	$+x$	x
$[NH_3]$	1.0	$+2x$	$1.0 + 2x$
$[Ag(NH_3)_2]^+$	0.25	$-x$	$0.25 - x$

Assuming that x is small because of the minimal dissociation of $Ag(NH_3)_2^+$, the $2x$ from the $[NH_3]$ and the x from $[Ag(NH_3)_2]^+$ can be dropped. Therefore, substitute these values into the equilibrium expression and solve for the $[Ag^+]$.

$$1.6 \times 10^7 = [Ag(NH_3)_2]^+/([Ag^+][NH_3]^2) = 0.25 \ M/([Ag^+](1.0 \ M)^2)$$
$$[Ag^+] = 1.6 \times 10^{-8} \ M \ Ag^+$$

To calculate the ion product, Q, multiply the $[Ag^+]$, 1.6×10^{-8} M, by the $[Cl^-]$, 0.0025 M.

$$Q = [Ag^+][Cl^-] = 1.6 \times 10^{-8} \ M \times 0.0025 \ M = 4.0 \times 10^{-11}$$

Because Q, 4.0×10^{-11} is smaller than the K_{sp} of AgCl, 1.6×10^{-10}, no precipitate forms.

SUMMARY

Buffer solutions are those that resist changes in pH. They consist of a weak acid and its conjugate base. The basic component of the buffer neutralizes small amounts of added acids, and the acidic component neutralizes small amounts of added bases. Each buffer solution has a fixed capacity to maintain a constant pH. The buffer capacity of a solution depends on the concentration of the components and how close the molar ratio of the components is to one.

An acid-base titration is the systematic addition of a base (or acid) of known concentration to an acid (or base) of unknown concentration. A plot of the pH of the solution versus the addition of either acid or base is a titration curve. The shape of a titration curve depends on the general type of acid and base titrated.

The equilibrium that establishes between a partially soluble ionic solid and its ions is a solubility equilibrium. This equilibrium is described by using the solubility-product equilibrium expression. The product of the molar concentrations of the dissolved ions raised to the power equal to their coefficients in the equation equals the solubility-product equilibrium constant, K_{sp}. This equilibrium constant allows us to calculate the solubility of solids.

Solubility product equilibrium expressions help us to predict if a precipitate forms in a precipitation reaction. If the ion product, Q, is less than K_{sp} then no precipitate forms because the concentration of the ions is too small to establish equilibrium. If Q equals K_{sp} then the solution just becomes saturated, and when Q exceeds K_{sp} then a precipitate falls from solution.

Complex ions result when Lewis bases, ligands, combine with metal ions. Complex ions can be used to change the solubility of partially soluble solids. A ligand bonds to dissolved metal ions and forms soluble complex ions. This removes the metal ions in equilibrium with the insoluble solid and shifts the equilibrium to the right, towards the dissolved ions. Complex ions are in equilibrium with the ions result from their dissociation.

CHAPTER 17 REVIEW EXERCISE

1. Calculate the pH of buffers that have equimolar amounts of the following weak acids and their conjugate bases. (a) $HClO_2 - ClO_2^-$, $K_a(HClO_2) = 1.2 \times 10^{-2}$ (b) $HOCN - OCN^-$, $K_a(HOCN) = 3.3 \times 10^{-4}$

2. (a) Calculate the pH of a buffer that contains $0.350\ M$ HNO_2 and $0.375\ M$ $NaNO_2$. The K_a of HNO_2 is 4.0×10^{-4}. (b) What is the pH of the buffer after the addition of 5.0 mL 0.10 M HCl to 175 mL of this buffer?

3. Given $0.10\ M$ $HC_2H_3O_2$ and $0.10\ M$ $NaC_2H_3O_2$ explain how 0.50 L of a buffer solution is prepared with a pH of 4.95. The K_a for acetic acid is 1.8×10^{-5}.

4. A student prepares a buffer by dissolving 25 g sodium propanoate, $NaC_3H_5O_2$, in 450 mL of 0.44 M propanoic acid, $HC_3H_5O_2$. Calculate the pH of the buffer using the Henderson-Hasselbalch Equation. The K_a for propanoic acid is 1.3×10^{-5}.

5. Calculate the pH of an ammonia-ammonium ion buffer solution that is prepared by mixing 150 mL of 0.88 M NH_3 and 150 mL of 0.66 M NH_4Cl, assuming that the volumes are additive.. The K_b of NH_3 is 1.8×10^{-5}.

6. Buffer A consists of 2.000 M $HC_2H_3O_2$ and 2.000 M $C_2H_3O_2^-$, and buffer B consists of 0.0200 M $HC_2H_3O_2$ and 0.0200 M $C_2H_3O_2^-$. (a) Calculate the pH change that occurs when you add 0.015 mol HCl(g) to 1.00 L of each of these buffers. (b) Which has the greater buffer capacity?

7. Calculate the pH of the solution after the addition of each of the following volumes of 0.2500 M NaOH to 50.00 mL 0.2500 M HF. The K_a of HF is 7.2×10^{-4}. (a) 0.0 mL (b) 10.00 mL (c) 25.00 mL (d) 35.00 mL (e) 45.00 mL (f) 49.00 mL (g) 49.90 mL (h) 49.99 mL (i) 50.00 mL

8. A student dissolves 1.50 g benzoic acid, $HC_7H_5O_2$, in 300 mL of solution. The K_a of benzoic acid is 6.3×10^{-5}. (a) If a 30.00 mL aliquot is removed and titrated, what is the pH after the addition of 2.50 mL 0.100 M NaOH? (b) How many mL of 0.100 M NaOH are needed to half neutralize the 30.00 mL aliquot? (c) What is the pH when it is half neutralized? (d) How many mL of 0.100 M NaOH are needed to change the pH of 30.0 mL of the solution to 5.00? (e) What is the pH at the equivalence point?

9. Consider the titration of 50.0 mL 0.100 M acetic acid, $HC_2H_3O_2$, with 0.100 M NaOH. Calculate the volume of NaOH required to produce a pH value of 5.50.

10. An experiment is performed to measure the solubility of AgBr in water. At 298 K, 1.3×10^{-5} g AgBr dissolves in 100 mL of water. Calculate the K_{sp} of AgBr.

11. Calculate the molar solubility of BiI_3. The K_{sp} of BiI_3 is 8.1×10^{-19}.

12. (a) Calculate the molar solubility of PbI_2 in a solution that contains 5.0 g NaI per liter. (b) What is the molar solubility of PbI_2 in pure water? The K_{sp} of PbI_2 is 1.4×10^{-8}.

13. What is the molar solubility of $Zn(OH)_2$ in a buffer that has 0.5 M NH_3 and 0.35 M NH_4^+? The K_{sp} of $Zn(OH)_2$ is 4.5×10^{-17}, and the K_b of NH_3 is 1.8×10^{-5}.

14. Calculate the value of Q and determine if a precipitate forms when 40 mL 0.025 M $Pb(NO_3)_2$ is mixed with 60 mL 0.0090 M KI. The K_{sp} of PbI_2 is 1.4×10^{-8}.

15. A student prepares 95.0 mL 0.010 M $AgNO_3$ and mixes it with 95.0 mL 0.100 M HI. What percent of Ag^+ remains in solution after the addition of the HI? The K_{sp} of AgI is 1.5×10^{-16}.

16. Determine if a precipitate forms when equal volumes of the following solutions of $AgNO_3$ and NaBr mix. The K_{sp} of AgBr is 5×10^{-13}. (a) 0.01 M $AgNO_3$ and 0.0001 M NaBr, (b) 4×10^{-5} M $AgNO_3$ and 1×10^{-8} M NaBr

17. Explain why the molar solubility of $BaCO_3$ is greater than that predicted from a K_{sp} calculation.

18. A solution contains 0.35 M Cd^{2+} and 0.35 M Ni^{2+}. (a) What is the maximum carbonate ion concentration that can be added to precipitate the maximum amount of the less soluble ion, leaving the other in solution? (b) What percent of the less soluble ion precipitates from the solution? The K_{sp} values of cadmium(II) carbonate and nickel(II) carbonate are 8.7×10^{-9} and 1.4×10^{-7}, respectively.

19. Calculate the minimum concentration of NH_3 that prevents the precipitation of AgCl in a solution with 0.010 M Cl^- and 0.10 M Ag^+. The of AgCl is 1.6×10^{-10}, and the K_f of $Ag(NH_3)_2^+$ is 1.6×10^7.

20. When Fe^{3+} combines with the thiocyanate ion, SCN^-, it produces $[FeSCN]^{2+}$, which has a formation constant, K_f, of 9.0×10^2. (a) Write the complex ion equilibrium expression for $[FeSCN]^{2+}$. (b) If 50 mL 0.50 M Fe^{3+} is mixed with 50 mL 0.50 M SCN^-, what is the molar concentration of uncomplexed Fe^{3+} that remains in solution?

ANSWERS TO REVIEW EXERCISE

1. (a) 1.92, (b) 3.48
2. (a) pH = 3.43, (b) pH = 3.42
3. 0.31 L $C_2H_3O_2^-$ and 0.19 L $HC_2H_3O_2$
4. 5.01

5. 9.38

6. (a) Buffer A $\triangle$pH = 0.01, Buffer B $\triangle$pH = 0.85, (b) Buffer A

7. (a) 1.88, (b) 2.54, (c) 3.14 (d) 3.51, (e) 4.10, (f) 4.83, (g) 5.84, (h) 6.84, (i) 8.12

8. (a) 3.61, (b) 6.15 mL, (c) 4.20, d. 10.62 mL, e. 8.33

9. 42.53 mL

10. $K_{sp}(AgBr) = 4.8 \times 10^{-13}$

11. $K_{sp}(BiI_3) = 1.3 \times 10^{-5}$ mol PbI_2/L

12. (a) 1.3×10^{-5} mol PbI_2/L, (b) 1.5×10^{-3} mol PBI_2/L

13. 6.7×10^{-8} mol $Zn(OH)_2$/L

14. $Q = 2.9 \times 10^{-7}$, $Q > K_{sp}$, a precipitate of PbI_2 forms

15. 3.3×10^{-11}%

16. (a) yes, (b) no

17. The carbonate ion, CO_3^{2-}, is a weak base and is converted to HCO_3^-; thus, this shifts the solubility equilibrium farther to the right then expected.

18. (a) 4.0×10^{-7} M CO_3^-, (b) 94%

19. 0.83 M NH_3

20. (a) $Fe^{3+}(aq) + SCN^-(aq) \longrightarrow [FeSCN]^{2+}(aq)$, (b) 0.017 M Fe^{3+}

18

Chemical Thermodynamics— Free Energy, Entropy, and Equilibria

*T*he first law of thermodynamics states that the energy of the universe is constant or more simply that energy cannot be created or destroyed. Mathematically, the first law is expressed as follows.

$$\triangle E_{sys} + \triangle E_{sur} = 0 \qquad (18.1)$$

This equation states that energy lost by a system is gained by the surroundings and vice versa. When the first law of thermodynamics is applied to chemical systems, it allows us to predict the amount of energy either gained or released in chemical changes.

Now let us consider what determines the value of the equilibrium constant, K, for a system? More specifically, we want to consider why, under certain conditions, a liquid either vaporizes or freezes, or why a precipitate either forms or dissolves, or why a chemical reaction mixture either yields more products or reactants upon reaching equilibrium. The answers to these questions come from an understanding of the second and third laws of thermodynamics. These two laws, along with the first law, are the most fundamental laws of nature.

18.1 SPONTANEOUS CHANGES AND ENTROPY

Spontaneous Changes

What is a spontaneous change? It is a change that takes place without any outside influence. Examples of a spontaneous process include: the flow of heat from a hotter body to a colder one, the melting of ice at room temperature (298 K), and a gas expanding and filling its container.

THE REVERSE OF SPONTANEOUS CHANGES

In all cases, the reverse of a spontaneous process is nonspontaneous. This means that a non-spontaneous change requires some outside driving force. For example, a body becomes warmer only after heat is added, or at 298 K, heat must be removed to change liquid water to ice.

Predicting Spontaneous Processes

In general, many exothermic reactions and other processes that release energy are spontaneous; however, some are not. For example, above 273 K the spontaneous melting of ice is an endothermic process. Many salts dissolve spontaneously in water endothermically. In some cases, reactions are spontaneous at certain temperatures and nonspontaneous at others. This shows that standard enthalpy changes are not always good predictors of reaction spontaneity and that temperature is sometimes a factor to be considered. What thermodynamic property is used to predict whether a reaction is spontaneous or not? In other words, what property is the driving force in nature for spontaneous processes? It is entropy, S, and entropy changes, $\triangle S$, along with enthalpy changes, $\triangle H$, that allow us to predict if a reaction is spontaneous.

Entropy, S

Entropy, S, is a quantitative thermodynamic property that explains the randomness or disorder in a system. Think of "randomness" and "disorder" as terms used to describe the lack of organization. More disordered systems (less organized), such as gases, have higher values for their entropies than less disordered systems (more organized), such as crystalline solids.

UNITS OF ENTROPY

Entropy is a physical property; thus, each substance has a characteristic entropy, just as it has a density or melting point. The entropy value assigned to a substance is called its absolute entropy or just entropy, for short. The values listed in most thermodynamic tables are standard molar entropies, $S°$, which means the conditions are 1 atm and 298 K. The units $J/(K \cdot mol)$ are used most often, instead of $kJ/(K \cdot mol)$, because the values of entropies are small compared to values such as enthalpies of formation, $\triangle H_f°$, which most often have units of kJ/mol.

Entropy, Possible Arrangements, and the Third Law

Entropy is the thermodynamic property that indicates the number of arrangements or states available to a system under a fixed set of conditions. Stronger intermolecular forces among particles in the solid phase limit the number of possible arrangements (states) these particles can take. However, the absence of significant intermolecular forces among gaseous particles allows them to take many possible arrangements (states). The more possible arrangements or states a system has the greater its entropy. Let's consider theoretically a perfectly organized solid at absolute zero, 0 K; e.g., He(s) at 0 K. Such a solid could only have one possible arrangement; thus, its entropy is zero. This relationship, known as the third law of thermodynamics, was proposed by Ludwig Boltzman (1844-1906) in the following equation

$$S = k \ln W \qquad (18.2)$$

in which S is the entropy of a substance, k is Boltzman's constant, ln is the natural logarithm, and W is number of possible arrangements or states (sometimes called microstates) for a system. Boltzman's constant, k, has the value of 1.38×10^{-23} J/K and equals the ratio of the ideal gas constant, R, to Avogadro's number, N_A.

Problem 18.1   What is the entropy of a perfect crystal that has only one possible arrangement?

Solution 18.1   Because a perfectly ordered solid has only one possible arrangement, the value of S equals 0 because the natural logarithm of 1 is 0.

$$S = k \ln W = k \ln 1 = 0 \text{ J/K}$$

Problem 18.2   A sample of 50 diatomic molecules (near 0 K) can only orient themselves in two possible arrangements. (a) What is the total number of possible arrangements that this can system have? (b) What is the entropy of this system?

Solution 18.2

(a) The value of W, the number of possible arrangements, is 2^{50} or 1.1×10^{15}.

(b)
$$S = k \ln W$$
$$= 1.38 \times 10^{-23} \text{ J/K} \ln 1.1 \times 10^{15} = 4.8 \times 10^{-22} \text{ J/K}$$

Entropy and Temperature

Entropy increases with increasing temperature. At 0 K, absolute zero, the entropy of a perfectly ordered substance is 0 J/K. As heat is added to this substance the average kinetic energy of its particles increases and thermal motion of the particles increases. Subsequently, the number of possible arrangements of moving particles should be greater than those that are stationary.

Entropy Changes– Increases in Entropy

Entropy changes, $\triangle S$, like enthalpy changes, $\triangle H$, are state functions, which means they only depend on their initial and final states and are independent of the path taken. Thus, an entropy change, $\triangle S$, is defined as the final entropy, S_{final}, minus the initial entropy, S_{initial}.

$$\triangle S = S_{\text{final}} - S_{\text{initial}} \tag{18.3}$$

If the entropy of the final state is greater than that of the initial state, then the value of $\triangle S$ is greater than 0, or, in other words, it has a positive value. Such changes describe those going from a less random to a more random state—the system becomes more disorganized.

Entropy Changes– Decreases in Entropy

The decrease in entropy occurs when the final entropy state is less than its initial entropy state. In this case, $\triangle S$ is less than 0, which means it is a negative number. Such changes describe systems going from a more random to a less random state—the system becomes more organized.

Problem 18.3 For each of the following changes predict if the value of the entropy change, $\triangle S$, is greater or less than zero. (a) a sample of Fe cools from 50°C to 25°C, (b) solid iodine sublimes

Solution 18.3

(a) As Fe atoms cool, their average kinetic energy decreases, which means that fewer possible arrangements exists. Thus, $\triangle S$ is less than zero (negative).

(b) Iodine sublimes when I_2 molecules break free from the crystalline state and enter the vapor state ($I_2(s) \longrightarrow I_2(g)$). Because molecules in the gas phase are more randomly distributed than those in solid phase, $\triangle S$ is greater than zero (positive).

Entropy Changes, Probability, and Spontaneous Processes

Isolated systems—those that do not transfer energy or matter to the surroundings—tend spontaneously to increase their entropy. To understand why such systems tend spontaneously to become more disorganized, consider the simple isolated system in which two gaseous particles (X and Y) are distributed in two connected glass bulbs. This system can have four different arrangements (states). Both particles can be in the left bulb, both can be in the right bulb, X can be in the left and Y in the right, or X can be in the right and Y in the left.

Because each of these four arrangements is equally likely, the probabilities that both particles are either in the left or right bulbs are both $\frac{1}{4}$ [$\frac{1}{2} \cdot \frac{1}{2} = (\frac{1}{2})^2$]. In other words, there is one chance in four for either of these arrangements. The likelihood of one particle in each bulb is $\frac{1}{2}$ ($\frac{1}{4} + \frac{1}{4}$) because two arrangements have one particle in each. Which of these possibilities is more random? Particles that are more spread out are more random than those that are more closely grouped. Thus, the more random arrangement is when one particle is in each bulb. The less random arrangement is when the particles are together in one bulb. Hence, the more random arrangement, one particle in each bulb, is more probable (one chance in two, $\frac{1}{2}$), and the less random arrangement, two particles in either the left or right bulb is less probable (one chance in four, $\frac{1}{4}$).

This simple systems tends to go spontaneously from a state of lower probability to one of higher probability in which the lowest probability state is the most ordered and the highest probability state is the least ordered. In other words, these systems go spontaneously from a lower entropy state, more ordered and less probable, to a higher entropy state, less ordered and more probable. Overall, isolated systems, those not affected by the surroundings, have a natural tendency to go spontaneously to a more disordered state ($\triangle S_{sys} > 0$). This is one of the many equivalent statements of the second law of thermodynamics.

18.2   SECOND LAW OF THERMODYNAMICS

Entropy and the Second Law

Most chemical reactions are not isolated systems and can exchange energy with the surroundings. Hence, our initial statement of the second law of thermodynamics at the end of the previous section most be broadened in order to become more useful. Besides the change in entropy of the system, $\triangle S_{sys}$, the change in entropy of the surroundings, $\triangle S_{sur}$, must also be considered. Therefore, the total entropy change, $\triangle S_{total}$, equals the sum of the entropy change in the system, $\triangle S_{sys}$, and the entropy change in the surroundings, $\triangle S_{sur}$.

$$\triangle S_{total} = \triangle S_{sys} + \triangle S_{sur} \tag{18.4}$$

The combination of the system and the surroundings is the universe (uni = sys + sur). Hence, the total entropy changes in the system and surroundings, $\triangle S_{total}$, equals the change in entropy in the universe, $\triangle S_{uni}$.

$$\triangle S_{uni} = \triangle S_{sys} + \triangle S_{sur} \tag{18.5}$$

Our previous discussion showed that the entropy of an isolated system increases in a spontaneous process. Hence, a more general way to state the second law of thermodynamics is that a spontaneous process causes an increase in the entropy of the universe. Mathematically, this can be shown as follows.

$$\text{Spontaneous Process} \qquad \triangle S_{uni} = \triangle S_{sys} + \triangle S_{sur} > 0 \tag{18.6}$$

This means that the increase in entropy can be either in the system or surroundings or in both.

Entropy Changes in the Surroundings and the Second Law

The entropies of gases are greater than those of liquids. For example, the standard entropy of $H_2O(g)$, $S°$ ($H_2O(g)$), is 189 J/(K · mol) and that of $H_2O(l)$ is 70 J/(K · mol). If the $\triangle S_{sys}^{o}$ for the condensation of water, $H_2O(g) \longrightarrow H_2O(l)$, is calculated, then the following is obtained.

$$\triangle S_{sys}^{o} = S_{H_2O(l)}^{o} - S_{H_2O(g)}^{o} = 70 \text{ J/K } - 189 \text{ J/K } = -119 \text{ J/K}$$

The negative value for this change, -119 J/(K · mol), shows that the final state ($H_2O(l)$) is more ordered (less disorganized) than the initial state ($H_2O(g)$). Although the entropy of the water decreases upon condensing from the vapor to the liquid state, this process occurs spontaneously at temperatures below 373 K (the normal boiling point of water). How can this apparent contradiction of an earlier statement that spontaneous processes increase entropy be explained? The answer comes from the recognition that the process being considered is not occurring in isolation from the surroundings. Thus, what happens to the entropy change of the surroundings, $\triangle S_{sur}$, must also be considered.

ENTROPY CHANGES IN THE SURROUNDINGS AND q_P

Two factors influence the entropy change of the surroundings. It is beyond the scope of this discussion to prove this rigorously, but the first factor is the maximum heat that can be transferred from the system to the surroundings at constant pressure, q_P. If the system loses heat to the surroundings, the additional thermal energy disorganizes the surroundings, and if the system gains heat, the surroundings lose heat causing less disorganization. Thus, $\triangle S_{sur}$ is proportional to $-q_P$.

$$\triangle S_{sur} \propto -q_p \tag{18.7}$$

The minus sign in front of q_P indicates that if heat is lost by the system, $q_P < 0$, then the entropy change in the surroundings increases ($\triangle S_{sur} > 0$), and if heat is gained by the system, $q_P > 0$, then the entropy change in the surroundings decreases ($\triangle S_{sur} < 0$). Recall that the heat flow at constant pressure is the enthalpy change of the system, $\triangle H$. Hence, the proportionality may be changed as follows.

$$\triangle S_{sur} \propto -\triangle H \tag{18.8}$$

Equation 18.8 shows that if a process is exothermic ($\triangle H < 0$), then the entropy change of the surroundings is positive ($\triangle S_{sur} > 0$), more random, and if the process is endothermic ($\triangle H > 0$), then the entropy change of the surroundings is negative ($\triangle S_{sur} < 0$), less random.

ENTROPY CHANGES IN THE SURROUNDINGS AND TEMPERATURE, T

The second factor that influences the entropy change in the surroundings is the Kelvin temperature, T. If the surroundings is at a high temperature, then it is highly disorganized already from the thermal energy and the heat flow from the system has little effect on the entropy change. However, if the surroundings is at a lower temperature, then added heat from the system causes a more significant change in the entropy. This means that the entropy change in the surroundings, $\triangle S_{sur}$, is inversely proportional to the Kelvin temperature, T. Therefore, the entropy changes in the surroundings tend to be larger at low temperatures than they are at higher temperatures. Including this in the proportionality, Eq. 18.8, gives the following equation.

$$\triangle S_{sur} = \frac{-\triangle H}{T} \tag{18.9}$$

Problem 18.4   Use Eq. 18.9 to show why water vapor condenses spontaneously to liquid water at room temperature, 298 K. The molar enthalpy of vaporization of water, $\triangle H_{vap}$, is 44 kJ/mol at 298 K.

Solution 18.4   The molar enthalpy of vaporization is the amount of heat needed to vaporize one mole of liquid to vapor at a fixed temperature. Therefore, the heat released when one mole of water vapor condenses to liquid is $-\triangle H_{vap}$ or -44 kJ/mol ($-44{,}000$ J/mol). Substituting this value and room temperature, 298 K, into Eq. 18.9 gives the $\triangle S_{sur}$, $+148$ J/K.

$$\triangle S_{sur} = \frac{-\triangle H}{T} = \frac{-(-44{,}000 \text{ J})}{298 \text{ K}} = +148 \text{ J/K}$$

Our results show that $\triangle S_{uni}$ equals $+29$ J/K.

$$\triangle S_{uni} = \triangle S_{sys} + \triangle S_{sur} = -119 \text{ J/K} + 148 \text{ J/K} = +29 \text{ J/K}$$

This means that the overall entropy change is positive—an increase in the entropy of the universe. Therefore, water vapor condenses spontaneously to liquid water at 298 K.

Problem 18.5   (a) Calculate the total entropy change, $\triangle S_{uni}$, when one mole of liquid mercury, Hg(l), changes to mercury vapor, Hg(g), at 298 K. The molar entropy of vaporization of Hg is 99J/(K · mol), and the molar enthalpy of vaporization is 59.1 kJ/mol. (b) Explain the results. (c) What effect should a temperature increase have on the spontaneity of this process?

Solution 18.5

(a)
$$\Delta S_{uni} = \Delta S_{sys} + \Delta S_{sur}$$

ΔS_{sys}, 99 J/(K · mol), is known. Thus, the ΔS_{sur} may be calculated by using Eq. 18.9. To calculate the entropy change of the surroundings, substitute the molar enthalpy of vaporization, 59,100 J/mol (59.1 kJ/mol) and the temperature, 298 K, into the equation.

$$\Delta S_{sur} = -59,100 \text{ J/mol}/298 \text{ K} = -198 \text{ J/(K · mol)}$$

Therefore, by adding ΔS_{sys} and ΔS_{sur} gives ΔS_{uni}.

$$\Delta S_{uni} = 99 \text{ J/(K · mol)} + (-198 \text{ J/(K · mol)}) = -99 \text{ J/(K · mol)}$$

(b) The negative value, -99 J/(K · mol), shows that the vaporization of Hg(l) at 298 K is nonspontaneous. Just looking at ΔS_{sys}, it would not be expected that Hg(l), with a more ordered structure, would go spontaneously to the less ordered mercury vapor, Hg(g). However, the ΔS_{sur} is significantly more negative at 298 K. Thus, the overall entropy change of the universe is negative.

(c) If the temperature is increased, ΔS_{sur} decreases and at some point ΔS_{sur} equals ΔS_{sys} and an equilibrium establishes—the boiling point. At even higher temperatures, the value of ΔS_{sur} is smaller than ΔS_{sys} and the liquid mercury spontaneously changes to mercury vapor.

Entropy, Chemical Reactions, and the Second Law

Hess's law can be used to calculate the standard enthalpy change, $\Delta H°$, for a reaction. When applying Hess's law, take the sum of the standard enthalpies of formation of the products ($\Sigma \Delta H_f°$(products)) and subtract the sum of the standard enthalpies of formation of the reactants ($\Sigma \Delta H_f°$(reactants)).

$$\Delta H° = \Sigma \Delta H_f°(\text{products}) - \Sigma \Delta H_f°(\text{reactants}) \tag{18.10}$$

Similarly, the entropy change, $\Delta S°$, for a chemical reaction can be calculated. This is accomplished by finding the sum of the standard entropies of the products ($\Sigma S°$(products)) and subtracting the sum of the standard entropies of the reactants ($\Sigma S°$(reactants)).

$$\Delta S° = \Sigma S°(\text{products}) - \Sigma S°(\text{reactants}) \tag{18.11}$$

Problem 18.6 (a) Calculate the standard entropy change, $\Delta S°$, in which $N_2(g)$ combines with $H_2(g)$ to produce $NH_3(g)$.
$$N_2(g) + 3H_2(g) \longrightarrow 2NH_3(g)$$

The standard entropies of $N_2(g)$, $H_2(g)$, and $NH_3(g)$ are 192, 131, and 193 J/(K·mol), respectively. (b) Explain the results. (c) Why can't the result from part (a) be used to predict if this reaction is spontaneous?

Solution 18.6

(a) $\Delta S° = \Sigma S°(\text{products}) - \Sigma S°(\text{reactants})$

$= [2 \text{ mol} \times S°(NH_3)] - [(1 \text{ mol} \times S°(N_2) + (3 \text{ mol} \times S°(H_2)]$

$= [2 \text{ mol} \times 193 \text{ J/(K · mol)}] - [(1 \text{ mol} \times 192 \text{ J/(K · mol)})$

$\qquad + (3 \text{ mol} \times 131 \text{ J/(K · mol)}]$

$= -199 \text{ J/(K · mol)}$

(b) Four moles of gaseous reactants produce only two moles of gaseous products. Entropy increases with a larger number of particles in the system and decreases with a smaller number of particles. Hence, the entropy of this reaction should decrease. As predicted, the sign of the entropy change for this reaction is negative. This means that the system goes from a more random to a less random state.

(c) Without calculating the entropy change in the surroundings (ΔS_{sur}), a prediction cannot be made about the spontaneity of this reaction. Calculating the ΔS_{sur} shows that it is a more positive value (309 J/K) than ΔS_{sys} (−199 J/K). Thus, this reaction is spontaneous as written.

18.3   FREE ENERGY

Gibbs Free Energy (Free Energy), G

It is more convenient to use one thermodynamic property to predict if a reaction is spontaneous. The American scientist Josiah Willard Gibbs (1839-1903) proposed such a property. He introduced the thermodynamic function G, which is sometimes called Gibbs free energy (or free energy for short) to honor him. It is defined as follows:

$$G = H - TS \tag{18.12}$$

in which G is free energy, H is enthalpy, T in the Kelvin temperature, and S is entropy. Why is G called free energy? Equation 18.12 shows that if TS, the portion of energy that represents the amount of disorder in the system, is subtracted from the enthalpy, H, which represents the total energy change, what remains is the energy that can become disordered and thus can effect change and do useful work. In other words, a given amount of energy may be divided into the energy that can be used to do work, free energy (G), and the energy that cannot be converted to work (TS).

MAXIMUM USEABLE WORK, w_{max}

One of the best ways to understand free energy is to think of it as the maximum useable energy that a system can transfer—in other words, the maximum work, w_{max}, that a system can do on the surroundings ($\Delta G = w_{max}$).

Free Energy, Enthalpy, and Entropy Changes

The spontaneity of a chemical reaction is related to the free energy change, ΔG, at constant temperature and pressure. The following relationship between free energy change and enthalpy and entropy changes at constant temperature and pressure is derived from Eq. 18.12.

$$\Delta G = \Delta H - T\Delta S \tag{18.13}$$

In Eq. 18.13, ΔG is the free energy change, ΔH is the enthalpy change, ΔS is the entropy change, and T is the Kelvin temperature. This is called the Gibbs-Helmholtz Equation.

FREE ENERGY CHANGE AND THE ENTROPY CHANGE OF THE UNIVERSE

If free energy changes are linked to the spontaneity of reactions, then free energy changes are related to the change in entropy of the universe, ΔS_{uni}. This relationship can be expressed as follows.

$$\Delta G = -T\Delta S_{uni} \tag{18.14}$$

Rearranging Eq. 18.14 and solving for ΔS_{uni}, gives the Eq. 18.15.

$$\Delta S_{uni} = \frac{-\Delta G}{T} \tag{18.15}$$

If $\triangle S_{uni}$ is greater than zero (positive), then a reaction is spontaneous. Hence, the minus sign in front of $\triangle G$ means that for spontaneous reactions the free energy changes are always less than zero (negative). In other words, all spontaneous reactions release free energy. $\triangle G$ is the free energy of the products minus the free energy of the reactants.

$$\triangle G = G_{products} - G_{reactants} \tag{18.16}$$

If $\triangle G$ is less than zero, then $G_{products} < G_{reactants}$ or free energy must flow from the system to the surroundings in spontaneous reactions.

Problem 18.7   Consider the reaction of the decomposition of $NO_2(g)$ at 298 K.

$$2NO_2(g) \longrightarrow 2NO(g) + O_2(g) \quad \triangle G° = +69.7 \text{ kJ}$$

Calculate the change in entropy of the universe, $\triangle S_{uni}$, and state if the reaction is spontaneous.

Solution 18.7   Use Eq. 18.15 to find $\triangle S_{uni}$.

$$\triangle S_{uni} = -\triangle G°/T = -69.7 \text{ kJ}/298 \text{ K} = -0.234 \text{ kJ/K}$$

Because there is a decrease in the entropy of the universe, the decomposition of NO_2 is nonspontaneous.

Gibbs-Helmholtz Equation and Chemical Reactions

Equation 18.13 shows that the value of the free energy change, $\triangle G$, for a reaction depends on the enthalpy change, $\triangle H$, and product of the Kelvin temperature, T, and entropy change, $\triangle S$. Most often, this equation is used when $\triangle G$, $\triangle H$, and $\triangle S$ are in the standard state. The equation then becomes

$$\triangle G° = \triangle H° - T\triangle S° \tag{18.17}$$

EXOTHERMIC REACTIONS IN WHICH THE ENTROPY INCREASES

The standard molar enthalpy changes, $\triangle H°$, of exothermic reactions are negative and the standard molar entropy changes, $\triangle S°$, of reactions that become more disordered are positive. Substituting a negative value for $\triangle H°$ and a positive value for $\triangle S°$ always produces a negative value for $\triangle G°$ ($\triangle G° < 0$). Whenever $\triangle G°$ is negative the reaction is spontaneous. All exothermic reactions in which the entropy increases are spontaneous under all temperature conditions.

Problem 18.8   Consider the formation of $HF(g)$ from the elements.

$$H_2(g) + F_2(g) \longrightarrow 2HF(g) \quad \triangle H° = -542 \text{ kJ} \quad \triangle S° = 14 \text{ J/K}$$

(a) Calculate the value of $\triangle G°$ and explain the result. (b) What is the $\triangle G°$ of the reverse reaction? Is this reaction spontaneous?

Solution 18.8
(a) Use Eq. 18.17 to calculate the free energy change.

$$\triangle G° = \triangle H° - T\triangle S°$$
$$= -542 \text{ kJ} - (298 \text{ K} \times 14 \text{ J/K} \times 1 \text{ kJ}/1000 \text{ J}) = -546 \text{ kJ}$$

The answer, -546 kJ, is less than zero. Hence, this reaction is spontaneous. The combination of two highly reactive gases, H_2 and F_2, should react spontaneously.

(b) If reactions that release free energy are spontaneous, then those that absorb free energy are nonspontaneous. A reaction that has a $\triangle G°$ value greater than zero is nonspontaneous. The formation of two moles of HF from the elements releases 546 kJ of free energy ($\triangle G° = -546$ kJ). Hence, the decomposition of 2HF to H_2 and F_2 is nonspontaneous because it requires the addition of 546 kJ of free energy ($\triangle G° = +546$ kJ).

ENDOTHERMIC REACTIONS IN WHICH THE ENTROPY DECREASES

All endothermic reactions in which their $\triangle S°$ values are less than zero are nonspontaneous. Recall that the enthalpy changes of endothermic reactions are positive and the entropy changes of reactions that become less random are negative. Substituting a positive value for $\triangle H°$ and a negative value for $\triangle S°$ always produces a positive value for $\triangle G°$ ($\triangle G° > 0$). Whenever $\triangle G°$ is positive, the reaction is nonspontaneous.

Problem 18.9   Consider the formation of hydrazine, $N_2H_4(l)$, from the elements.

$$N_2(g) + 2H_2(g) \longrightarrow N_2H_4(l) \qquad \triangle H° = 51 \text{ kJ} \qquad \triangle S° = -333 \text{ J/K}$$

Calculate the free energy change and predict if the reaction is spontaneous. Explain the result.

Solution 18.9   Use Eq. 18.17 to calculate the value of $\triangle G°$.

$$\triangle G° = \triangle H° - T\triangle S°$$
$$= 51 \text{ kJ} - (298 \text{ K} \times -333 \text{ J/K} \times 1 \text{ kJ}/1000 \text{ J}) = 150 \text{ kJ}$$

The calculated value for $\triangle G°$ is 150 kJ. Because it is a positive value, this reaction is nonspontaneous at standard conditions. Once again this is not unexpected because hydrazine is a reactive liquid. In general, reactions that produce unstable products, such as hydrazine, are nonspontaneous.

Problem 18.10   Use the following thermodynamic data to calculate the $\triangle G°$ for the reaction in which $PF_5(g)$ forms from $PF_3(g)$ and $F_2(g)$ at 298 K.

$$PF_3(g) + F_2(g) \longrightarrow PF_5(g)$$

Compound	$\triangle H_f°$ kJ/mol	$S°$, J/(K · mol)
$PF_3(g)$	−919	273
$F_2(g)$	0	203
$PF_5(g)$	−1577	301

Solution 18.10
First, calculate the $\triangle H°$ and $\triangle S°$.

$$\triangle H° = \Sigma\triangle H_f°(\text{products}) - \Sigma\triangle H_f°(\text{reactants})$$
$$= (1 \text{ mol} \times \triangle H_f°(PF_5) - [(1 \text{ mol} \times \triangle H_f°(PF_3) + (1 \text{ mol} \times \triangle H_f°(F_2)]$$
$$= -1577 \text{ kJ} - (-919 \text{ kJ} + 0 \text{ kJ}) = -658 \text{ kJ}$$
$$\triangle S° = \Sigma S°(\text{products}) - \Sigma S°(\text{reactants})$$
$$= (1 \text{ mol} \times S°(PF_5)) - [(1 \text{ mol} \times S°(PF_3) + (1 \text{ mol} \times S°(F_2)]$$
$$= (1 \text{ mol} \times 301 \text{ J}/(K \cdot \text{mol}) - [(1 \text{ mol} \times 273 \text{J}/(K \cdot \text{mol})$$
$$+ (1 \text{ mol} \times 203 \text{ J}/(K \cdot \text{mol}))]$$
$$= -175 \text{ J/K}$$

Finally, calculate $\triangle G°$ by substituting the values of $\triangle H°$ and $\triangle S°$ into Eq. 18.17.

$$\triangle G° = \triangle H° - T\triangle S°$$
$$= -658 \text{ kJ} - (298 \text{ K} \times -0.175 \text{ J/K} \times 1 \text{ kJ}/1000 \text{ J})$$
$$= -606 \text{ kJ}$$

TEMPERATURE EFFECTS ON SPONTANEITY

Problem 18.11 Consider the reaction in which solid Ag_2O decomposes to $Ag(s)$ and $O_2(g)$.

$$Ag_2O(s) \longrightarrow 2Ag(s) + \tfrac{1}{2}O_2(g) \qquad \triangle H° = 31 \text{ kJ/mol} \qquad \triangle S° = 67 \text{ J/K}$$

(a) Calculate the standard free energy change and describe what it means. (b) What effect would increasing the temperature have on the spontaneity of this reaction? (c) Above what temperature is this reaction spontaneous?

Solution 18.11

(a)
$$\triangle G° = \triangle H° - T\triangle S°$$
$$= 31 \text{ kJ} - (298 \text{ K} \times 67 \text{ J/K} \times 1 \text{ kJ}/1000 \text{ J})$$
$$= 31 \text{ kJ} - 20 \text{ kJ} = 11 \text{ kJ}$$

This reaction, as in most decomposition reactions, requires the addition of heat—an endothermic reaction. Because a highly ordered ionic solid, $Ag_2O(s)$, goes to Ag, a metallic solid, and O_2, a gas, the system becomes more disordered; therefore, its entropy change is positive ($\triangle S° > 0$). At 298 K, this reaction is nonspontaneous because $\triangle G°$ is greater than zero.

(b) This calculation shows that the $T\triangle S°$ term is smaller than the $\triangle H°$ term. If the temperature is increased sufficiently, then the $T\triangle S°$ becomes larger than $\triangle H°$, producing a negative $\triangle G$ (free energy change at nonstandard conditions), which means that the reaction is spontaneous at higher temperatures[1].

(c) Solve the equation for T for the case when $\triangle G$ equals zero. Any temperature above this value gives a $T\triangle S°$ term larger than $\triangle H°$.

$$\triangle G = \triangle H° - T\triangle S°$$
$$0 = 31 \text{ kJ} - (T \times 67 \text{ J/K} \times 1 \text{ kJ}/1000 \text{ J})$$
$$T = 4.6 \times 10^2 \text{ K}$$

For temperatures above 4.6×10^2 K, the decomposition of silver oxide is spontaneous, and for temperatures below that, the reaction is nonspontaneous.

Calculating Free Energy Changes from Free Energies of Formation, $\triangle G_f°$

The standard free energy change, $\triangle G°$, for a reaction can be calculated from $\triangle H°$ and $T\triangle S°$. Since $\triangle G°$ is a state function, the $\triangle G°$ of a chemical reaction can also be calculated from standard free energies of formation, $\triangle G_f°$, by using the following relationship.

$$\triangle G° = \Sigma \triangle G_f°(\text{products}) - \Sigma \triangle G_f°(\text{reactants}) \qquad (18.18)$$

---

[1] For this statement to be valid, the assumption must be made that the values of $\triangle H°$ and $\triangle S°$ are independent of temperature. This is a reasonable assumption for this reaction.

Problem 18.12 Calculate the free energy change, $\triangle G°$, for the complete combustion of methane.

$$CH_4(g) + 2O_2(g) \longrightarrow CO_2(g) + 2H_2O(l)$$

The standard free energies of formation for $CH_4(g)$, $CO_2(g)$, and $H_2O(l)$ are -51, -394, and -237 kJ/mol, respectively. The $\triangle G_f°$ for O_2 is 0 kJ, because it is an element in its most stable form.

Solution 18.12 Substitute the given values in Eq. 18.21 as follows.

$$\triangle G° = \Sigma \triangle G_f°(\text{products}) - \Sigma \triangle G_f°(\text{reactants})$$
$$= [(1 \text{ mol} \times \triangle G_f°(CO_2)) + (2 \text{ mol} \times \triangle G_f°(H_2O(l)))]$$
$$- [(1 \text{ mol} \times \triangle G_f°(CH_4)) \times (2 \text{ mol} \times \triangle G_f°(O_2))]$$
$$= [(1 \text{ mol} \times -394 \text{ kJ/mol}) + (2 \text{ mol} \times -237 \text{ kJ/mol})]$$
$$- [(1 \text{ mol} \times -51 \text{ kJ/mol}) + 2 \text{ mol} \times 0 \text{ kJ/mol}]$$
$$= -817 \text{ kJ}$$

Free Energy Changes and Equilibrium Systems

If the free energy change, $\triangle G$, equals zero, a system is at equilibrium. Thus, for equilibrium systems at any constant temperature and pressure, zero can be substituted into Eq. 18.13 for $\triangle G$ and solved for the entropy change, $\triangle S$.

$$\triangle G = \triangle H - T\triangle S$$
$$0 = \triangle H - T\triangle S$$
$$T\triangle S = \triangle H$$
$$\triangle S = \triangle H/T \quad \text{(Equilibrium systems)} \quad (18.19)$$

Equation 18.19 shows that when a system is in equilibrium, the entropy change, $\triangle S$, equals the enthalpy change, $\triangle H$, divided by the Kelvin temperature, T. When standard conditions are present ($T = 298$ K), Eq. 18.20 results.

$$\triangle S° = \triangle H°/T \quad (18.20)$$

Problem 18.13 (a) Calculate the molar entropy of fusion of ice, $H_2O(s)$. The $\triangle H_{fusion}$ of ice is 6.01 kJ/mol, and its melting point is 273 K. (b) Calculate the molar entropy of vaporization of water, $H_2O(l)$. The $\triangle H_{vap}$ for water is 40.7 kJ/mol, and its boiling point is 373 K.

Solution 18.13

(a)
$$\triangle S_{fus} = \triangle H_{fus}/T_{mp}$$
$$= 6.01 \text{ kJ/mol}/273 \text{ K} = 0.0220 \text{ kJ/(K} \cdot \text{mol)} = 22.0 \text{ J/(K} \cdot \text{mol)}$$

(b)
$$\triangle S_{vap} = \triangle H_{vap}/T_{bp}$$
$$= 40.7 \text{ kJ/mol}/373 \text{ K} = 0.109 \text{ kJ/(K} \cdot \text{mol)} = 109 \text{ J/(K} \cdot \text{mol)}$$

Problem 18.14 The enthalpy of vaporization, $\triangle H_{vap}$, of liquid ammonia, $NH_3(l)$, is 23.3 kJ/mol and its entropy of vaporization, $\triangle S_{vap}$, is 97.2 J/(K $\cdot$ mol). Estimate the normal boiling point (1 atm) of liquid ammonia in °C.

Solution 18.14

$$\triangle S_{vap} = \triangle H_{vap}/T_{bp}$$
$$T_{bp} = \triangle H_{vap}/\triangle S_{vap}$$
$$= 23.3 \text{ kJ/mol}/(97.2 \text{ J/(K} \cdot \text{mol)}) \times 1 \text{ kJ/1000 J}$$
$$= 240 \text{ K} = -33 \text{ °C}$$

18.4 FREE ENERGY AND CHEMICAL EQUILIBRIA

Free Energy Changes at Nonstandard Conditions

The equation to compute the standard free energy change is Eq. 18.17.

$$\triangle G° = \triangle H° - T\triangle S° \qquad \text{(standard state)}$$

If you use this equation, the pressure of the gases must be 1 atm, the temperature is fixed at 298 K, and the concentration of dissolved reactants must be 1 M. When the conditions change from the standard state, the above equation does not apply. Instead, Eq. 18.13 must be used

$$\triangle G = \triangle H - T\triangle S \qquad \text{(nonstandard conditions)}$$

in which $\triangle G$ is the free energy change at nonstandard conditions. Note that if a reaction begins at standard conditions as soon as the reactants begin to change to products, standard conditions are no longer present.

To understand the relationship between free energy change and equilibrium, the relationship between free energy change at nonstandard conditions, $\triangle G$, and the standard free energy change, $\triangle G°$ must be considered. This relationship is expressed as follows:

$$\triangle G = \triangle G° + RT \ln Q \qquad (18.21)$$

in which $\triangle G$ is the free energy change at nonstandard conditions, $\triangle G°$ is the standard free energy change, R is the ideal gas constant (8.314J/(K $\cdot$ mol)), T is the Kelvin temperature, ln is the natural logarithm, and Q is the reaction quotient. The reaction quotient, Q, for the following general equilibrium

$$xA(g) + yB(g) \rightleftharpoons zC(g)$$

is

$$Q = \frac{P_C^z}{P_A^x P_B^y}$$

What is the meaning of Eq. 18.21? The nonstandard free energy change, $\triangle G$, of a reaction depends on two factors: the standard free energy change, $\triangle G°$, and the quantity $RT \ln Q$. At a constant temperature, T, $\triangle G$ only depends on the composition of the reaction mixture, Q, because $\triangle G°$ is constant.

Problem 18.15 Consider the following gas-phase $NO_2 \rightleftharpoons N_2O_4$ equilibrium.

$$2NO_2(g) \rightleftharpoons N_2O_4(g)$$

The $\Delta G°$ for this reaction is -6.0 kJ/mol. Calculate ΔG at 298 K when initially 1.0 atm of both NO_2 and N_2O_4 are present. (b) Calculate ΔG at 298 K when initially 10 atm NO_2 and 5.0 atm N_2O_4 are present. (c) Explain the results.

Solution 18.15   For both parts of this problem use Eq. 18.21 in which

$$Q = \frac{P_{N_2O_4}}{P^2_{NO_2}}$$

(a) In this problem both the reactants and products are in the standard state–1.0 atm. Under these conditions the value of $Q = 1$.

$$Q = P_{N_2O_4}/P^2_{NO_2} = 1.0 \text{ atm}/(1.0 \text{ atm})^2 = 1.0$$

Substituting the values into the Eq. 18.21 gives the following.

$$\Delta G = \Delta G° + RT \ln Q$$
$$= -6.0 \text{ kJ/mol} + RT \ln 1 = -6.0 \text{ kJ/mol}$$

(b) Once again calculate the value of Q and substitute into Eq. 18.21.

$$Q = P_{N_2O_4}/P^2_{NO_2} = 5.0 \text{ atm}/(10 \text{ atm})^2 = 0.050$$
$$\Delta G = \Delta G° + RT \ln Q$$
$$= -6.0 \text{ kJ/mol} + (8.314 \text{ J/(mol} \cdot \text{K)} \times 1 \text{ kJ}/1000 \text{ J} \times 298 \text{ K} \times \ln 0.050)$$
$$= -6.0 \text{ kJ/mol} + (-7.4 \text{ kJ/mol}) = -13.4 \text{ kJ/mol}$$

(c) The answer, -13.4 kJ/mol, shows that this mixture ($P_{N_2O_4} = 5.0$ atm and $P_{NO_2} = 10$ atm) has a more negative free energy change than that of a standard state mixture. This is expected because the initial mixture contains a greater partial pressure of reactant compared to that of the product than in part (a).

Relationship of $\Delta G°$ and K

At equilibrium the free energy change equals zero ($\Delta G = 0$). Thus 0 is substituted for ΔG in Eq. 18.21, and at equilibrium the reaction quotient equals K.

$$\Delta G = \Delta G° + RT \ln Q \quad \text{(nonequilibrium reaction mixture)}$$
$$0 = \Delta G° + RT \ln K \quad \text{(at equilibrium)}$$

Solving the equation for the standard free energy change, $\Delta G°$, gives Eq. 18.22—one of the most important equations in chemistry.

$$\Delta G° = -RT \ln K \tag{18.22}$$

This equation states that if K is greater than 1, which means the products are favored at equilibrium, then $\Delta G°$ is less than 0—a spontaneous reaction.

Problem 18.16   Consider the following equilibrium.

$$H_2(g) + Cl_2(g) \rightleftharpoons 2HCl(g)$$

The standard enthalpy change, $\Delta H°$, for this reaction is -92 kJ and the standard entropy change, $\Delta S°$, is -95 J/K. Calculate the equilibrium constant, K_p, at 298 K for this reaction.

Solution 18.16   First, calculate $\triangle G°$ using Eq. 18.17.

$$\triangle G° = \triangle H° - T\triangle S°$$
$$= -92\text{ kJ} - (298\text{ K} \times -95\text{ J/K} \times 1\text{ kJ}/1000\text{ J}) = -64\text{ kJ}$$

Then, calculate K_p using Eq. 18.22.

$$\triangle G° = -RT \ln K_p$$
$$-64\text{ kJ} = -8.314\text{ J/K} \times 1\text{ kJ}/1000\text{ J} \times 298\text{ K} \times \ln K_p$$
$$\ln K_p = 26$$
$$K_p = e^{26} = 1.7 \times 10^{11}$$

Problem 18.17   Consider the following gas-phase reaction in which methane, CH_4, combines with chlorine gas, Cl_2, to produce methyl chloride, CH_3Cl, and hydrogen chloride, HCl.

$$CH_4(g) + Cl_2(g) \rightleftharpoons CH_3Cl(g) + HCl(g)$$

The equilibrium constant, K_p, for this reaction is 7.58×10^{17} at 298 K, and the standard enthalpy change, $\triangle H°$, is -99 kJ/mol. Calculate the entropy change, $\triangle S°$, of the reaction in J/K.

Solution 18.17   First, calculate $\triangle G°$ from Eq. 18.22.

$$\triangle G° = -RT \ln K_p$$
$$= -8.314\text{ J/(mol} \cdot \text{K)} \times 1\text{ kJ}/1000\text{ J} \times 298\text{ K} \times \ln 7.58 \times 10^{17}$$
$$= -102\text{ kJ}$$

Then, calculate $\triangle S°$ from Eq. 18.17.

$$\triangle G° = \triangle H° - T\triangle S°$$
$$-102\text{ kJ} = -99\text{ kJ} - (298\text{ K} \times \triangle S°)$$
$$\triangle S° = 0.0010\text{ kJ/K} = 10\text{ J/K}$$

SUMMARY

*S*pontaneous changes occur by themselves without outside intervention. The reverse of a spontaneous process is always nonspontaneous. The driving force for spontaneous processes is a thermodynamic property called entropy. One way to define entropy, S, is a measure of the randomness or disorder in a system. Entropy is a measure of the number of possible arrangements or states that a system can take. The relationship between possible arrangements and entropy is as follows, S = k ln W, in which S is entropy, k is Boltzman's constant, ln is the natural logarithm, and W is the number of possible arrangements of a system. This relationship leads us to the third law of thermodynamics, which states that a perfect crystal at absolute zero has an entropy of 0 (perfect order).*

The spontaneity of a chemical reaction depends on its change in entropy. An increase in entropy ($\triangle S > 0$) means that the products are more disorganized than the reactants. A decrease in entropy

($\triangle S < 0$) means the products are more organized than the reactants. An increase in entropy is the driving force of spontaneity in isolated systems. Isolated systems tend spontaneously to become more random. Because chemical reactions are usually not isolated systems, the entropy changes in both the system, $\triangle S_{sys}$, and the surroundings, $\triangle S_{sur}$, must be considered. The second law of thermodynamics states that a spontaneous process increases the entropy of the universe, which is the sum of the entropy changes in the system and surroundings. Mathematically, this can be shown as follows.

$$\text{Spontaneous Process} \qquad \triangle S_{uni} = \triangle S_{sys} + \triangle S_{sur} > 0$$

The entropy change of the surroundings depends on both the Kelvin temperature and enthalpy change of the system. It can be calculated as follows.

$$\triangle S_{sur} = -\triangle H/T$$

Gibbs free energy is the most convenient thermodynamic property used to predict if reactions are spontaneous. It is defined as follows, $G = H - TS$, in which G is free energy, H is enthalpy, T is the Kelvin temperature, and S is entropy. The TS represents the disordered component of energy and the enthalpy represents the total energy, and what remains is the energy that can become disordered and thus can effect change and do work. Free energy is a measure of the maximum useable energy of a system. Reactions that release free energy, $\triangle G > 0$, are spontaneous and those that absorb free energy, $\triangle G < 0$, are nonspontaneous. Free energy changes are calculated from enthalpy changes, and the product of the Kelvin temperature and entropy change.

$$\triangle G° = \triangle H° - T\triangle S°$$

The relationship between free energy changes and chemical equilibrium is expressed as follows

$$\triangle G = \triangle G° + RT \ln Q$$

in which $\triangle G$ is the free energy change at nonstandard conditions and Q is the reaction quotient. As a reaction proceeds in loses free energy until it reaches equilibrium. At this point $\triangle G$ equals zero; thus, $\triangle G° = -RT \ln K$, which states that the natural logarithm of the equilibrium constant times $-RT$ equals the standard free energy change in a reaction.

CHAPTER 18 REVIEW EXERCISE

1. For each of the following changes decide if it is spontaneous or nonspontaneous. (a) hot tea cools to room temperature, (b) water vapor condenses to liquid water at 400 K and 1 atm, (c) a red dye distributed throughout water concentrates in one region of the water

2. For each of the following changes predict if the value for the entropy change, $\triangle S$, is greater or less than zero: (a) $N_2(g)$ condenses to $N_2(l)$, (b) sugar (sucrose) dissolves in water, (c) $Si(s)$ combines with $O_2(g)$ and produces $SiO_2(s)$

3. Calculate the entropy changes, $\triangle S°$, for the following change:

$$C(graphite) \longrightarrow C(diamond)$$

The entropies of graphite and diamond are 6 J/(mol · K) and 2 J/(mol · K), respectively. (b) Explain the result of part (a).

4. For each of the following changes of entropy in the system and surroundings, determine if the process is spontaneous or nonspontaneous:
   (a) $\Delta S_{sys} = -10$ J/K $\Delta S_{sur} = +15$ J/K, (b) $\Delta S_{sys} = -10$ J/K $\Delta S_{sur} = -15$ J/K

5. Calculate the entropy change in the surroundings, ΔS_{sur}, at 298 K, for the oxidation of carbon monoxide, $CO(g)$ to $CO_2(g)$.

$$CO(g) + \tfrac{1}{2}O_2(g) \longrightarrow CO_2(g) \qquad \Delta H° = -283 \text{kJ}$$

6. The standard entropies, $S°$, of $CaCO_3(s)$, $CaO(s)$, and $CO_2(g)$ are 93, 40, and 214 J/(K · mol), respectively. Calculate the standard entropy change, $\Delta S°$, for the decomposition of $CaCO_3(s)$ to $CaO(s)$ and $CO_2(g)$.

$$CaCO_3(s) \longrightarrow CaO(s) + CO_2(g)$$

   (b) Describe the meaning of this $\Delta S°$ value.

7. Consider the following reaction.

$$CS_2(l) + 3O_2(g) \longrightarrow CO_2(g) + 2SO_2(g)$$

Compound	$\Delta H_f°$, kJ/mol	$S°$, J/(mol · K)
$CS_2(l)$	87.9	151
$O_2(g)$	0	205
$CO_2(g)$	−393	214
$SO_2(g)$	−297	248

   Calculate the standard entropy change for this reaction. (b) Calculate the standard entropy change for the surroundings in this reaction. (c) What is the total entropy change, ΔS_{uni}, for this reaction?

8. Calculate the $\Delta G°$ for the oxidation of Cl_2 to Cl_2O from the following thermodynamic data:

$$Cl_2(g) + \tfrac{1}{2}O_2(g) \longrightarrow Cl_2O(g)$$

   The standard enthalpies of formation of $Cl_2(g)$, $O_2(g)$, and $Cl_2O(g)$ are 0, 0, 80.3 kJ/mol, respectively. The standard entropies of $Cl_2(g)$, $O_2(g)$, and $Cl_2O(g)$ are 223, 205, and 266 J/(K · mol).

9. Calculate $\Delta H°$, $\Delta S°$, and $\Delta G°$ for the following reaction:

$$2KCl(s) + 3O_2(g) \longrightarrow 2KClO_3(s)$$

   The standard enthalpies of formation of KCl, O_2, and $KClO_3$ are −436, 0, and −391 kJ/mol, respectively. The standard entropies of KCl, O_2, and $KClO_3$ are 83, 205, and 143 J/(mol · K), respectively.

10. The standard free energy change, $\Delta G°$, for the following reaction:

$$Fe_2O_3(s) + 3CO(g) \longrightarrow 2Fe(s) + 3CO_2(g)$$

   is −29.4 kJ. The standard entropies of Fe_2O_3, CO, Fe, and CO_2 are 90, 198, 27, and 214 J/(mol · K), respectively. Calculate the standard change in entropy of the universe, $\Delta S_{uni}°$, for this reaction. (b) What is the standard entropy change of the reaction, $\Delta S_{sys}°$? (c) What is the standard entropy change of the surroundings, $\Delta S_{sur}°$?

11. Find the temperature range over which the following reaction is spontaneous:

$$N_2(g) + \tfrac{1}{2}O_2(g) \longrightarrow N_2O(g)$$

The $\triangle H°$ for this reaction is 82 kJ and the $\triangle S°$ is −74 J/K. Assume these values do not vary with temperature.

12. Calculate the standard molar free energy change, $\triangle G°$, and determine if the following decomposition reaction is spontaneous. The standard molar free energies of formation for $CaCO_3$, CaO, and CO_2 are −1129 kJ/mol, −604 kJ/mol, and −394 kJ/mol, respectively.

$$CaCO_3(s) \longrightarrow CaO(s) + CO_2(g)$$

13. The enthalpy of vaporization, $\triangle H_{vap}$, of ethanol, $C_2H_6O(l)$, is 42.6 kJ/mol and its entropy of vaporization, $\triangle S_{vap}$, is 122 J/(K · mol). Estimate the normal boiling point of ethanol in °C.

14. Consider the following equilibrium:

$$2NO_2(g) \rightleftharpoons N_2O_4(g)$$

If the standard free energy change, $\triangle G°$, for this reaction is −6.0 kJ, calculate $\triangle G$ when initially 1.0 atm NO_2 and 20 atm N_2O_4 are present. Explain the meaning of your answer.

15. Calculate the equilibrium constant at 298 K for the formation of nitrous oxide, $N_2O(g)$, from N_2 and O_2.

$$N_2(g) + \tfrac{1}{2}O_2(g) \rightleftharpoons N_2O(g)$$

The standard enthalpy change, $\triangle H°$, for this reaction is 82 kJ, and the standard entropy change, $\triangle S°$, is −74 J/K. Calculate the equilibrium constant, K_p.

16. The standard free energies of formation of ethanol liquid and vapor are −174.8 kJ/mol and −168.5 kJ/mol, respectively. Calculate the vapor pressure, in torr, of ethanol at 298 K.

17. Consider the formation of HBr(g) from $H_2(g)$ and $Br_2(g)$.

$$H_2(g) + Br_2(g) \rightleftharpoons 2HBr(g)$$

At 298 K, the equilibrium constant, K_p, for this reaction is 1.28×10^{19}. If the standard entropy change, $\triangle S°$, for this conversion is 22 J/K, what is the enthalpy change?

18. Consider the following equilibrium.

$$H_2(g) + I_2(g) \rightleftharpoons 2HI(g)$$

The standard free energy change, $\triangle G°$, for this reaction is 1.3 kJ. Calculate the free energy change, $\triangle G$, at 298 K for each of the following reaction mixtures: $P_{H_2} = 10$ atm, $P_{I_2} = 5.0$ atm, $P_{HI} = 10$ atm, (b) $P_{H_2} = 10$ atm, $P_{I_2} = 10.0$ atm, $P_{HI} = 1.0$ atm, (c) $P_{H_2} = 10$ atm, $P_{I_2} = 5.0$ atm, $P_{HI} = 5.4$ atm

ANSWERS TO REVIEW EXERCISE

1. (a) spontaneous, (b) nonspontaneous, (c) nonspontaneous
2. (a) $\triangle S < 0$, (b) $\triangle S > 0$, (c) $\triangle S < 0$
3. (a) −4 J/(mol · K), (b) The entropy of this system decreases, which means the sp^3 hybridized C atoms in diamond are more organized then the sp^2 hybridized C atoms in graphite.
4. (a) $\triangle S_{uni} = +5$ J/K, spontaneous, (b) $\triangle S_{uni} = −25$ J/K, nonspontaneous
5. $\triangle S_{sur} = 950$ J/(K · mol)

6. (a) $\Delta S° = 161$ J/K, (b) The products (an ionic solid and gas) are more random than the reactants (an ionic solid).

7. $\Delta S° = -56$ J/K, (b) 3.61 kJ/K, (c) 3.55 kJ/K

8. $\Delta G° = 98.0$ kJ/mol

9. $\Delta H° = 90$ kJ, $\Delta S° = -495$ J/K, $\Delta G° = 237$ kJ

10. (a) 98.7 J/K, (b) 12 J/K, (c) 87 J/K

11. The reaction is not spontaneous at any temperature.

12. $\Delta G° = 131$ kJ/mol, The reaction is not spontaneous.

13. $bp_{ethanol} = 76.2°$ C

14. $\Delta G = 1.4$ kJ/mol, A positive free energy change indicates that the reaction with 1.0 atm NO_2 and 20 atm N_2O_4 is spontaneous from right to left because of the high initial partial pressure of N_2O_4 compared to that of NO_2.

15. $K = 5.8 \times 10^{-19}$

16. 60 torr

17. $\Delta H° = -102$ kJ

18. (a) 3.0 kJ, (b) -10.1 kJ, (c) 0.0 kJ

19

Electrochemistry

*E*lectrochemistry is the area of chemistry that is concerned with both the conversion of chemical energy to electrical energy and the conversion of electrical energy to chemical energy. These conversions take place in electrochemical cells. A voltaic cell, also called a galvanic cell or battery, is the electrochemical cell in which chemical energy changes spontaneously to electrical energy. An electrolytic cell is the electrochemical cell in which electrical energy changes nonspontaneously to chemical energy.

Reactions that produce and consume electricity in electrochemical cells are oxidation-reduction reactions—redox reactions. Oxidation occurs when electrons are lost and reduction occurs when electrons are gained (Section 5.4).

19.1   VOLTAIC CELLS (GALVANIC CELLS)

Redox Reactions

A voltaic cell is a device that spontaneously produces electricity in an electric circuit as a result of a redox reaction. Let's consider what happens when a strip of Zn metal is placed into a solution of copper(II) sulfate, $CuSO_4(aq)$. The Zn strip dissolves and solid Cu forms on the surface of the Zn. In time, the Zn dissolves, solid Cu forms, and the solution changes from the blue color associated with the Cu^{2+} ions to the colorless solution associated with the Zn^{2+} ions. The overall and net ionic equations for this reaction are as follows.

$$Zn(s) + Cu^{2+}(aq) + SO_4^{2-}(aq) \longrightarrow Zn^{2+}(aq) + SO_4^{2-} + Cu(s)$$
$$Zn(s) + Cu^{2+}(aq) \longrightarrow Zn^{2+}(aq) + Cu(s)$$

Separating the net ionic equation into two half-reactions, shows that the Zn atom undergoes oxidation when it releases two electrons, and the Cu^{2+} ion undergoes reduction when it gains two electrons.

$$Zn(s) \longrightarrow Zn^{2+}(aq) + 2e^- \qquad \text{(Oxidation)}$$
$$Cu^{2+}(aq) + 2e^- \longrightarrow Cu(s) \qquad \text{(Reduction)}$$

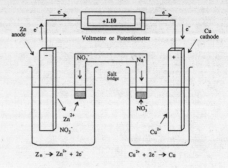

Fig. 19.1

Components of a Voltaic Cell

A voltaic cell is constructed when the oxidation half-reaction is physically separated from the reduction half-reaction, forcing the electrons to travel through an external circuit. Figure 19.1 shows a diagram of a voltaic cell with a Zn strip immersed in a solution of $Zn(NO_3)_2(aq)$ and a Cu strip immersed in a solution of $Cu(NO_3)_2(aq)$. Each of these metals in its respective solution is termed a half-cell. The half-cells are connected with a wire and voltmeter or potentiometer on one side and a salt bridge on the other side. When the electrical circuit is completed, electrons flow from the Zn electrode to the Cu electrode. The Zn releases the electrons and the Cu^{2+} takes in the electrons. Oxidation occurs at the anode, and reduction occurs at the cathode. Hence in this voltaic cell, the Zn strip is the anode and the Cu strip is the cathode. The anode is the negative electrode because its half-reaction is the source of electrons (negatively charged particles) and the cathode is the positive electrode because its half-reaction takes in the electrons.

CELL NOTATION

A cell notation is used to designate the components of voltaic cells. It is as follows

$$\text{anode|anode electrolyte||cathode electrolyte|cathode}$$

in which the anode is the substance that releases electrons, the anode electrolyte is the solution in which the anode is immersed, the cathode is the substance at the cathode, and the cathode electrolyte is the solution in which the cathode is immersed. The single vertical line, |, separates components in different phases that are physically in contact. The double vertical lines, ||, represents the salt bridge or any porous barrier that separates the anode from the cathode.

Problem 19.1 (a) Write the cell notation for the Zn-Cu cell previously discussed. (b) Write the cell notation for a cell that has an Al anode and a Ni cathode. (c) Write the balanced half-reactions for the Al-Ni voltaic cell.

Solution 19.1 (a) The cell notation for the Zn-Cu cell is as follows.

$$Zn(s)|Zn^{2+}(aq)||Cu^{2+}(aq)|Cu(s)$$

(b) The cell notation for a voltaic cell that has an Al anode and a Ni cathode is as follows.

$$Al(s)|Al^{3+}(aq)||Ni^{2+}(aq)|Ni(s)$$

(c) $\qquad$ $Al(s) \longrightarrow Al^{3+}(aq) + 3e^-$ $\qquad$ (Anode)

$\qquad$ $2e^- + Ni^{2+}(aq) \longrightarrow Ni(s)$ $\qquad$ (Cathode)

The net overall cell reaction is obtained after equalizing the electrons released and taken in (6 e^-) and adding the two half-reactions.

$$2Al(s) + 3Ni^{2+}(aq) \longrightarrow 3Ni(s) + 2Al^{3+}(aq)$$

Problem 19.2 A voltaic cell is constructed using $Pb(s)$ and $Pb(NO_3)_2(aq)$ for one half-cell and $Zn(s)$ and $Zn(NO_3)_2(aq)$ for the other. If Zn is a better reducing agent than Pb and the salt bridge contains an aqueous solution KNO_3, answer each of the following. (a) Which metal is the anode? (b) Which metal is the cathode? (c) Which ions move toward the anode? (d) Which ions move toward the cathode? (e) Which metal is the negative electrode? (f) Which metal is the positive electrode? (g) Write its cell notation.

Solution 19.2 First, determine which substances are oxidized and reduced. If Zn is a better reducing agent than Pb, then Zn more readily donates electrons. Thus, Zn undergoes oxidation and Pb^{2+} in $Pb(NO_3)_2(aq)$ undergoes reduction.

$\quad$ (a) The anode is the site of oxidation; hence, $Zn(s)$ is oxidized to $Zn^{2+}(aq)$ at the anode $\quad$ ($Zn(s) \longrightarrow Zn^{2+}(aq) + 2e^-$).

$\quad$ (b) The cathode is the site of reduction; hence, $Pb^{2+}(aq)$ is reduced to $Pb(s)$ on the cathode $\quad$ ($2e^- + Pb^{2+}(aq) \longrightarrow Pb(s)$).

$\quad$ (c) Anions migrate towards the anode. Therefore, the NO_3^- ions from the salt bridge and from $\quad$ the $Pb(NO_3)_2$ solution move toward the anode.

$\quad$ (d) Cations migrate toward the cathode. Hence, the Zn^{2+} produced from the oxidation of Zn, $\quad$ and K^+ ions from the salt bridge move towards the cathode.

$\quad$ (e) The anode is the negative electrode; thus, Zn is the negative electrode.

$\quad$ (f) The cathode is the positive electrode; therefore, Pb is the positive electrode.

$\quad$ (g) $Zn(s)|Zn^{2+}(aq)||Pb^{2+}(aq)|Pb(s)$

19.2 STANDARD REDUCTION POTENTIALS AND CELL POTENTIALS

Cell Potential, $\mathcal{E}$, and Electromotive Force (EMF)

$\qquad$ The electrons from the negative anode in the voltaic cell travel through the external circuit to the positive cathode. Each different redox reaction has a different capacity to push the electrons through the circuit. For example, if a strong reducing agent, one that readily gives up electrons, and a strong oxidizing agent, one that readily takes in electrons, are used in a voltaic cell, electrons can more readily be pushed through the circuit than if weaker reducing and oxidizing agents are used. The greater the tendency to push electrons through a circuit, the more useful work can be done. The capacity that a voltaic cell has to push electrons through a circuit is called the electromotive force, emf, of the cell or the cell potential, $\mathcal{E}$. A cell with a higher electromotive force delivers higher-energy electrons than a cell with a lower electromotive force.

VOLT, V

$\qquad$ The SI unit for electromotive force is the volt, V. One volt is the emf just needed to give 1 J of energy to that number of electrons having a charge of 1 coulomb, C—the charge on 6.2×10^{18} electrons.

$$1 V = \frac{1 J}{1 C} \qquad (19.1)$$

Another way to think of the volt is that if 1 C of charge travels between electrodes that differ by one volt, then 1 J of energy is released. This can be more readily understood if Eq. 19.1 is rearranged as follows.

$$1\,J = 1\,C \times 1\,V \tag{19.2}$$

Standard Cell Potentials, $\mathcal{E}^\circ$

Cell potentials are precisely measured using a voltage-sensing device called a potentiometer. This instrument gives the voltage of the cell when an infinitesimal current flows. Attaching a potentiometer to a Zn-Cu cell at 298 K with 1 M aqueous solutions of Cu^{2+} and Zn^{2+} gives us its standard cell potential, $\mathcal{E}^\circ$, of 1.10 V.

$$Zn(s) + Cu^{2+}(aq) \longrightarrow Zn^{2+}(aq) + Cu(s) \quad \mathcal{E}^\circ = 1.10\,V$$

Cell potential is an intensive property—one that is independent of its mass and volume. If another combination of metals such as Zn and Sn are selected for the electrodes, a different standard cell potential is measured because Sn^{2+} has a different capacity to undergo reduction than does Cu^{2+}. The standard cell potential, $\mathcal{E}^\circ$, for a voltaic cell with Zn and Sn is 0.62 V.

$$Zn(s) + Sn^{2+}(aq) \longrightarrow Zn^{2+}(aq) + Sn(s) \qquad \mathcal{E}^\circ = 0.62\,V$$

Half-Cell Potentials

It is convenient to assign each half-cell a potential so they can be added to obtain the overall cell potential. The only problem with such a method is that no way exists to measure experimentally the voltage for a half-cell. Instead the overall cell potential is measured with the half-cell of interest and a reference half-cell that is assigned a potential of 0.0 V. Thus, the overall cell potential is just that of the half-cell of interest.

STANDARD HYDROGEN ELECTRODE, SHE, AND STANDARD REDUCTION POTENTIALS, $\mathcal{E}^\circ_{RED}$

In chemistry, this reference half-cell is the standard hydrogen electrode, SHE, in which H^+ ions are reduced to hydrogen gas, $H_2(g)$. This half-cell potential is called the standard reduction potential, $\mathcal{E}^\circ_{red}$ (or just $\mathcal{E}^\circ$, for short).

$$2H^+(aq, 1\,M) + 2e^- \longrightarrow H_2(g, 1\,atm) \qquad \mathcal{E}^\circ_{red} = 0.0\,V \tag{19.3}$$

The 0.0 V potential assigned to this reference half-cell has no physical meaning because a potential of any value could have been assigned. Assigning 0.0 V as the value of standard hydrogen electrode indicates that if a voltaic cell is constructed with the standard hydrogen electrode as one half-cell and the other half-cell is a stronger reducing agent, then the H^+ ions are reduced to $H_2(g)$ as shown in Eq. 19.3. But if the other cell is a weaker reducing agent (a stronger oxidizing agent), then it forces the reverse reaction in which H_2 molecules are oxidized to H^+ ions. The half-cell potential for this is also 0.0 V.

$$H_2(g) \longrightarrow 2H^+(aq) + 2e^- \qquad \mathcal{E}^\circ = 0.0\,V$$

In either direction the half-cell potential for the standard hydrogen electrode is zero. Hence, the voltage measured is that produced by the other substance.

STANDARD REDUCTION POTENTIALS, $\mathcal{E}^\circ_{RED}$, AND REDOX

A table of standard reduction potentials presents a list of common half-reactions and their standard reduction potentials. Listed in the top quarter of such a table are the half-reactions that most readily undergo reduction, the strongest oxidizing agents. Listed in the bottom quarter of this table are the half-reactions that most readily undergo oxidation, the strongest reducing agents. At the top of this table is F_2 (the strongest oxidizing agent listed), which can remove electrons from the substances listed below it. The standard reduction potential, +2.87 V, of F_2 is the most positive value listed. At the bottom of the table is Li (the strongest reducing agent listed) which donates electrons to all of those listed above it. Its standard reduction potential, −3.05 V, is the most negative value listed. Therefore, a substance with a higher positive standard reduction potential more readily undergoes reduction than one with a lower value. A substance with a more negative standard reduction potential undergoes oxidation more readily than one with a less negative value.

Problem 19.3   The standard reduction potentials of Cl_2 and Br_2 are +1.36 and +1.06 V, respectively. Which is the stronger oxidizing agent?

Solution 19.3   The higher positive value for Cl_2 indicates that Cl_2 is a stronger oxidizing agent (more readily takes in electrons) than is Br_2.

Problem 19.4   The standard reduction potential for Sn^{2+} is −0.14 V.

$$Sn^{2+} + 2e^- \longrightarrow Sn(s) \qquad \mathcal{E}° = -0.14V$$

What is the standard reduction potential for each of the following?
  (a) $Sn(s) \longrightarrow Sn^{2+}(aq) + 2e^-$
  (b) $2Sn(s) \longrightarrow 2Sn^{2+}(aq) + 4e^-$

Solution 19.4
  (a) Whenever a half-reaction is reversed, the sign of the half-cell potential must be changed. When the reactants and products are switched, the half-cell potential for the oxidation of Sn to Sn^{2+} and $2e^-$ is +0.14 V.
  (b) Doubling the coefficients in this equation has no effect on the standard reduction potential because it is an intensive property. The number of electrons transferred changes, but the electromotive force remains the same.

Calculating Cell Potentials from Standard Reduction Potentials

To calculate a cell potential, $\mathcal{E}°$, first obtain the two standard reduction potentials, $\mathcal{E}°_{red}$, for the half-cells. Then determine which half-cell undergoes reduction by identifying the one with the more positive or less negative standard reduction potential. This half-cell is the cathode. The other half-cell is the anode, the site of oxidation. To calculate the standard cell potential add the standard reduction potential of the cathode half-cell to the negative of the standard reduction potential of the anode half-cell.

$$\mathcal{E}°_{cell} = \mathcal{E}°(cathode) + (-\mathcal{E}°(anode)) \tag{19.4}$$

An equivalent way to express this relationship is to subtract the standard reduction potential of the anode from the standard reduction potential of the cathode.

$$\mathcal{E}°_{cell} = \mathcal{E}°(cathode) - \mathcal{E}°(anode) \tag{19.5}$$

Problem 19.5   (a) Calculate the cell potential for a voltaic cell that has Al and Pb electrodes and state which is the anode and cathode. (b) Write the cell notation for this voltaic cell.

Solution 19.5   (a) The standard reduction potentials for Al and Pb are −1.66 and −0.13 V, respectively.

$$Al^{3+}(aq) + 3e^- \longrightarrow Al(s) \qquad \mathcal{E}° = -1.66 \text{ V}$$
$$Pb^{2+}(aq) + 2e^- \longrightarrow Pb(s) \qquad \mathcal{E}° = -0.13 \text{ V}$$

Because the standard reduction potential of Pb^{2+} is less negative (more positive) than that of Al^{3+}, Pb^{2+} undergoes reduction and Al undergoes oxidation. Hence, the Al/Al^{3+} half-reaction must be reversed and the sign of its $\mathcal{E}^\circ$ must be changed.

$$Al(s) \longrightarrow Al^{3+}(aq) + 3e^- \qquad \mathcal{E}^\circ = +1.66 \text{ V}$$
$$Pb^{2+}(aq) + 2e^- \longrightarrow Pb(s) \qquad \mathcal{E}^\circ = -0.13 \text{ V}$$

To obtain the overall cell reaction, equalize the electrons released by the oxidation half-reaction and taken in by the reduction half-reaction ($6\,e^-$). Then add the half-reactions, canceling the electrons. Multiplying the equations to equalize the electrons has no effect on the magnitude of the half-cell potentials because they are intensive properties. To obtain the overall cell potential, $\mathcal{E}^\circ$, add the two half-cell potentials.

$$2Al(s) \longrightarrow 2Al^{3+}(aq) + 6e^- \qquad \mathcal{E}^\circ = +1.66 \text{ V}$$
$$3Pb^{2+}(aq) + 6e^- \longrightarrow 3Pb(s) \qquad \mathcal{E}^\circ = -0.13 \text{ V}$$
$$\overline{2Al(s) + 3Pb^{2+}(aq) \longrightarrow 3Pb(s) + 2Al^{3+}(aq) \qquad \mathcal{E}^\circ_{cell} = +1.53 \text{ V}}$$

At standard conditions this cell produces 1.53 V and Al is the anode, the negative electrode, and Pb is the cathode, the positive electrode. (b) The cell notation is $Al(s)|Al^{3+}(aq)||Pb^{2+}(aq)|Pb(s)$.

Spontaneity of Reactions and Standard Reduction Potentials

Standard reduction potentials are used to determine if a redox reaction is spontaneous in the standard state. Reactions in voltaic cells are spontaneous and their $\mathcal{E}^\circ$ values are positive. Hence, all redox reactions with positive $\mathcal{E}^\circ$ values are spontaneous. If the $\mathcal{E}^\circ$ for a reaction is negative, then it is nonspontaneous. In other words, the reverse reaction is spontaneous.

Problem 19.6 (a) Will a strip of Pb(s) dissolve in a 1 M Zn^{2+} solution? Will a strip of Zn(s) dissolve in a 1 M Pb^{2+} solution?

Solution 19.6 (a) Begin by writing the equation for the reaction.

$$Pb(s) + Zn^{2+}(aq) \longrightarrow Zn(s) + Pb^{2+}(aq)$$

Use an $\mathcal{E}^\circ$ table to find the needed half-reactions and standard reduction potentials.
$$Pb^{2+}(aq) + 2e^- \longrightarrow Pb(s) \qquad \mathcal{E}^\circ = -0.13 \text{ V}$$
$$Zn^{2+}(aq) + 2e^- \longrightarrow Zn(s) \qquad \mathcal{E}^\circ = -0.76 \text{ V}$$
Reverse the Pb/Pb^{2+} half-reaction, change the sign of its standard reduction potential, and add the half-reactions to get the desired chemical equations.

$$Pb(s) + Zn^{2+}(aq) \longrightarrow Zn(s) + Pb^{2+}(aq) \quad \mathcal{E}^\circ = -0.63 \text{ V}$$

Adding the corresponding half-cell potentials gives a negative $\mathcal{E}^\circ$ value which means this reaction is nonspontaneous. Therefore, a strip of Pb does not dissolve in a 1 M Zn^{2+} solution. (b) The reverse reaction is spontaneous because it has a positive $\mathcal{E}^\circ$ value. Therefore, a Zn strip dissolves in a 1 M Pb^{2+} solution.

$$Zn(s) + Pb^{2+}(aq) \longrightarrow Pb(s) + Zn^{2+}(aq) \quad \mathcal{E}^\circ = +0.63 \text{ V}$$

Problem 19.7 Will a strip of Cu dissolve in 1 M H$^+$ and form Cu^{2+}?

Solution 19.7 The standard reduction potential for Cu/Cu^{2+} is +0.32 V.

$$Cu^{2+}(aq) + 2e^- \longrightarrow Cu(s) \quad \mathcal{E}^\circ = +0.32 \text{ V}$$

This reaction must be reversed to predict if Cu dissolves and forms Cu^{2+}.

$$Cu(s) \longrightarrow Cu^{2+}(aq) + 2e^- \quad \mathcal{E}^\circ = -0.32 \text{V}$$

A 1 M H^+ solution is reduced to $H_2(g)$ in the standard hydrogen half-reaction. The $\mathcal{E}^\circ$ value for the standard hydrogen electrode is 0.0 V.

$$2H^+(aq) + 2e^- \longrightarrow H_2(g) \quad \mathcal{E}^\circ = 0.0 \text{ V}$$

Hence, when this value is added to the potential for Cu the result is -0.32 V. A negative value indicates that Cu does not dissolve in 1 M H^+.

19.3 THERMODYNAMICS OF REDOX REACTIONS

The Relationship of $\mathcal{E}^\circ$ and $\triangle G^\circ$

The sign of the standard potential of a reaction, $\mathcal{E}^\circ$, is related to the spontaneity of a redox reaction. Therefore, the $\mathcal{E}^\circ$ value is related to the standard free energy change, $\triangle G^\circ$. Recall that if the $\triangle G^\circ$ of a reaction is less than zero (negative), then the reaction is spontaneous. If the $\triangle G^\circ$ of a reaction is greater than zero (positive), then the reaction is nonspontaneous. If the $\mathcal{E}^\circ$ value for a reaction is greater than zero, then the reaction is spontaneous, and if the $\mathcal{E}^\circ$ value is less than zero, then the reaction is nonspontaneous. Therefore for a spontaneous reaction, it can be concluded that G° is proportional to $-\mathcal{E}^\circ$ because G° must be negative and $\mathcal{E}^\circ$ must be positive.

$$\triangle G^\circ \propto -\mathcal{E}^\circ \tag{19.6}$$

It is beyond the scope of this discussion to show how this proportionality is converted to an equation. It can be shown that this relationship is

$$\triangle G^\circ = -nF\mathcal{E}^\circ \tag{19.7}$$

in which G° is the standard free energy change, n is the number of electrons transferred in a reaction, F is Faraday's constant, and $\mathcal{E}^\circ$ is the standard cell potential. For nonstandard conditions, Eq. 19.7 becomes the following.

$$\triangle G = -nF\mathcal{E} \tag{19.8}$$

THE UNIT FARADAY

Faraday's constant, F, is named for Michael Faraday (1791–1867). One faraday is the electric charge in coulombs, C, possessed by one mole of electrons.

Problem 19.8 (a) Calculate the numerical value for one faraday in C/mol e^-. The charge on one electron is 1.60210×10^{-19} C. (b) What is the value of one faraday in J/(V mol)?

Solution 19.8
(a) 1.602×10^{-19} C/mol $e^- \times 6.022 \times 10^{23} e^-$/mol $= 9.647 \times 10^4$ C/mol.
(b) One V is 1 J/C; hence, 1 C is J/V or 9.647×10^4 J/CC mol.

Calculating Standard Free Energies, G°

Problem 19.9 Consider a redox reaction that transfers two moles of electrons and has an $\mathcal{E}^\circ$ value of +1.00 V. (a) What is the free energy change in kJ for the reaction? Explain the answer. (b) What is the free energy change in kJ for a redox reaction that transfers two moles of electrons and has a $\mathcal{E}^\circ$ value of -1.00 V. Explain the answer.

Solution 19.9

(a) Substituting into Eq. 19.7 gives the following.

$$\triangle G^\circ = -nF\mathcal{E}^\circ$$
$$= -(2.00 \text{ mol e}^- \times 9.65 \times 10^4 \text{ J}/(\text{V} \cdot \text{mole}^-) \times 1.00 \text{ V})$$
$$= -1.93 \times 10^5 \text{ J} \times 1\text{kJ}/1000 \text{ J} = -193 \text{ kJ}$$

This rather large negative standard free energy change indicates the reaction is spontaneous. Such reactions have large equilibrium constants, K.

(b) Repeating this calculation with -1.00 V with 2.00 moles of electrons transferred, $+193$ kJ is obtained for the standard free energy change. This value tells us the reaction is nonspontaneous with a small equilibrium constant.

Problem 19.10   Calculate the standard free energy change, $\triangle G^\circ$, for the following reaction.

$$Cl_2(g) + 2I^-(aq) \longrightarrow I_2(s) + 2Cl^-(aq)$$

Solution 19.10   First calculate the standard potential, $\mathcal{E}^\circ$, for the reaction. This is accomplished by obtaining the standard reduction potentials and then calculating $\mathcal{E}^\circ$. The standard reduction potentials for Cl_2 and I_2 are as follows.

$$Cl_2(g) + 2e^- \longrightarrow 2Cl^-(aq) \quad \mathcal{E}^\circ = +1.36 \text{ V}$$
$$I_2(g) + 2e^- \longrightarrow 2I^-(aq) \quad \mathcal{E}^\circ = +0.54 \text{ V}$$

To obtain the overall equation, reverse the I_2/I^- half-reaction and change the sign of its reduction potential to negative (-0.54 V). The overall potential of the cell, $\mathcal{E}^\circ$, is calculated as follows.

$$\mathcal{E}^\circ = \mathcal{E}^\circ(Cl_2) + \mathcal{E}^\circ(I_2) = +1.36 \text{ V} + (-0.54 \text{ V}) = 0.82 \text{ V}$$

Given the standard potential, use Eq. 19.7 to calculate the standard free energy change, $\triangle G^\circ$. In calculating the $\mathcal{E}^\circ$ value, we found that two moles of electrons ($n = 2$ mol) are transferred in the reaction.

$$\triangle G^\circ = -nF\mathcal{E}^\circ$$
$$= (2 \text{ mol e}^- \times 96,500 \text{ J}/(\text{C} \cdot \text{mol e}^-) \times 0.82 \text{ V})$$
$$= 1.6 \times 10^5 \text{ J} = 1.6 \times 10^2 \text{ kJ}$$

The Relationship of $\mathcal{E}^\circ$ to K

Since a relationship exists between $\triangle G^\circ$ and the equilibrium constant, K, there must also be one between $\mathcal{E}^\circ$ and K. Equation 19.7 from the last subsection gives the relationship between $\triangle G^\circ$ and $\mathcal{E}^\circ$.

$$\triangle G^\circ = -nF\mathcal{E}^\circ$$

The relationship between $\triangle G^\circ$ and K is as follows (Eq.18.23).

$$\triangle G^\circ = RT \ln K \qquad (19.9)$$

Quantities equal to the same thing are equal.

$$-nF\mathcal{E}^\circ = -RT \ln K \qquad (19.10)$$

Rearranging Eq. 19.10 and solving for $\mathcal{E}^\circ$ gives the following equation

$$\mathcal{E}^\circ = \frac{RT}{nF} \ln K \tag{19.11}$$

in which $\mathcal{E}^\circ$ is the standard potential, R is the ideal gas constant, T is the Kelvin temperature, n is the number of electrons transferred, F is Faraday's constant, ln is the natural logarithm, and K is the equilibrium constant. At standard conditions the temperature is 298.2 K, R equals 8.314 J/(mol · K), and F equals 96,485 J/(C · mol e^-). Equation 19.11 can be simplified by substituting these constant values into the equation and creating a single constant value.

$$\mathcal{E}^\circ = \frac{0.02569}{n} \ln K \tag{19.12}$$

Equation 19.12 shows that if K is greater than one, then $\mathcal{E}^\circ$ is greater than zero, because the natural logarithms of numbers greater than one are positive and both the constant (0.02569) and n are positive values. If K is less than one, then $\mathcal{E}^\circ$ is less than zero because the natural logarithms of numbers less than 1 and greater than zero are negative.

Problem 19.11 One of the most commonly used batteries is the lead storage battery. The anode and cathode half-reactions for this battery are as follows.

$$Pb(s) + SO_4^{2-}(aq) \longrightarrow PbSO_4(s) + 2e^- \qquad \mathcal{E}^\circ = +0.36 \text{ V}$$
$$PbO_2(s) + SO_4^2(aq) + 4H^+(aq) + 2e^- \longrightarrow PbSO_4(s) + 2H_2O(l) \qquad \mathcal{E}^\circ = +1.68 \text{ V}$$

Calculate the equilibrium constant, K, for the lead storage battery at 298 K.

Solution 19.11 Equation 19.12 is used to calculate the equilibrium constant, K, from the cell potential, $\mathcal{E}^\circ$. Hence, first obtain the overall cell potential, $\mathcal{E}^\circ$, and the number of electrons transferred. To begin, add the two half-reactions that give the overall cell reaction and then add the half-cell potentials to get the cell potential, $\mathcal{E}^\circ$. The cell potential is +2.04 V and two moles of electrons transfer. Hence, substitute these values into Eq. 19.12 and solve for K.

$$+2.04 \text{ V} = (0.02569/2) \ln K$$
$$\ln K = 159$$
$$\text{antiln} (\ln K) = \text{antiln} (159)$$
$$K = e^{159} = 1.13 \times 10^{69}$$

The Relationship of $\mathcal{E}$ and $\mathcal{E}^\circ$—The Nernst Equation

Under standard state conditions, the concentrations of solutions must be 1 M and the pressures of gases are 1 atm. If the concentrations of the solutions in electrolytic cells are not 1 M or if reactions do not begin with 1 M solutions, then the Nernst Equation is used. It is as follows

$$\mathcal{E} = \mathcal{E}^\circ - \frac{RT}{nF} \ln Q \tag{19.13}$$

in which $\mathcal{E}$ is the nonstandard cell potential, $\mathcal{E}^\circ$ is the standard cell potential, R is the ideal gas constant (8.314 J/(mol K)), T is the Kelvin temperature, n is the number of moles of electrons transferred, F is Faraday's constant (96,500 J/(V mol)), ln is the natural logarithm, and Q is the reaction quotient. The Nernst Equation may be simplified by inserting the numerical value of RT/F in which T is 298 K, yielding Eq. 19.14.

$$\mathcal{E} = \mathcal{E}^\circ - \frac{0.02569}{n} \ln Q \tag{19.14}$$

THE RELATIONSHIP OF $\mathcal{E}$, $\mathcal{E}^o$, AND Q

In voltaic cells, $\mathcal{E}$ is always greater than one. When the reaction quotient, Q, in the Nernst Equation (Eq. 19.14) is greater than one, then the term $(0.02569/n) \ln Q$ is positive. However, the minus sign that precedes this term in Eq. 19.14 decreases the value of $\mathcal{E}$. Therefore, when Q is greater than one, then $\mathcal{E}$ is less than $\mathcal{E}^o$. Note that when Q is greater than one, more products are usually found in the reaction mixture. This means that the reaction has a smaller tendency to occur. In contrast, when the reaction quotient, Q, is less than one, then the term $(0.02569/n) \ln Q$ is negative. The minus sign in front of this term increases the value of $\mathcal{E}$. Thus, when Q is less than one, then $\mathcal{E}$ is greater than $\mathcal{E}^o$. This means that the reaction has a greater tendency to occur.

Problem 19.12 A voltaic cell has Sn and Ag electrodes. (a) Predict the voltage of this cell at 298 K when $[Sn^{2+}] = 1.0\ M$ and $[Ag^+] = 1.0\ M$. (b) Predict the voltage of this cell at 298 K when $[Sn^{2+}] = 0.0010\ M$ and $[Ag^+] = 0.75\ M$. (c) Predict the voltage of this cell at 298 K when $[Sn^{2+}] = 0.75\ M$ and $[Ag^+] = 0.0010\ M$.

Solution 19.12 The standard cell potential for the Sn/Ag cell should be calculated first, and then substituted into the Nernst Equation to obtain the values of $\mathcal{E}$. The standard reduction potentials for Sn and Ag are -0.14 V and $+0.80$ V, respectively. Because Ag^+ has the higher reduction potential, Ag^+ undergoes reduction at the cathode, and Sn undergoes oxidation at the anode. Reversing the Sn/Sn^{2+} half-reaction, equalizing the electrons, and adding them together gives us the following overall cell reaction.

$$Sn(s) + 2Ag^+(aq) \longrightarrow 2Ag(s) + Sn^{2+}(aq)$$

To calculate the $\mathcal{E}^o$ value, add the half-cell potentials as follows.

$$\mathcal{E}^o_{cell} = \mathcal{E}^o(\text{cathode}) - \mathcal{E}^o(\text{anode}) = +0.80\ V - (-0.14\ V) = +0.94\ V$$

(a) Because both ions are in the standard state, $1.0\ M$, then $\mathcal{E}$ equals $\mathcal{E}^o$ because Q equals 1 and the natural log of 1 is 0.

$$\mathcal{E} = \mathcal{E}^o - (0.02569/n) \ln[Sn^{2+}]/[Ag^+]^2$$
$$= +0.94\ V - ((0.02569/2\text{mol e}^-) \ln[1.0\ M/(1.0\ M)^2]) = +0.94\ V$$

(b) $\mathcal{E} = +0.94\ V - ((0.02569/2\ \text{mole}^-) \ln[0.0010\ M/(0.75\ M)^2])$
$= +0.94\ V - (-0.081\ V) = +1.02\ V$

(c) $\mathcal{E} = +0.94\ V - ((0.02569/2\ \text{mol e}^-) \ln[0.75\ M/(0.0010\ M)^2])$
$= +0.94\ V - 0.17\ V = +0.77\ V$

Problem 19.13 A chemist wants to measure the molar concentration of Fe^{3+} in an aqueous solution to accomplish this, the chemist constructs a voltaic cell in which the cathode has a strip of $Fe(s)$ immersed in an unknown concentration of Fe^{3+} and the anode is a standard Zn half-cell. The potential of the cell is 0.65 V. If the standard cell potential for a Zn/Fe cell is 0.72 V, what is the molar concentration of Fe^{3+}?

Solution 19.13 Begin by writing the equation for the reaction. If Zn is at the anode, it undergoes oxidation to Zn^{2+} ($Zn(s) \longrightarrow Zn^{2+}(aq) + 2e^-$). At the cathode Fe^{3+} is reduced to Fe ($Fe^{3+}(aq) + 3e^- \longrightarrow Fe(s)$). Equalizing the electrons that are released and taken in shows that six electrons transfer from the anode to the cathode ($n = 6$). Adding the two half-reactions gives the following overall cell equation.

$$3Zn(s) + 2Fe^{3+}(aq) \longrightarrow 2Fe(s) + 3Zn^{2+}(aq)$$

To calculate the unknown concentration of Fe^{3+}, substitute the known values into the Nernst Equation and solve for the molar concentration of Fe^{3+}. The cell potential, $\mathcal{E}$, is +0.65 V. The standard cell potential is +0.72 V. The number of moles of electrons transferred, n, is 6, and the standard concentration of Zn^{2+} is 1.0 M.

$$\mathcal{E} = \mathcal{E}° - (0.02569/n) \ln[Zn^{2+}]^3/[Fe^{3+}]^2$$

$$0.65 \text{ V} = +0.72 \text{ V} - (0.02569/6 \text{ mol e}^-) \ln(1.0 \text{ M})^3/[Fe^{3+}]^2$$

$$0.07 \text{ V} = -(0.02569/6 \text{ mol e}^-) \ln(1.0 \text{ M})^3/[Fe^{3+}]^2$$

$$\ln(1/[Fe^{3+}]^2) = 16.4$$

$$[Fe^{3+}] = 3 \times 10^{-4} \ M \ Fe^{3+}$$

19.4   ELECTROLYSIS AND ELECTROLYTIC CELLS

Converting Electrical Energy to Chemical Energy

Voltaic cells produce electricity spontaneously, which means they release free energy ($\triangle G° < 0$). Electrolytic cells operate opposite to that of voltaic cells, which means electrolytic cells require a constant source of free energy (electricity). In other words, the reactions in electrolytic cells occur nonspontaneously ($\triangle G° > 0$).

Electrolysis

The term electrolysis is used to describe any nonspontaneous reaction that only takes place with the addition of electrical energy. The same fundamental principles that apply to voltaic cells also apply to electrolytic cells.

ELECTROLYSIS OF MOLTEN SODIUM CHLORIDE, $NaCl(l)$

An electrolytic cell with molten sodium chloride, $NaCl(l)$, results when inert electrodes are immersed in liquid NaCl and a direct-current (DC) source of electricity such as a battery or a DC power supply is attached. The DC source pumps electrons into the cathode, the site of reduction, and withdraws electrons, from the anode, the site of oxidation. Recall that NaCl is an ionic solid. When $NaCl(s)$ melts (producing $NaCl(l)$), some of the resulting ions, Na^+ and Cl^-, are free to move. Therefore, in this electrolytic cell Na^+ ions accept electrons and are reduced to liquid sodium, $Na(l)$, and the Cl^- ions release electrons and are oxidized to chlorine gas, $Cl_2(g)$. Hence, the anode, cathode, and overall reactions are as follows.

$$
\begin{array}{ll}
2Cl^-(l) \longrightarrow Cl_2(g) + 2e^- & \text{(Anode)} \\
\underline{2Na^+(l) + 2e^- \longrightarrow 2Na(l)} & \text{(Cathode)} \\
2Na^+(l) + 2Cl^-(l) \longrightarrow 2Na(l) + Cl_2(g) &
\end{array}
$$

SIGN CONVENTION IN ELECTROLYTIC CELLS

Note that the sign convention for the anode and cathode of electrolytic cells is opposite to that in voltaic cells. The anode is the positive electrode because the power supply withdraws electrons, and the cathode is the negative electrode because the power supply pumps in electrons. Also note that the cathode, as in voltaic cells, attracts the cations, Na^+, and the anode attracts the anions, Cl^-.

ELECTROLYSIS OF WATER, $H_2O(l)$

In the electrolysis of water, an electric current decomposes water to its component elements, $H_2(g)$ and $O_2(g)$.

$$2H_2O(l) \xrightarrow{\text{elec}} 2H_2(g) + O_2(g)$$

Nothing happens after applying a DC current because of the very low concentration of dissolved ions. Recall that at 298 K, the molar concentrations of H^+ and OH^- are only 1.0×10^{-7} M in pure water. Therefore, to initiate the electrolysis of water, a small amount of a strong acid such as H_2SO_4 must be added. At that time, bubbles of $O_2(g)$ evolve from the anode and bubbles of $H_2(g)$ form at the cathode. Two possible oxidations can take place at the anode. They are as follows.

$$2H_2O(l) \longrightarrow O_2(g) + 4H^+(aq) + 4e^- \qquad \mathcal{E}° = -1.23 \text{ V}$$
$$4OH^-(aq) \longrightarrow O_2(g) + 2H_2O(l) + 4e^- \qquad \mathcal{E}° = -0.40 \text{ V}$$

If the pH of the water is low as a result of the addition of acid, the oxidation of water to produce O_2 is the principal half-reaction that produces O_2 because of the very low OH^- concentration in an acidic solution. However, if the water is neutral, pH = 7, then the OH^- half-reaction is the more predominant one at the anode because of its more favorable electrode potential.

At the cathode, two possible reductions can occur. They are the reduction of either the H^+ ions or H_2O molecules to hydrogen gas, $H_2(g)$.

$$4H^+(aq) + 4e^- \longrightarrow 2H_2(g) \qquad \mathcal{E}° = 0.00 \text{ V}$$
$$2H_2O(l) + 2e^- \longrightarrow H_2(g) + 2OH^-(aq) \qquad \mathcal{E}° = -0.83 \text{ V}$$

Because H_2O and H^+ ions are in equilibrium, both half-reactions describe the same process. In the first half-reaction, the $[H^+]$ is 1 M at standard conditions. In the second half-reaction, the $[OH^-]$ is 1 M at standard conditions. In a 1 M acid solution, the OH^- concentration decreases to 10^{-14} M and the $\mathcal{E}$ value for the second half-reaction equals 0.00 V.

Problem 19.14   A solution of copper(II) sulfate, $CuSO_4(aq)$, undergoes electrolysis using inert Pt electrodes. On the surface of one electrode O_2 bubbles evolve and Cu plates out on the other. Explain why these products result, and write the anode, cathode, and overall balanced equation.

Solution 19.14   To account for the products of this electrolysis reaction, first consider what chemical species are present to undergo oxidation and reduction. Because $CuSO_4$ does not hydrolyze in water, the principal species present are Cu^{2+}, SO_4^{2-}, and H_2O.

    (a) Anode reaction

        Oxidation occurs at the anode. Thus, the two possible oxidations are that of H_2O or SO_4^{2-}. However, only O_2 is observed at the electrode. This means that SO_4^{2-} less readily undergoes oxidation under the conditions of the cell.

$$2H_2O(l) \longrightarrow O_2(g) + 4H^+(aq) + 4e^- \qquad \text{(Anode)}$$

    (b) Cathode reaction

        Reduction occurs at the cathode. The two possible reductions are that of H_2O and Cu^{2+}. Because Cu forms at the cathode, Cu^{2+} undergoes reduction more readily than water. This can easily be determined from their standard reduction potentials.

$$Cu^{2+}(aq) + 2e^- \longrightarrow Cu(s) \qquad \mathcal{E}° = +0.32 \text{ V}$$
$$2H_2O(l) + 2e^- \longrightarrow H_2(g) + 2OH^-(aq) \qquad \mathcal{E}° = -0.83 \text{ V}$$

        The standard reduction potential for Cu^{2+} is significantly more positive than that for H_2O.

    (c) Overall reaction

$$2H_2O(l) \longrightarrow O_2(g) + 4H^+(aq) + 4e^-$$
$$\underline{2Cu^{2+}(aq) + 4e^- \longrightarrow 2Cu(s)}$$
$$2Cu^{2+}(aq) + 2H_2O(l) \longrightarrow O_2(g) + 4H^+(aq) + 2Cu(s)$$

Stoichiometry of Electrolytic Reactions

Michael Faraday was the first to show the stoichiometric relationships in the 19th century. Hence, many scientists call the stoichiometric relationships in electrolytic reactions Faraday's law of electrolysis. One statement of Faraday's law is that the number of moles of products formed during electrolysis is directly proportional to the number of moles of electrons that pass through the cell.

ELECTRIC CURRENT

It is most convenient to measure the electric current the flows through the cell. The SI unit of electric current is the ampere, A. Think of the ampere as a measure of the amount of charge in coulombs, C, that flows past a point in an electric circuit per second.

$$1A = \frac{1C}{1s} \tag{19.15}$$

Thus knowing the current, in amperes (A), and the amount of time, in s, we can calculate the electric charge that passes through the cell by rearranging Eq. 19.15.

$$\text{Coulombs (C)} = \text{amperes (A) seconds(s)} \tag{19.16}$$

Problem 19.15   (a) If a current of 10.0 A passes through an electrolytic cell for 1.00 min, calculate the amount of electric charge. (b) How many moles of electrons flow through this cell?

Solution 19.15

(a) $C = A \times s = 10.0\ A \times 1.00\ min \times 60\ s/min = 600\ C$

(b) To calculate the number of moles of electrons, use Faraday's constant, F, as a conversion factor from charge to moles of electrons.

$$\text{Mol e}^- = 600\ C \times 1\ \text{mol e}^- /96,500\ C = 6.22 \times 10^{-3}\ \text{mol e}^-$$

Problem 19.16   What mass of Pb(*s*) forms at the cathode when a current of 5.00 A flows through a solution of $Pb(NO_3)_2$ for 25.0 min?

Solution 19.16   Whenever solving a stoichiometry problem, always write the equation for the reaction first. In the electrolysis of $Pb(NO_3)_2(aq)$, $Pb^{2+}(aq)$ is reduced to Pb(*s*).

$$Pb^{2+}(aq) + 2e^- \longrightarrow Pb(s)$$

This equation shows that two moles of electrons produce one mole of Pb. To solve this problem, begin with the current, 5.00 A (5.00 C/s), and the time, 25.0 min, and calculate the number of coulombs, C, of charge transferred. Then, the number of coulombs can be converted to the moles of electrons using Faraday's constant, 96,500 C/mol e$^-$. The remainder of the problem is straightforward stoichiometry. Two moles of electrons produce one mole of Pb, and the molar mass of Pb is 207 g/mol.

$$5.00\ C/s \times 25.0\ min \times 60\ s/min \times 1\ \text{mol e}^- /96,500\ C$$
$$\times 1\ \text{mol Pb}/2\ \text{mol e}^- \times 207\ \text{g Pb/mol Pb} = 8.04\ \text{g Pb}$$

Problem 19.17   How many minutes does it take to produce 35.0 g Fe(*s*) by passing a 20.0 A current through a solution of $Fe(NO_3)_3(aq)$?

Solution 19.17 Again begin the problem by writing the equation for the reduction of $Fe^{3+}(aq)$ to $Fe(s)$ ($Fe^{3+}(aq) + 3e^- \longrightarrow Fe(s)$). This equation shows that three moles of electrons produce one mole of solid Fe.

$$35.0 \text{ g Fe} \times 1\text{mol Fe}/55.8 \text{ g} \times 3 \text{ mol e}^-/1 \text{ mol Fe}^{3+} \times 96,500 \text{ C/mol e}^-$$
$$\times 1 \text{ } s/20.0 \text{ } C \times 1 \text{ } min/60 \text{ } s = 151 \text{ } min$$

SUMMARY

Electrochemistry is the study of both the conversion of chemical energy to electrical energy in voltaic cells (galvanic cells) and the conversion of electrical energy to chemical energy in electrolytic cells.

A simple voltaic cell consists of two electrodes immersed in electrolyte solutions connected by an external circuit and a salt bridge or a porous cup. The anode is the negative electrode because it is the source of electrons. The cathode is the positive electrode because it takes in electrons. The electrons from the anode flow through an external electric circuit and are taken in by the cathode. At the cathode the electrons are accepted by the cations in solution. The salt bridge, which is either a tube filled with inert salt such as $NaNO_3$ or a porous barrier, completes the circuit. Cations migrate towards the cathode and anions move towards the anode.

The capacity that a voltaic cell has to push electrons through a circuit is called the electromotive force, emf, of the cell or the cell potential, $\mathcal{E}$. The SI unit of electromotive force is volts, V. The cell potential may be calculated from standard reduction potentials, $\mathcal{E}^o_{red}$. A standard reduction potential is the voltage produced by a reduction half-cell at standard conditions relative to the standard hydrogen electrode, which is assigned a value of 0.0 V.

The more positive the standard reduction potential, the more readily a substance undergoes reduction—a better oxidizing agent. The more negative the standard reduction potential, the more readily a substance undergoes oxidation—a better reducing agent. A cell potential is obtained by subtracting the standard reduction potential of the anode from that of the cathode. All voltaic cells are spontaneous, and their standard cell potentials are always positive.

Reactions with positive $\mathcal{E}$ values are spontaneous, those with negative $\mathcal{E}$ values are nonspontaneous, and those that equal zero are at equilibrium. The relationship between $\triangle G^o$ and $\mathcal{E}^o$ is $\triangle G^o = -nF\mathcal{E}^o$. Because $\mathcal{E}^o$ is related to $\triangle G^o$, and $\triangle G^o$ is related to the equilibrium constant, then $\mathcal{E}^o$ is related to K as follows.

$$\mathcal{E} = \frac{RT}{nF} \ln K$$

The more positive the $\mathcal{E}^o$ value, the farther the equilibrium lies towards pure products, and the more negative the $\mathcal{E}^o$ value, the closer the equilibrium lies towards pure reactants. At all other conditions except standard conditions, the Nernst Equation is used.

$$\mathcal{E} = \mathcal{E}^o - \frac{RT}{nF} \ln Q$$

In an electrolytic cell, electrical energy changes to chemical energy. All electrolytic cells are nonspontaneous and require an outside energy source. Electricity is pumped into the cathode, the site of reduction, and pumped out of the anode, the site of oxidation. In an electrolytic cell, the substance that most readily reduces plates the cathode and the substance that most readily oxidizes forms at the anode. The amounts of products produced at the electrodes are predicted using Faraday's law, which states that the number of moles of products formed during electrolysis is directly proportional to the number of moles of electrons that pass through the cell.

CHAPTER 19 REVIEW EXERCISE

1. Write the cell notation for each of the following: (a) anode = Zn/Zn^{2+} and cathode = Sn/Sn^{2+} and (b) anode = Ni/Ni^{2+} and cathode = Ag/Ag^+

2. A voltaic cell has $Mg(s)$ and $Mg(NO_3)_2(aq)$ for one half-cell and $Cd(s)$ and $Cd(NO_3)_2(aq)$ for the other. If Mg is a better reducing agent than Cd and the salt bridge contains a solution of $NaNO_3$, answer each of the following: (a) Which substance is the anode? (b) Which substance is the cathode? (c) Which ions move toward the anode? (d) Which ions move toward the cathode? (e) Which metal is the negative electrode? (f) Which metal is the positive electrode? (g) Write its cell notation.

3. Calculate the standard cell potentials, $\mathcal{E}°$, for each of the following:

    (a) $Pb(s)|Pb^{2+}(aq)||Hg^{2+}(aq)|Hg(l)$
    (b) $Fe(s)|Fe^{3+}(aq)||Cu^+(aq)|Cu(s)$

4. Completely describe the voltaic cell, including the standard cell potential, that has the following half-reactions.

$$Fe(OH)_2(s) + 2e^- \longrightarrow Fe(s) + 2OH^-(aq) \qquad \mathcal{E}° = -0.88 \text{ V}$$
$$NiO_2(s) + 2H_2O(l) + 2e^- \longrightarrow Ni(OH)_2(s) + 2OH^-(aq) \quad \mathcal{E}° = +0.49 \text{ V}$$

5. Use standard reduction potentials to determine in which of the following solutions will a strip of Cd dissolve and form $Cd^{2+}(aq)$. (a) 1 M $H^+(aq)$, (b) 1 M $Al^{3+}(aq)$, (c) 1 M $Hg_2^{2+}(aq)$, (d) 1 M $Cr^{3+}(aq)$, (e) 1 M $Ba^{2+}(aq)$

6. Use standard reduction potentials to predict which of the following solutions dissolves a strip of Ag: (a) 1 M $Au^{3+}(aq)$, (b) 1 M $Sn^{2+}(aq)$, (c) 1 M $MnO_4^-(aq)/H^+(aq)$, (d) 1 M $H^+(aq)$.

7. Calculate the standard potential, $\mathcal{E}°$, for each of the following reactions:

    (a) $H_2(g) + I_2(g) \longrightarrow 2HI(g) \qquad \Delta G° = 2.6 \text{ kJ}$
    (b) $P_4(g) + 6Cl_2(g) \longrightarrow 4PCl_3(g) \quad \Delta G° = -1.1 \times 10^2 \text{ kJ}$

8. Use the standard reduction potentials to calculate the standard free energy change, $\Delta G°$, for the following reaction:

$$I_2(s) + 2Br^-(aq) \longrightarrow Br_2(l) + 2I^-(aq)$$

9. Calculate the equilibrium constant for the following redox reaction:

$$Sn(s) + Ni^{2+} \longrightarrow Ni(s) + Sn^{2+}(aq)$$

10. Calculate the equilibrium constants, K, for each of the following reactions.

    (a) $Br_2 + 2I^- \rightleftharpoons I_2 + 2Br^-$
    (b) $3Pb^{2+} + 2Cr \rightleftharpoons 2Cr^{3+} + 3Pb$

11. A student constructs a voltaic cell using Sn and Al. (a) Predict the voltage of this cell at 298 K when $[Sn^{2+}] = 1.0$ M and $[Al^{3+}] = 1.0$ M. (b) Predict the voltage of this cell at 298 K when $[Sn^{2+}] = 0.0050$ M and $[Al^{3+}] = 0.50$ M. (c) Predict the voltage of this cell at 298 K when $[Sn^{2+}] = 0.50$ M and $[Al^{3+}] = 0.0050$ M.

12. The same chemist uses exactly the same set-up as in Problem 19.13 to measure the unknown concentration of another Fe^{3+} solution. This time the measured cell potential was 0.59 V. Calculate the molar concentration of the Fe^{3+}, $[Fe^{3+}]$.

13. A solution of sodium sulfate, $Na_2SO_4(aq)$, undergoes electrolysis using inert Pt electrodes. O_2 bubbles evolve from one electrode and H_2 bubbles are released from the other. Explain why these products result, and write the anode, cathode, and overall balanced equation.

14. What mass of $Ag(s)$ forms at the cathode when a current of 12.0 A flows through a solution of $AgNO_3$ for 10.0 hr?

15. How many hours does it take to produce 127 g Cu by passing a 16.5 A current through a solution of $Cu(NO_3)_2$?

16. (a) Calculate the standard cell potential, $\mathcal{E}°$, for a voltaic cell that has Fe/Fe^{2+} and Cu/Cu^{2+}. (b) What is the cell potential at 298 K when $[Fe^{2+}] = 0.0010\ M$ and $[Cu^{2+}] = 1.0$ M? (c) What is the cell potential at 298 K when $[Fe^{2+}] = 0.10\ M$ and $[Cu^{2+}] = 1.0$ M? (d) What is the cell potential at 298 K when $[Fe^{2+}] = 1.0\ M$ and $[Cu^{2+}] = 0.010$ M?

17. What volume of O_2 at STP result when 850 mA flows through water with added acid for 1.00 day?

18. Use the electrochemical data to determine the K_{sp} of AgCl.

19. Two electrolytic cells are connected in series. One produces Ag from $AgNO_3$ and the other produces Pb from $Pb(NO_3)_2$. (a) Calculate the masses of Ag and Pb produced in their respective cells when 25.0 A passes through the cells for 2.00 hr.

ANSWERS TO REVIEW EXERCISE

1. (a) $Zn(s)|Zn^{2+}(aq)||Sn^{2+}(aq)|Sn(s)$ (b) $Ni(s)|Ni^{2+}(aq)||Ag^+(aq)|Ag(s)$

2. (a) Mg, (b) Cd, (c) NO_3^-, (d) Na^+, Cd^{2+}, (e) Mg, (f) Cd, (g) $Mg(s)|Mg^{2+}(aq)||Cd^{2+}(aq)|Cd(s)$

3. (a) 0.99 V, (b) 0.56 V

4. Anode = $Fe/Fe(OH)_2$, Cathode = $NiO_2/Ni(OH)_2$, $\mathcal{E}° = 1.37$ V,
   $NiO_2(s) + 2H_2O(l) + Fe(s) + 2OH^-(aq) \longrightarrow Fe(OH)_2(s) + Ni(OH)_2(s) + 2OH^-(aq)$

5. $1\ M\ H^+$, $1\ M\ Hg_2^{2+}$

6. Ag dissolves in Au^{3+} and $1\ M\ MnO_4^-/H^+$

7. (a) -0.013 V, (b) 0.95 V

8. $\triangle G° = 1.1 \times 10^2$ kJ

9. $K = 1.8 \times 10^{-5}$

10. (a) 3.8×10^{17}, (b) 7.5×10^{61}

11. (a) $\mathcal{E} = 1.52$ V, (b) $\mathcal{E} = 1.46$ V, (c) $\mathcal{E} = 1.56$ V

12. $[Fe^{3+}] = 2.6\ 10^{-7}\ M$

13. Anode reaction = $2H_2O(l) \longrightarrow O_2(g) + 4H^+(aq) + 4e^-$
    Cathode reaction = $2H_2O(l) \longrightarrow H_2(g) + 2OH^-(aq)$
    Overall reaction = $2H_2O(l) \longrightarrow 2H_2(g) + O_2(g)$

14. 483 g Ag

15. 6.50 hr

16. (a) 0.76 V, (b) 0.85 V, (c) 0.79 V, (d) 0.70 V

17. 4.26 L O_2

18. 1.6×10^{-10}

19. 201 g Ag, 193 g Pb

20

Nuclear Chemistry

Nuclear chemistry is the study of the nucleus and how it changes. The nucleus is the very small dense region within an atom that contains the nucleons—the protons and neutrons. In this final chapter, we will consider radioactivity and nuclear changes.

20.1 THE NUCLEUS AND NUCLEAR STABILITY

The Nucleus—Atomic and Mass Numbers

The atomic number, Z, is the number of protons, and the mass number, A, is the sum of the protons plus neutrons in the nucleus of an atom (Sec. 3.1). Subtracting the atomic number from the mass number gives the number of neutrons, N, in the nucleus.

$$N = A - Z \tag{20.1}$$

Collectively, the protons and neutrons in a nucleus are called the nucleons.

NUCLEAR COMPOSITION NOTATION

When writing the nuclear composition for an atom, place the mass number as a superscript to the left of the symbol and the atomic number as a subscript, also to the left of the symbol. For example, to show the symbols for the carbon-12 and oxygen-16 atoms, write $^{12}_{6}C$ and $^{16}_{8}O$.

Isotopes and Nuclides

Isotopes are atoms with the same atomic number but with different mass numbers. In nuclear chemistry, the term isotope is used to refer to different forms of an individual element. For example, $^{235}_{92}U$ and $^{238}_{92}U$ are two isotopes of uranium. However, the term nuclide is used to refer to atomic forms of different elements. For instance, $^{1}_{1}H$, $^{4}_{2}He$, and $^{12}_{6}C$ are three different nuclides.

The Strong Force (Nuclear Force)

The stability of a nucleus is the result of a force called the strong force—one of the four forces of nature (gravity, electrostatic, strong nuclear, and weak nuclear). The strong nuclear force (strong force, for short) is the force of attraction between nucleons that acts only over distances less than 10^{-15} m. At distances greater than 10^{-15} m, the strong force decreases rapidly to zero. Hence, if two protons are separated by more than 10^{-15} m they repel each other. However, if they are separated by less than 10^{-15} m, the strong force binds them. The strong force also holds neutral particles such as neutrons.

Nuclear Stability— Nuclear Shell Model

Which nuclides are stable, and which are unstable? Nuclear scientists believe that the nucleons in an atom are organized in various energy levels and shells, like the shells that electrons occupy. This theory is called the nuclear shell model. Recall that the noble gases have the most stable arrangement of electrons. The nucleus also has "magic numbers" associated with stable nuclear configurations. Nuclides that have 2, 8, 20, 50, 82, or 126 protons or neutrons are usually more stable than other nuclides. For example, six stable isotopes of calcium ($Z = 20$) exist: ^{40}Ca, ^{42}Ca, ^{43}Ca, ^{44}Ca, ^{46}Ca, and ^{48}Ca. In contrast, only two stable isotopes of potassium ($Z = 19$), ^{39}K and ^{41}K, and only one stable isotope of scandium ($Z = 21$), ^{45}Sc, exist in nature. Five stable nuclides with a neutron number of 20, ^{36}S, ^{37}Cl, ^{38}Ar, ^{39}K, and ^{40}Ca, exist, but no stable nuclides with either 19 or 21 neutrons are known.

NUCLEAR STABILITY—ODD AND EVEN NUCLEONS

Nuclides that have even numbers of nucleons, those with an even number of protons and neutrons, are more stable than those with either an odd number of protons or an odd number of neutrons.

NUCLEAR STABILITY—*N/Z* RATIOS

Nuclear stability also correlates with the ratio of the number of neutrons to the number of protons. In nuclides with low mass numbers ($A < 41$), the most stable ones are usually those with the same number of protons and neutrons ($N/Z = 1$); e.g., $^{12}_{6}$C, $^{16}_{8}$O, $^{32}_{16}$S, and $^{40}_{20}$Ca. For higher-mass nuclides ($A > 41$), this is not true. The most stable nuclides have a larger number of neutrons than protons ($N/Z > 1$).

NUCLEAR STABILITY—HIGH-MASS NUCLEI

All nuclides with atomic numbers greater than 83 ($Z > 83$) are unstable. This means that all of the isotopes of the elements beyond bismuth ($Z = 83$) are radioactive.

Problem 20.1   Select the more stable nucleon from each of the following pairs: (a) $^{40}_{19}$K or $^{40}_{20}$Ca, (b) $^{59}_{27}$Co or $^{64}_{29}$Cu

Solution 20.1   To predict if a nuclide is more stable than another, first write the atomic number, Z, and calculate the neutron number, N. Then, check to see if one of these values equals one of the "magic numbers." Next, see if these values are odd or even. If both Z and N are even, it is probably more stable than if one or both values are odd.

 (a) ^{40}K has an atomic number of 19 and a neutron number of 21. ^{40}Ca has an atomic number of 20 and a neutron number of number of 20. One of the stable nuclear configurations for atoms is 20 and in ^{40}Ca both Z and N equal 20. Neither Z nor N equals a stable nuclear configuration in ^{40}K; thus, ^{40}Ca is more stable than ^{40}K. Another way to obtain the same prediction is that ^{40}Ca has an even number of protons and neutrons, while ^{40}K has an odd number of nucleons. Nuclides that have an even number of nucleons are more stable than those that do not.

 (b) The Z and N values for ^{59}Co are 27 and 32, respectively. One of these two values is even. The Z and N values for ^{64}Cu are 29 and 35, respectively. Both value for ^{64}Cu are odd. Hence, a good prediction is that ^{59}Co is a more stable nuclide than ^{64}Cu.

20.2 RADIOACTIVITY

Radioactive Decay

Unstable nuclei decay spontaneously and release different types of matter and energy. These spontaneous nuclear changes are called radioactive disintegrations or radioactive decays. An atom that undergoes such changes is said to be radioactive.

Types of Radioactive Decay

Radioactive atoms can release alpha particles, α, beta particles, β, and gamma rays, γ. In addition, two other means by which unstable atoms decay will be considered: electron capture and positron emission.

Alpha Particles, α

Alpha particles, α, are high-mass particles, having the mass of a helium nucleus and a 2+ charge. Alpha particles are helium nuclei that have been ejected from the nucleus at a speed approximately one-tenth the velocity of light, c ($c = 3 \times 10^8$ m/s). The symbol for an alpha particle is either ${}^4_2\alpha$ or ${}^4_2\text{He}^{2+}$. Compared to β and γ emissions, α particles have the smallest capacity to penetrate matter (penetration power). As α particles penetrate matter they ionize the atoms they encounter. Alpha particles have a greater capacity to ionize matter than either β or γ emissions because of their higher mass and charge.

Alpha Decay

An α particle is composed of two protons and two neutrons. Thus, when a nucleus releases an α particle, its atomic number decreases by two and its mass number decreases by four. To show what happens during radioactive decay, nuclear equations are written. Nuclear equations give the symbols, mass numbers, and atomic numbers of all the species involved. The general nuclear equation for alpha decay is

$$ {}^A_Z X \longrightarrow {}^{A-4}_{Z-2} Y + {}^4_2\alpha \tag{20.2} $$

in which ${}^A_Z X$ is the parent nuclide, ${}^{A-4}_{Z-2} Y$ is the daughter nuclide, and ${}^4_2\alpha$ is an alpha particle. The parent nuclide undergoes radioactive decay and produces the daughter nuclide.

Problem 20.2 (a) Write a nuclear equation that shows the alpha decay of the radionuclide ${}^{226}_{88}\text{Ra}$. (b) Write the equation for the alpha decay of the daughter nuclide of ${}^{226}_{88}\text{Ra}$. (c) Write the equation for the alpha decay of ${}^{242}_{94}\text{Pu}$.

Solution 20.2 When writing nuclear equations, always remember to obey the law of conservation of mass/energy.

(a) ${}^{226}_{88}\text{Ra} \longrightarrow {}^{222}_{86}\text{Rn} + {}^4_2\alpha$

(b) ${}^{222}_{86}\text{Rn} \longrightarrow {}^{218}_{84}\text{Po} + {}^4_2\alpha$

(c) ${}^{242}_{94}\text{Pu} \longrightarrow {}^{238}_{92}\text{U} + {}^4_2\alpha$

Beta Particles, β

Beta particles, β, are high-energy electrons. Thus, they are usually symbolized as either ${}^0_{-1}e^-$ (${}^0_{-1}e$) or ${}^0_{-1}\beta^-$ (${}^0_{-1}\beta$). The subscript -1 is written to represent its negative charge and a superscript 0 represents its mass number because it has no nucleons. Like α particles, β particles travel at a high velocity often in the range of 0.5 to 0.7 c. They penetrate a greater thickness of matter than do α particles before being absorbed. Beta particles can penetrate more matter than α particles because of their smaller mass, higher velocity, and lower charge. Their ability to ionize matter is much less than that of α particles, but significantly greater than that of γ rays.

Beta Decay

Beta decay occurs in nuclei that have a high neutron to proton ratio. Some neutrons undergo a spontaneous change, producing a beta particle, ${}_{-1}e^-$; a proton, ${}^1p^+$; and an antineutrino, $\bar{\nu}$.

$$ {}^1_0 n^0 \longrightarrow {}^1_1 p^+ + {}^0_{-1} e^- + \bar{\nu} $$

The daughter nucleus has the same total number of particles because a neutron changes to a proton. In other words, the mass number remains the same. However, the atomic number increases by one because of the additional proton in the nucleus. Therefore, the general nuclear equation for beta decay is

$$^A_Z X \longrightarrow ^A_{Z+1} Y + ^0_{-1} e + \bar{\nu} \tag{20.3}$$

Beta decay cannot be explained by the strong force alone. It is related to the weak force—a basic force of nature.

Problem 20.3 Write equations for the beta decay of each of the following: (a) $^{14}_6$C, (b) $^{39}_{18}$Ar, (c) $^{131}_{53}$I.

Solution 20.3

(a) $^{14}_6$C $\longrightarrow$ $^{14}_7$N + $^0_{-1}$e + $\bar{\nu}$
(b) $^{39}_{18}$Ar $\longrightarrow$ $^{39}_{19}$K + $^0_{-1}$e + $\bar{\nu}$
(c) $^{131}_{53}$I $\longrightarrow$ $^{131}_{54}$Xe + $^0_{-1}$e + $\bar{\nu}$

Gamma Rays, γ

Gamma rays have no mass or charge; therefore, the symbol for gamma rays is just the symbol gamma, γ. Gamma rays are a type of electromagnetic radiation that travel at the velocity of light, c. Their penetration power is greater than that of either α or β rays because of their minimal interaction with matter. A thick wall of lead or some other dense substance is required to block gamma radiation. Gamma rays are the least ionizing radiation of the three types discussed because of their smaller degree of interaction with matter.

Gamma Emission

Gamma emission takes place without a measurable nuclear mass change because γ radiation is a type of electromagnetic energy. All types of electromagnetic radiation have both wave and particle characteristics. Thus, nuclei that possess excess energy become more stable by releasing quanta (photons) of γ radiation. After γ emission, the nucleus decreases to a lower energy state. A similar emission of electromagnetic energy occurs when electrons move from higher energy orbitals to lower energy ones and release photons, hν.

EQUATIONS OF GAMMA EMISSIONS

To represent γ emission in an equation, either an asterisk, *, or the letter m is placed next to the symbol, indicating a nucleus with excess energy. These nuclei are said to be in a metastable state, m. Usually within less than 1 ns, a metastable nucleus releases a γ ray and reaches a more stable state. After the release of the γ ray, the same nucleus is present in a lower energy state; hence, the asterisk or the m is removed.

$$^A_Z X^* \longrightarrow ^A_Z X + \gamma \tag{20.4}$$

Most often γ emission accompanies other types of radioactive decay. For example, if a nuclide releases an α particle and produces a daughter nuclide in a metastable state, it can then release a γ ray and becomes more stable.

Positron Emission

Positron emission is another means by which nuclei decay. A positron is an antielectron—a type of antimatter. The symbols $^0_1 e^+$ or $^0_1 \beta^+$ are used for positrons because they have the same properties as "regular" electrons, but they carry a positive charge. When they encounter "regular" electrons they annihilate each other and produce two γ rays ($^0_{-1} e^+ + ^0_1 e^+ \longrightarrow 2\gamma$). When β rays are emitted, the nucleus has a high neutron-to-proton ratio. In positron emission, it is exactly the opposite—these nuclei have a high proton-to-neutron ratio. During positron emission a proton changes spontaneously to a neutron and releases a positron and neutrino.

$$^1_1 p^+ \longrightarrow ^1_1 n^0 + ^0_1 e^+ + \nu$$

Note that during positron emission, a neutrino is released and in β emission an antineutrino is released. The general equation for positron emission is

$$\tfrac{A}{Z}X \longrightarrow \tfrac{A}{Z-1}Y + \tfrac{0}{1}e^+ + \nu \tag{20.5}$$

Problem 20.4 Write the equation that shows the positron emission of $\tfrac{22}{11}Na$. Explain the equation.

Solution 20.4

$$\tfrac{22}{11}Na \longrightarrow \tfrac{22}{10}Ne + \tfrac{0}{1}e^+ + \nu$$

Electron Capture, EC

Closely related to positron emission is electron capture, *EC*. During electron capture, a proton in the nucleus captures an electron, usually one in the lowest energy shell. This proton changes to a neutron and a neutrino is released.

$$\tfrac{1}{1}p^+ + \tfrac{0}{-1}e^- \longrightarrow \tfrac{1}{0}n^0 + \nu$$

Usually one of the outer-level electrons fills the vacancy left by the captured electron, releasing an x-ray.

$$\tfrac{A}{Z}X + \tfrac{0}{-1}e^- \longrightarrow \tfrac{A}{Z-1}Y + \text{x-ray} \tag{20.6}$$

Both electron capture and positron emission produce the same nuclear transformation, and in many cases they compete with each other. Electron capture occurs more often in high-mass nuclides because the lowest energy orbitals have small radii, which makes it easy for the nucleus to capture an electron.

Problem 20.5 Write an equation for the electron capture of $\tfrac{7}{4}Be$. Explain the equation.

Solution 20.5

$$\tfrac{7}{4}Be + \tfrac{0}{-1}e^- \longrightarrow \tfrac{7}{3}Li + \text{x-ray}$$

Problem 20.6 Write a nuclear equation for each of the following: (a) the α decay of $\tfrac{210}{84}Po$, (b) the β decay of $\tfrac{227}{89}Ac$, (c) the positron emission of $\tfrac{13}{7}N$, (d) the electron capture of $\tfrac{73}{33}As$

Solution 20.6

(a) $\tfrac{210}{84}Po \longrightarrow \tfrac{206}{82}Pb + \tfrac{4}{2}He^{2+}$

(b) $\tfrac{227}{89}Ac \longrightarrow \tfrac{227}{90}Th + \tfrac{0}{-1}e^-$

(c) $\tfrac{13}{7}N \longrightarrow \tfrac{13}{6}C + \tfrac{0}{1}e^+$

(d) $\tfrac{73}{33}As + \tfrac{0}{-1}e^- \longrightarrow \tfrac{73}{32}Ge + \text{x-ray}$

Problem 20.7 What is the missing component for each of the following nuclear changes? (a) $\tfrac{77m}{34}Se \longrightarrow \tfrac{77}{34}Se + ?$, (b) $\tfrac{218}{85}At \longrightarrow ? + \tfrac{4}{2}He^{2+}$, (c) $\tfrac{234}{90}Th \longrightarrow \tfrac{234}{91}Pa + ?$

Solution 20.7

(a) Because the nucleus went from a higher-energy state to a lower one and the nucleus did not change composition, this is gamma decay; thus, γ is the missing component.

(b) In this nuclear change an alpha particle is released; thus, the daughter nuclide is $\tfrac{214}{83}Bi$.

(c) The mass number remains constant and the atomic number increases by one; thus, this is beta decay. The missing component is $\tfrac{0}{-1}e^-$ or $\tfrac{0}{-1}\beta^-$.

20.3 QUANTITATIVE ASPECTS OF NUCLEAR RE-ACTIONS

Units of Nuclear Energy—J, kJ, and eV

The SI units for energy the joule, J, or the kilojoule, kJ, are often used. However, for convenience, many nuclear scientists use a non-SI unit called the electron volt, eV. One electron volt is the energy needed to accelerate an electron by a potential difference of one volt. To calculate the number of electron volts, take the charge on an electron, 1.602×10^{-19} C, and multiply it by the number of volts, V (J/C). Thus, one electron volt is equivalent to 1.602×10^{-19} J. The product of the charge in coulombs times the voltage is the number of joules. The electron volt is a small unit of energy. Hence, the most commonly encountered units are the kilo, mega, and gigaelectron volts—keV, MeV, and GeV, respectively.

Equivalence of Mass and Energy

A result of Einstein's special theory of relativity is that energy and mass are equivalent. This relationship may be expressed as follows

$$\triangle E = \triangle m\, c^2 \tag{20.7}$$

in which $\triangle E$ is the change in energy, $\triangle m$ is the change in mass, and c is the velocity of light, 3.00×10^8 m/s. In words, this equation states that for each mass change there is an associated energy change and vice versa. Therefore, a loss of mass results in the production of an equivalent amount of energy and vice versa.

Problem 20.8 Consider the exothermic reaction in which methane, CH_4, undergoes complete combustion.

$$CH_4(g) + 2O_2(g) \longrightarrow CO_2(g) + 2H_2O(g) \qquad \triangle H^\circ = -802 \text{ kJ}$$

Calculate the loss of mass, $\triangle m$, in this reaction. Explain the result.

Solution 20.8 Equation 20.7 can be used as follows to calculate this loss of mass.

$$\triangle E = \triangle m\, c^2$$
$$-802 \text{ kJ} \times 1000 \text{ J/1 kJ} = \triangle m \times (3.00 \times 10^8 \text{ m/s})^2$$
$$\triangle m = -8.91 \times 10^{-12} \text{ kg} = -8.91 \times 10^{-9} \text{ g}$$

This calculation shows that the change in mass is on the order of magnitude of 10^{-9} g (1 ng). This mass is not measurable under normal circumstances because most analytical balances can only detect masses of 1×10^{-4} g. Thus, mass-energy equivalence has little importance in normal chemical changes.

Problem 20.9 Consider the following nuclear fusion reaction that occurs in the sun.

$$^3H + {}^2H \longrightarrow {}^4He + {}^1n$$

(a) Use the following table of masses to calculate the mass loss, $\triangle m$, in this reaction.

Nuclide/Particle	Mass, u
^3H	3.01605
^2H	2.01410
^4He	4.00260
^1n	1.00866

(b) Calculate the energy, in J/atom and MeV/atom, that is equivalent to this mass loss. (c) Convert the energy to kJ/mol.

Solution 20.9

(a)
$$\triangle m = \text{mass}(^4He + {}^1n) - \text{mass}({}^3H + {}^2H)$$
$$= (4.00260 \text{ u} + 1.00866 \text{ u}) - (3.01605 \text{ u} + 2.01410 \text{ u})$$
$$= -0.01889 \text{ u}$$

(b) Use Eq. 20.7 to find the $\triangle E$ that is equivalent to this mass loss, $\triangle m$. Before substituting into this equation, the mass in atomic mass units, u, is converted to kilograms, kg. This is accomplished by knowing that one u is equivalent to 1.6605×10^{-27} kg.

$$\triangle m = -0.01889 \text{ u} \times 1.6605 \times 10^{-27} \text{ kg/1 u} = -3.137 \times 10^{-29} \text{ kg}$$

Next, substitute this mass change into Eq. 20.7.

$$\triangle E = \triangle m \, c^2$$
$$= -3.137 \times 10^{-29} \text{ kg} \times (2.998 \times 10^8 \text{ m/s})^2 = -2.819 \times 10^{-12} \text{ J}$$

Knowing that 1 eV is 1.602×10^{-19} J, our answer can be converted to eV and MeV.

$$\triangle E = -2.819 \times 10^{-12} \text{ J} \times 1\text{eV}/1.602 \times 10^{-19} \text{ J}$$
$$= -1.760 \times 10^7 \text{ eV} \times 1 \text{ MeV}/1 \times 10^6 \text{ eV} = -17.60 \text{ MeV}$$

(c)
$$2.819 \times 10^{-12} \text{ J/atom} \times 6.0220 \times 10^{23} \text{ atoms/mol} = 1.698 \times 10^{12} \text{ J/mol}$$
$$1.698 \times 10^{12} \text{ J/mol} \times 1 \text{ kJ}/1000 \text{ J} = 1.698 \times 10^9 \text{ kJ/mol}$$

Nuclear Binding Energy

When nucleons combine to form a nucleus, they release energy just as atoms release energy when they form chemical bonds. In other words, the nucleus is more stable than the individual particles from which it is made. The energy needed to separate the nucleons in a nucleus is the nuclear binding energy. Think of the nuclear binding energy as the energy released when the nucleons combine to form the nucleus. Because of the equivalence of mass and energy, if energy is released in the formation of the nucleus, then an equivalent amount of mass is lost. This means that the actual mass of the nucleus is less than the sum of the masses of its nucleons. The difference between the actual mass and the sum of the masses of the nucleons is called the mass defect, $\triangle m$.

Problem 20.10 Consider the nucleus of deuterium, ^2H. It consists of just a proton (1.00782 u) and a neutron (1.00867 u). The measured mass of ^2H is 2.01410 u. (a) What is the nuclear binding energy in MeV. (b) Explain the result of part (a).

Solution 20.10

(a)   Total mass = mass(proton) + mass(neutron)

$$= 1.00782 \text{ u} + 1.00867 \text{ u} = 2.01649 \text{ u}$$

$$\triangle m = \text{(actual mass of nucleus)} - \text{(sum of the masses of the nucleons)}$$

$$= 2.01410 \text{ u} - 2.01649 \text{ u} = -0.00239 \text{ u}$$

Next, change the mass loss in atomic mass units, u, to kg.

$$\triangle m = -0.00239 \text{ u} \times 1.6605 \times 10^{-27} \text{ kg}/1 \text{ u} = -3.97 \times 10^{-30} \text{ kg}$$

Then, substitute this mass change into Eq. 20.7.

$$\triangle E = \triangle m\, c^2$$
$$= -3.97 \times 10^{-30} \text{ kg} \times (2.998 \times 10^8 \text{ m/s})^2 = -3.57 \times 10^{-13} \text{ J}$$

Finally, convert the answer from J to MeV.

$$\triangle E = -3.57 \times 10^{-13} \text{ J} \times 1 \text{ eV}/1.602 \times 10^{-19} \text{ J}$$
$$= -2.23 \times 10^6 \text{ eV} = -2.23 \text{ MeV}$$

(b) The nuclear binding energy for the deuterium nucleus is −2.23 MeV. In other words, a deuterium nucleus releases 2.23 MeV when it forms or a deuterium nucleus requires 2.23 MeV to separate it into its component nucleons. The large values of nuclear binding energies are the result of the strong nuclear force that binds the nucleons.

EQUIVALENCE OF MASS DEFECT AND NUCLEAR BINDING ENERGY

To simplify the conversion of mass defects to nuclear binding energies, 1 u is equivalent to 931.5 MeV.

Problem 20.11   What is the nuclear binding energy for ^{12}C? The actual mass of ^{12}C is 12.00000.

Solution 20.11   The ^{12}C nucleus consists of six p^+ and six n^o. Thus, calculate the total mass as follows.

$$6p^+ \times 1.00782 \text{ u}/p^+ = 6.04692 \text{ u}$$
$$6n^o \times 1.00867 \text{ u}/n^o = 6.05202 \text{ u}$$
$$\text{Total mass} = 6.04692 \text{ u} + 6.05202 \text{ u} = 12.09894 \text{ u}$$

Then, calculate $\triangle m$.

$$\triangle m = 12.09894 \text{ u} - 12.00000 \text{ u} = 0.09894 \text{ u}$$

Use the conversion factor 931.5 MeV/u to find the nuclear binding energy from the mass defect.

$$0.09894 \text{ u} \times 931.5 \text{ MeV/u} = 92.16 \text{ MeV}$$

Nuclear Binding Energies per Nucleon

Nuclear binding energies per nucleon are used to compare the stabilities of nuclei. Think of the nuclear binding energy per nucleon as the average binding energy for the nucleus. For example, the nuclear binding energy for ^{2}H was 2.23 MeV. Subsequently, its nuclear binding energy per nucleon is 2.23 MeV/2, which equals 1.11 MeV/nucleon. A more stable nucleus has a higher nuclear binding energy per nucleon than a less stable one. The lowest values are around 6 MeV/nucleon and the highest approach 9 MeV/nucleon. These values lie along a curve that initially rises rapidly until it reaches mass numbers near 50, and then the curve gradually decreases. The atom with the highest nuclear binding energy per nucleon is ^{56}Fe (8.8 MeV/nucleon). Therefore, ^{56}Fe has the most stable nucleus. Because atoms tend spontaneously to go to their lowest energy states, low-mass atoms, $A < 56$, tend to undergo nuclear fusion reactions until they reach the most stable ^{56}Fe nuclear configuration. In contrast, high-mass atoms tend to undergo nuclear fission reactions, also to reach more stable nuclear configurations.

Problem 20.12 What is the nuclear binding energy per nucleon for ^{6}Li? The actual mass of ^{6}Li is 6.01512 u.

Solution 20.12 The ^{6}Li nucleus consists of three p^+ and three n^o. Thus, calculate the total mass as follows.

$$3p^+ \times 1.00782 \text{ u/}p^+ = 3.02346 \text{ u}$$
$$3n^o \times 1.00867 \text{u/}n^o = 3.02601 \text{ u}$$
$$\text{Total mass} = 3.02345 \text{ u} + 3.02601 \text{ u} = 6.04947 \text{ u}$$

Then, calculate $\triangle m$.

$$\triangle m = 6.04947 \text{ u} - 6.01512 \text{ u} = 0.03435 \text{ u}$$

Use the conversion factor 931.5 MeV/u to find the nuclear binding energy from the mass defect.

$$0.03435 \text{ u} \times 931.5 \text{ MeV/u} = 32.00 \text{ MeV}$$

Finally, divide this energy by the number of nucleons.

$$32.00 \text{ MeV}/6 \text{ nucleons} = 5.333 \text{ MeV/nucleon}$$

SUMMARY

*N*uclear chemistry is the study of the nucleus and how it changes. The nucleus is the very small dense region within an atom that contains the nucleons—the protons and neutrons. The nucleus is bonded by the strong or nuclear force, which acts on nucleons separated by less than 10^{-15} m.

The stability of a nuclide depends on its composition. Nuclides with 2, 8, 20, 50, 82, and 126 protons or neutrons are more stable than those with other compositions. Atoms with both an even number of protons and neutrons are generally more stable than those with odd numbers of protons and neutrons. Nuclear stability also correlates with the ratio of neutrons to protons. Small atoms are most stable when they have an equal number of protons and neutrons, while higher-mass atoms are most stable when they have more neutrons than protons. All atoms with an atomic number greater than 83 are radioactive.

Alpha particles are high-energy helium nuclei, $^4_2He^{2+}$ or $^4_2\alpha$, that have a low penetration power. When an atom undergoes α decay, its atomic number decreases by two and its mass number decreases by four.

Beta particles are high-energy electrons, $^0_{-1}e^-$ or $^0_{-1}\beta^-$, that have a penetration power greater than α rays but less than γ rays. During β decay, a neutron changes to a proton releasing a β particle and an antineutrino, . The daughter nuclide in β decay has the same mass number as the parent and an atomic number of $Z + 1$.

Gamma rays, γ, are a type of electromagnetic radiation. They have a higher penetration power than either α or β rays. In γ emission, an unstable nucleus releases a γ ray and drops to a lower energy state.

Positrons are antielectrons, ${}^0_1e^+$. If a positron and electron collide, they annihilate each other and produce two γ rays. In positron emission, a proton changes to a neutron, releasing the positron and a neutrino. The daughter nuclide in positron emission has the same mass number and has an atomic number of $Z - 1$.

Electron capture occurs when a proton attracts an electron in a low energy level. This proton changes to a neutron and a neutrino is released. When a higher-energy electron fills the vacated orbital, the atom releases an x-ray.

The energy needed to separate the nucleons in a nucleus is the nuclear binding energy. Thus, when a nucleus forms it releases the nuclear binding energy. According to Einstein's equation, $\triangle E = \triangle mc^2$, a release of energy, $\triangle E$, has an equivalent loss in mass, $\triangle m$. The difference in the sum of the masses of the nucleons and the mass of the nucleus is the mass defect.

CHAPTER 20 REVIEW EXERCISE

1. Consider the nuclide ${}^{126}_{52}\text{Te}$ to answer the following: (a) What is its mass number? (b) What is its atomic number? (c) How many protons and neutrons are in its nucleus? (d) What is the atomic mass of the element Te?

2. Write the symbol for the nuclides with the following characteristics: (a) $A = 121$, $Z = 51$, (b) $A = 152$, $Z = 62$, (c) $N = 100$, $Z = 69$

3. Considering the composition of their nuclei, predict which nuclide is the most stable of each of the following pairs: (a) ${}^3_1\text{H}$ or ${}^4_2\text{He}$, (b) ${}^{12}_6\text{C}$ or ${}^{14}_6\text{C}$, (c) ${}^{64}_{30}\text{Zn}$ or ${}^{65}_{30}\text{Zn}$

4. Select the more stable nucleon from each of the following pairs: (a) ${}^{138}_{56}\text{Ba}$ or ${}^{133}_{56}\text{Ba}$, (b) ${}^{125}_{50}\text{Sn}$ or ${}^{89}_{39}\text{Y}$, (c) ${}^{198}_{79}\text{Au}$ or ${}^{195}_{78}\text{Pt}$.

5. Write the nuclear equations for each of the following. (a) the β decay of ${}^{32}_{14}\text{Si}$, (b) the electron capture of ${}^{55}_{26}\text{Fe}$, (c) the α decay of ${}^{252}_{100}\text{Fm}$, (d) the positron emission of ${}^{68}_{31}\text{Ga}$.

6. Write a nuclear equation for each of the following radioactive changes: (a) β decay of ${}^{194}\text{Os}$, (b) α decay of ${}^{232}\text{Th}$, (c) β decay of ${}^{47}\text{Ca}$, (d) γ emission of ${}^{89}\text{Sr}^*$

7. What nuclide results after each of the following nuclear changes? (a) ${}^{131}\text{I}$ releases a β particle, (b) ${}^{214}\text{Pb}$ undergoes two successive β emissions, (c) ${}^{218}\text{At}$ undergoes two successive α decays followed by a β decay

8. Complete each of the following equations:

    (a) ${}^{196}\text{Pt} + ? \longrightarrow {}^{197}\text{Pt} + {}^1\text{H}$
    (b) ${}^{94}\text{Mo} + ? \longrightarrow {}^{95}\text{Te} + {}^1\text{n}$
    (c) ${}^{13}_7\text{N} \longrightarrow {}^{13}_6\text{C} + ?$
    (d) ${}^{235}_{92}\text{U} + {}^1_0\text{n}^o \longrightarrow ? + {}^{143}_{54}\text{Xe} + 3{}^1_0\text{n}^o$

9. (a) How much energy in electron volts, eV, is needed to accelerate an electron through a potential difference of 75 V? (b) What is the equivalent amount of energy in J? (c) Convert 2.0 J to eV. (d) Convert 2.0 eV to J.

10. Consider the following nuclear fusion reaction:

$$^6\text{Li} + {}^2\text{H} \longrightarrow 2{}^4\text{He}$$

(a) If the masses of ^{6}Li, ^{2}H, and ^{4}He are 6.01512 u, 2.01410 u, and 4.00260 u, respectively, calculate the $\triangle m$ for this nuclear fusion reaction. (b) What is the $\triangle E$ in MeV? (c) What is the equivalent amount of energy, $\triangle E$, in J for this reaction? (d) What is the $\triangle E$ in kJ/mol ^{4}He?

11. The mass of a proton is 1.00783 u and the mass of a neutron is 1.00866 u. (a) If the mass of a ^{59}Co nucleus is 58.9332 u, what is its nuclear binding energy in J and MeV?, (b) What is the nuclear binding energy per nucleon?

ANSWERS TO REVIEW EXERCISE

1. (a) 126, (b) 52, (c) 52 p$^+$, 74 n^o, (d) 127.6

2. (a) $^{121}_{51}$Sb, (b) $^{152}_{62}$Sm, (c) $^{169}_{69}$Tm

3. (a) $^4_2$He, (b) $^{12}_6$C, (c) $^{64}_{30}$Zn

4. (a) ^{138}Ba, (b) ^{89}Y, (c) ^{195}Pt

5. (a) $^{32}_{14}$Si $\longrightarrow$ $^{32}_{15}$P + $_{-1}\beta^-$

   (b) $^{55}_{26}$Fe + $_{-1}$e$^-$ $\longrightarrow$ $^{55}_{25}$Mn

   (c) $^{252}_{100}$Fm $\longrightarrow$ $^{248}_{98}$Cf + $^4_2$He

   (d) $^{68}_{31}$Ga $\longrightarrow$ $^{68}_{30}$Zn + $_1\beta^+$

6. (a) $^{194}_{76}$Os $\longrightarrow$ $^{194}_{77}$Ir + $_{-1}\beta^-$

   (b) $^{232}_{90}$Th $\longrightarrow$ $^{228}_{88}$Ra + $^4_2\alpha$

   (c) $^{47}_{20}$Ca $\longrightarrow$ $^{47}_{21}$Sc + $_{-1}\beta^-$

   (d) $^{89}_{38}$Sr* $\longrightarrow$ $^{89}_{38}$Sr + γ

7. (a) ^{131}Xe, (b) ^{214}Po, (c) ^{210}Pb

8. (a) ^{2}H, (b) ^{2}H, (c) $^0_1$e$^+$, (d) $^{90}_{38}$Sr

9. (a) 75 eV, (b) 1.2×10^{-17} J, (c) 1.2×10^{19} eV, (d) 3.2×10^{-19} J

10. (a) 0.02402 u, (b) 22.37 MeV, (c) 3.584×10^{-12} J, (d) 1.079×10^9 kJ/mol

11. (a) 517.3 MeV, (b) 8.768 MeV/nucleon

Index